ALL THAT GLITTERS
A LIFE

Michael Hilliar

carrowmore.ie

First published 2018

www.carrowmore.ie
info@carrowmore.ie

British Library Cataloguing in Publication Data.
A catalogue record for this book is available from the British Library.

isbn 978-1-9999915-5-5

Typesetting and origination by Carrowmore

PREFACE

Adolf Hitler had come in the night, let down from a big black zeppelin. From behind the hedge, I could see him clearly as he ran into the back bog where no one could find him, on that fearful first week of May, 1945. I shuddered to think he was alive and well in Ireland. For it was that old de Valera who had arranged for the amazing escape. Imagine! Just to spite the British and Winston Churchill, de Valera had ensured there would be no retribution for all the evil Hitler had done. I could see the bulrushes moving as Adolf struggled about in his waist-high waders. It wouldn't be much fun with the moorhens and ducks, yet he was safe in Ireland, hiding until it was time to sneak away under the shifting clouds and corpse-coloured moonlight.

That was the Free State for you, sheltering this monster, for there were dark and ominous foxes of Fenian subversion across the border from me. Hitler was smuggled in a lorry load of pigs through Newry to freedom, dressed as a farmer, hunched low in the passenger seat. He should have been with the pigs! The most dreadful things had been happening, the rats were fleeing the Reich Chancellery and all that time the Pope had never once mentioned the plight of the Jews.

The Irish Free State. Sweet Afton cigarettes and the smell of burning turf; the green, white and Papal yellow; ornate Catholic Church interiors; slim girls, quick as sparrows, flicking a few drops of holy water, crossing themselves leaving; post boxes painted green over the royal crown and cipher. Wasn't it amazing that Admiral Lord Nelson was left standing on top of his column above O'Connell Street? The bullet marks at the GPO, reminders of treason and shame. Dirty Dublin, de Valera, rebel stuff, base neutrality, condolences to the German Ambassador on Hitler's suicide. It saddens me that no one will ever believe the night I saw him arrive.

Famine and disease; filthy, narrow laneways leading nowhere. Children without shoes on their little feet. Second-hand clothes, far too big, for they've no hands. Holy things; hunger strikes; mother of God statues, blue and white; floating red-lit lanterns in Catholicism's dark shadows; priests black and numerous as crows; nuns that can fly.

At Drogheda there's a man's head, syrupy yellow in a glass case, the relic of a blessed someone. I was startled on entering the church. Here are miraculous cures and Catholic superstition. I caught lice in my hair when I came to Dublin during the war, mother was sure. Lord Haw Haw was an Irishman and Hitler's half-brother had worked in the Shelbourne hotel and married a Bridget from Tallaght. Fragments of adult conversation filtered through to my young mind: "Normandy"; "Dresden"; "Berlin"'and "out of Belsen, like walking skeletons they were."

Years later, when alone in the Fenian capital of my childhood's troublesome fears, with my shadow growing long and short in the lamp light as I walk around Fitzwilliam Square, I see through green curtains, parted somewhat, and view recklessness, gaiety and sin.

Their National Museum mesmerizes me beyond comprehension: an asylum of moonlight-gilding madness and netherland. Who were these people, then and now? Anomalous and superstitious? Cunning and querulous? Madness entwined. They fashioned gold and silver objects like never seen before. The weirdness of Irish existence was encapsulated in a decorated bronze shrine enclosing the arm of a saint. The designs on it are an unimaginatively complex taunting. There is a fearful creativity here. Memorabilia of the Irish Republican Brotherhood. It is suddenly claustrophobic in the museum, stifling; I have to get away out of this. The rain has stopped, sunshine is warming Grafton Street, where the girls are very pretty.

CHAPTER 1

With a thumping crackle and too much filth from its exhaust, the motor bike eventually starts. I drive north over the Boyne waters, where Stuart and Nassau fought for the crown. Blue Dutch guards, Irish Enniskilleners, French Huguenots led by Caillimotte and gallant old Schonberg. William himself, his arm in a sling ploughing into the river on a white horse... triumphant. There's not a movement from the Free State customs, gone asleep in their corrugated, unpainted, green huts. Whereas her Majesty's Revenue and Customs are alert, waving me on through, back to loyalist Ulster. The sky is clearing to a pale, golden blue over the snow-brushed Mournes; I can see the familiar shape of Slieve Croob in the distance. I will soon be home, there are signs pointing to Ballynahinch. At the cross-roads, on the flag pole above the red telephone kiosk, the Union Jack is defiantly flying, as if by benign providence. Across the narrow road, nailed to a tree, a sign proclaims 'Jesus Saves'. No doubt it was written in the happiness of having been born a Protestant.

Gazing out the dormer window an hour after midnight, I view a Jacobean planter landscape of shadows and moonlight intermittently illuminated from under the fast moving clouds. Sounds flow from the little stream that tumbles hurriedly from the mountain through the hedged fields on either bank. Cattle stand strange and motionless in the field below. Here are the blue-grey slated homesteads of Ulster's good, God-fearing Protestant people, white washed and tar bottomed, the thick-rooted gate pillars the same, with pointed caps to keep the fairies away, all scattered to the distance in wondrous luminosity. Magherhamlet, Church of Ireland, lies behind the sloping field and bend of the road where my maternal ancestors lie buried beneath the wet Ulster earth. It's in the blood. The fearful throb of the Lambeg drum is being practised well before the Twelfth, hands and drum sides bloodied. 'For the freedom of the present, for the future that awaits'.

Morning sees Fred Hennan on his ubiquitous grey Ferguson ploughing the same sloping field, turning the dull winter green into fresh brown, two furrows at a time by invention of the hydraulic system. A flock of hungry seagulls follows behind: one of the most pleasing and ancient sights to behold. Secure in his Presbyterian beliefs and ever watchful as forbears were, there will be no change.

Suspicious and pawky-humoured men are dressed in seemingly discarded Sunday suits: waist-coated, hob-nail booted, flat-capped, smoking Gallagher Blues or Greens. Their ever present collie is alert and never far away. As a youth talking to a girl on the bridge, the story went, Fred jumped into the stream to hide when he saw his mother approaching. She who had bought an expensive fur coat the week after their father was buried. Fred and his brother Bob never married, working the farm together, taking a holiday to Blackpool in turns each year and never once crossing the border. During the Hungarian revolution and Cuban missile crisis, with its threat of nuclear war, a worried Fred would drive over on his Fergie to talk man-to-man about the situation with my father.

The eaves of the bedroom conceal two rusty rifles from the gun running in 1914. Here, too, are a pile of last century's dog-eared *Punch* magazines, their cartoons maliciously portraying Paddy Irish as a lazy, drunken, rebellious, malevolent, simian-faced fool, not to be trusted. A collection of assorted books, thick and forbidding, by eminent Protestant Divines. 'Evening and morning and at noon will I pray and cry aloud and he shall hear my voice.'

* * *

Just after the war, out of nowhere, Father's disturbing loud and clear English commanding voice came from the foot of the stairs. Dressed in Royal Air Force blue, with striped sleeves and coloured ribbons on his chest, his return was an awful shock. Seeing a total stranger in bed with mother. I had to get away fast and hide in the byre where uncle Leslie was milking the cows, crouched into the fat udder, left tit to right tit, squeezing the steaming milk out. He was oblivious as I watched him, a father figure, a hero and capable of anything. For here was a refuge. The byre was warm from cows and the dogs barked a welcome greeting. Stepping carefully, I made my way past sharp implements concealed under hay in the windowless dark. But soon enough came the spectre of Father at the entrance, stark and forbidding against the daylight, my escape blocked.

Father had something in his hand, for I snatched it away and managed to squeeze past him, ignoring the fact he was calling after his son. Over the fields to the back bog, breathless, hesitantly opening a Churchman's cigarette tin. Inside was a swastiked iron cross attached to a broad, red-centred ribbon with stripes of white and black at either edge.

The medal was hot coal burning, burning! If Hitler was still in the bog there'd be trouble taking this from one of his soldiers. Hitler would know. Were the bulrushes suddenly rustling to the breeze? Or was it him, leader of the Nazis? The first ever gift from my father and it was most disturbing. This Hun, the former owner, was a cruel murderer, lying dead, soaked in his pure Aryan blood. Coalscuttle-headed, member of the cruel master race, ice cold, blue-eyed face. Served him bloody right. Should I throw it away? No, no. It is too mesmerizing.

On my return, I listened furtively to the hushed talk of England and Father's war. The tranquility of the air was disturbed; the certainties of my happy, fatherless childhood in Northern Ireland were disintegrating. Life wasn't going to be carefree from now on.

In the past year there had been County Down and walks on Tyrella beach; cycle trips to the mysterious Ballynoe Stone circle; rides on the back of aunt Mary's bicycle around by Ballydugan lake. There, the ever-present, hazy-blue, familiar-shaped Slieve Donard stood in the distance behind reeds and water that reflected an ever-changing Irish sky. On Sundays there had been trips to Hollymount church.

* * *

The American army were camped at the Downpatrick race course and what could be more exciting than getting close up to a Sherman tank stuck in a ditch on the Bonecastle road? One evening, as I rounded up the hens, with dark closing in, they came by on manoeuvres. Helmeted, with rifles and black-smeared faces and all of them smoking sweet-toasted, 'Lucky Strike', the Americans had us surrounded.

Less pleasure had come from picking potatoes.For they were the curse of Ireland years before, according to some. It seemed to me strange and ghostly how potatoes grew underground in all different sizes. Somehow, with each handful, I sensed a whispering sadness.

The clock striking one from Downpatrick Cathedral meant it was time to go home, where dinner would be waiting. My evenings had been spent in and out of hedgerows, where hares and rabbits frolicked for Leslie to shoot. War-time rationing of meat was never a problem for us, but a sorrow for the animals.

From the distance, with a scythe, Leslie is a disconcerting scarecrow-like figure, one that draws ever closer, cutting the headrigs on each side of the field. The cruel shape in Leslie's big, strong hands goes swish, swishing the quivering stalks down and there is no avoiding the jolt that comes with a sensation of time passing and my own mortality. The old Fordson Major and Binder came to turn the corn into sheaves to be stooked. The ricks were brought back to the yard and stacked. It was always a joyous occasion when the thrasher arrived and when it was left for the evening, ready to start the next morning, then I would be hypnotized by the toffee-red machine and all the moving parts on the long belt attached to the tractor.

I had always been aware that mother became apprehensive when the postman called: who could she be expecting? Eamonn de Valera? Adolf Hitler? The Pope, black as soot down the chimney from spiteful south wind? Old Rosie Hogg had a framed picture of bad Pope Pius II in her cottage above the mantelpiece; he was mean-faced and steely eyed. My brother John used to taunt me: "he'll catch you and burn you alive."

* * *

Going to bed, the paraffin lamp and candlelight made shadows dance up the narrow stairs to play on the landing walls. Snuggling safe in bed, I could feel the earth turning slowly, a great big sphere of life floating in the depth of space. I was young, yet aware, bathed by the lemon-green glow of the faithful moon, which peeped in at the gable window, that I was born of Ireland.

At the end of aunt May's feather bed there was a large, very old, iron-strapped wooden trunk packed solid with letters from America and legal agreements with Lord Dunleath's agent for rent to be paid twice a year in Downpatrick. But Dunleath could still hunt, fish and shoot over the land and the corn had to be ground in his mill. The letters of careful, faded script, lovingly kept, tied in bunches with red and black ribbons, per sailing ship from New Orleans with a captain Abraham McTaggart, must have taken ages to arrive home. Mother would read them when asked.

Our forebears would leave by horse and cart to Newry, then sail around Antrim and Donegal and afterwards undergo a stormy passage across the Atlantic to New Orleans. They never returned. Some did well in construction and cotton and kept slaves. Always, though, their haunting sadness of loss came through as Mother turned the pages, their memories of Ireland flooding over them like cool water. They described how they were unable to sleep; that there was no escaping the constant chirping of cricket sounds; the stifling, tropical nights. Negroes were invisible and at night seemed spooky with just the whites of their eyes showing. So many left. They had done so as far back as the eighteenth century.

* * *

There was another way of leaving. We crossed the Irish sea from Belfast to Liverpool on the *Ulster Prince*. It was exciting yet upsetting to watch the lights of Belfast recede into the darkening horizon. In the morning, I was surrounded by strange voices and took a long train journey past factories with tall, smoking chimneys, past coal mines and past the far too many houses that blighted the countryside. Dazed and confused after a long day, I had arrived. But where?

Awakened by aero engines close overhead, I found myself in a newly created world of concrete, enormous hangers and flying machines. Father's car had fluttering pennants on the front mud guards; air men saluted him.

Half-a-dozen decommissioned Lancaster bombers were parked across the runway by the house we had been provided with. I had been warned to leave them well alone, but John and I soon found out how to get inside. The bombers provided us with a mysterious fantasy playground of mustard greens inside. And views through the out-of-shape perspex of these incredible creations had a noble majesty, a quasi-religious effect. We felt the ghostly presence of young airmen as avenging knights, delivering firey destruction and death: just retribution on wicked Germans, their Gomorah.

I was in the pilot's seat for taking off; the navigator's seat on approaching the enemy; a rear gunner, giving a short burst; or a bomb aimer, crying 'bombs away' over Dresden. The hollowing, clambering noise echoed as we ran amid camouflaged blacks, browns, greens. Near the big roundels — bullseye on blue — are tiny swastikas in rows. There were whispering sighs along the fuselage, a tick-tacking of expanding sheets, rivets contracting.

It was a morning of light wind and occasional sunshine; starlings swept over the runway; the orange windsock cone waved lazily; air men's voices carried faintly from aftar.

In the afternoon, it was very different. We went to London. I can remember the coloured telephones on the desk at the Foreign Office and watching the trooping of the colour from a window above Horse Guards parade. At Hampton Court, there was a portrait of Edward VI as a very young boy, wearing the most amazing reds. The televised coronation was shown from a raised platform for the whole village of Ellesmere; I'd been allowed there from school but the flickering, silvery-grey twelve-inch screen was meaningless from the back of the hall.

A Bishop of Cashel and Lismore, Thomas Arnold Harvey DD, went to the same school as me. His brother won the Victoria Cross. I thought about this, during the minute's silence early one November. Our school's war dead were written in golden names on the chapel wall, among them was the terrifying junior housemaster called Snotty Cooper who had kept his canes in a spent brass shell case. Father's Mater and Pater were very old and peculiar. My grandfather had war medals kept upstairs in a top drawer, they had St George on horseback, trampling hunish symbols. He was photographed wearing bearskin in the Grenadier Guards, India. Father's brother in the Royal Navy gave me half-a-crown at the West Byfleet railway platform, Mother saying I didn't deserve it. Which made me think of the English rose called Diana Ogilvy-Wedderborn at the London Central; the fact that I never laid a hand on her was a big mistake. And now comes a loud knock on the bedroom door.

* * *

"Time to get up, we need you to give us a hand."

"For what?"

"Pigs to be weighed, the Ulster transport will be here tomorrow for them," Father replies and there's no escaping that hated chore. I will reek of pig now, I think, wheeling the gated weighing cage into their pens. Its handles are as sharp as knives. I help to catch and drag each squealing, terrified pig into the cage as the lever is pulled down, contacting the Salter scales until the pointer's momentarily still, recording the exact weight. Fearful eyed, huddled together in corners, this death-selecting intrusion indicates which lives are to be cut short. Father is Dr Mengele, using a pot of red paint to mark those of the desired weight. They will be gassed. The same method as was used on the Jews: men women and little children. Thank God there's no castration today, it was an even worse chore, to catch them when much younger, cradle them up by the hind legs, feeling them wriggle and twist as their testicles are cut out by Leslie or John with a sharpened pen knife and splash of Jeyes fluid. Father's life in Ulster with pigs is perhaps more fraught than were his war years.

CHAPTER 2

Awake. Confused. I'm not a child. I'm twenty-two years old and I'm on the roof of the Marquess of Ormonde's stables, across the Parade from the massive, cylindrical-towered castle of Kilkenny. Lying on the slanting slates, I feel warm from the midday June sun directly above; there is just the occasional puffy white cloud to provide a welcoming, cool shadow across my forehead. I climbed up through the clock tower from the lofts above the long-abandoned, carved stalls below. It was Kilkenny's air and my sly sleep that induced such fanciful imaginings.

I have to go see a Robert Haughton, the Marquess of Ormonde's estate agent, this afternoon. He lives in the fine Georgian house-cum-office on the Parade next door to the stables. Dark hair, oiled flat and parted on a round pinkish, countenance; bleary eyes from under unusually thick eyebrows. He wears hush puppies and grey flannel drainpipe trousers, with a countryman's check shirt, tweed jacket and a narrow, green woollen tie. The estate agent lights a Sweet Afton automatically and, leaning over, places the shaking match on an ashtray that boldly proclaims in mulberry coloured letters on white: 'Everybody is drinking Smithwicks Ale'. His smoke rises lazily and soon there is a dirty nicotine haze around us. My task is to explain the plans for the future to a man who's been drinking.

There comes a light touch on the door, which opens to a handsome, reddish-haired, smiling face, asking, "Would you both like a cup of tea?"

"Ah, no thank you." I reply to her, watching her enter with some curiosity now, a fine figure of mature womanhood. Robert raises both hands in an abrupt negative gesture, so that she knows to leave the room. His slowful words are conducive to sleep and forgetfulness. The minutes stretch away. Why am I here?

"The keys, I've come to collect the stable keys." I suddenly remember, reality intruding harshly.

"Ah, yes indeed you have. The Export Board phoned yesterday, a Paul Hogan I think it was, mentioned your coming." Haughton gets up awkwardly and leaves. Returning from gentle voices across the hallway outside, he holds two sets of large, labelled keys.

"These are for the stables and these the castle, you might like to have a look around this afternoon. But leave them back in the morning for his Lordship will be over from England this week anytime. This key is for the wicket in the main door, it will let you through to the open courtyard behind and this the castle to get inside. You're to keep the stable ones for I have another set as they're removing grain from there at the moment," he holds up each key, a magician with mysterious choices for me to make: which to open?

In the castle's long corridors, I wander lost in Kilkenny's yesterdays, which unfold in so many different rooms, empty of everything but silence and the feel of the presence of those long past. There's a leak in the weird, angel-painted, high roof of the Long Gallery that leaves a large puddle in the middle of the faded, parquet floor. A slow and gentle destruction is underway. From diamond-shaped, lead window panes the sunlight is fading gently to darkness, spreading Kilkenny's subtle spell upon my feeling of solitude. From the highest circular tower room, I look down upon the silvery, flowing Nore and across the old city to St Canice's Cathedral and Round Tower. The girl typing in Haughton's office, who I caught a glimpse of as I left, was very pretty in her blue overall.

Night closes upon me, in the crescent curve of the stable's cobblestone courtyard; the circular windows above are as portholes of a mysterious ship, sailing where? With the sky clouding over now, a dull glow reflects the city lights. There are sounds: a passing car, pubs closing and a dog barking. Somehow this feels like an ending and a beginning. The dusty telephone on the high window ledge by the door at the front is marked Kilkenny 14. The directory for the whole of the Twenty-Six Counties is hardly an inch thick. I float about in this other-worldliness, unlocking a cold room which has no working lights and realisation slowly comes that I am looking at a household cavalry breastplate and horse-hair matching helmet. Also here are magic books with geometric star-shaped designs; a heavy, fearsome, sheathed sabre; waxy, coloured maps of whole counties on the wall (of property once owned by the Ormondes and clearly marked). Those must be rent books, with so many names paying in pounds, shillings and even pence. Large, elaborate gilt-framed paintings are stacked, leaning untidily over, forgotten and damaged. Despite the gloom, I recognise the merry monarch King Charles II, who, strangely, comes alive. Smiling, bewigged and swarthy with thick, sensuous lips.

Hedonistic king what are you doing in Kilkenny? That mocking look of sated contentment says take all the cunt you can get while you're in Kilkenny.

* * *

The few people who pass me on High Street as I walk towards Parliament Street, glance at me furtively. Why am I wandering at this time? Well lit, surreal shop windows display a sad collection of items for s ale, from the dubious pleasures of colourful sweets in jars; assorted tobaccos; a new dress and pair of shoes (pre-war).

There are lodgings for me on James's Street with a Sarah Coogan that Haughton booked on my behalf. A care-worn woman, she is silently distressed at my arriving at this late hour. She shows me up a short, narrow stair to a small room and immediately asks for three pounds and ten shillings rent, a week in advance, without meals, as agreed beforehand. Carefully, I count three green, Free State pounds and a worn English ten shilling note into her small, outstretched, grasping hand. She has to be peasant-like and cunning to survive.

The room is panelled in long strips of cream, painted fitted wood, with the Sacred Heart of Jesus at the foot of an iron tight bed, crucifix above. There's a lavatory and wash basin but no bath to use and she'll tidy the room each day, with the sheets changed once a week. I lose the day in dreamy sleep: dreaming of the blue-coated girl naked beside me and King Charles laughing heartily at my waking moist effusions.

* * *

Three grave and dull-grey suited men are silently attacking boiled eggs toast and tea in the dining room downstairs; I glimpse into the breakfast room as I leave in the morning, glad not to be joining them. On the way to the stables, under the fine bay Tholsel arcade, a hand on the shoulder stops me and I turn to a short, balding rotund figure with mischievous eyes, who exclaims, "you must be the new man starting work in the castle stables; isn't it great news for Kilkenny?

"That's right, I'm the man," I reply.

"I'm Peter Farrelly the Town Clerk. Come on up to my office for a chat then."

I follow him through an entrance nearby, to a large room above the arcade and street below. A feeling of unseen webs brushing my face contributes to the dusty, old atmosphere; there are two single light bulbs without shades, barely emitting any light.

"Take a seat," says he, settling expansively behind his wide, cluttered desk. "And when exactly will this exciting new enterprise begin?"

"I'd say by the time the workshops are ready, it would be well into next year. The builders won't even be starting for some weeks yet," I explain.

"It's designs for Irish industry and prototypes sort of thing I was reading about; will there be many new jobs for Kilkenny then?

"No doubt there will be in time, I've to set up the silversmithing workshop."

"Silversmithing indeed," says he, slightly baffled, shaking his head. "We've a silver mug and cups here made a few hundred years ago, I'll show you." Farrelly goes over to a metal filing cabinet, drawing something out. "Oh, I must show you these too." Now he has lifted up a large biscuit tin, placed onto his desk. Inside it are parchments and scrolls and fragment of seals. "Most are in Latin and Norman French, they go back to when the Normans first arrived here in the twelve hundreds, so I've been told." He does not sound as though he cares much and tosses them towards me.

Forgotten words, written beautifully long ago in now-faded ink. I peruse the indecipherable text in a momentary silence that is broken as the door is rudely flung open by the Town Sergeant, breathless in his shabby, blue-piped, red outfit. He is shouting. "We have a new Pope, it's Paul, Paul the Sixth! a Giovanni Montini!"

"Put out the Papal flags right away with the tricolour," exclaims Farrelly, an automation in overdrive now, standing up quick as a Jack-in-the-box. "Isn't that great news, a new Holy Father and another Italian it seems, so be it, thank God." The silver and the parchments are forgotten in the excitement of this Holy distraction. He sees me to the door and adds, 'is it the North you're from I detect?" His voice is hushed as we part.

"Born in Downpatrick; my home's County Down," I reply.

"Ah, the Black North, would you believe it, I've never been up there."

I stumble light-headed into Kilkenny's soporific air, to get a bite to eat at the Club House Hotel, which had been recommended to me. There it is on Patrick Street, comfortably old with an easy-going few in the bar discussing the news from Rome. Framed, spy cartoons of Westminster's nineteenth century parliamentarians and lords are positioned around the lobby, staircase and landing walls. In the butter-and-cream dining room are antique sideboards, tables set on crisp white cloths and stag's heads, looking down from above. I'm hungry now with that smell of food. The freckle-faced, carrot-headed waitress is nicely proportioned, in high black with a white apron chest high. She serves three ample courses for a modest seven shillings and six pence.

The stomach best satisfied now, I find a state of total awareness and grace is to be found here over coffee and the low mummers of the other diners, who are unaware of the profoundity of this hour. I must freeze the memory of this day somehow: the sudden beauty of the woman bending so near, clearing the dirty plates away and a warm feminine scent that draws me to her. I could sit sphinx-like, enthralled and contented in her innocent and naturally sensuous movements. Southern voiced and bewitching, she is aware that I am watching her, she rests lightly on the door frame, her lips quiver a smile at me, then she leaves.

The Protestants of Kilkenny are aware that one of their kind has arrived in the city. Glad of another for their diminishing flock perhaps, yet how would they know which denomination, if any, I belong to? It is as uncanny as the accuracy of swallows flying back from Africa in spring. I have read that some moths can smell a mate seven miles away. These things do happen, over time nature builds a mechanism for survival in adverse conditions. A sensory instinct, extra sensory perception. Maybe it's just in my name? In any case, I am invited to tea by Dean Gash of St Canice's and a Lady Bellew. It is an invite that I can't really refuse. They'll want to know all about the stables and what's going on, what is the reality of the mystery in the many words thrown about in Dublin? It will be as though I have a fancy box of chocolates from which to choose the most interesting to offer them. I must learn to levitate, to believe Kilkenny is happening. And on parting they will probably say, "maybe we'll see you at church on Sunday?"

*   *   *

At the tea party (myself, Lady Bellew, the curate, the dean and their wives), I feel slightly uncomfortable and caged, as though I am being viewed by odd and inquisitive strangers, whose hands touch me and poke me through bars. From the dean and his wife sentences come as in a muffled and careful drum beat. They are specimens of a species thought long dead, preserved and kept alive, sleeping in tall glass jars, reminders of a bygone age. Lady Bellew's no fool, dusty titled and 'All from above'. Feisty and sharp in sensible tweeds, she listens bewildered and doubtful as I explain the mysteries of gold and silversmithing.

"A new golden age come to Kilkenny, imagine!" The lady says, her tone of doubt loud and clear.

"And why not Elaine? It sounds like a good idea," the dean interjects helpfully.

"It all seems a little peculiar to me, the State getting involved in the making of silver at taxpayers' expense. And who buys silver these days anyway? More a liability if you ask me, the first thing a thief would steal and where will you sell it anyway?" She eyes me directly.

"Coras Trachtala will take care of that side, they have a lot of contacts in America with the likes of Nieman Marcus and Tiffanys." I like the

Irish bit, it sounds good, but it's a smokescreen and I feel silly, really, as I haven't a clue.

"Coras Trachtala, what's that? Who are they?"

"The Irish Export," I reply.

"Oh, really. Well, we shall see young man." Lady Bellew is hardly convinced. Sitting back and silent now, she regards me in a curious way, what does she want? I wonder at her age.

In a subtle interrogation, they confirm their beliefs: I'm one of their kind. The curate's from Belfast, with that abrasive manner associated with the defiant and besieged. His new wife is English and weirdly attractive, lips far too red, with a pirate-like patch over one eye and with legs to die for. She carelessly crosses them back and forth, while I try not to notice. Does she realise what she's getting into? I suppose she's finding the scene highly amusing and is trying to keep a straight face, while the bee in the curate's bonnet is the *Ne temere* decree, which I've vaguely heard of before.

For a Protestant to marry a Catholic here, she must sign a promise to bring up any children of the union as Catholic it seems. In time, there'll be none of us left if this goes on, or so the curate believes. I would have thought it just a piece of paper, signed under duress and surely therefore not valid? And who would marry a girl immersed in Catholic superstitious belief, without birth control? The Dean and his wife don't seem perturbed about the decrees. Life goes on much as before. The Dean even lent the church hall to the other side and they behaved themselves very well.

* * *

Well, maybe the curate's right, I think, getting into bed, gazing at the Sacred Heart's unwelcome presence. Who makes up such superstitious nonsense? The room is closing in upon me; I'm buried alive, suffocating in Catholic intrusion.

Awake! The new day frees me from my dreams.

Ascending the steep steps to St Canice's Cathedral, I see crows pecking about warily among the gravestones of the long dead. It is a soft day in sunshine and cloud, no one's about, the door is open. I enter to wander among grey stone and carved effigies of Ormondes lying in full armour. Men and women remembered, in and out of living consciousness. Dust particles float in sunlight. A new world is before me.

CHAPTER 3

I'm thinking of the day that Paul Hogan introduced William H. Walsh to me at the Export Board on Lower Baggot Street by the Grand Canal. Hogan was the Board's 'Industrial Design Assistant' (as printed in black on his white card). Through my father's enquiries in Dublin, I was by chance led to Hogan and his cerebral and enthusiastic plans for what they were beginning to call Kilkenny Design. Hogan took Father and I to a fine meal in the Bailey, this flashman of movement and words, dizzying us with wine. And on that day he offered me this job. Did he know what he was doing?

William Walsh. Seemingly, a sallow Italian gangster with tired looks, baggy flesh under dark eyes, immaculately dressed (tailor made with a difference, George Jensen silver cuff-links protuding from a white shirt). When Hogan brought me to him, Walsh was smoking Carrolls No 1, the red and white opened packet on his desk. He was on the phone. His smile was also an invitation that I be seated. From carpets to furniture and paintings, his was a modern office and when little Miss Anna Livia wheeled in a trolley of tea with a plate of chocolate, cream and jam biscuits, I became aware somehow that I was joining a carnival procession which was about to set off.

"Do you like my new sculpture?" asked Walsh after Hogan had introduced us. He was nodding towards the rear of the office. Going over to inspect the piece, I saw it was a casting of a charioteer pulled by a prancing horse the colour of aged copper green. I could see the tiny pieces of clay that made up the original model. Cuchulainn, cattle raids and heroic tales no doubt.

"Interesting, who is the artist?"

"Oisin Kelly, do you know his work?" Walsh said.

"I've heard the name alright," I lied.

"We can use him when your workshop is ready ..." Walsh began his speech, with Hogan nodding affirmatively now and then. Hogan was smoking the extra-long Kingsway in a red, flip-top pack. Before lighting up, he would grip it in his teeth with a grinning, peculiar look that was purposely mad.

From the sugar rush of sweet biscuits and tea and from inhaling the ever thickening cloud of smoke, came a disturbing, woozy feeling. I found it hard to understand what they were saying. They mentioned with familiarity a number of names: Ake Huldt, Gunner Petersen, somebody Sorensen, an Erik Herlow and Kaj ... was it Frank? These were saints of Scandinavian design it seemed. I tried to listen attentively, not to enter into the surreal. All the same, their words created in me the sensation that I was falling, just before hitting the ground.

They had to make a start somewhere, to take craft-based design and design for craft-based industries. The metal workshop would be the first to produce a range of silver to see how shops and industry reacted, with prototypes coming later. This could hopefully be the type of cross-fertilization expected between art, craft and design, the epitome of the Scandinavian model. Automatically, I agreed with all that they said. For they were the pair that chose me for the job in Ireland. Yet somehow, ever so faintly, it occurred to me to wonder did they know how to translate their words into reality? It was just a passing thought, quite inconsequential.

There was an enormous black Jaguar Mark 10, 4.2 parked in the Reserved space just outside the building they shared with the Tourist Board. The tricolour, shamrock and three-coiled spiral logos of the other two flags in green and blues flew on separate flag poles above us. Atlantic blown between mountain and sea. On the way out with Hogan, I was feeling drunk and gasping for fresh air, when I asked him curiously, "who owns the Jaguar?"

"O'Driscoll the Bord Failte boss, and all on the house, over the top if you ask me to be seen in a yoke like that!"

* * *

It was last Easter that Hogan drove me down to Kilkenny in his Morris Minor — at a shocking speed — to choose the first workshop for silversmithing. We measured it with string bought in Woolworths on the High Street there. I had stayed in the Ormond Hotel the night before and couldn't believe the meal and room were all paid by the Board. Dublin, the Old Fenian city, seemed foreign and so different from Belfast; the

Liffey cut it in two, with the raucous cries of seagulls never far away. A whiff of treason blew in the softly penetrating cries of easy and subtle subversion. I found it hard to sleep that night, from the southern siren calls of women and smell of drink and from floating in a sea of mixed emotions.

* * *

Now in St. Canice's Cathedral, the noise of a side door closing towards the altar brings me back to the present. A small, dark figure approaches and introduces himself, "I'm the Sexton, the dean has told me all about you, welcome to St Canice's."

There, again, how did he know I was the one the dean mentioned?

"You're the silversmith, come on and I'll open the safe and show you our silver, it's very old you know." He speaks with pride and an evident delight that he has someone to show it to. Plain, simple, Crowned Harp silver chalices, the hallmarks are seventeenth century.

The lazy day progresses. I am feeling somewhat stupefied. While parked beside Haughton's, the same blue-coated girl I saw in there before appears. I watch her in the mini's rear view mirror as she walks down the Parade. Nice. In bright yellow now. I should try to ask her out somehow. She momentarily turns around, as if aware I am watching.

On this warm and sunny afternoon, I take the road to wherever it may lead, the sign says to Stoneyford. The county is subtle, hypnotizing, the views are extraordinary. I'm bowled over, engulfed in an amorous embrace. And I drive on in careless and spellbound in wonder at each slow turn. The rising, faraway, pale-purple horizon must be Mount Leinster; there are fields of fat black and brown cattle; a small Protestant church is tucked contentedly away, shaded by trees, with nothing to disturb it. I park beside the graveyard and my fingers gently caress the colourful lichen gravestones. I think of the many generations gone to that brightness above. Moments that cannot hold and soon will be those, 'transitory dreams given o'er, whose images are kept in store by memory alone'.

Stoneyford is a wide and empty village, little changed from the last century. Turning right towards Kells, I find myself on an even more enchanting way, entering the slipstream of the middle ages. On the slope below are high, straight walls between square towers, some kind of fortified priory perhaps? Space open to the sky; thick, ivy-tumbled walls with tiny wild, blue, yellow and pink flowers growing between stones. A piece of fallen moulding there. Is that an angel hidden amongst the ragwort and thistle? Crows 'kaaah kaah' above me, having lots of handy places to nest and hide. A warm light breeze breathes the presence of those who prayed here long ago. Heaven was waiting, but surely it was already here

I don't want to leave, for what more is there really to see apart from this? Suffused in timelessness all around, the evening slowly dies to night; the only sounds are of the river now, flooding past the old watermill.

* * *

There's a sign to Kilree High Cross and Round Tower that I follow; it's not far to the marked spot. Over a stile, I climb into to a field of freshly mown hay; long-abandoned in the ditch is an old McCormack reaper, sinister and warlike, an ancient chariot. I can just make out the dull shape of an abandoned, roofless church as an island, partly screened by dark Cyprus trees. Behind the standing sentinel is the high Round Tower. Moving around, the full moon is growing brighter behind a High Cross decorated with spirals, frets and figures; it casts a long shadow on a ground turned silvery. The scene becomes ever more mysterious and it occurs to me that there is no understanding any of this. Two curious cows draw rear and stare, then turn and canter off.

The clock is striking midnight when I return to Kilkenny and park the Mini in the stables. Locking the main door behind me and leaving, I notice someone in a long field-grey overcoat by the castle railings. Are my pre-concieved notions creating a reality? Getting into bed, the Sacred Heart of Jesus has the face of Adolf Hitler.

* * *

I have to see a William Cleere in his builder's yard on the Ormonde Road this afternoon, along with Niall Montgomery, who will be the architect for the stables. Cleere is a touchy, little man I met once before at his office in Merrion Square. A Joycean scholar according to Hogan, who even knew the famous man in Paris. I could never get through *Ulysses* from beginning to end. I saw Montgomery just now parked in Canal Square, furtively eating sandwiches in his bottle-green Peugeot, for whatever reason he'll keep to himself.

Cleere drives a big maroon Zephyr and is a chain-smoking, Gold Flake man. His foreman is a Mr Sowersby, a sad man who comes up from Cork every Monday morning to Kilkenny and returns on Friday evening again. Sowersby's suit is well worn. You'd be sure Cleere was a hard sort of man to work for, but apparently Sowersby has a large family to keep and must not offend his employer. I thought he was from Wales when I first met him, having never heard a Cork accent before.

All four of us are here: Cleere, Sowersby, Montgomery and I. I have the rough plans made when I took measurements with a length of string. Handing the plans to Montgomery, I see him scan them briefly.

Obviously he is not pleased. "I can't work from these, you've hardly any measurements." He passes me back the plans.

"There's enough there to go on, all we need is a small room at both ends, one for an office, one for polishing. And new floor and a roof with plenty of light along the side over the work benches."

"But without exact plans, which I intended to draw up from your ones, the builders won't know where to start!" Montgomery is clearly annoyed.

"Not to worry, I'll be there with them all the time and can show them exactly what I want as we go along, measurements and all. You can manage with that Mr Cleere surely?" Turning to him.

"Well yes, yes we can, it shouldn't be a problem," Cleere replies hesitantly, looking to Montgomery who exasperated, raises both hands from his knees and throws his head up to the sky. The architect is thin and awkwardly puppet-like, with his bowler hat, thick glasses over a rat nose, greying moustache, suit, cane and briefcase.

"If we go back to the stables, I can show you now, as you have the main measurements and you can then do your plans exactly as you want." I am conciliatory, we don't need a row.

"Seems like a good idea," Mr Sowersby suggests helpfully.

Montgomery lowers his head with a sigh, "Let's go then. No, no I need to walk." This, directed to Cleere, who was heading for his Zephr.

In the stables, by the lean-to, Montgomery takes copious notes and measurements as I describe to him what's needed. Then he leaves with few words, saying the plans will be ready when he returns next week. The three of us watch him disappear under the archway out of sight.

"A difficult man, I'd say there," Sowersby muses to himself.

"Now, now, none of that!" Cleere rebukes Sowersby, smiling, weakly apologetic. I don't say anything, but I agree with the foreman.

* * *

It will be some months before the workshop is ever completed and there's all that equipment ordered in London to collect and store somewhere soon. They have at least started a man with the task of clearing the weeds between the cobblestones. A tedious job, done on his knees, ragged, methodical and slow; he's glad of the work no doubt and perhaps grateful for the few shillings he's getting paid?

* * *

He called across to me, "A grand soft day, sir."

"Yes, indeed you're right," I reply.

I can't help but compare my own position. A hundred pounds a month and eight and three farthings a mile motoring expenses. Not bad for a start. How long can it last? The old, blue, faded-gold, Roman numerical clock reminds me of Time's tricks. From under the stable's cupola comes Robert Haughton, the estate agent, and with him a well-dressed, rather distinguished-looking gentleman.

"Can I introduce you to the Marquis of Ormonde?" says a smiling Haughton.

I take the nobleman's outstretched hand, his appearance is faintly familiar somehow. Early seventies, I would say, with fallen bloodhound looks; dark-eyed and with white, neatly-parted hair.

"This is the first man to begin work here, as I said to you earlier about the conversion of the stables to a design centre." Haughton explains to the Marquess.

"What will you be doing then?" The Marquess asks.

"We'll be making silver hollowware and jewellery and prototypes for industry."

"I see, I see, how very interesting. Tea pots and candlesticks sort of thing do you mean?"

"Well yes," I reply, "once we get started and see how this develops."

"Extraordinary. To be making silver tea pots in the old stables, what a turnaround, what do you say Robbie?"

"I haven't really thought about it your Lordship."

"Well the best of luck on your endeavours then." The Marquess is clearly bewildered though and moves off with Haughton to look around. I can faintly hear muttering about silver tea pots. It is strange alright, come to think about it, making silver tea pots here.

I suddenly remember that he's the boy (about nine or ten then) in the photograph taken in the Long Gallery with King Edward VII and Queen Alexandra. The picture that is hanging in Haughton's office. His youthful world has been turned upside down since then. In the pink and gold Debretts at home, which I looked at when I knew I was coming to Kilkenny, I discovered a Lord James Arthur Norman Butler born in 1893. Harrow; Lieutenant Colonel Seventeenth and Twenty-First Lancers; Honourable Corps of Gentlemen-at-Arms; Military Cross in the Great War; ancestor accompanied Henry II into Ireland. They were Chief Butlers and Lord Justices, with grants of the Prisage of Wines and Regalities of Tipperary, with a right of a Palatine. They numbered Lord High Treasurers, Lord Lieutenants and a Captain General and Commander-in-Chief attained of high treason. These Dukes, Marquesses, Earls, Viscounts and Barons wore a silver gilt coronet of strawberry leafs and balls. They dressed in fur coats of crimson velvet, edged with the white winter coat of a stoat. And there was James, the fifth earl, who fell into the hands of the Yorkists at Towton and was beheaded at Newcastle in 1461. From there to this grand, soft day in Kilkenny, shaking the hand of James' descendent. Hands across the centuries to the Norman invasion of the late twelfth century; with the only movement and sound now the scraping of the man clearing the weeds.

High on the main castle door, on painted wood, are the Ormonde arms. The shield is quartered, indented blue and gold, with three gold covered cups on red, a rampant red lion with a swan between two gold annulets and a red saltire on ermine. 'Butler A Boo' bellows the motto.

* * *

There she goes, it's now or never. So I roll down the windows and stop the car beside her. "Can I give you a lift?"

Startled, she turns, hesitates. "I'm going to Stoneyford, if you're going that way?"

"Yes I'm going to Kells to look around the old priory." As good a fib as any. She gets in, blushing and confused. King Charles' crude advice comes to mind, I'm all too aware of those knees, her cleave of breast and lilt of soft words. Femininity's attractions. She automatically straightens her skirt down. I drive on.

"Have you been working in Haughton's for long?" I ask.

"Far too long, but sure, where else is there to work in Kilkenny?" Her reply is weary.

"I suppose you've heard about the design business?"

"Very little, other than what Mr Haughton occasionally mentions, and you can be sure he'll be making something out of it. You've already started there haven't you?"

"Yes, but it will be sometime yet before my workshop is ready." And silence in the mile or so of the familiar road now. I know she's in a spin and I'm not sure which way this will go. It is out of the question to stop the car and take things further now.

"Is this where you live?" We are coming into the village.

"Yes, you can let me out here, by the Shell petrol pump."

A bird out of a cage, she flies to the nearest door without another word, but turns, smiling, and waves. A swish of dark hair, shoulder-length; a round, elfin face; nice legs. Without a name. She'd know mine though.

Where now in another, long summer evening? I have all of Kilkenny's overflowing emporium of sights to choose from. There is nothing physically dramatic here, yet I succumb all the more to temptation in the form of the sweep of river and folds and the strange soldiers and bishops carved at Jerpoint. With little Miss Eire pressed hard against gravel stone and wet grass and my fingers between her thighs, moist and inviting. It would be breaking and entering into the divine mysteries of the Catholic faith made glorious flesh. The Normans came to Thomastown, with their presence somehow still lingering; they intermarried and were here to stay.

There's a light mist rising along the banks of the Nore, a veil to hide her voluptuous figure, to make discovery of it all the more alluring. Descending to the tree-lined village of Inistioge, I feel as though this is not real. Over the wide, fast-flowing river. As fast as time, this evening has gone forever under the old stone bridge joining the Barrow to Waterford and the Celtic Sea.

In the 'Spotted Dog' I order a Smithwicks, the Kilkenny-brewed beer. It is served by a young waif of a girl, whose head is barely above the counter. I sit across opposite an oldish man, who has a curled pipe in his mouth and a near-empty pint glass of Guinness on the table before him. You would think he was asleep, in the five minutes or so that ensue without a sound.

"We burnt them out you know." He suddenly erupts, looking over at me.

"Who's them then?" I ask quietly.

"The Tighes."

"The Tighes?"

"The Tighes of Woodstock, we burnt the whole house down, the biggest blaze you ever did see."

"Is that so?"

He subsides again, to the silence of his delinquent memories. It was with the Republicans, I suppose. Marching up to the big house with their fire torches blazing. The child stares continually at me in a most disquieting manner. Time to go.

"Good night." To himself.

In reply, he barely nods his worn head, full of those memories, all we, have in the end. Outside, I can see the lonely, egg-yoke 'Afton' sign glowing under a changed, wind-up, black-overcoat threatening night sky.

There's a message left at Coogan's from Haughton to call Paul Hogan at the Export Board. Saying I am to expect Walsh down to look over the stables on Saturday with the Marquess of Queensbury, Sir Basil Goulding and Louis le Brocquy, the painter of isolated, blurry beings who confronts the problems of existence and meaning. Another Marquess indeed. Was it the eighth or ninth that got Wilde put away?

CHAPTER 3

Exiting from a regal, black Austen Princess that parks across by the castle entrance, a green-uniformed, peak-capped chauffeur opens the rear door to let them all out. Walsh is wearing a most unusual tweed jacket, slanting bird-like front to rear, with a red handkerchief in the breast pocket. Le Brocquy is casual smart, not a hair out of place on the fair round face of the low countries. Queensberry is in his mid-thirties with the quiet confidence of a true blue: Harrow or Eton educated. Goulding's much the same in manner but older, his family is in fertilizers mostly now. Used to be railways and banking as well, Hogan had told me, and he was a keen collector of modern art. His son, Timothy, is a budding artist.

Walsh is like a child with a new-found toy as he proudly leads the way, explaining where this and that workshop will eventually be. I follow him up to the loft's front in a confident hum of agreement and praise at the idea and everything he says. Each them gaze through the big round windows in turn, words lost to the sloping and heavy crossover beams above. Le Brocquy takes out a soft blue packet of Gauloises cigarettes, expertly tapping one out to light it with a slim, silver lighter in a most graceful and confident manner. It would almost tempt one to the habit and their rather pleasant smell is now in the air. Moving on down the wooden stairs, I wonder if the footsteps of our passing are heard. Is the whispering wind in the eaves concerned about how will this end?

Invited to join the group for lunch, I walk past the curious glances from Kilkenny's own. Surely, such well-dressed, distinguished strangers can only be going to the Club House Hotel? Le Brocquy is complaining about the British press having almost ignored President Kennedy's stay in

Ireland. The adulation in Ireland for such a glamourous boy is misplaced, I would have thought. The familiar waitress appears, as if she's been crying, her face carries an awful upset as she shows us to the prepared table: what could be wrong?

In the lavatory, Walsh is suddenly beside me, in an uncomfortable moment really when it's out and he can't be seen to wait prudishly. It's just a long sheet of metal without divisions, both of us helpless to nature's call, relieving straight ahead. With a naughty peep at his little limp, white, uncircumcised penis. In the peep, the cosmos was created they say, from the infinitesimal weird stuff.

There's a choice of red or white wine. In the flow of conversation, I feel I'm riding a shooting star. Walsh is describing his new crimson-coloured, poplin dinner jacket, which is being woven by a Mr O'Connor in the Coombe. O'Connor will be given a room to set up his loom here soon. Queensberry is beginning to look slightly apprehensive at this talk, while Le Brocquy and Goulding are clearly enjoying their day out. They've both just been invited to be Board members of the Kilkenny Design Workshops. I will have to try and get serious about this, the making of silver teapots, as the other Marquess kept repeating to Robbie Haughton and himself.

Returning to the waiting Princess, a touch light headed from the wine, we find the chauffeur fast asleep, his head a dead mask to the great unknown. Walsh gives three loud raps on the window screen and he's awake with a fearful start, poor man. Then away they go, disappearing into Rose Inn Street, while back at the stables it's starting to rain, silent and deserted again. This is Saturday afternoon in Kilkenny, late June, 1963.

* * *

It is an afternoon for drifting, I've nothing else to do. So to Tynan's Bridge House Bar then, cool and low lit, with a ceiling of dark, fitted wood. I'm entering a world of departed souls. I sit in the farthest corner with a glass of the now familiar, wondering why? Why haven't I started to design a new range of silverware to be ready when the workshop is finished? There is a stasis in my mind; I'm drowning in Kilkenny, pulling away into the unreal. Made drowsy with shadowing, convoluted images that only Salvador Dali could understand, a figment of my imagination (or not) at the speckled-pink, marble counter turns around to frighten me. It is a man in a dirty mackintosh drinking from a liquor glass. Is it Adolf Hitler? I leave hastily; outside the rain has stopped. Canal Square is a furnace of blazing sunlight and rising water vapour.

* * *

I notice seashells in the black paving stones on nearly every street. Kilkenny was once under the depths of a Boreal Sea, Triassic or Tarassic. Will our bones be the same? Delahunty's, at the corner of James's and High Street, is an awful, new and garish rainbow-coloured pub on the inside of the renovated older building. There are two men here that I have seen before, seated together at an empty, glass-covered table, the older reading a newspaper. They cast looks over to me as I enter.

"Aren't you the chancer they're on about in this ridiculous article?" Showing me a page about the Workshops in the local *Kilkenny People*.

"I wasn't aware of it, but yes that's me they're writing about." Glancing at the page, I see the word innovative. I've never been called that before.

"So you're going to light an exciting new path for Irish industrial design, according to this?" One of them says mockingly.

"Well exciting or not, that's the general intention. I suppose." It occurs to me now that Hogan did mention he'd let the paper know about me, a press release he called it.

"So tell us, what will your job be then?"

"I've to start the metalwork department, we'll be doing prototypes for industry and the manufacture of silverware."

"Silverware!" He exclaims loudly.

"Yes silverware."

"Silverware. Jesus, John did you ever hear the likes?" The man addresses his younger companion, who has the glazed appearance of someone with far too much drink in him.

"Feckin' hilarious if you ask me."

"What sort of silverware?" The interrogation continues.

"I'll be making silver hollowware, teapots and the likes." Too late to recall it, the word falls out of my subconscious, it was stuck in the mind somehow.

"Teapots, silver teapots, I don't believe it, you're having us on?"

"No, this is a serious attempt by the state to improve visual awareness and help the crafts industry to get a start."

"Ah, bullshit," says John, "I've never heard such a load of rubbish in my life. Who are they trying to cod up there by the castle? Money for old rope if you ask me. Sit down for God's sake man and what'll you have to drink?"

"A glass of Smithwicks would be fine."

"Make it a pint for this man, Tom and I will have the same," John says to the barman, who is clearing the table.

The amount of drink they can consume in the evening is unreal, as they continue to slag me off to one another. The pints make for a dulling sensibility and infect me with ominous doubts about the Design Centre. The older man is Tom Eastwood, an English soldier from the Lancashire Fusiliers in the war, Kilkenny Gas Works now. What is he doing here? His companion is the much younger John Young of Eagle Star Insurance. A solid, granite-grey building on the corner Patrick Street and The Parade. John is paving his way to certain destruction at this rate for certain.

I have a sour taste in my mouth and am contemplating images of mortality.

The television above the bar is now playing Eire's anthem over pictures of rivers and mountains. We stand, unsteadily. St Bridget's Cross and final crackle of an ending, which is the echo of the beginning.

"You can have a bite of supper with us as if you want?" Eastwood invites me. We are in the street now, the cool air calming. In the darkly moving Colliers laneway, I can smell the cooking of unhealthy food. Arriving at a dirty kitchen in limelight, I see tanks of boiling fat. God knows what's in them. To a smiling, sweating man in rolled shirt sleeves and a filthy apron, Eastwood raises three fingers: "The usual."

Without asking me for my choice, if there is one?

Here comes dripping chips and something I cannot identify, wrapped in newspaper, warming to the hands. I offer to pay, but he refuses, unconcerned. They share a room to the side of Delahunty's and we return there, to complete chaos. What are these? Pigs, pigs trotters, yes. No, no, I can't eat this. The pair of them silently devour the food with an unnerving intensity and speed. Young is finally asleep, fully clothed on his storm-tossed bed.

"Have you no home to go to?" Eastwood snarls at me in his own dismay at another day having ended like this. So I leave.

Next day there is a figure at the castle, who seems to be waiting for me. Furtively, gazing over, as would an animal afraid to come any closer. He strays from the castle to the stables and watches from a safe distance. Should he even be here? Hesitantly he steps towards me and I remain, until he can touch me lightly, beggar-like on the arm, "I'm related to the Butlers; Viscount Mountgarret you know," says he, a Mr Punch in a heavy, torn, tan overcoat with a hollow, deep voice, which comes from under a purple, wide-pared nose. It is obviously important for him that I should know this.

"My goodness," I reply.

"We go back a very long way."

"Is that so?"

"Oh yes indeed."

"How far?"

"Hundreds of years. We're a branch of the Butlers that own the castle you know."

"Amazing."

"The first was a Richard Butler, second son of the eighth Earl of Ormonde."

"Extraordinary."

"Yes." His face is alight at his having finally managed to import his genealogy to me.

"One of Kilkenny's aristocracy you might say," I observe.

"Ah now, none of that, you do keep this under your hat." There is false modesty in his reply and he winks at me with a knowing smile.

"Nice to have met you then," I say, shaking his hand.

"And you too Sir, good luck and God bless."

Leaving him a much happier man it seems, I cross the enclosed court-yard. He waves, with his secret to keep as a bond between us, he's maybe thinking. After this sad encounter, I will give him a wave every time I see him.

* * *

Are they swifts or swallows; what's the difference? The birds dive bullet-fast, skimming just above the ground, then way up again and again over the wide acres of lawn, stretching to the gentle airy blues rising at the rear of the castle. Such acrobatic displays. The crows look slow and cumber-some by comparison to the ethereal little wizards above them in the sky. And they mutter a faint, 'tsink, tsink' twitter in their passing. The swifts feed on the way, they mate and even sleep on the wing, I was told. At dusk, they circle higher and higher until disappearing from sight.

I treasure the daylight and freedom, for beneath this verdant expanse is a tunnel leading to the kitchens from the iron gate, with steps down in the wall by the roadside. The servants would have come in darkness to wait upon the castle owners then and would not have been seen: the view is only for those above them.

Eight pounds is a high price to pay for a ticket to the ballet at the Gaiety, Bolshoi though it is. I had the idea to ask her to come, for she'd hardly refuse the once-in-a lifetime invitation while they're here. She's in a new dress from Duggan's (established since 1853), which I saw her coming with the day before. There's a madness in my desire and going this far is hardly necessary. It is an expensive impulse, designed to impress; for who else in Kilkenny would take her to Swan Lake?

I get a peck on the cheek as she gets into the car. So near, so far. She is well groomed and as excited as can be, fresh as flowers picked with the morning dew, that tight little arse clearly shows the elastic stretching underneath. *Curve of thigh, heeled shoes that perfectly shape; Oh Miss Eire, you, I would love to penetrate.* We will return by the mound of Ardscull under thick summer trees, the starry night is a mystery of life: space-time throwing us together. How to be careful though? The way it is down here, I can't buy Durex anywhere. I will have to ask Graham in Castleward, but that's too far. I wouldn't do it without one. It takes just one of the racing millions to hit and ignite. It's too risky to pull away, all mess, no pleasure. I must show respect, it's a Catholic country and she'd be crucified in Stoneyford. Ann Boleyn kept Henry waiting, mind you, he cut off her head eventually. Nobody messed with Henry, who finished with the monasteries and the Pope even.

A woman is playing a harp on Grafton Street, green, white and orange ribbons tied to the frame. Danny Boy is a mournful tune, their music is always sad.

A drunken beggar says, "bless ye for a shilling, sir?" Then we have to ignore the lowering after we pass him, "yez mean ould fecker!"

All Ireland is there in the two of them.

What a crowd! This is a big event for Dublin. The city is lucky to get the Bolshoi. This will be an evening to remember, one that will never come again. We settle down in suspense: the lights go low and I take her hand, nervously. I feel I hold it without totality, there is something bothering her. Maybe, this is too early, or am I imagining a lack of response? The curtains part, the stage is set in a frost-like blue. You could hear a pin drop. A doll-like woman in fluffy white is pirouetting with amazing control. This needs years of practice from an early age. I never before appreciated ballet as I do now; it is what the Russians do best.

Between this and Kilkenny there is not a deal of difference. Kikenny is just another stage, but I have a part to play in it, making up my words as I go along. The Marquesses and Baronets of a medieval city; the backdrops of painted greens; rivers; castles; rains in forgotten places. Round towers; Celtic Crosses in moonlight and swirling mist. The county could be a painting by Giorgione or Correggio with their mysterious countrysides of dreamy blues and yellowy greens. Men wearing masks in workshops will be making silver objects. It is hard to know yet what they will craft.

I'm startled back to the show, by the Soviet Army's chorous and band, with their lusty marching songs that would carry you anywhere on thundering crescendos of male voices. The balalaiks are strumming and the brasses are blaring. Such dramatic effects, with a quality of tone and discipline that is unequalled. Sorrowful and haunting. Far away.

Kamarinskaya.
Bandana.
Kalinka.
You Are always Beautiful.
Snow Flakes.

Volga Boat Song.
Annie Laurie.
Tipperary.

Wouldn't you just know they'd have to sing that, in perfect English too.

It is humid and ominous outside, with spiteful little gusts of wind occasionally troubling us. There is a rolling black, purplish threatening sky coming towards us as the crowd slowly leaves well satisfied.

"Did you enjoy that then?" I ask her.

"Oh, God I did; such a performance, the way she did the dying swan at the end and the Russian Chorus, such rousing music. Surely they're not all a Godless nation to be able to sing like that?"

I like her reply. "Would you want a drink before we leave?"

"Ah, no, me Mam will be waiting, anxious for me to get home."

Is that it then? I unlock the car, which I parked the far side of Stephen's Green. What now? Spots of rain and distant thunder. Out of the shadows a dark figure suddenly confronts me, wearing an official-looking harp badged cap, needlessly, he guides me out with overly dramatic gestures and a mad face of false gaiety and outstretched hand.

Somewhere between Naas and Athy, the sky erupts in a flood of rain, with lightning and loud thunder. I have to stop the car as I am unable to see ahead. Terrified, with atavistic fear in her eyes, she crosses herself and begins, "our Father which art in Heaven ..." She is in world-ending mode, Day of Judgement, her many sins before her. Another flash and thunder is very near. Silly girl, it is only electricity from the clouds to the ground and not the work of God.

With an arm round her shoulder and a hand on her knee, she hardly seems to notice or mind what's slowly beginning to happen now in this cataclysmic night. From her stocking tops to the suspenders which hold them, to the inside of her thighs, naked flesh. My fingers feeling the moistness beneath her scant briefs and her mouth is receptive to mine. With the other hand, I am unbuttoning a breast. Freed from constraint, it is budding out, small and firm. Lightning illuminates everyting again momentarily. The Mini's an awkward little space to be doing this with the long gearstick in the way. I ease her over to me, raising her dress. Her bottom automatically lifts to oblige me, it is as if she is hypnotized. She's wonderfully hot and sweetly sour beneath as I ease her legs apart. But it has to be second best for me: on her stomach and thigh, suspenders and stockings, coming all over her dress. The miracle that is a spoonful of trouble or joy. Yet I've nothing to wipe it off with. She's panicking as she angrily pushes me away. She looks aghast and helpless at the mess with raised hands, not wanting to touch it, as if it were poison. There's an oily cloth in the side door compartment and I hand to her.

"Just look at my new dress, if Mam sees this! And this filthy rag will make it even worse!"

"Nothing to worry about, we just got carried away, there was no penetration."

"We! You, you mean, will you please take me home now?"

The lightning and thunder easing somewhat, I'm able to drive on. She doesn't say a word until we reach Castlecomer, then she begins to sob quietly, saying, "You're a Protestant aren't you?"

"Well, yes, I suppose you could say so."

She continues to sob without another word, drying her tears once we are beyond Kilkenny and nearing Stoneyford, she says, "I don't want to see you again. I've a boyfriend in Limerick and he'll be back in Kilkenny soon."

There's a light waiting on her house, God help the poor girl, what have I done?

CHAPTER 4

Iarnrod Eireann on the side of the train; Iarnrod Eireann slips easy and gentle from the tongue. Iarnrod Eireann, watching them load machinery and crates of tools onto an old Bedford lorry in the freight yard of Kilkenny's railway station. What a day it was, sauntering into Edwards on the Euston Road, casually ordering a new Taylor spinning lathe with every accessary and the big Canning polisher. As many hammers and stakes as I could possibly want, no expense spared, all paid for by the Irish Export Board. Then to H.S. Walsh on the Clerkenwell Road, not as the poor art student of yesterday, counting every penny. I gave the familiars quite a surprise with my orders on that day. The very best of every Swiss file, six of each. Sandbags and six draw plates; twelve gross of Ideal Number Three piercing saw blades; rulers and scribers; angle poise lights; loupes and magnifiers; swansdown; reflex; stitched and hard felt mops. Bars of lustre and rouge; pliers and shires; borax cones and dishes and more. The list was long, as were the six leg vices.

The entire staff gathered in amazement, continually in and out of the store room, with the occasional, "we'll have to order the balance of these."

Until finally I said, "send the invoice to," I loved the next bit, "Coras Trachtala," pausing, "Wilton Terrace, Dublin, Eire."

"To who?" said the beige-coated, Capstan-Full-Strength man.

"Coras Trachtala, Wilton Ter..."

"What sort of a word is that?" he interrupted me.

"It's Irish for Export Board."

"Oyeaa." He cocked his sharp cockney eye at me, "how do you spell it then?

"COR AS TRA CH TA LA." Slowly and clearly too, while he laboriously wrote down each letter.

"Blimey mate, that's a weird word and where does all this lot go to then?"

"Kilkenny Castle, Kilkenny, Eire. No better make Republic of Ireland." Don't want to upset them.

"What are you? Some kind of a Lord then?" He looked up at me, surprised.

"No, but I certainly feel like one today."

"The Irish were neutral during the war, weren't they?"

"Not the North."

"Still part of us, the North are they?"

"Yes they are."

"Are you Irish?"

"What do you think?"

"Hard to say really, your voice has something that's not quite English."

"Not quite. Anyway, as soon as they pay you, send it all to that address." Pointing to his paper.

"Coros Trochtoloo, that's Irish for Export Board, did you know Sarah?" As I was leaving, I heard him joking to the girl.

* * *

I volunteer to sit on the open rear of the lorry on one of the crates, while the driver and his two assistants squeeze into the front. High and slow, we move through the narrow streets and busy traffic, with a good view of Kilkenny's endeavours over the centuries on both sides of us. The Priory of St John the Evangelist; the faded Home Rule Club; the fine tradition of signwriting and Celtic, shop-front lettering found in the Book of Kells; the looming castle to the left over John's Bridge. There's an apprehension form in me as we cross it, this could be on a tumbril to my execution. I am thinking of Louis XVI and Maria Antoinette.

"There goes yer man, coding everyone, off with his head!"

The sudden loud taunting voice from the street is John Young's, directed up at me as the lorry turns into the Parade.

"Silver teapots for sale, cheaper by the dozen, come on up to the castle and buy one!" Tom Eastwood is just as loud and with raised, clapping hands. People stop and stare, some clapping as well. "Jesus man, will you come on down out of that nonsense up there," he calls.

"Is it gold or silver you have in those crates?" asks John.

"Chancer ..."

Their mocking voices carry all the way up to the castle. There, Robbie Haughton comes out of his office and seeing the arrival, stops, curious, then turns and follows closely behind us into the stables. He watches bemused as the contents are unloaded — with difficulty —through the narrow door of a small room, near to where the workshop will be.

"My goodness that's a queer looking yoke, whatever is it for?" says Robbie, in a rather flippant mood, touching the crate.

"It's a spinning lathe, for turning up metal."

"And how does it work then?"

"The complexities and knack of metal spinning is really beyond words to describe, like riding a bicycle, one day it just comes."

"Is that so?" He shakes his head at the heavy, disassembled pieces of grey machinery before him.

"You basically have a circular shaped chunk of wood or metal screwed into the lathe centre, turning at speed, with a circle of silver pressed lightly on the chuck from behind. Both spinning together, the silver is gradually levered over with a metal tool onto the shape of the chuck." I explain this to him but see he is none the wiser.

"It sounds awfully complicated and what's that yoke for?" Robbie asks, nodding towards the polisher.

"A polisher: when the workshop's up and running, you can come and see them both operating, if you're really that interested."

"God, maybe I will." The estate agent replies half-heartedly. He remains a while longer then leaves, overtaken by the Iarnrod Eireann three driving past. From those two boyos on The Parade, to Robbie Haughton, is this beginning to unravel in my head before it even begins? Has a very singular moment arrived?

* * *

Cleere's maroon Zephr glides into the courtyard, a strange intrusion unrelated to anything in the old, laboriously-quarried, stone-built stables. Two different worlds are side-by-side here and pulling apart, yet as a silversmith, I will be as one with the stables. For there will be no mass production here, only tedious hammer work using methods little changed in hundreds, no, thousands of years. Do they really know what they're doing? Silver teapots. I will never say those words to anyone in Kilkenny again.

"Can we have a word?" The builder calls me to come over, beside him is Sowersby, down low on the wide bench.

"We'll be starting your workshop in about a fortnight," he says.

"Did Montgomery come down yet?" I ask.

"No, but he sent his plans drawn up, they are fairly straightforward, so we can begin on the roof and walls."

"In about a fortnight?"

"Well yes, give or take a few days either way. Montgomery will be here the week we begin." Cleere lights a Gold Flake and inhales with deep satisfaction.

Leaning on the side of the car, I notice his fingers are heavily stained with nicotine. Sowersby smiles weakly at me, preoccupied; he doesn't say a word. There's a St Christopher medallion hanging from a short chain and rosary on the rear view mirror and a little Virgin Mary standing, rubber-suctioned on the dashboard. Can't be too careful it seems. They drive through the archway to the rear of the stables.

* * *

I feel disconnected by this slow, unfolding pursuit in Kilkenny's high summer time. I'm clouded with confusion and a lack of concentration for the job: carelessly indifferent about when it will start. It is though I have fallen under a tropical sea, whose strangeness comes fishlike, in slow-motion, each new experience confounding past reason and sense. Something about Kilkenny presses on my imagination.

For the next few days, I drift aimlessly, seeing Miss Eire turn the other way. Well what's her problem? The Bolshoi ballet and a stormy night together? Quite an experience, costing enough and not to be ashamed of. The rain and lightning and thrills we all live for. Violence and decay looks behind every smiling face and rose bloom. No harm was done to her, despite my being a heretic and all; she obviously knew about me before-hand, as they all do in Kilkenny somehow.

Something profound and even peculiar emanates from me here, a quirkiness of imagination. Is that possible? They're looking for Irishness without obvious Irishness, an Irishness instantly recognisable as Irishness, but an Irishness never seen before. I will have to go and seek in the grave-yard of their past, among the leaning and fallen lichen-covered stones. The shapes and words on the gravestones can hardly be deciphered. I notice the faint movement of ivy and summer grasses and I pick up a heavy, rusted iron cross, the ends split in two and curled about each other. I'm unnaturally drawn to these places now, but I'll never get any kind of normality from them.

The road leads to Knocktopher, where there's a grey and sadly aban-doned, bricked up Protestant Church in the village, amidst an overgrown graveyard with surrounding walls. Not a soul about in the short walk to the singular, lofty remains of a church or abbey in another graveyard, where I can see across to a big Gothic-style house in lovely spacious grounds of natural spreading oak and chestnut trees. There's a British, racing-green Jaguar parked outside the main perpendicular-shaped doorway. Someone is living in fine style and comfort, to own this memorable setting. It gives me a faint feeling of unease though, as I stand there a while in the silence. What haunting secrets are here?

At the half door of a tiny village shop, stooping to enter, I ask the old woman behind the counter, "who lives in the big house up the road?"

"Ah, sure, that's the Langrishe's. Sir Terence, they own the whole village and they used to own a lot more years ago here; thousands of acres it was then. Why do you ask?" Looking at me, her face suddenly changes, becoming a mite suspicious.

"I was just passing through and stopped for a walk, curiosity really."

"Killed the cat, now can I get you anything?" she says, as if adding: and that's all the information you're going to get out of me.

"A Mars bar would be just fine."

*　*　*

The next morning, as I awake, I wonder was Knocktopher in a dream or did I really visit the village yesterday evening?

There's a dance on in the city, Irish Town end. As an anthropologist studying the natives from long ago would listen and read, submerged in their culture, I attend, entering the risen Hottentot race. The dance hasn't started yet. Males and females wait, watching each other from opposite sides of the dance floor. Males tanking upon on alcohol, females wary and safe together. Eyes painted with black eyeliner, in high heels and tight fitting skirts to pump out the legs and arse. Small wonder it was a pope started a witch craze to burn so many of them alive, for the Devil comes in many guises. My subconscious fires are flickering and swirling, creating images. I'm going to go native and ask a dark and sylphlike woman to dance. Brendan Boyer's performance would be a hard act to follow in Botswana or the Congo.

"You're not from around here are you?" She shouts so I can hear her above the loud music and homogenized moving mass.

"No, indeed I'm not, but I'll be living here now I think."

"So where are you from?"

"The North I suppose."

"You suppose?

"Well, a good bit of England as well."

"So you're a Brit?"

"If that's what you think. What about yourself then, where are you from?"

"Gortnahoo, Tipperary."

"That's a long way to come, how did you get here?"

"We hitched."

"At this time of night?"

"No problem, there's loads come for the Royal Showband, they're the best."

"Dark night and lonely laneways, anything could happen to you."

"I'm not bothered, life's short, anything for a bit of fun." She eyes me provocatively.

The dance ending, I'm not quick enough to ask her for another, as bird-like she's back in the flock. Discussing me with two companions probably, seeing as they look over at me intently. Smeared with aniseed and given a head start, Essex's men would have hunted them with dogs for sport then. At the entrance outside there's been a fight, blood is pouring from one primate's nose. It's a distressing sight, with the other jeering, "yez feckin gobshite, that'll teach you to leave her alone!"

Stag like, the winner is triumphant.

I must get away out of this, on atavistic wings winds are brushing over-head. I am in the streets of a suddenly foreign city. Silent and starving, out of the woods they come to take their revenge. Footsteps come hurrying footsteps behind, frightening me foolishly. I'm touched on the shoulder and I turn to the dark girl. "Do you have a car, can you give us a lift? Please" Her hands are upturned; she is helpless and distressed.

"Into Tipperary? Sure that's miles away."

"Ah, go on, you seem like a nice bloke."

"You told me you'd have no problem getting home."

"I was wrong this time, sorry." Lowering her eyes, she is the wee woman, helpless and begging for help.

"The car's up by the castle, it's very late."

"I know." Her voice is plaintive and she looks even more vulnerable, but cute as a fox now. It could be interesting, into the heart of Eireann with her alone, why not?

"Come on then if you insist, up to the castle with me."

"Ah no, you go on, I'll wait here, I have to say a few words and goodbye to someone."

You wouldn't know what you were getting into; I was, however, commit-ted now.

Returning in the car, she's there and opening the passenger side door and pulling up the seat, out of nowhere two girls dart in, with a, "I hope you don't mind, we're all going in the same direction together." She speaks with a cheeky grin, sitting down beside me and closing the door, a fait accompli. The little bitch. I have to hand it to her though, she doesn't miss a trick, laughing in chorus with the two in the back at her clever deception. Away we go then, headlights boring into the mysterious land-scape, a journey to what mysteries hidden by night's fold?

Signs to Tullaroun, Freshford and Urlingford. A constant awareness of the scent of three women so close to me, it is overpowering. Could this be a ghost train of Irish history? Who are these boisterous creatures? Harridans of their religion and race? Singing Perry Como's awful hit song about stars and moonbeams in jars. One of the girls wants to stop for a pee, dear God.

The entrance to a gate will have to do, her pale bottom two moon spheres just off the ground, unashamedly in your face: that's what we think of you. But there's something else, as out of the gloom, gliding ship-like, the remains of a castle or tower draws near; a looming presence mute and inscrutable. I am aware of the spirits of past lives, whose existence was precarious and painful. Shouldn't this be from a place with a more settled history? A Somerset or Dorset? At a crossroads corner the headlights momentarily illuminate the Virgin Mary standing in a golden recess. All three girls cross themselves, robotic and weird. Where do they get that Mariolatry from, it's not in the Gospels is it?

We must be into Ormonde's Palatine by now, Norman avarice thrust deep into Ireland's bounteous heartland. How was it then, by flame and sword? Slipping in and out of reality, so close together, but I am in haunted isolation.

"Is it far now?" I ask.

"We're nearly there. You don't say much do you?"

"Things on my mind."

"Like what?"

"You wouldn't understand."

"I think you're a quare one."

"Leave him alone Kathleen, isn't he good to be driving us home?" says one from behind.

"I think he's just shy and that's nice in a man," says the other.

"Well I don't know." Kathleen is a touch sulky. I should throw her out, to come all this way to hear her say that. Mind you, it's a shame she isn't on her own though.

This is it, Gortnahoo, inconsequential, a forgotten habitation in the surrounding sea-green of Tipperary. Who has even heard of it?

"You can let Maria out here, we're a bit further on," says Kathleen, really pumping the well of tolerance dry. But I might yet end up with her alone! No, it's not to be, as the pair get out together further on. Here are cottages on a road signed to Cashel and Clonmel. There is just a fleeting kiss from both of them in the end.

I drive on to Cashel without thinking why, a hidden hand drawing me towards the town in the first faint glow of morning. The whole of Tipperary belongs to me.

Coming around a bend in the road, quite suddenly rising before me, is the famous Rock of Cashel, silhouetted against the lightening sky. It is an arrow, piercing my heart exquisitely. Now and hereafter, out of a fairy tale, a medieval illuminated manuscript. I am earthbound no more. Ireland is surreal, I have a miraculous and momentary understanding of the mystery that I glimpse, fleetingly, and then it is gone. Climbing the high grass and rock face, I find amidst the ancient, pre-Norman, roofless ecclesiastical wall, a perfect Round Tower. My hands grope carvings; I watch the sun rise over the great plain of Tipperary and I find it hard to hold back the tears.

CHAPTER 5

Farrelly, the Town Clerk, I recognise. I don't know the rest, crowding around me as if I were almost a celebrity. I'm embarrassed. They are avid for information, but what can I say? I'm as ignorant as they. *Rome wasn't built in a day and silversmithing was a fine old Irish tradition once here; it will revive. Kilkenny will be the precursor of the whole metal working industry in Ireland, you know...* It is complete nonsense. Yet again words about good design fulfilling an important function for Ireland in the twentieth century don't mean anything at times like this and are soon forgotten. It's a comfortable hour or two for happy people with plenty to drink. I was invited to this gay little gathering by the proprietor of the *Kilkenny People*, John Kerry Keane. He lives in a fine modern house, it's so unusual for Kilkenny for me to be in one. I have to get away out of that Sarah Cougan's; I believe there's an empty room on the Parade. That's all I need, at least there won't be any Sacred Hearts. Here comes Farrelly beaming, with a drink in his hand.

"Aha, our man from the Black North and how are you finding life in Kilkenny?" he asks.

"Just fine, couldn't be better, extraordinary place."

"Indeed it is, any activity up at the castle then?"

"My equipment's arrived and the builders will be starting in a few days."

"So things are beginning to move?"

"Slow but sure."

"Ah, yes, but you know this will really put Kilkenny on the map, what they're doing."

"Yes it will hopefully. I see you've still got the Papal flags out. Why is that?"

"God man, you were there when the news broke, for the new Pope of course!" He is squinting, his face puzzled.

"That was a while ago now; you really believe all that religion do you?" I shouldn't be asking.

"But of course, I couldn't live without the one true Catholic Church, 'You are Peter, and on this rock I will build my church...' You know that don't you?"

I'm surprised at the question and fail to reply.

"How do you think all this came about? You, me, the sun, moon and stars: created by God." Lifting up his arms and spilling his drink.

"Then who made God?"

"Ah, you Protestants, you're all atheists at heart, questioning everything. God is eternal; didn't Jesus die on the cross for our sins? His resurrection opened the gates of everlasting life for us." This is said forcibly.

"I wouldn't be so sure about that."

"You must be joking! Do you believe in God at all?" he says, shocked at my reply.

"I really don't know, does anyone?" I say, smiling solicitously. No need to upset him, these agreements lead nowhere, they go in circles, are dangerous even. Best if I leave it alone. He will never change, how could he?"

"Mother and Head of All Churches of the City and Earth." Farrelly recites provocatively, his forefinger raised.

"Where does that come from?"

"The Lateran basilica Rome, in Latin of course, I was there last year." He says this proudly, emptying his drink, more relaxed.

"My goodness, Rome's the one city I must go to, did you see the Pope?"

"We certainly did, but I'm away for another drink now, you're a terrible heretic you know!" Playfully, he pokes me in the ribs with his clenched fist.

Flagrant Immorality on Friary Street. Thus the article headline reads in the *Kilkenny People* that is lying on a side table in the hallway I pass when going to the lavatory. The miracle of wine turning into water takes place with a gushing sound and I'm taken aback: the bathroom has a bidet. It must be the only one in Kilkenny (Ireland even), amazing. I'd love to have a bath here right now: towels on heated rails; a choice of soaps; soft toilet rolls; tissues. Opening the larger, mirror-fronted cabinet, I find a cornucopia of scented bottles, tubes, jars, razors and toothbrushes. Never mind, I'll wash the face. The hot water comes immediately, relaxing, ahh, yes, yes. But the water turns very grey, which is most disturbing.

Returning, I find a small space for myself and am left alone. They've lost interest in the future wonders of Kilkenny Design, for a while at least. Farrelly is across the room eyeing me; he shakes his head at me and I wonder will the worm of doubt eat at a fraction of his certainties in bed tonight? Where am I going to live? Will I settle here eventually? Or am I just a pilgrim passing?

After many strange, "good nights" and "God blesses", I walk back in the landscape-altering glow of the moon above the city and I think it was nice of Keane to invite me into his comfortable house for the evening. Perhaps I should have asked him for a bath?

Sarah has a written me a message, to call a Hubert Butler from Bennetsbridge, now who would that be? I ask her.

"I've heard the name all right, there was some kind of row here years ago, he insulted the Pope or was it the Papal Nuncio?" she replies.

"Sounds interesting, what did he look like?"

"There were two of them, himself and his wife I think, in their early sixties I'd say."

"They give any reasons why they wanted to see me?"

"No, just to call the number you have there."

* * *

Hubert Butler has invited me to lunch at Maidenhall Bennetsbridge, the village near Kilkenny by the Nore. After a short drive at midday, nearly asleep, I hit a bump and am awakened just before I crash into the ditch. It is frightening. In those milliseconds, I am aware that my life could come an abrupt ending, on a summer's day Kilkenny. There's a little field of buttercups the other side of the hedge. It would be pleasant just to lie down there and fade into the effervescence of Kilkenny.

A laneway leads to comfortable, old house in pleasant and leafy surroundings. As I lift my arm to rap on the knocker, a sudden whoosh of realization comes: this is a unique place. I am struck from out of nowhere, as if by a heart attack. I'm still dazed as the door opens to the welcome of this Hubert Butler and his wife Peggy. Shown into a warm mellow room, I see the sunlight filtering in from the wavering trees outside.

Like the Crow Fool in Durer's woodcut, I try to explain Kilkenny Design to them. With a crow in each hand and on the head, in a slippery, fouled courtyard between store room and stables. They are a grey and comforting, softly-spoken pair, who have a kindness and a natural curiosity. I enjoy a simple meal with them, appreciative that they have gone to all this trouble to host me. An atmosphere that is hard to pin-point or fathom pervades them though; I sense that benign southern Protestant sadness in a whispering of regrets. He has an extraordinary knowledge of Ireland and especially his beloved Kilkenny. Obscure saints, cult centres, holy wells, tribes, extraordinary miracles and ancestors come to life and flit about the room. His descriptions of castles and their past owners, of the dispossessed, of archaeological finds and round towers are like sparkling waters falling from a rocky, secret place thick with ferns. The Nore is in his veins.

I will have to visit the Cantwell Fada, the crusader of Kilfane, the ruins of Desart Court and the round tower at Tullaherin, whose Lord was killed in a duel. Murdered. He had changed religion, not centuries ago, but yesterday, the story-telling transcending time. This is becoming exquisitely painful listening. Was it Cleere or Young that said Butler was an obsessed old fecker who went about upsetting people, with all sorts of bees in his bonnet?

* * *

Coras Trachtala want to purchase some of the silver I made as a student in London for presentations. Well now, what to charge for the tea set, fruit bowel, vase and gilt cigarette box? I haven't a clue, for time was of no importance then, but even so, with the weight of silver there's no need to sell myself short. I have suddenly found myself at the end of this pot of Irish gold. I put the silver on Hogan's desk.

"There you go Paul, three hundred pounds for the lot." I'm glad to be rid of them.

"Are you sure that's enough? Why don't you make it three-fifty, or you could round it up to four if you like, it's not a problem. Go on up to Michael Clark in accounts and he'll pay you right away," says he most generously.

"Would you like me to make that out in guineas?" asks a smiling Michael, pen in hand.

"Whatever you say yourself Michael, that would be fine." Why not, someday this is going to end.

* * *

I'm in the Tower of London, summoned there at a moment's notice by William Walsh, who had me flown to London to check out harps and shamrocks in the Jewel House for reasons I don't understand. Was it some wealthy Irish American who told him they were here? Are we stirring the pot for Irish reclamation? Do some of the crown jewels belong to Ireland? From the Imperial Crown and other crowns, to the orbs of kings and queens, ampulla and spoons, sceptres, swords, maces, sacramental and banqueting plate, I am closely scrutinizing every item. The most Illustrious Order of St Patrick is here on display, along with the Garter, Thistle and Bath. Why? It has plenty of harps on the golden chain, with a few shamrocks alright on the Star and Badge, these look more like tre-foils. And that's all there is to report. This whole episode is bizarre. Never mind. Did Walsh really think there were jewels stolen which should be returned? Still, I get to stay in the Intercontinental, three courses, full English breakfast, existential. Floating as a cloud that Kilkenny was dreaming, expenses paid.

* * *

Farrelly is coming towards me on the High Street; there is no avoiding him. "I was thinking what you said to me the other night about God, you were joking of course?" says he, stopping.

"No I wasn't joking. I very much doubt if there is a God." My reply probably sounds somewhat surprised and irritated.

"Do you know, you're the first man that's ever said that to me?" he responds pointedly.

"It's only an opinion and sure we'll all find out soon enough."

"But then it'll be too late for you."

"Too late for what?"

"Your immortal soul."

"What do you mean?"

"To deny God in this life is denying your soul everlasting happiness in the next, you'll roast in Hell!"

"Oh really." I am chuckling.

"You shouldn't be flippant about this now. Take my advice, turn to God!" says he in all seriousness, letting me pass, to move on.

And there's the curate from Belfast, the other side of the street, watching it all. I hurry on fast up to the stables. As I have to sort out living in Paddy Delahunty's ramshackle, high Georgian, brick house on the Parade. I can have a room on the ground floor, without Catholic iconography and with a lavatory and a sink (with just a cold-water tap) in the basement below. The hallway is a store room for bags of cement, scaffolding poles and planks of timber. All this inconvenience for a hefty three pounds a week. But I just have to get away from the house on James's Street.

There's Paddy coming out under the broken fanlight pillard door, a dusty figure in an oversize jacket with the cuffs rolled back.

"I'll be moving in tomorrow, if that's all right with you Paddy?" I ask.

"Not a bit of bother, whenever you like," he replies gayly.

"I'll go on in to leave a few things, do you have a key?"

"Ah no, there isn't one, but you needn't worry, your gear will be alright."

"Are you sure?"

Paddy frowns in surprise. "Of course."

"What about the front door?"

"It's never locked, you may come and go as you please. No women mind you." He laughs down the high stone steps.

This will just have to do. I'm gazing around the large, much-painted, high stucco ceilinged room. Impressive old Kilkenny marble fireplace, iron grate full of soot and fallen sticks, carpetless wooden floor: a fine gentleman's residence once. A heavy antique bed, probably cheap at an auction, I bet. His wife was supposed to have made it up by now. Still, it's not so bad really, to be alone in austere splendour here, right beside the stables.

I'm watching Paddy outside through the window, this builder of sorts, loading his A40 with cement, connecting it to a trailer with mixer on. I don't believe this, now he's even tying a ladder on the roof. And off he goes in a fierce cloud of dirty exhaust smoke, near well laden down and slow moving

Up to the third floor and see about this bed then. I knock on the open door. Paddy's wife is sitting in a pink dressing gown at the kitchen table covered with many messy breakfast leftovers. Exhausted, pale and thin, with dark greying hair and a pretty face, finely lined, she is prematurely aged, a baby bottle in one hand, the other holding a cranky child on her knee. It's an awkward time.

"Sorry to disturb you, I was wondering about the bed, did Paddy tell you I'd be moving in tomorrow?" As if she doesn't hear me, she turns away, unperturbed. "Do you know about the bed?" I repeat.

"The bed?" she replies bewildered.

"Yes, you were to make up the bed for me."

"Ah, no. Paddy never said anything to me about you or any bed. Sure I've enough on my hands here as you can see." She smiles to the child lovingly, the bottle sucker in his mouth again.

"Do you have anything I can put on the bed then? I can do it myself."

"No I don't. But if you go on down to the Monster House they should be able to sort you out. It's for that old yoke on ground floor isn't it?" says she, now surrounded by small faces staring at me, as if they have suddenly come out of the woodwork.

"Yes, but Paddy did say..."

"Never you mind Paddy." She cuts me off somewhat annoyed. "He's no right to be making promises like that without first checking with me. There's a mattress on the bed, so a few sheets and blankets is all you need."

"In the Monster House?"

"The Monster House, yes."

I'm irritated and regret having paid Paddy in advance. On leaving, I look at an etching on the landing wall: a large, askew framed image of the Duke of Wellington riding over the field of Waterloo with a young lady seated with him. The duke has a nice outfit, I love his boots. What a find. In this house of all places. 'Prayer to St Theresa, please pick me a rose from the heavenly garden and send it to me with a message of love.'

I will get sheets and blankets from mother at home. There's nothing doing here for a while. It seems the boys from Coras Trachtala are sleeping, so I will let them lie.

CHAPTER 6

In limbo and feeling an indeterminate carelessness again, I cross the border into Newry. For whatever reason, I've never liked the largely nationalist town. Onwards into this land of milk and honey, for God's chosen people, the thirteenth tribe of Israel, the new Jerusalem. I sense the great Protestant wind that drove Spain's armada to ruin and I find my thoughts are blown back to the classroom of an English education.

Approaching the stunted remains of De Courcy's little motte and bailey castle at Clough, the Union flag flutters in the same wind, a gentle breeze now. Downpatrick, then past the old defunct railway station and on up the hill of English Street — the hangman's drop bricked up above in the wall of the old jail — to park in front of the Cathedral.

The grave of my maternal grandparents is just the other side of the graveyard gate. To the left, slightly higher, is the great granite slab from the Mourne Mountains covering the supposed remains of Saints Patrick, Columcille and Bridget. Here are sublime views of marshes and tumbling greens. South over the Mournes and way beyond, is a place that only exists in the imagination, it is called Kilkenny. A chimera from here.

I enter the cathedral's musty and damp odorous embrace. Here, I used to sit in that old stall, with himself freshly Brylcreamed, shoes polished and face cutthroat-razor shaved. Our Sunday mornings had a meticulous ritual, which involved me watching him get ready. I collected the money on a blue velvet-covered brass plate; it was a most responsible position. I would gaze at those beautiful coat-of-arms around the walls of the aisles, designs that were so fascinating. The Downshire's had a gold-spotted leopard and reindeer holding their shield. Others, whose names flitted from mother's lips, canary-like in the background, included: Stewarts of Lawrencetown, Annesleys of Castlewellan, Delacherois of Donahadee, Kers of Portavo, Johnstons of Ballykilbeg (who mother took me to see once), Hamiltons of Killyleagh, Beauclerks of Ardglass, Craig Lauries of Myra Castle, Fordes of Seafarde, Gordons of Delamont, Stewarts of Mountstewart, Nugents of Portaferry and Halls of Narrowater. Hall married his nurse, who was a Catholic and converted, I heard them say. There is poetry in this place and these names, yet within these walls I somehow feel a sense of decay and Protestant decline.

There are wreaths of red red poppies on the war memorial by the road leading out of Downpatrick to Strangford. Realisation comes to me for a moment that I'm blessed to have been born here and to have had my first awareness of life in these surroundings. Turning into Viscount Bangor's sylvan estate, I make for a workshop in the Castle Ward farmyard dominated by a Jacobean tower house, overlooking the sea-green lough. I can see him through a window, unaware of me, bent to concentrate on fastidious workings of gold and silver. In his Opti Visor, he looks like a large insect. He is totally absorbed in his artistry and I wonder what little difference is there between the two of us? It's shame to distract him but I open the unlocked door. Annoyed, he turns to me and upon recognising his visitor, cries out in his loud and friendly northern voice, "what about you, I suppose you're up to get your freebees on the National Health; have you no conscience?"

"So, what are you making then Graham?" I ignore his remark.

"I'm setting this amethyst in a cross for the Bishop of Down, before you so rudely interrupted."

"Very nice. You certainly get some interesting jobs," I say, admiring his fine workmanship.

"But of course, they come only to the best." Graham leans back and stretches his arms, smiling wide at me, boastfully playful. He's a big man with dark, wavy hair and a pointed beard. We studied metal-working together in our College of Art days in Belfast, in riot and foolishness and for my part, the subject had been taken by mere chance.

The workshop for his solitary endeavours was a long, single-storey room, with the usual confusion of scattered tools and piles of jewellery that he was still working on.

"Graham where can I get Durex?"

"Durex!" Mock horror.

"Yes. Just to be on the safe side, if the situation arises."

"And you obviously think it will?"

"Who knows? Not yet anyway; well very nearly, just the once."

"But my dear fellow, you're now living in the South of Ireland where such use is strictly forbidden."

"So it seems."

"And don't you forget it. Catholics believe sex is only for procreation within marriage, and not pleasure for its own sake. Serves you right to be working down there, ha ha ha."

"So where do I go?"

"It's not a problem my friend, you'll get them in Blake's surgical supplies, Pottinger Entry, between High Street and Ann."

"I won't hold you up, I can see you're a busy man."

"It's not a problem, we'll have a coffee before you go."

How time flies...

"You go carefully now, and don't be overdoing it with the fair colleens." Graham speaks with amusement, getting back to his setting, a true friend.

* * *

I don't know what it is about asking for these, they are only common sense really and I shouldn't feel embarrassed, walking furtively towards the man. He's a small round figure in a white coat, behind the counter at Blakes.

"Can I get some Durex?" I ask him boldly.

"Indeed you can Sir, they come in packets of three and a gross, plain or feather lite."

"That's twelve in a packet?"

"Correct."

"God, I'd hardly need that many."

"You're obviously not from the Free State then?"

"Why do you say that?" I am surprised.

"We sell a lot to certain individuals from there. The other day I sold fifty packets to a regular from Dublin."

"Fifty packets of a gross?"

"Oh yes."

"That's ... see six hundred if my arithmetic's correct, that's an awful lot."

"The record was a hundred."

"A hundred gross?"

"And the feather lite as well."

"Twelve hundred featherlike, my goodness that's hard to believe!"

"Not really if you take the population of Dublin as a whole."

"A mere drop in the ocean as they say."

"Mind you they're breaking the law, civil and canon, but sure where there's a willie there's a way," says he, winking with a dirty little laugh.

"Would you give them a discount for that many?"

"Five percent."

"A nice little earner on black market prices to the desperate," I say, thinking aloud.

"It all comes from the Pope and Saint Augustine for them you know. They'll outbreed us Protestants here eventually!" He shakes his head seriously.

"Not if you keep selling them at that rate surely? I'll take six of the feather lite." I have a sudden urge to get away out of this.

In the Crown Liquor Saloon, I experience a reversal of those earlier postive feelings about my home, feelings are now strangely distorted amidst the crowded and loud Ulster speak. Saint Augustine. Durex. Smuggling them across the border with the cattle and pigs. I look at these people as if for the first time, in a new and disturbing light, by the ornate, coloured glass, under the dark patterned ceiling, in secretive conspiratorial booths. Standing by the bar waiting to be served, I watching as would a spy, an ornithologist closely observing the species... they are unexpectedly foreign. How amazing! With a nudge on the arm, from someone beside me, my attention returns to the waiting barman.

"What'll you have Sir?"

"A glass, no pint of... Guinness." Where did that come from? Out of nowhere; I've never even tasted the stuff before. Warm and creamy smooth, where have you been until now?

Approaching the old homestead from Ballynahinch, Nicky Annett is sitting by the red waterworks gate in the tall summer grass of the ditch with his collie dog. The pair of them totally in tune with each other's every movement and sounds, opposite the laneway to his farm. Mother maintains that Nicky lives mostly on Ormo white bread, spread with butter and rhubarb and ginger jam. I would see them together, crossing over the fields: a mysterious, loping bachelor figure in a real world all of his own. A single Tilley lamp light at his window. Ulster nights, unmanageable, and him dreaming of a moth that flew down the chimney and turned into a naked woman.

"Hi Nicky, how are you?" I stop the car beside him. He does not recognise me at first, I'm away in a far place. Then he removes his cap and brushes back his grizzled scalp.

"Boys a boy, the boy up from the South. Your father told me you're working down there now."

"In Kilkenny, do you know it?"

"Not atall, I was in Newry a few times, the nearest I ever got to the border." Pausing for a while, there is something on his mind, then he adds, "there's terrible quare things going on these days, you wouldn't know what's going to happen eventually."

"Is that right?"

"I tell you for sure."

A black-faced, horned sheep comes up behind him the other side of the iron gate. Aware, the dog turns flickering, bared teeth at the silent intruder. A brief interlude in life's journey, with man, dog and sheep. It is trivial, yet startlingly profound, Creation's magic, found here by a narrow, County Down roadside.

With blue-green colours of sky and gentle sloping hills on both sides, I pass the overgrown remains of an ancient ring fort surrounded by ash trees. Ulster's confusion is in my head. Turning into the steep driveway of the farmyard, I'm home. There's no one about, but a mongrel dog, woken by the noise, comes slinking hesitantly towards me, tail lowered. I'm aware of the faintest movement of pigs, half-hearted squeaks behind walls and half-doors. There are the smells of dung, diesel and Ervine's of Newry's meal bags. I'm now in Protestant Ulster's comforting embrace and feel the light touch of my maternal ancestors. Patting the dog — who is wagging his tail now — I approach the door. There's a tall, black pump with a long, carving ball-ended handle. I remember once pulling the covering up and looking down into a damp, cavernous chamber below. It was frightening in its size, over a pool of cold, dark water stretching under the house and yard. All calm and peaceful above, an awful tragedy waiting to happen one day should the surface crack and break! God only knows what's lying under the ground here and in the bones of inherited memories handed down to each new generation.

Father's reading Irish history. I open the book randomly and read a few lines. *A fortnight later Cromwell with 3000 ironsides reached Dublin, the great guns echoing forth their welcome, and acclamations of the people resounding in every street.* You wouldn't have thought so, but the author is Professor of Irish History, Queens University Belfast.

I pick up their wedding photograph: All Saints Church, Srinagar Kashmir 1935. Then another of himself with six heavily coated airmen, British Military Mission to Russia, Air Section at Archangel 1941. Conjugal love and momentous events in far off places, one of the few.

He comes in with an effluvium of pigs, wearing a blue boiler suit and muddy wellington boots.

Mother makes a simple tea. She finds blankets and sheets in the deep, bottom drawer upstairs. There's a small cardboard box underneath, it has a curious looking brooch inside, one I've never seen before. Taking it from me, she gazes at it... and she's no longer here.

"Where did that come from?" I ask.

"I had a boyfriend in the 16th Hyberdad Regiment, he gave it to me to wear, it's their badge in platinum. I met him in Ambala but his regiment was posted to Thal or the North West Frontier, he... never mind, it was a long time ago." Quietly spoken, her eyes are moisting as she puts the brooch back in the box and closes the drawer. The she leaves the room.

I feel awkward... but I take the brooch out again, Indian made, inter-twined numerals and letters, hardly platinum though and what is the story behind this artefact?

There's no knowing the workings of the mind in dreams or in military matters. With those two Dubliners from Kimmage who came to Belfast to join the Irish Guards. Our hands raised together, swearing allegiance to Queen Elizabeth II. In grey ill-fitting raincoats, shroud like, anaemic and corpse pale, risen from the dead Ireland of de Valera's disappearing Irish. Did they speak soft and shyly? Smoke Woodbine cigarettes right down to the smallest butt as if the only sustenance to survive on somehow? In the throbbing stern of the Ulster Prince or was it the Monarch? On that blackest night crossing the Irish Sea, they were cold and forgotten, then sitting in a dirty railway carriage waiting at Heysham in Lancashire's dismal early morning winter lights. Two innocents abroad, one even taking out his rosary beads, lips moving in silent prayer. The dark mid-land towns flew past on their journey to where?

From London to Caterham, they could hear shouts from the parade ground drawing near. Sleeping in a prefabricated dormitory quarter called Passchendale... awake!

I am in my bed at home. Looking out over the familiar landscape of Nicky Annett's imagination. From the window, in the glow of the full moon, I can see an enormous yellowy-white moth with the body of Miss Eire flying over me!

CHAPTER 7

A feather light touch on the nose awakens me again in disquieting circumstances. I am surrounded by Delahunty's brood, who are laughing and running around the room, looking into everything. They can't expect me to live like this? Annoyed, I get out of the antique bed unwashed and unfed, showing them away like vermin. Has anything been taken?

But lo and behold the builders have started work on the workshop. Entering the stables, I see there's a lorry and men with Sowersby unloading materials. Going over to him, I ask, "do you need me for anything yet?"

"No, no, Montgomery's plans that he took from your instructions are clear enough for the moment. This is Seamus Butler who'll be in charge when I'm not here," says Sowersby, introducing a small and wiry man to me. We shake hands.

These psychedelic days may soon be over, or maybe they are just beginning? Having basked in the sun's terrifying heartbeat, which I've seen close up in pictures and from where we all came, I will have to try and get serious about Kilkenny and register with the Assay Office in Dublin.

* * *

I enter the Assay Office from Ship Street under a big, stone-archway side gate. Dublin Castle is mostly a collection of scattered, Georgian-type buildings that have seen better days. Empty rooms behind dirty windows, an overgrown garden, high walls, wandering and lingering yesterdays. A chapel, two massive drum towers. The seat of British rule in Ireland, they say, for nearly eight hundred years. I find that the Assay Office is a small two-storey, red-brick building sadly out of place beside and below the much larger castle proper. Steep steps lead up to a gable-end, an open door and a short corridor. On pressing the bell by the hatch, it opens to the extraordinary beauty of Irish womanhood in full bloom... her sudden and unexpected appearance is startling and painful. Marie Mulcahy, Marie Mulcahy, like rare Irish honey, thick and cunt sweet on the tongue. I can see her lovely brown eyes and she's aware of the effect she has upon me.

"I phoned you yesterday about getting my maker's mark registered, there's three of them here in different sizes." I hand them to her, smiling and staring silently. She holds the markers without looking at me.

"Ah, yes, that's right. The Captain would like a word with you." Her voice is low and siren-like.

"The Captain?"

"Captain Le Bas the Assay Master, he wanted to see you. I'll let you in and get these marked, you'll need to fill out a registration form."

Following after her curvaceous and scented body (cruel world), I'm shown into a small office. "The Captain will be with you in a short while." As she leaves, she is laughing lightly and knowingly.

The blue and red Dublin Assay quartered arms with two unicorns is framed behind his desk. Captain of the Assay, or even captain in the army, these are hardly ranks to hold onto in civilian life. I'm as apprehensive as if I were at school waiting to see the housemaster. What could he want?

Le Bas is a slight, balding man in a bit of a sweat, it seems. He flings a newspaper down on his desk in front of me. "What's the meaning of this?"

He is pointing to a picture in the *Sunday Independent* of the tea set I recently sold to Coras Trachtala. *The coffee set Americans are talking about. Now in the home of Mr Melvin D. Dawley, President of New York's top flight store of Lord and Taylor is an Irish silver coffee service (pictured above). No ordinary coffee service is this – it is the beginning of a battle in shape, form and design which Irish industry has begun.*

Whoever wrote this? It continues: *Mr Haughey, Chairman, Coras Trachtala, presented the coffee set to Mr Dawley at a reception at the Irish Export Centre, in Ireland House, New York. The design is the work of a young man just out of his twenties now designer silversmith for Kilkenny Design Workshops Ltd. The company was set up to produce designs for any Irish metal producing company.*

They have printed so many errors. I am not out of my twenties and it was a tea set, not a coffee set.

"So what's your problem. Captain?"

"Your IRISH, silver coffee set hasn't been hallmarked!"

"It was hallmarked in London."

"All foreign gold and silver goods have to be hallmarked at the Dublin Assay office before they can be sold here. Understand. You're breaking the law, we never hallmarked this ENGLISH made coffee set." The Captain is most forceful.

"With the London hallmark as well?"

"Yes!" Hitting the desk with his fist.

"What is the import mark?"

"A Bouget."

"A Bouget." I repeat.

"A Bouget with date letter and fineness mark."

They could have purchased it in the North, that'll fox him. No, best to keep on his right side, eat humble pie, roll over dog-like. I have to live with this.

"God, I never knew Captain, I do apologize. It's in New York now according to this stupid article."

"What are you doing down there anyway? We've been reading a lot about Kilkenny in the papers these days," he says, slightly more mollified now.

"It's all talk at the moment, as you can see, it'll be some months before we will require your services, but I'm registering anyway." He'll like that.

"You'll be producing designs for the Irish metal industries?"

"That's doubtful, no matter what they say, Kilkenny will end up being an arts and crafts undertaking, in my workshop at least. Lots of silverware to be hallmarked." I smile at him.

"The trade here will hardly take kindly to this," he says.

"I can well imagine, unfair competition, state subsidies, free publicity."

"Indeed."

"I'm really sorry about the tea set, it never crossed my mind, you still have the crown on the harp, the badge of the RUC."

"And we'll never get rid of it," Le Bas says emphatically, "comes from our royal charter granted by Charles I, the King Majesty's stamp, the Harp Crowned." Sitting behind his desk now and lighting an Afton Major, he inhales to the full, relaxing and contemplative. I wouldn't want to get on his wrong side though.

With a light tap on door, Marie enters with pen and form. "You just fill out this and you're registered with the Company of Goldsmiths of Dublin." She speaks with a minx-like, butterfly touch and she's gone, but still there. The Captain, slightly annoyed at the interruption, slap's his hand on it.

"Le Bas is a most unusual name, where does that come from?"

"French Huguenot originally. We left France just after the Saint Bartholomew day massacre in fifteen seventy-two."

"Protestant refugees you were?"

"Oh yes, well before the revocation of the Edict of Nantes in sixteen eight-five by Louis fourteenth, nearly a hundred years later."

"Extraordinary."

"We came to England and eventually Ireland, and as silversmiths."

"Are yez all right there?" shouts an inebriated man in a ragged, belted coat, as I leave at the gate. There is a loud yelping wail from a herring gull, perched on a gable end. That Marie melting all over; what is a Bouget?

* * *

We'll have Kilkenny silver again.
City to be Silver Centre.
Ancient Tradition Revived.
A craft that was practised on the Nore as far back as 850BC and knew its glorious years between 1650 and 1700 before finally dying out, will soon be revived in Kilkenny. Within two months it is expected that articles of silver will be manufactured...

I glance, dismayed, at the *Kilkenny People*'s latest edition in the newsagents on High Street.

They've put a shoe under the sheets and been into everything. I will have to get a lock, or leave stuff in the stables. The builders are not here, but the old roof and side are nearly gone; where are they? Maybe it's a Holy day; I can't think of which one. There's been a fire by the pathway of discarded woodworm and dry rot wood, the charcoal remains are still smouldering and warm. So they must have been working yesterday.

Miss Eire is coming through the far archway. "You're to phone Mr Hogan right away," she shouts over, turning and leaving. Not a chance there, shame. Could have gone up to the loft together, quickly now, or this evening.

Paul Hogan wants something for the Irish Building stand at Olympia in London and a packaging prize. What can we do? Le Bas mentioned Gunning's and there's a firm that does aluminium fittings for the building trade. I could give each a try.

I do not yet have even a table to work on, but work in a dusty space, curled in one of the thick, round windows. I draw with paper and pencil on a flat piece of wood. Is this an historical moment, as pencil touches paper, is this what Kilkenny Design will be?

* * *

There is a large (blue and white, as always) statue of the Virgin Mary in the front reception of Gunning's, the ecclesiastical metal workers in Fleet Street. Nonchantly, I run a hand up her demure side, when comes a hollow, deep voice, as if risen from the dead.

"Don't be doing that, you do leave her alone!" Drawing back, I'm caught unawares. A tall, gaunt woman is behind the counter now, with a face of malignant disapproval. Immaculately conceived from one pope out of the blue and wasn't it the awful Pacelli Pope who dreamed up her physical assumption into heaven? The same pope who never once condemned the Holocaust or the plight of the Jews.

"It was only a friendly rub, and no harm was done."

"She's not to be touched. And what can I do for you?"

"I've to see Larry Gunning."

The owner appears in a soiled apron; I'd say he has a keen antenna for business. I show him the design I did in Kilkenny, which he studies carefully, then, turning to me, Larry smiles. "Is this the way forward we've been reading about lately?"

"That's nothing to do with me, what they write about. Can you make it?"

"Should be no problem, it's an unusual looking yoke. I'll work out a price and let you know," says Larry, evidently somewhat amused. Old hands, uninterested in new tricks.

"You don't have to, just make it as fast as you can."

"Are you sure?"

"Well roughly then, I won't hold you to it."

His lips move silently a while at the design again. The Virgin, Aryan, blue-eyed and fair skinned, benoventy watching over us. The young Jewish woman of Nazareth in Galilee.

"Shouldn't be more than one hundred and fifty, maybe less." He is confident.

"When will you have it?"

"Give me two, or three weeks at the most."

"I'll call you in a fortnight then."

"Would you like to have a look around our workshop?" Unexpectedly, he makes this most unusual offer.

Here are men busy at half-moon benches. They look up at me from their mysterious workings on Catholic religious artefacts with suspicion. A chalice here, a monstrance there, and I wouldn't know what those other items are for. I watch a man hammer up a silver flagon from the drawing and template beside him.

"This is a tabernacle for a church in Florida." From somewhere I remember the tent of the wandering Israelites. "And candlesticks for Cross Michael's new cathedral in Galway," Larry explains.

"Cross Michael?"

"The Bishop of Galway."

In the polishing shop, the two polishers are like coal miners from the dirt of polishing silver and brass. Grey, wary faces, they have the worst job in the trade. As with the pigs, the smell here impregnates ones clothing, simply by being near the room. From spinners to chasers, engravers and so on, everything done under the one roof. You couldn't teach these Dubliners anything. Well-made and Catholic-designed for their religion worldwide. For how long though, with the many changes coming from the Second Vatican Council?

"Would you ever be interested in new, modern domestic silverware?" I ask him.

"We can always look at what you're about in Kilkenny," replies Larry half-heartedly. I know full well he thinks Kilkenny is a joke.

With difficulty I find Unidare in dreary Finglas on the North side. In preparation for a Celtic-inspired abstract design made from aluminium extrudings, I have them cut up various lengths and weld them together on their premises. In little over an hour, out of nowhere, without drawings, it is finished and looks fine.

Parking the car in Fitzwilliam Square, I have time for a mixed grill in the Shelbourne Hotel (side entrance off Kildare Street), making sure to keep the receipt. I am aware of being in this divided island of consciousness turning into dreams. From the precision of Unidar's extrudings and loud noise of men and machines, to Larry Gunning's silent, mocking undertones and Kilkenny's subtle seduction. A whiskey in their spacious bar, with customers well content in the comforts of easy talk, alcohol and nicotine. It is getting late and time to leave.

There are women along by the railings, concealed in the darkening and overhanging trees. Their high-heeled legs are visible: still and sauntering temptation. Opening the rear door, the aluminium construction on the back seat seems to shudder and melt to the heart's quickening heat. Catching her eye, I nod and smiling, she approaches hesitantly, scented and warm. She has a face of insane beauty, yet somehow with a desperation drawn out of famine and dispossession. I feel a sudden strangeness over me, sublime and exquisite in the moment, as I beckon her to get in the car. She directs me to a narrow laneway and there in the depth of old Ireland, we cling madly. I am locked helpless in her embrace.

There's a two hour journey back to Kilkenny, through Naas and Athy and I'm as fearful as if I were in a boat on a stormy sea. Until, as I arrive at the wide calming waters of Castlecomer, with the moon riding gently over Kilkenny, I feel for my wallet. It has gone.

By the banks of the Nore, wide and immutable, I drive onwards past Hubert Butler and his ten thousand saints. Under the high castle walls, contemplative in the silent, silver hours. A seed of worry grows to extraordinary shapes in my thoughts, ridiculous and weird. I am thinking about elongated, sweeping silver sauce boats; extended belly vases and coffee pots more like elegant plumbing than silversmithing. Candelabra and letter openers are always useful and make a nice gift. Condiment sets with emerald green glass liners and coasters to slide a rare claret across fine, antique tables. Salad servers and napkin rings with the men of Jerpoint chased playfully around. Or maybe it's a kind of torc-inspired jewellery they would like, variations on the Gleninsheen Gorget perhaps? For this will not be George Jenson overnight.

* * *

This Norwegian-inspired concept in Walsh's head, that seems like a great idea for Kilkenny, will work itself right in the long end. Articles for sale; prototypes and commissions for Irish industry; old Ireland will be transformed. I'm seated in the Marble City Bar, when I hear the taunts of Eastwood and Young. The two bad pennies have turned up yet again, both immediately spied me upon entering.

"And how many fancy tea pots did you make today?" Eastwood calls over. Young is more interested in the barman's attention, silently thumping the counter with his clenched fist. They mean no harm.

My emotional world is bursting over, in the beauty of the blue-green island and with a realization of the too-fragile, flickering fire. The Prince of Denmark's march somehow. I'm fearful, passing the loud cries of the enormous man-child on the corner of Rose Inn on High Street: dressed in filthy rags he sells the *Herald* as if in supplication to an indifferent God.

A Virgin-coloured Sunbeam Rapior drives into the stables just as the builders are leaving. They've been doing just fine the last few days. And getting out is an almond-skinned Andalusian-looking woman, lovely at first sight, smiling as I approach. Who could she be? Miss Anna Rose Carrigan from Coras Trachtala, introducing herself as Walsh's new secretary, wants to be shown around the stables and Kilkenny. She has a gorgeous tight arse and fine legs, which I appreciate as she goes up the loft staircase before me. It is painful to be with such thoughts. I picture us on the wide dusty plank floor, flesh against rough stone walls, or sitting in those big circular windows. All in vain. We gaze out on both sides, from the castle to the courtyard, as Seamus Butler strolls across the stones, inconsequential and abstract below us. Taking out a soft white packet of Kent cigarettes, she offers me one, saying, "They're very mild." Smiling at me as Eve would to Adam, and why not this time?

Anna has a gold lighter, drawn from within a crocodile skin handbag. The well-made clicks allow us to light our cigarettes, then she shuts the bag. Her eyes momentarily glaze over, inhaling, for one can't normally get these in Ireland. Certainly, they are mild and toasted and smoking Kents is a far-too-easily acquired habit, like le Brocquy's Gauloises before. She could be American, Argentinian or Brazilian.

Her parents probably purchased farmland, with horses faintly whispering in the background. This is just a job for a while and something for her to do.

Sherry in the Club House before lunch, slipping into nonsense like drowning in syrup or the pea soup. I have a roast beef that I hardly touch and I would rather have coffee with another Kent than dessert. It is time to step out of this dance, for she has more to do. As this day runs into the next and the following weeks.

We must sort a small room for Walsh's weaver from the Coombe. This means upsetting Montgomery, who was never consulted. He's in a sulk, threatening to resign, or what? We get chairs and tables and clean up the front loft for Professor Edna Martin from the Art and Design School in Stockholm. She is coming for a textile seminar and needs some where to stay. We book her into the Rose Hill Hotel, a rather nice old house by the Callan road on the way out of Kilkenny.

* * *

I'm at the back not listening to a word the professor is saying to the students and others from Dublin and beyond. I'm watching the beautiful blondes, Astrid, Brigitte and Helena. The Swedish sold iron ore to the Germans and locked up Allied sympathizers. I can't think of a single Swede that did much for humankind. King Gustov Adolf, the Protestant lion of the north. Well hardly.

* * *

O'Connor's loom is a fragile, old-wooden, clattering contraption which is easily installed. He's in the smallest room of the rear crescent upstairs, looking out to the metal workshop, which is separate behind. His is tedious work. I'm watching as the thin thread of the weft from the bobbin flies across the many threads of the warp. Left to right hand, hardly more than a few yards a day. He's contented and happy enough, though, away from those still remembered violent riots of the Dutch and Flemish Huguenot weavers who escaped from persecution to settle in the Coombe.

Most afternoons, O'Connor sleeps. Oblivious to the slow and dripping sadness of all that history. He's old man now, who only speaks when spoken to. William Walsh will be so pleased with the dinner jacket, made from this hand-woven, truly Irish poplin.

Another load of building material appears through the archway. I'll need to order silver soon, Also sulphuric acid and Calor gas from Eastwood at the gas works. And I'll have to hire another silversmith or two. There's one in London who might be interested. Someone young would be best, maybe, when the time comes.

This is a day of light winds and intermittent cloud. One Kilkenny hour follows another and here's Robbie Haughton in his green Wolsey. The relative of the Butlers Mountgarret, with the bond between us, a secret familiarity, nods as he passes, his pedigree safe. Does everyone know? Hogan's in Denmark, and I'm told he was the boyo who stole the disputed painting from the Tate Gallery in 1957. I must make something on silver for the Irish pavilion at the New York world's fair next year.

Like a great ring of pure and endless light,
All calm, as it was bright
And round beneath it, Time in hours, days years,
Driven by the spheres.

* * *

Ireland can't possibly exist. This is the conclusion of the many tangled, overloaded, connecting sparking points of my fevered brain. From one person to another, I travel at the speed of light. The trophy design must be shown to the mysterious and sinister director of the Arts Council, a Jesuit Priest. Then there is an envious, disgruntled letter from a Pádraig Ó'Mathuna, challenging me to make an exact copy of the Tara Brooch.

The awesome Long Cantwell of Butler's lovely Kilfane, makes me think of broken walls and forgotten lives. The statue stands before ruins that are now home to many crows. In the sudden silences, Ireland can only be found in some unintelligible mathematical formula of time and space. It would take an Albert Einstein or Enrico Fermi to make sense of the place. To split the Irish conundrum: for could it be that Adolf Hitler is having tea with Eamon de Valera and Dublin's Archbishop John Charles McQuaid?

In my dream, Paul Hogan was wearing a coal scuttle helmet and William Walsh was in the uniform of a high ranking SS officer with the Knight's Cross with oak leaves and swords, it was frightening.

An old lady runs Alwright and Marshall, the silversmith's, on Fade Street. She is pleasant but wary enough, poking into her business. I couldn't pull the wool over her eyes, I could tell. On display were Celtic wire-edged trays, Georgian reproduction strawberry dishes and dairy maid tea sets, with few examples of worthwhile Irish design, according to the Scandinavian Design Group in Ireland. They had no appreciation of the material and its possibilities: little real understanding of the intricate early Christian motifs, the interlaced animals. There was too much of an emphasis on ornamentation, no feeling for the simple strength and rhythm of the originals. The many Ardagh chalices as tea pots, are only shallow and worthless imitations.

No, no, I couldn't even contemplate how I would design these items. A Holy Ghost Father is collecting his new, reproduction De Burgo-O'Malley chalice and paten. Case beautifully made, he's delighted. The customer had always been right.

CHAPTER 8

Friday evening, in the little, carmine-coloured bar of the Club House, I am waiting on John Young to arrive. He's half an hour late and obviously not coming. I should never have bought the insurance policy from him, one that hopefully pays two thousand pounds at forty. A long way off, with inflation, and might I even be as dead as the empty glass before me? He'd get the commission right away. So the least he could do is stand me the promised few drinks and a meal.

"Are you waiting for Young?" says Tom Eastwood on entering.

"He was to buy me a meal."

"He'll never turn up, I know what he's like," Eastwood says sitting down beside me, highly amused. Turning to the bar, he pauses surprised. "Wow, who is that girl? Never seen the likes of her in Kilkenny before!"

There's a strikingly beautiful girl now behind the bar counter, with another. Her dark hair is tied in a bun; both of them are in blue coats.

"I'll ask her to the dance, you never know your luck with women, it's always a wheel of fortune. I'd pass for thirty-five in this light, no ordinary Paddy Mick this, a man of the world." Tom winks mischievously.

"You're far too old for her Tom, you can see she's still a teenager, probably."

"Not a problem, I'll get you a drink, and remember a man's only as old as the woman he feels. Just you watch me, a Smithwicks isn't it?" Generous to a fault and over he goes.

And soon enough they're laughing with him. He returns with the drinks. The earth shattering moments are usually unremarkable, not until days, even years after, do I come to realise their nature. Here, there was no eureka moment. Just a dull evening outside on Patrick Street, with passers-by, the smell of food, the sound of voices and the mellow glow of Scotch and Irish whiskies, tempting me to a subtle dulling of the senses, to make the evening soft and manageable.

I can see the girls are talking about us, they are looking over, she is smiling weakly, as Tom calls over to her. "What about my young friend then, will you go to the dance with him?"

She looks at me with startling grey eyes, extraordinary eyes. Yes, say yes! Then to Tom, "Sure, he'd have no interest in me. It'll be at least ten when I'm finished here." Her Kilkenny voice is melodious and lilting.

"He'll wait then, isn't that so?" says Tom, nodding his head with a silent yes.

"Yes if you'd like?" This to her, causes the momentary blush of a pink rose to appear on her beautiful cheeks. "I'll meet you outside at the front door, at say half past ten then?"

She doesn't say yes, but she doesn't say no. The other girl is plain, bewildered and clearly envious of the fact that her companion is attracting so much attention. Furtive glances across the room, a grand Canyon between the sexes, and Eastwood's copious advice on women.

Draining his glass, he disappears into the darkening city, with a, "let me know how you get on?" That was a strange encounter

Following him out, I check, it is half past nine.

I wait in the car; autumn is drawing near, it is cold enough on the gaseous, yellowy, old sloping street. The sky is overcast, masking all heavenly movement. Customers, the few who come to and from the now mysterious hotel, are curious about me. I shouldn't be parked here. She's not coming. True, she never promised she would. I faintly hear the clock striking eleven, as if taunting me. My watch is slow. Can I try inside, without even her name? It will look bad, what will the management think? Your man from the Design Centre this hour after their barmaid, imagine!

I think back over that chance meeting with Eastwood. I would never be here but for Young, the mean sod. Fireflies have a phosphorescent glow in the night, distorting it. Would she even remember me in the morning? The dance must be nearly over; it's too late, time to leave. Feeling like this. It was those grey eyes: a tunnel to Ireland's troubled past, piercing me painfully, yet orgasmic.

A mosaic of scattered pieces rise in my thoughts.

Geraldine would come to the high gate from the corrugated, iron-roofed cottage nearby. Her face would be dirty with running snot; she had no shoes on her poor wee feet during the war. Mother would give them milk, butter and potatoes, even coal sometimes. Always on the other side of that gate, were Spenser's Irish. 'Out of every corner of the woods and glens they came weeping forth upon their hands, for their legs could not carry them, they looked like anatomies of death, they spoke like ghosts crying out of their graves, they did eat the dead carrion, happy where they could find them. Yea, and one another soon after, in so much as the very carcasses they spared not to savage out of their graves.'

Myriad thoughts come to me in the silent hours, in a type of fever that brings diffuse imaginings. I'm unable to think clearly. A mirage, maybe, is coming towards me from High Street below… I'm in wonder at this. She is wearing a ragged, white coat with her hair let down to her waist. She is nearly beside me!

I get out of the car, and, "I was waiting for you."

She stops startled! I will never forget her appearance until the day die. This 'heavenly beautie' entering my blood stream as Ireland. I'm transfixed.

"I didn't think the pair of you were serious, I've already been to the dance and I'm going back to my room." She speaks with a mixture of concern and distrust.

"Come on then, there's still time, the dance won't be over until midnight, we can drive down."

"I don't know now if I should or not, it's very late." Now she's like a hunted animal, wondering which way to turn.

"You've nothing to fear, I'm not into pillage and rape." And immediately from the look on her face, I sense shouldn't have said the last word. There is silent suffering and oppression here. "It's the Royal Showband isn't it?" I ask.

"Yes it is. I suppose it'll be all right, I'll go then, if you're really sure?"

Going over to the other side and opening the car door, she gets in, looking surprised. Nervously settled in beside me, she has the smell of a wild thing: rain on blackthorn bloom, boggy places and dark woods. These scents will provide strange and unexpected memories to hold long into the future.

I'm always vaguely aware that I'm entering into this other Ireland. Only, I'm taking deeper steps this time. And where are they leading? In a tartan top, beige pleated skirt and tan shoes, she's away with the music, in a seemingly happier, ephemeral state. A stranger, although one of their own, she draws many an inquisitive glance. The dance over, standing to the National Anthem, she hesitantly reaches for my hand expectantly; I take hers and press tightly.

My car is a biblical chariot hurtling to eternity, her eyes are moonlight on water beside me. Where is this mysterious girl from? Realising it is well past midnight, she urges me to take her back to the hotel. The doors are locked and no one can be reused.

"I'll loose my job over this, where can I go now?" says she, upset as a wind in the graveyard.

"Were you staying in the hotel?"

"Yes, it went with the job."

"I'll take you home then."

"No, no, its miles away, you wouldn't understand." She shuts me out. Ghostly, starving images appear in my thoughts, of outcasts from the years long before. Those who went down on bended knees at the big house. Obscure and without substance. In moments like this, something awakens from deep in my consciousness, something impossible to understand.

"Not to worry, I've a room on the Parade, you can sleep in my bed, there's nothing to fear." She doesn't reply and as if sleep-walking gets back in the car and turning to me asks, "will I be all right?"

Like two prisoners escaping in the night, we hurry from the stables where I'm parked, overshadowed by Ormonde's mighty castle, to Delahunty's. I show her into the old, musty and untidy, masculine room.

"Before you get into bed, put this wedge under the door, so you'll not be disturbed by the children upstairs. I'll give you three knocks in the morning for you to let me in." I wouldn't dream of trying anything with her.

"You don't have to," she says sitting on the bed, apprehensive as I'm about to leave.

"Yes I do, and don't forget the wedge."

Outside, on the steps overlooking The Parade, it will soon be early morning light. I'm dazed by the dubious enterprise of making silver in a fantasy city that's an invention of my mind, as is everything that happened here before me. This beauty has fallen out from the multigreen curtain of Kilkenny, one which I can rarely see behind... Uncomfortable, I sleep fitfully in the wide round window... The loft is rising upwards at the far end, then sinking, sliding into the sea. I am afloat, surrounded by all sorts of ghostly creatures, with Farrelly's head that of a shark, smiling horribly.

Awake, awake... Where is this, what am I doing here?

This Kilkenny living is not easy sometimes. Standing, I stretch, sore from the awkward position I had slept in. My thoughts come slowly around to the night before. Will she still be there?

Panic churns my stomach. Amazing, I have never felt this before. It mightn't be the same though, after the night's deceits and many lies. It would be a shame if she's gone. Hopefully not. In growing excitement, I go get her something to eat. It's a short walk to Crotty's for milk, chocolate digestive biscuits and two sticky buns. Returning the sunshine that suddenly sweeps across the wide Parade, I'll soon see. Knock, knock, knock. I wait in the silence of a quickening heartbeat experience a minute of listening that stretches to an eternity.

The door opens to a young woman as miraculous as I remembered her, no falsehood there. 'This glorious ornament of heavenly grace, over feeble eyes in subdued hearts do tyrannize', wrote Spenser, more or less.

She is without shoes and her legs are bare, echoing a coy remembrance I have of her, when my imagination set her in Irish poverty last night.

"I thought you might have flown and I'd never see you again."

"Without a penny in my pocket, where could I go?" she replies sharply.

"Where do you live then?"

"It's beyond Freshford." Hesitantly, as if not wanting to answer.

"Is that far?"

"About twelve miles."

"Wouldn't have been a problem last night."

"It was too late. Can I have some of those biscuits and a drink of milk. Do you have a cup?"

We sit on the side of the bed together, eat and drink.

"I don't even know your name."

She pauses, undecided, then boldly like throwing a stone, tells me, "Mary, I'm Mary Malone."

"A good Irish name."

"If you say so and yours I already know."

"How come?"

"I recognise you from the papers."

"Is that so."

"Oh, yes," she says as if she'd been aware for some time.

"Will you go back to the hotel?"

"I'll have to collect my few things, I'm not working there anymore, they'll fire me anyway."

"That's awful and all my fault, what can I do for you?"

"You could give me the bus fare to Freshford if you like."

"Don't be silly, I'll drive you home."

"We'll see." There is scepticism in her voice now.

What have we here? The indefinable, poignant inheritance from a scarred land and its ancient race. Nothing else will matter much from this day forward but her. Kissing her lightly on the cheek, she touches me with her hand, holding mine as if to keep it.

"Come and I'll show you my workshop, there's a running tap and sink there, where you can brush your teeth with my toothbrush. The builders finish at One on a Saturday, so no one will be there."

"Would it matter if they were?" she asks pointedly.

"Not for me, but maybe for you, the way builders are with such a pretty girl in sight as you."

"Getaway. I'll go around to the hotel first, and get this over with."

"Will I come with you?"

"No, no, I can handle myself." Spoken defiantly.

"And you will be back. I'll meet you up by the stables entrance, won't I?" I find I am almost pleading.

She replies tentatively as though surprised. "Yes, I'll see you there."

There are other mysteries here, the whisperings of darkened stories smoldering from Kilkenny's recent past!

Across the crescent courtyard, a disturbed crow flies off and settles warily at the apex of the far roof. Streaks of blue, cream and white lie still and high as the background to the building. Under the archway I go and through to the nearly completed metal workshop on the ground floor. A newly slated roof slopes down from the rear wall to wooden windows along the front; they will let in plenty of daylight. It is looking good and all going to plan in spite of Montgomery. In a week or two, I will be ready to begin. What? Thunder and lightning, blazing silver and gold!

I have to get the head around silver circle sizes in gauge eleven and twelve. Square wire and round, with hard and easy silver solder and William Walsh impatient to get two pieces the same as he saw in the Danish *Mobilia* Magazine. Shouldn't be too difficult though, a most peculiar request. I must keep a sharp eye on him if he doesn't find his Renaissance in Irish silver, whatever that means in his dreams. I am under a heavy cloud from the many siren calls. Their appeals to my art dull my awareness and common sense somehow.

Here comes Mary: Mary Malone in all her dark and sweet cunning deceit. Mary Malone, the name is a perfect poem in just two words, soft as butter, with taste of wild raspberries and fresh cream. Does King Charles Stuart, askew and cobwebby in the Marquess of Ormonde's estate office, which I am now passing, share my thoughts of softness and fleshy delight? I can see she's rushed and upset, with a small battered case without a handle under her arm. She has a perfect figure and moves as if dancing towards me in fast quick steps.

"The old witch, she called me a tart imagine, I don't deserve that!" Mary exclaims angrily. She is delightfully flushed, breathless and I am thinking that the making of gold and silver is nothing to the living miracle of a female Kilkenny heartbeat.

"All because I made you return to the dance. Let me go and explain to them, it's the least I can do."

"You will not. I never liked working there anyway, and if that's what they think of me, they can keep it!"

"Are you really sure?"

"I am indeed." Emphatically spoken, without a doubt.

"This is where I'll be working." I point towards the workshop.

"Doing what?"

"Silversmithing."

"What does that mean?"

"Making the most amazing articles in silver." My hands are out-stretched, joking.

"Is that right? In Kilkenny of all places, seems weird." Mary shakes her head slowly, puzzled, as well she might be.

"Only time will tell, whatever comes of this." I reply, with a tinge of panic, as puzzled as she. I am imagining the arrival of many Scandinavian academics, with Walsh and Hogan in tow, eager to please them. This is a strange improbability. Is it chance? Or as predetermined as the moving spheres? For there'll never be another opportunity to create my silverware in the fantasy that's Kilkenny. May it last as long as lasts, with Mary just as she is now, upset and confused. All I know is that I will be with her what-ever happens, from this day on, to the very end, just as I will breathe air.

"Will I take you home now?"

"Not yet, show me the sink where I can clean my teeth."

"Oh yes, and you'll see all the machinery that's going into the workshop there."

I sense that she doesn't really want to go home; we spend the afternoon together, which drifts far too soon into nightfall. We eat salmon sand-wiches with tea in the Metropole Hotel at the bottom of James's Street. She's only seventeen, the flower of the county and a mysterious beauty, with secrets here waiting to be found. From where were her forebears? In her inclinations I sense a sadness, as a movement on water, a gentle lap-ping on shoreline.

The road leads out from Kilkenny, past St. Canice's to Freshford. There are few lights now, the odd approaching car, in a landscape that undulates darkly on both sides of us. We drive towards Laois and Tipperary. Wasn't Laois the Queen's county or was it the King's? I think about bloody Mary and her husband, the Catholic fanatic Spanish King Philip. There's the glimmer of inquisitions and the many burnings in the old county names. She's silent beside and looking straight ahead, even more disturbing in the fast changing shadows and dashboard light. It is as if the wings of time are flying above us. Coming into Freshford, she says to turn right, by a small Romanesque church with a double recessed doorway and gable step that I admire. By the dim village light, she is even more precious, like a jewel set in gold.

"Why are you stopping?" she asks nervously.

"Admiring the old church, it's extraordinary, don't you think?"

"I never really thought so, passing it so many times in all kinds of weather." She replies indifferently, "it's Protestant you know."

"So, where do we go now?" Without commenting on her last statement.

"First turn left." I drive into a narrower winding road, leading to God knows where? We come to a crossroads by an obviously Catholic church (pebble dashed, a whitish sailship waiting at anchor).

"You can let me out here." She turns to me tearful and without another word is out of the car, running away up the hill, animal-like, almost back to its own. The fox and the hare... What now?

I will have to climb that hill, however high, to find her again.

CHAPTER 9

In the empty days that follow, my mind wanders between imagination and reality. I collect the silver trophy I designed for Gunnings: it is well made, but somehow disappointing in the finish. Delivering it to Hogan, he semed pleased enough. He was back from Denmark and has given up the Kingsway, instead smoking little Dutch cigars out of a hinged tin. Our long conversation is about nothing in particular: the certain repeated words I'd heard before, how he was looking forward to the new silver that will be made. A Rolf Middelboe from Denmark is coming to start printed textiles and David Reeves will be in the pottery workshop. There'll be Oisin Kelly, in a few weeks. I've to get him the other small room beside O'Connor, without upsetting Montgomery.

"Doing what exactly? I ask, as Hogan leans back on the two legs of his chair and lights another cigar. The smoke I'm inhaling is pleasantly hallucinogenic.

"Our artist-in-residence; a free spirit doing his own thing a day or two each week. It will be interesting to see what comes of it. He's very good with animals and birds you know."

"I see I see…" Preposterous silver articles are taking shape above his head.

On the way out there's Wesley Burroughs, a lighthouse of subtle warning and good sense.

* * *

"Well my boy, did she make a man of you the other night?" Eastwood calls across the crowded Marble City bar with his distinctive Lancashire voice, irritating me.

"No she did not and I certainly didn't try and where were you anyway, you still owe me that meal Mr John Young!" Young is seated beside Eastwood as usual, well away in the drinking humour.

"Sure you'd never have met the girl if it wasn't for me. Tom tells me she's a looker, so ain't you the lucky one." Young replies, carelessly amused. If I could only find her.

* * *

The Parade is deserted this late hour. Looking out from the window of the big old room, I watch autumn leaves scurry in occasional little gusts of a breeze. There is fragility in everything. The grandson of the great Duke once used to parade his troops up and down there; I was told that was how the street got its name. I must return to the crossroads by Freshford soon. Will it even be there? Where did she disappear to? Girls like her just don't live up laneways, in out-of-the-way places. No, she must live in a world of Venetian masked and sinister clowns, gypsy encampments, travelling performers. She's probably miles away by now, continually moving, drawn by horses. Wearing bright colours to the sounds of haunting music. A people not of the present, treated as outcasts, like the 'treacherous Jews'.

More Irish trickery, a will-o-the-wisp over the faintly blue bog. The white owl in the pine plantation with big, yellow eyes that stared at me and never flew. For there was grace and nobility here, you could clearly see that. Wandering and wondering, in and out of sleep... time squeezes like an accordion in and out, from days to months and even years. Before and back again in the living that's Kilkenny. To the extraordinary of the seemingly ordinary. As with the blind who are made to see for the first time, I'm puzzled beyond comprehension. I feel like spilled mercury in extra slow motion, as it makes the most incredible meeting with a reality it can never hold.

There's a self-contained flat on the third floor of Haughton's; it has a bathroom on the landing. I can move in any time and another two flats will be ready soon. Should I get in touch with the silversmiths at Vanders and Naylor Brothers? The two I met while they were doing their apprenticeship at the Central. What would they make of Kilkenny? A slow drowning in the moist soft air. They would eventually be into women and breeding and the curious character of the silversmithing. One I could see ending up in the graveyard: a regular Kilkenny man forever. The other would probably leave. Look at Eastwood and the old Black and Tan, who, after terrorizing the land, married an Irish girl and settled peacefully in some midland town.

From the flat window, I can see the large Frenchified dowager Marchioness's house beyond Haughton's garden below. I'm living in reasonable comfort at last, like floating in a balloon.

So the setting up of this ancient and mysterious craft begins, we are moving in all the tools and machinery at last. The silverware will be ever so slowly made and hallmarked Irish in every detail. Eight half circle spaces are cut out of the thick wooden benches, with leather aprons underneath to catch the filings and scrap. Green, angle-poise lights above each place, file and hammer racks, the lathe screwed onto the floor by the wall, same as the polisher in the small end room. A ventilated covering over the hearth, by which is a metal turntable with sheets of asbestos on top and a tank of heated ten percent sulphuric acid and water beside. A filing cabinet, an adjustable architect's desk (the very best money could buy), and a wide chest of drawers for paper and working drawings.

Already, there were too many faces at the long windows peering in, making me a prisoner, caged in a freak show. They come right up to the glass, a hard shielding for viewing. I can well imagine the hillarity of the lads at Gunning's at this. Never mind, whatever, it was important just to get started, to get the wheels turning.

William Walsh and Paul Hogan suddenly enter without knocking, startling me, like detectives out of nowhere, addressing me with just a few words. They stand over me stoney-faced; I'm mostly silent. What are they about? I'm nervous that the pair from the Export Board, to whom I owe this position, are watching me, wondering what is it that I'm making? The Viscount Mountgarrets' relative is at the rear window as well.

I'm dishing a silver circle with a ball-faced hammer on the circular recess carved out of the old tree trunk. Then I strike a Friendly match to the hissing sievert and brass torch head and the blue yellow flame comes from the grey cylinder of calor propane. I anneal the silver now to a cherry red heat for a few seconds. It cools slightly to an oxidized black from the small amount of copper it contains, before I quench it in the sulphuric acid and water mixture and spitting, the silver turns turns white and soft: it is ready to work again. I wish they'd all go away. Walsh gets a tiny splash of the corrosive mixture on his jacket sleeve; there will be a hole there in a day. Drying the piece with the torch flame, I then fashion it with the hammer. Striking is a tedious effort and I'm out of practice, doing this in the twentieth century!

They soon leave, somewhat confused I would say, at what they have started. Snared by Mountgarret on the pathway outside, I can see my employers trying to get away, which they do eventually. And dear God, he's not coming on in is he, could this become a habit?

"You'll have my two pieces ready soon?" Walsh interrupts me again in the afternoon.

"This is what I'm already doing," I say pausing, with silver and hammer in hands.

"Good man, I'll leave you in peace then." With an encouraging smile and spring in his step this time Walsh leaves. I, on the other hand, am perplexed and annoyed.

* * *

The day I move into Haughton's is a day of celebration. Soaking thankfully in a bath of hot water, I enjoy the quiet. There is a little cooker and refrigerator behind a screen in the single room. More than enough for my needs. This is a benign world where I can experience existential drift, with just the occasional bark of their Scottie dog to remind me of the world outside. Enclosed in warm conviviality, today Kilkenny is a soft pillow to lie on. I luxuriate in the hours from evening to morning, here alone, my belongings neatly put away. A pot of tea and scrambled eggs on toast, a tin of peaches, comfortable old armchair, no children, no smell of cement, no Walsh and cold water. If only these few hours would last forever.

Across the creaking landing to the far side of the house, I look out over the Parade and as ever am drawn to the castle, an hour after midnight. There's a clear sky and a near full moon makes angled shadows from the castle. Then comes the inevitable cloud, veiling the ephemeral beauty in brief modesty, in softer, diffused moonlight. As the wind flies to Freshford and beyond, heart of Ireland, heart of sorrows. Where did she go? Opening the window to the sound of restless Kilkenny night air, I wonder, where is she sleeping?

* * *

This silver for Walsh is difficult enough to make, a bowl and pair of candlesticks with cunning Scandinavian simplicity. Sure, he went to Kilkenny College. I could have tried something really different, incorporating and maybe abstracting ideas from the county far and wide. There are lots of ideas in their cats and castles, in the very stones and scenery about here: Butlers, saints, the crows of Kilree round tower (the crows that are always in and out of the high places). The Freshford door I saw with her the other night. I could easily drown in the stuff. I'm not going to be pushed around, we'll see soon enough. They'll hardly leave alone. Head down, I'm only an employee, remember... hammer on!

There she is, yes it is her, in a blue coat waiting on the Parade by the J J Kavanagh bus that goes through Freshford to Urlingford. It is truly amazing. I hold the moment again, forever and ever. She looks uneasy as I apporach, wondering which way to turn or whether I'll want to walk past?

"Are you on your way home? Come on up to my new flat above Haughton's here, I can take you home later."

She is confused, looking radiantly innocent and sweet in the suddeness of our unexpected meeting. She is about to enter the lime and cream bus, which is waiting ready to leave. And she is speechless.

"We can have a cup of tea together and something to eat," I add.

She wavers a smile and, "well alright then, but I won't stay late." She is cautious, with a mind of her own, yet clearly pleased.

Taking her, small, cold hand, I lead her to the door and up the stairs to the new world of my very own. "I'll turn the fire on and you sit there and get warm, while I make the tea." Pointing to the four-bar electric fire and the armchair. "Would you like a piece of fruit cake?"

"That would be nice," she replies softly.

"Take your coat off and throw it on the bed." From the other side of the partition, putting the kettle on. "Isn't this a great place compared to the last? I can do all my own cooking and there's a bath as well."

"It's very cosy all right, the other room was so big and drafty from under the door."

"Were you afraid?"

"Yes I was a bit, you could have stayed with me, I wouldn't have minded," says she, a touch rebuking perhaps, but hopefully respecting my behaviour.

"I've started work, and my arm and shoulder ache from hammering silver."

"You must be pleased then, in spite of the pain."

"Well yes and no, it's a funny old trade this silversmithing, more a throwback to the way they worked in the middle ages you know. So tell me about yourself, what have you been doing since you ran away from me in the dark that night?"

She remains silent. I sense I should go easy there, where secrets abound, ever so faintly like mice: you think see them, but can't be quite sure.

"God you're very nosey." Her eventual reply is playfully mocking, "I'm trying to get a job in Woolworths for Christmas and some money before I go to London."

Against the sound of the kettle boiling, I feel a sudden confusion and a tightening apprehension at thought of her leaving. To Hogarth and Dicken's Great Wen, where the philandering Sir Harry Fetherstonehaughs and Honourable Charles Grevilles live, and so many more ...

"What will you do there?"

"Study to be a nurse."

"Will you miss Kilkenny?"

"No. I hate it?" She replies vehemently.

"As much as that?"

"Yes I do."

"I see ..." Seeing the mice definitely there now. "Would you like some butter and strawberry jam with your cake?"

"That would be nice." Spoken with the slow, flowing voice of Kilkenny's female time.

She's obviously hungry, devouring three thick slices of cake, spreading plenty of butter and jam on each. I see her as an atavistic embodiement of Ireland, somehow sad and impoverished. A bitter cocktail drawn from those haunted country laneways of Irish superstition. Should I dare to drink it? To enter their world, but terrified and with my mind clouding subconsciously from an ancestral aversion. Understanding none of this.

Sitting opposite her, I'm transfixed with desire and the knowledge that soon she'll be gone again into the mysteries of rural Kilkenny, like a fog of incense covering their churches. The hedged fields, the stones, the stones (always) and the distant rising hues. Her little hand pinching the last crumbs, as if a prisoner, or aware of a coming famine. As if this were her last meal. Why do I have such bizarre imaginings? I'm torn apart, a stand of broken glass deep in the heart. Or walking on thin ice, the cracks suddenly sounding me, freezing the blood. For she'll never understand what she possesses in full measure until years from now. I'm smitten forever and chained to her as the very soil she walks upon and came out of.

Finishing her tea, shaking the few miniscule crumbs off and rubbing her hands well satisfied, she smiles without in my way realizing the effect she has upon me. The skirt just above the knees; glorious, grey eyes (a touch mischievous now, even flirtatious) and a relaxed posture, enjoying the pleasant aftertaste of tea and cakes with sweet butter-fat filling. Clearing away the cups and plates, I eye the delights beneath her blouse. Ancient mounds, military or sepulchral, cover the land. Hers are for pleasure and hopefully will succour he who climbs there. Kneeling before this pagan, Roman altar, she is a holy well to bathe and drink from. Her lips are eager to please, my arms encircling her as though around ould Ireland, ring-fencing her forever, but no, she draws back as I struggle to back down.

"Would you like to be on the bed for a while, you must be tired?" I suggest.

"But not for long, I've to be back before dark." There is a spark of apprehension in those so-grey eyes this time.

Wrapped in her wild, warm scent, made from light hedgerows and wet grasses and the long walk from the crossroads to Freshford, perspiring in light rain. We drift in a boat of sleep on the wide treacherous seas of the future, locked together but poles apart...

"God, Mam will be worried, me coming home again this late," she says, suddenly awake, sitting upright on the bed with a start.

We are on the road to Freshford again; it's my fate to fall into a whirlpool of these illuminated knots and dizzying interlacings. She's silently worried, or so I feel, wondering where is this taking her? It's hardly a problem surely? She's not exactly a child. Could there be a fearsome father (taken to the drink) and battered mother waiting for her?

"I'll explain to your Mam it's not your fault, so you've nothing to worry about."

"You will not, don't you dare." She looks at me, sharp eyed.

"Trust me, you'll be all right."

"We'll see."

Approaching the crossroads. "You can let me out here then."

"No, you can't walk up there in the dark." I turn the car into the lane.

"I wish you wouldn't, for I don't want you to see."

"See what?"

"Where I live."

The laneway is very narrow and rutted with big hedges on both sides, making it a kind of tunnel on entering; without the car headlights it would be pitch black.

"This is me now." Says this Mary Malone, mortified and obviously ashamed for me to see where she living. In a clearing is a mean, two-storey cottage with a single half-door. From one of the two bottom windows a dusty dim light faintly signals that indefinable sadness of Ireland I find so often.

"Do you want me to have a word with your Mam?"

"No, no, it doesn't matter, I'll be fine." She most definitely does not want to let me in.

"So when will I see you again?" I ask anxiously.

"Do you really want to now?"

"Of course I do. I'll come on Saturday afternoon about two, I've this silver to make; a couple of late nights should see it finished."

Accompanying the press of lips hungrily subsumed in each other are myriad shooting stars like tiny flashes of silvery light falling out of the heavens. Then a reluctant, "good night".

At the half-door she looks back and waves me on.

Turning the car at a field entrance further on and returning past the front of the cottage, I stop. All is quiet, not a voice. They can't have much. From now or the past hunger, years and the rent, the St George's of Freshford would ride past this cottage, oblivious!

CHAPTER 10

Too many interruptions and with the new telephone in the workshop there's even more. I will never get much made at this rate; I will have to give my two colleagues a call to come over from London. Will they?

Now who is this lightly tapping on the door? In a smart, dark blue suit, white shirt, knitted greenish tie; wearing soft brown booties and with a confident, Nordic, blondish, blue-eyed appearance. Rolf Middleboe introduces himself, with a look of enjoyment, amused even. He doesn't want to miss out on such an experience with the natives. He's staying at the Rose Hill Hotel and will be starting work early next year, so to his coming feels more like a holiday. There'll be no fixed rules for him.

I listen to his attractive, stilted English, which is so self-assured and charming he could fool anyone. He'd be about forty five, from Copenhagen. I must ask him about the German occupation.

"Ah, yes," says Rolf. "They came all of a sudden and the Government decided to offer no resistance, how could they? I well remember asking a German soldier in the city square behind a Maschinengewehr forty-two that could fire a thousand two hundred rounds a minute, what are you doing here? Do you know what he said to me? "I've come to protect you from Communists and Jews!"" As he goes on and on...

"Did you know that Hitler escaped to Ireland at the end of the war?" I interrupt him, speaking seriously.

"I can well believe it, you were neutral and nothing would surprise me about Ireland you know." Rolf replies with a big, happy smile, laughing as he finally leaves me.

Called to the phone, I hear voices that seem harsh and foreign in comparison to Rolf's. Hearing the busy sounds of London's silversmiths in the backyard, I'm momentarily immersed in the exquisite, the dreaming distances, the otherness I find in Kilkenny. Their words invade this place, to a peculiar reversal of time and ancestral belief. These are the raucous shouts of Cromwell's ironsides at the walls. I find a quickly-passing resentment against them rises up in me out of the blue, without reason, whispering at their Englishness.

Those soldiers stabled their horses in St. Canice's, defacing tombs and hanging priests wherever they found one. That's what Cleere said. It wasn't such a bad idea, perhaps, in 1650 when they captured Kilkenny. Or I could consider it just a blip, for they would have been on my side, those priest haters and iconoclasts. Like a drift of smoke, my resentment at their voices quickly passes. I must guard against becoming infected by evasive vapourings and carelessness. For these men certainly know their craft, no, no art! From an early age, you couldn't be better trained in the renaissance style of the old London apprenticeships: handed down by a master silversmith; learning beside him; absorbing his every move. Without too much airy-fairy, art school. Presenting a final master piece to be judged in the splendour of Goldsmiths Hall. Then freemen of the City of London, St. Pauls.

It was with great difficulty I got them a living wage. I had to bargain down to the last shillings and pence almost. Now what's the going rate for a silversmith here they ask? The thinking in the Export Board was that they were semi-skilled. After a stubborn resistance, with Hogan exercising his authority unnecessarily, I was given a final offer of fourteen pounds and ten shillings a week. A mild case of xenophobia perhaps at the English working man coming to Ireland, never mind the Scandinavian!

* * *

There's a lot of traffic coming into Kilkenny on the Freshford road this Saturday afternoon, for a hurling match probably. I'm in a death ride of daring and overtaking, racing towards blaring horns, flashing lights, coming head on without a care, a game of Russian roulette, extolling and boasting amongst themselves. Caught unawares in this frightening onslaught, like experiencing a sudden storm or a swarm of bees or the Hottentots bent on revenge again. They overtook on corners especially, laughing hysterically at the grief they caused: they must have been drinking. I decide I had better stop for a while at Three Castles, watching the madness race past, thankfully out of it until they are gone. There are no speed limits and it seems that any fool can get a driving licence here.

What is that lying on the floor of my car? I give a little start. Black and snake like and God it's her rosary beads, which must have slipped out of her pocket the other night. I knew all along she was Catholic; it couldn't have been otherwise. Picking it up, it feels weird, plastic and cheap. In daylight, the land of this region is rich and fertile. I'm alone now on the road. A calm sea of varied greens rolling brightly under big white blonde tinted clouds accompanies me into Freshford.

An old man with a stick, turning, gazes after me, I can see in the rear view mirror that he's thinking: who's that? He looks wary and puzzled: the car was Northern registered even!

Mary's obviously been waiting at the half door, top ajar, anxious and ready. She runs out to me and seats herself in the car, gesturing forward with body and arms. "Come on come on, let's go!"

"What's your hurry?"

"O, I just want to get away for a while, can't you tell?"

"So where to then?"

"I really don't care, anywhere will do." We continue on up the hill.

"Out of Ireland even?"

"That would be wonderful."

"You left your rosary beads in the car." I take them out of the side compartment, handing them to her.

"Ah, God, I was wondering where they were." In that quintessential voice of the Kilkenny country girl, sublime and innocent, but quick as the fox.

"Do you pray with them very often?"

"Now and then, before bed sometimes with Mam and..."

"And?" I repeat, but she doesn't reply. "It's the Hail Mary Mother of God prayer you say with them isn't it?"

"You know, of course." Her reply surprises me.

"Not really, we're heretics according to your church." I say this, wondering what she'll think. Hopefull, it won't be as difficult as the last time I used the phrase.

"Is that right?" she comments slowly. "Well, I wouldn't mind whatever you are, makes no difference to me." She jerks her head emphatically. As she does, absurdly, I see a white dove rise out of the burning pyre.

"There's a present for you on the seat behind."

"Cadbury Milk Tray, well I never had anything that size before." She reaches back eagerly, "can I open them now and have one?"

"Of course you can."

Her hand wavers over the delicious assortment, before she picks the one wrapped in pink foil. As the day melts into a kaleidoscope of gently shifting countryside from Kilkenny to Tipperary, as slow and sweet as thick golden syrup, we go wherever the notion takes us, without thoughts of when we will return. I've too much respect for her modesty and youthful caution to consummate this in the stops I find myself searching for. And there's the memory of Blakes Surgical Supplies, a harsh Northern intrusion to discourage me from even wanting to try!

We arrive at Holycross Abbey by the Suir. Beside the slow-flowing river sounds are sacred antiquities that haunt me on each new discovery. A flight of starlings turns above the roofless walls, across the pale, wandering evening moon. How did I arrive here with the living miracle of Mary, Mary Malone? The pages are torn into many pieces from those bizarre, illuminated Gospels I found and are scattered as the autumn leaves on the Parade in Kilkenny. My footsteps tread unaware over buried pagan gold and silver treasure, Christian objects, atomizing bones. Again, we go no further than an embracing kiss under the massive central crossing tower, the minutes like a waterfall. I'm unable to stop, despite seeing she's uneasy... and, yes!

"You seem to be in another world apart from me, amidst these old ruins, sure there's nothing here but emptiness and weeds!" She says cheekily, not wanting to stay. I was admiring the meticulous incidental carvings in the church.

"What else is there to see around here then?" I reply contrite.

"We could drive on to Tipperary. I would like to see it and get something to eat, I'm starving."

"After all those chocolates?"

"Yes!" She speaks boldly.

She's right, isolated and probably living on much the same food, day after day, in that cottage up in the darkening laneway, in her own emptiness and weeds.

In Tipperary find a sombre-fronted hotel; in the gloomy entrance is a peculiar smell. There is no one at the reception but there are female voices arguing faintly somewhere. In the dining room we find set tables, with a solitary man by the far wall, his back to us. Eventually, a young girl in black with a starched white apron comes over, glancing strangely at Mary, for some reason. The best on offer is a mixed grill, with a side board of thick apple pie and cream. Mary reads this in happy anticipation. It is more to her liking than the lifeless wonders of Holycross Abbey. She is living in the here and now, dealing with practicalities.

As were are seated and served, I am overcome by a sudden sense of unease in the room. A nightmare in my head or in reality? I'm not part of the scene but watching from outside. Looking at this mysterious Botticellian Venus enjoying her meal...

"Can I have another slice of that pie, it's delicious?" Mary asks, finishing the plate; her smile is guilty and most unladylike. I beckon to the waitress, who is pretending not to notice and who sulkily complies, wide-eyed at Mary.

In the moment he turns, his hypnotic, still-cold eyes are unmistakeably those of Adolf Hitler. Definitely, Adolf grown old and living in Tipperary is he? The moustache and drooping forelock, now all white as snow... it's shocking!

"Are you all right, you look as if you've seen a ghost?"

Mary observes me, touching me anxiously. She just wouldn't understand, coming from Holycross. And now Adolf Hitler. She would think me quite mad. I dare not look again at his awful, malevolent gaze.

"Nothing, nothing. I just thought I recognized someone over there." Thumb pointing behind.

"There's no one over there," Mary says, shaking her head.

"Yes there is, or was, didn't you see him?"

"No."

"Well, look over again then; see his pot of tea and left-over plate of brown bread and jam are still on the table.

"So, I still didn't see anyone, silly goose!"

* * *

I promise to return in a day or two that I know will feel like years. Parked some yards from the cottage gate, with my headlights on to guide her safely home, a prolonged, strangled shriek comes from the sudden, ghostly swoop of an owl across her path. She freezes and turns in the bright light: an embodiment of Ireland in the cold night air.

I get out. "It's only an owl looking for its supper, are you all right?"

Then she's gone, gone. *Of the wilde fruit, which saluage soyl hath bred, which being through long wars left almost waste, with brutish barbarism is overspread. And as so faire a land, as may be redd...*

I am far too attuned: just like dogs have their sense of smell and hearing sensitivities, I am too aware of the echoes of this country's past. There is something fateful and ethereal about my driving so late towards Kilkenny.

* * *

To the silver morning that follows yesterday's revelation, to heat and to hammer while my thoughts are on Mary. I experience the painful pull of two worlds. My images of Mary seem unreal, as in a *gentle Shore that making way*. The telephone is ringing, ringing like Middleboe's fearful Maschinengewehr might be. The voice of Walsh intrudes, waking me, enquiring about his silver again and crimson poplin now.

"The silver just needs hallmarking and then they're yours. I'll check with Mr O'Connor and post away if ready to you..." I answer him with barely subdued patience.

O'Connor's rather deaf from his many years at the loom, so I open his door slowly, so as not to frighten him. Then I knock above the sound of his weaving. "Sorry to disturb, but the boss is looking for his poplin." I speak loudly.

He straightens, hands on waist, his back and neck stretching. "Ah yes, game ball, all ready to go." And I see it is there on the window ledge wrapped in brown paper; he presents it to me softly.

It is addressed to Lorenzo de'Medici, somewhere in Florence. They say he had a shamrock farm down Wexford way, showing imagination and enterprise. I go to the post office on High Street past Woolworths, hoping she'll get the Christmas job. But is she going to London after? We shall soon see. Returning, Montgomery and Cleere are on the far side of the crescent with Seamus Butler, as drifting flotsam on the high seas of profundity. Their presence reminds to check Oisin Kelly's room beside O'Connor's is ready, as he could be arriving any day soon.

Striking my maker's mark into Walsh's silver candlesticks and bowl, I feel a kind of immortality in the knoweldge it will be there for years to come. Better get them into the assay and then set, so they can be collected whenever.

Miss Eire is coming towards me, appearing downcast, wearing a brave smile. Something's upsetting her, she's surely not going to stop and talk?"

"Will you take me to the rugby ball?" Asked without hesitation, admirably to the point.

"When is it?" I reply, surprised.

"The second of December." Her pretty face is inwardly skewered in regrets and embarrassment. I want to be as gentle as possible for she was sweet in the few times were together.

"I'll be away then and I'm sorry for what happened that night." It's a white lie, to avoid upsetting her too much.

"Ah, no matter then, I over reacted and sure anyway..." Her voice tapers away under wings of regret.

"And the boyfriend in Limerick?"

"That's finished!"

"Sure, I'm a heretic and you're better off with your own kind."

"Oh, I don't know about that anymore!" She speaks with a pronounced certainty, smiling weakly and then leaves, her womanly instinct knowing that there's not a chance.

* * *

In the car, embraced by sudden darkness, watching the cottage. Unexpectedly, the face of an old woman appears at the car window, she taps her finger on the glass to make me notice her. My thoughts are confused, falling into the randomness that can spring from memories of past histories, rocketing and exploding and falling, smoking like a spent fire-work.

"Will you come in, Mary's not ready yet." She leans into the window, which I roll down, shakened. Getting out to this apparition, at first I can hardly believe in this. She's far too old to be Mary's mother, grandmother then? Hardly. I follow her warily into the cottage, looking at the long, dark shawl that covers her shoulders. The room has an open fireplace, with goose wings to sweep away the ash remains. Two bursting, broken horse-hairs and three rocky, wooden chairs; a small dresser with tacky, scattered souvenirs from Tramore; the wicked, steely eyed Pius, Mary and Jesus; an odour of coal and dusted poverty; a grey cat eyeing me suspiciously from under the red and white oil cloth table.

"You be seated, she'll not be long." This is kindly said as she watches me. Sizing me over. "Would you like a cup of tea?"

"No, no, thank you." I reply bewildered, in subconscious shame and disbelief that I make fine silver, while here there would be no more than a thimble, hairpin or the plainest ring, such were their straightened circum-stances. It was as though they were William Wilde's wretched peasantry, whom he observed in 1848 with a ghostly appearance.

Here comes Mary, as fresh as the wild rose amongst woods and tumbled walls. She is surprised to see me inside and glances at the woman who must be her Mam. And there's another girl behind her giggling.

"Say hello to this young man, Nora," asks Mam.

Nora complies with a weak, "hello" and a mischievous look. She is way-ward and pretty enough, in a holed, fairisle jersey, shirt and ankle socks. Then another girl, even younger still, waif-like and sad, looks in and on seeing me, disappears up the stairs again.

"That's our little Eileen, she's very shy you know," explains Mam.

Now what do I make of this, of three young girls living in such condi-tions. Is Mary anxious to leave them?

In the short drive towards Gattabaun (she can't stay long), I ask her, "who's the old woman and two girls?"

"That's Mam..." And a long silence, until I turn to her, to encourage her to go on. "I'm boarded out they call it, the same as the others. I've only ever seen my mother a few times, she lives near Knocktopher."

"And your father?"

"I wouldn't know who he is; do you mind I'm that way?"

"Why would I? Sure it's you, not your parents that matter to me." The mystery clears somewhat.

Mary leans over and kisses me ever so lightly, her tears falling to the sound of little sobs of relief. Her birth is no longer secret and it doesn't matter.

"So Mam is the one that looks after you all?"

"Yes, she's very kind."

"Do you know where you were born?"

"Roscrea, the Bird's Nest they call it, in a place run by the nuns, awful witches they were." Her explanation is eager now. I decide to leave well alone, the rest is not important. Yet I am curious who the parents were... and them living in Knocktopher!

"Would you like to come to Dublin with me tomorrow, I've to go to the Assay. There's nothing for you to worry about, it'll be a nice drive and day out for you." I hold my breath, hoping she'll say yes.

"I'd love to, but I'll have to ask Mam first."

"It would be tomorrow, so I'd have to pick you up very early."

"Then turn around and I'll ask her." Mary sounds excited.

CHAPTER 11

Captain le Bas is most anxious to see the first silver from Kilkenny up for assay. Making sure, he puts a deep enough spread hallmark on of Hibernia, the Harp crowned, and the date letter V. But he is adamant in not letting me supervise exactly how I want it struck. For there's nothing worse than a light hallmark that's easily damaged and loses the sharp details when given a finish with the polishing mop. It is almost a family of sorts, the Dublin assay office, gently spinning dreams in the hallmarking of gold and silver. The place drowns me in fantasies and strange possibilities. I'm like a bird, lazy in the warm, damp air, rising higher and higher with a dull awareness, the spread of an island below is only a fiction created from myth and abstraction. Marie Mulcahy's smile, voice and name even are another song in themselves.

"We're too late for today's assay, so they'll have to post them on to Kilkenny. This bold captain's not for turning, they're a law onto themselves and rightly so I suppose, a nuisance though." I am explaining to Mary, who waited for me in the car, parked opposite the Birmingham Tower.

As we drive up Ship Street, she quietly suggests (with a pleasing docility in her now wayward grey eyes), "we could stay the night, so you could collect them tomorrow afternoon."

My heartbeats quicken from the signals above. I imagine us together in some hotel, jumping into the death of all earthly beings, to the momentous, sublime and ethereal. But I forgot to bring them, it hadn't occurred to me we might spend the night in Dublin together. God no, no; she's still a child almost. A Catholic country girl. I'm thinking about her suggestion and it is true that I'm anxious to collect the assay. We are a long way from the cottage. But the other is wishful thinking; in the heat of the moment it only takes one of the millions to hit the bull's eye. They are microscopic, I read that you need atomic, electronic magnification to see them; how truly amazing!

"What about your Mam?"

"I don't think she'd mind and even if she does, she's not my real mother. I'm seventeen now you know!" She speaks emphatically.

"If that's your wish then, it shall be granted." I'm happy to comply.

I phone the Assay and make her day, all at the Board's expense!

Walking up O'Connell Street by the Gresham Hotel, I remember the story of an uncle holed up for a week inside, with a bird's eye view of the GPO. And what a rising commotion unfolded before his eyes, of dead soldiers, dead horses; green flags; being unable to get out and home to Belfast. I imagine all this as we pass... and there were snipers.

They are suspicious at the Anchor Hotel, as if it's any of her business anyway! Is the sensation of wandering indifference found in all Irish hotels? Where you could spend days in a drowsy sanctuary from the busy world outside.

"Were you ever in Dublin before?" I ask Mary.

She is thrilled with the room and later, to be sitting down to a meal of whatever she chooses, with attention and service as she's never had before.

"Only once, when the school took us by bus to the Lemon's pure sweet factory when I was ten. They gave us each a bag of their boiled sweets to take back; it was great fun to be away for the day, if only had lasted forever!" Mary's words bring about a painful sadness in me, at the momentary gaiety she had in the big city. I can imagine the laughter in the speeding bus, a ship on the cold seas of her Ireland! Then left at the crossroads to what end? A dying day, alone she will have walked to that dusty shoebox, then to bed. Then looking through the little window at an even colder, bitter sweet lemon moon!

These moments of haunting reflection, this Ireland once again under the false light: the shaded hotel customers are the fire-eyed Germans, perusing the whores of Hamburg's Reeperbahn, which I once visited with the Goldsmith's money. Kilkenny was no more than silvered illusions in the early mornings, a chimera, ephemeral as Hitler was in Tipperary that other evening. And who is she really?

Slipping under the covers with my shirt on, God love her and what a blooming lovely pair they are, to touch them was more than enough for the night. A perfect gentleman. I'm going to buy her those fine, high-heeled leather boots which are for sale on Parliament Street, six pounds five shillings and sixpence, a nice surprise for her. But ghastly for the Jew in striped pyjamas, wearing a big yellow Star of David, lying on the pavement, reminding me of what they had so recently done! The terrors of the twentieth century. Ireland adrift back and forth on Time's pendulum. For here the Holocaust was no more than British propaganda, I heard they were laughing at the newsreels down here.

* * *

In the morning, we have the the full Irish and it's never been so good. Mary enjoying every mouthful in silent contentment and there'll be no bag of boiled sweets when she returns this time. Then I'm with Hogan in a pianoforte conversation about Walsh's silver and what to make for the New York World's Fair and... the minutes tick away to Mozart's Turkish Rondo, played this morning in sublime fashion. Hogan invites me for a spot of lunch in the Wellington, across the Grand Canal.

"I've a friend, do you mind if she comes?"

"Ah ha and who is she?"

"A girl I met a few weeks ago in Kilkenny."

"I seee, it didn't take you long then to suss out the Kilkenny women." His smile is weakly lascivious, "yes, of course bring her along." Now he's curious to meet her.

Mary is waiting in the car, which I had parked on Wilton Place and she is a bit shy and reluctant to come. I introduce her to Hogan, who has been waiting on Baggot Street bridge. He is obviously surprised at Mary's appearance. Entering the pub, when Mary heads for the Mná na hÉireann, Hogan asks, "Jesus man, how did you ever find her? What's the story there?"

With the waiter approaching, there's no need to reply. We order and Mary returns, male glances surreptitiously following her, giving me a fission of pride. To Hogan's subtle questioning of her, Mary proves skillful at evasion for an hour or so, until it is time to collect the assay. Walking towards the car, hand-in-hand, for no reason I turn around. Hogan is still there, where we parted on the steps of his office building, motionless, staring after her statue-like, malicious even, strange... Or is this my imagination?

* * *

Well now, what was the rush from Walsh? I've been asked to hold onto his silver for a while. Having set the hallmarks with the plainsher, I then brush it all over with a light scratch, in running water, leaving the fire stain in.

A phone call comes from Vanders' man, John Blagden, who has arrived in Dublin from London via Holyhead. He's just landed, can I meet him at the Kilkenny station? As he doesn't mind catching the train from Heuston. Sarah Coogan's is the best I can do for him at the moment for a place to stay and God only knows what he'll make of bedding down there. Blagden is doing the Design Centre a favour, coming this far for a lousy fourteen pounds, ten shillings a week.

In his words, which were almost nervous, I hear echoes of my time in London. His voice so obviously English compared to the easy sounds of gentle Kilkenny-speak. Blagden is paley goldfish-faced, with questioning eyes that are easily offended. Probably, one of his distant forebears was one of Wat Tyler's mob and years later another marched with Jack Cade, demanding the head of Lord Saye-and-Sele at the Standard in Cheapside. There's no point, however, in having second thoughts about him.

Blagden comes in the next morning. "Blimey that Sarah Coogan's a right one and the bloke nailed to the cross above the bed, gruesome! They'd all be religious here would they?"

"Oh yes, Catholic mostly, a few Protestants though."

"So what's the difference then?" he asks quizzically.

"God, John, you'd want to read your history about the popes, indulgences, Martin Luther, Salvation through faith alone."

"What's indulgences?"

"The selling of forgiveness of sins. A racket some popes dreamed up to make money for themselves, a ticket to heaven you might say!" I give him the design for a coffee set to make. It's not a problem for him. In just a few days, I see it coming along fine.

* * *

The Viscount Mountgarret is staring benevolently through the windows at John. On becoming aware of this, John stops, irritated, with hammer and silver in either hand. "Who is this man? Tell him to buzz off, is he a lunatic escaped from the asylum?"

"His ancestors were of great and noble birth John, related to Lord Ormonde, the owner of the castle, he told me."

"Yeah, but look at him now a weirdo!" The reply is without sympathy.

"That's a bit harsh John, it's his whole life in a way, so let him dream of his chief indented azure, crescent and a coronet of sixteen silver balls. Somehow, I think he would claim that as part of his reason for living."

"You're got me there; I'm not into the Lord and Lady stuff, we're just as good as they are; so bollocks to them all!"

To his own racecous laughter, John turns back to raising silver. The Viscount leaves, visibly upset by John having aimed a grimacing expression at him.

Soon John is complaining; he's suspicious Sarah's poking about into his things, having set a clever trap of carefully placed hairs for her to disturb. Making doubly sure to check after he's been away.

"What are the women like in Kilkenny then?" he asks.

"You can find out soon enough John, there's always a dance in the town most weeks, but be careful, you can't buy Durex here!"

"Can't get Durex, what do you mean?" I can hear the surprise in his voice.

"It's against the law, you'd have to get them from England or the North."

"You must be joking, why?" John is truly amazed now.

"Ireland's a Catholic country, John, at least in the South; that's just the way it is. But don't worry, I've some from the North, and they're easy enough to get up there. The politicians make the laws to please the Catholic Church, for the sake of their immortal souls, it seems."

John doesn't answer, shaking his head, clearly mystified.

And who is this now, lightly tapping on the window? David Reeves introduces himself as the ceramic designer, his Englishness sounding a class above John's. Tweed jacketed, with white shirt and plain narrow tie, wearing grey flannels and sensible worn leather shoes, he is a man of pleasant appearance and receding hairline.

"So this is the metal workshop, do you mind if I look around?" Eyes curious left and right.

"Go ahead, help yourself." I welcome him as he checks the lathe, turns the polishing machine on, and even picks up hammers and files.

"You're certainly got the best equipment, and all brand new." David says admiringly.

"Money was no object. So what do you think of this Kilkenny Design idea?" I ask him.

"Hard to say, certainly enough talk, but what I have noticed is you can't get fresh fruit anywhere in Kilkenny."

"Really!" I wouldn't have thought that was true. David takes out a packet of Senior Service, lighting up without offering one to either us.

"You can get apples and oranges easily enough."

"You'll have to show me where then," he's unconvinced.

"In the grocers, there's nearly always fruit with the vegetables, surely?"

"They're not the greatest and I like a wide variety: apples, oranges, pears and bananas."

"There's always tinned fruit." I suggest.

"I prefer fresh fruit," the ceramic designer replies rather sharply, yet I have a feeling of concern for him. Perhaps his too hasty judgement upon Kilkenny will change... He's striding away. With such a complaint he's hardly likely to stay. I should have asked him where was he going to live and...

"Do you have problems finding fresh fruit John?"

"I don't eat much fruit anyway, but maybe I should have an apple a day, you know what they say." John remained silent throughout the conversation, probably still somewhat dazed at thoughts of Ireland's Catholic morality!

* * *

Joe Cahill is a pleasant young man who looks older than his years. He talks slowly and is not going to be hurried or pushed around by anyone. He doesn't say much, but I think him cunning, observant and the owner of an elephantine memory. Joe is the first Kilkenny man to be given a job. Charged with candle making, he uses the little room beside the lavatory, which is nearly opposite us. He has a long list of materials to get and Oisin Kelly will do the designs. They are Irishy, in various colours, and shapes: square, thin, fat and round.

Joe watches at the comings and goings beside him, owl-like, from out of a narrow window. In these elasticated days, he doesn't comment on whether it's summer, autumn or winter in effusive old Kilkenny, city of slumbers and dreams. "Ah now, sure that's the way it is!" he says.

"What are they going to do with this silver when it's made?" John asks me casually one day, enjoying his recently acquired mid-morning habit of tea with Afton and Crotty's cake.

"We'll make up a collection of thirty or forty pieces and take it from there. We can hardly do time, materials and pricing yet, for who knows what they're really looking for?"

"A big change from Vanders, a sort of Alice in Wonderland you could say!" says John, transcendent from the comparison to his past working experience. He's settled down surprisingly well.

When John met the awkward pair, drinking pints together, Young's first comment was. "Another Englishman. Is there no jobs for the Irish by the castle there?"

"Maybe they've all gone to London, there's enough of them over there." John replied and soon he was away with them, back to the Middle Ages, walking with them up Collier's Lane, just like I had done.

I wonder will the subversion of place eventually seduce him? You wouldn't know. Everything is something of a novelty for John now, except for Sarah and the wait for his wages.

There's a greyhound fitfully asleep on a heap of coal. An old, ribbed, knackered carthorse tied outside the blacksmith's. There, mute in the sooty smoke half-light of the yellowy-red coke glow, the blacksmith heats, hammers, bends and quenches a thick rod of steel into a particular shape of stake that I need made. The only sound is that of heavy breathing from his blackened face. The whites of his eyes are ghostly, an inscrutable mask. It is raining heavily. What do the poor horse, dog and Mary do on a day like this? Ireland hangs heavy. A sudden, sharp wedge of bloody despair enters my head, like El Lissitzky's famous poster.

"You've to phone Mr Walsh, I told him you were at the blacksmith's. He seemed surprised I answered the phone, does he even know I'm working here?"

"He's a busy man John, it was through Paul Hogan and Michael Clarke that I arranged for you to come."

"I think he was annoyed you weren't here."

"Was he now? Let's see what he wants then." I am faintly disturbed at what John implies.

Hogan takes the call, Walsh had to go out. Calmed by the gentle words of Hogan's expansive mood — he'd be smoking one of those little Dutch cigars — I wait patiently for him to get to the point. "The Minister of Industry and Commerce, Jack Lynch, will be coming to the Workshop next week. So be prepared and make sure to be doing something interesting to show him, including the pieces for Walsh, which he'll collect. For they have to keep Industry and Commerce in the picture. That's where the money comes from for all this." Hogan explains the situation to me. I'm sanguine, John will soon be finished with the coffee set and can get started on a pair of salad servers and some letter openers.

"You'll meet William Walsh and the Minister in a few days John, they want us to put on a good show."

"Like what?"

"Demonstrating the mysterious craft of silversmithing from time immemorial."

At this John raises his eyes and tosses his head, "isn't it a bit early yet? We've only just started, there's not a lot for them to see."

"We can only do our best."

*   *   *

There's trouble brewing by Freshford. Mam's been crying and Mary's upset, explaining. "The priest has been after Mam for me going out with you, a forty-year-old Northern Ireland Protestant and says it must stop! He's threatened to pass us at the Communion rail if I continue."

This spiteful blast of Popish malice rekindles the embers of my Protestant upbringing and brings back folklore, which flares phantom-like in my mind. It is as if nothing has changed. This should not be happening in the 1960s. Popish trumpery, my mother called it, the cheek of the priest from Downpatrick going out to visit Rosie's daughter Mary for having only two children. The Free State was still riddled with such superstitious nonsense! Both sides certainly had a way of discovering my leanings.

"Mam got an awful fright when I opened the door to him, shouting in the dark, even darker black as the devil he was, not seeing fit to enter, as if what he said was the law and that was final, the end of the matter, obey!" Mary vividly recalls the scene.

I can well imagine him not wanting to come into such a humble abode. Where would he sit? Hardly by the mean fire and goose wings, where he'd be at a disadvantage, surrounded by a tired, old woman and three frightened orphan girls, explaining the Magisterium of the Roman church.

"Does this make any difference to you Mary?" I ask anxiously.

"No, no, of course not." This comes from the heart. Nora and little Eileen are both hovering shadows, helpless, confused and spellbound.

"What about you Mam?" I turn to their guardian.

"I'm really too old to care, if he passes us at Mass sure he'd be the sinner now. Mary's breaking no law, let him do his worst, I don't think he'd dare somehow!" There is defiance in her voice and she speaks with a smile.

Mary's aware of the parcel I have, which I hand to her. "There you are, this is for you."

She opens to the boots I bought, amazed and joyfully surprised. "Oh God they're lovely."

Excitedly, she puts them on, they are a perfect fit. Nora and even Eileen want to try too and of course they are far too big for the girls. I am saddened by this poverty and by the power of the priest. Mam is not even going to try wearing the boots, her feet are all swollen. Things may not be so bad, she says in the flow of conversation, he's only doing his job as he thinks, for sure isn't the Mass only a nonsense. Not to worry this will pass, as everything does... and now the room is merry.

"I used to work at the castle for Lord Ormonde, in the laundry mostly, had to starch his white shirts you know." Mam reminisces, "I'll always remember when the old century passed away into this. At the stroke of midnight, he gave a great fireworks display, the whole sky was lit up. Everyone was there, all the gentry were in the castle having a ball."

It occurs to me that she'd have remembered the old Marquess, who she would have met when he was a boy.

"Did you see the King and Queen when they came to Kilkenny?"

"Oh God I did, standing on John's Bridge, I was, the constabulary were everywhere and the soldiers on horseback escorting them on their open carriage... those days are long gone now." She says with wistful regret. "I never liked that de Valera fella, no, not at all!" She shakes her head, eyes gazing far away into her youthful past.

"Will you come to the Rugby ball with me Mary?"

"I'd love to!" Mary is excited, though she soon turns anxious, "what will I wear?"

"You leave that to me," says Mam, touching Mary's knee, obviously with something up her sleeve.

CHAPTER 12

A call the day before the visit from Paul Hogan, who is double checking everything is in place for the big day. I've to let Walsh do most of the spin with the Minister.

Lady Bellew and Peggy Haughton unexpectedly arrive early on the all-important morning, with bunches of flowers and a bag: what are they up to, entering here so boldly?

"We thought you'd like some flowers to brighten up the workplace for the Minister and his wife, with these Waterford glass vases to hold them," explains Lady Bellew, taking over, unwrapping and laying out the flowers on the bench. She ignores John, who is beside her, mesmerized by their intrusion. Peggy has been told of the impending visit, obviously, and is attractively dressed; a touch flirtatious perhaps, when she glances at me...

I'm uneasy, watching them pluck and pack, making the arrangements with cuttings of greenery here and there amidst the red, pink and white geraniums. It doesn't look right though, this is not a flower shop and they'll be arriving soon. Perhaps I should hide the flowers away; no, no, it's too late, I'd better leave them.

When they finally depart, John laughs out loud. "Crazy old cow, that lady what's her name?"

"Bellew. Lady Elaine Bellew, John, the widow of an Irish aristocrat of ancient dignity and inherited title." I reply with supercilious mockery.

"Well, kiss my arse, that's what I say to the lot of them!" His voice sounds crudely brutal, far from the natural gentleness of the Irish accent. The crowded geraniums seem like have festering wounds, that they are raw from the awful cut-glass vases. The flowers have a lingering, dead smell; they crowd the workbenches and speak of hidden dreams in the mischievous airs of Kilkenny.

It is these dreams that I am attempting to designing and make into silver. They are elusive and glimpsed only under moonlight, perhaps at Kilree and Kells. The beauty of coy Kilkenny girls; the view from the graveyard at Knocktopher...

Suddenly, a large killer shark, cold and shocking, is visible through the near window: a black Ford Zephyr. Jack Lynch and his wife Maureen get out, armed garda driving the car, with another Zephyr behind. Do they expect an assassination attempt? William Walsh and Paul Hogan running across from the rear archway, seeming clown-like and ridiculous in their hurry to catch up and welcome the Minister. Hogan is carrying a large biscuit tin!

With cursory introductions (Walsh forgets John's name), the group enter our workshop. Taking the coffee pot from John – I'm hoping he won't drop it – Walsh holds sway with the now familiar rhetoric about Kilkenny Design. We are designing prototypes for industry. Spearheading this approach is important. We have to start somewhere, for the security of protectionism and tariffs in place since the 1930s is ending and the free market of Europe is bound to come. The economic importance of good design is not generally understood by Irish industry. The decision to initially tackle craft-based design and design for craft-based industry makes sense. I am no longer really listening but I appreciate that Walsh means well. He is a small man, Napoleonic.

"We have a few finished pieces here, you can see," I say, leading them into the small office. Here I display Walsh's silver and am met by a strange silence: is it of approval or disappointment? I feel more relaxed now all the same. Jack Lynch takes out his pipe and having filled his pipe from a small round tin of Mick McQuaid, lights up, all his motions automatic. The scare about smoking and lung cancer has obviously made Walsh start to smoke a pipe too. But lacking the expertise of Lynch, his efforts are surprising and awkward. His is a large, curved Sherlock-Holmes-style Peterson pipe. The American Indians who introduced us to the practice would have been amused by it. Maureen Lynch has silky, blue hair and wears blue-shaded glasses; an attractive woman, admiring the flowers. Both looking somewhat mystified and both doing their best to show interest.

Paul Hogan is the first to leave the display, whispering, "Walsh will collect his silver tomorrow, well done, I think he's well pleased, and there's some ideas from Oisin Kelly inside the tin, see what you can do."

This is good to know; I'm soothed by the drifting, easy talk from the other room. They speak about our work as an ancient craft worth preserving and a great export earner in the years to come... The Lynch's are finally Zehpred away, they are a softspoken pair. Walsh will be staying with the Haughton's tonight.

Opening the tin, I see a tangle of pink plasticine shapes, which I show to John.

He shakes his head. "What on earth are those? Are they serious in silver?"

"Oisin Kelly is a well-thought-of artist John."

"That Walsh certainly has the gift of the blarney, although a lot of what he said does make sense," replies John, unusually reflective, as we begin to wrap the silver for collection. "Do you charge him? For they'll be expensive enough. How many hours, and what was the weight of silver?"

I answer, "about fifty hours and just under ninety ounzes. It's up to himself, and I'm not going to ask him."

In the middle of the courtyard is a lovely new pale and dark chocolate Triumph 2000, which we both walk over to. Leather seats, wooden dashboard, shaped so as to be a pleasure to drive, parked and making out a claim.

"Is that Walsh's car?" John asks.

"Yes, isn't she a beauty?"

"He's doing all right for himself then." We stop to admire the vehicle.

Out to the Parade, to a sudden, loud blast from an unusual-sounding horn! Good God! Hogan's driving an enormous finned, blue and white American car: Baick, Pontiac or Oldsmobile. No it's a Cadillac!

Glancing over toward the sound, I see Hogan has a face of reckless abandon: what a lark, down to Kilkenny and back to Dublin in a yoke like that. The car looks surreal in the setting of old Kilkenny.

* * *

I must forget normality, as the next morning I watch Walsh walk off with his three pieces of silver. He was full of praise, which creates a matching contentment in me. Long into the future will I remember these golden sunsets and silver sunrises, the mysterious nights and incredible days. Silver and gold, miraculous metals made from massive, exploding stars, supernovae, star of Bethlehem, blasting heavy elements produced by nucleosynthesis, particularly in the short waves, guiding the Magi in search of Jesus. Made in the Irish twenty carat.

Is this over the top? My hand is raised, holding a water jug. And why not? I have designed and worked out the price based on a twelve inch diameter circle, gauge eleven, weight about thirty ounces with the spout and handle. Over a thousand pounds. It is an awful lot but they can only say no. I will ask Hogan. He mentioned that Coras Trachtala got a few million every year and made sure to spend it all by the end of the year, so they'd get more in the next!

"What do you say, John, to making a water pitcher in twenty carat gold?"

"Are you serious?" He pauses and looks up at me, incredulous. "I'd love to have a chance to make something with gold that pure; it would be even softer than silver, imagine. We made an eighteen carat chalice last year, but spun up, the lads all had to have a piss in it!"

I'm not surprised by the heathen English and London apprentices.

I explain to Hogan on the phone about the golden idea.

"You're an awful bloody chancer at that price, but leave it to me. I'll have a chat with Michael and Walsh will have to approve; it could be interesting." His answer is surprisingly positive. It's extraordinary that they even take seriously an item like my proposed water pitcher and I feel their naivety and innocence.

Then, where would they sell it? Maybe it was not such a good idea? The state of the country, Mary and those girls living in that cottage. And me asking to work with twenty carat gold.

* * *

"Any chance of that flat yet? I don't think I can put up living with Sarah much longer." Enquires John wearily. "There's a priest staying, on about the Brits as if what happened to Ireland years ago was my fault! He said the Black and Tans threw his father in the Suir at Caher. That the six counties are under British occupation; I can't wait to get out of there."

"Patience John, the other two will be vacant very soon."

"Who were the Black and Tans anyway?"

"Ah, it's a long, complicated story, goes back eight hundred years."

"But nothing to do with me." John adds quiety to himself.

It is starting to pour heavy rain; loud thunder and crack of lightning overhead. John and I look at each other, with a momentary, atavistic fear of Gods. When the Black and Tans shot the Protestants Curate in Downpatrick, mother was going to school and saw it happen. They thought he was a priest!

* * *

The television, which is on for some reason, is showing de Valera and Kennedy again, amidst the waving, smiling adoring crowds. I never thought much of those American Catholic Kennedys. The fecund matriarch Rose; old man Joe's Chicago connections; the election that the mafia swung; dismissing the British in 1940, for Germany would be victorious.

"What's this about Kennedy then?" I ask the barman.

"Kennedy's been shot, he's dead!"

No…

"Where did this happen?"

"Dallas Texas." The barman answers casually, pulling a pint, for this life does go on.

Who'd want to murder the President? Kennedy had it all and was still young. The twenty six counties will be in mourning, total shutdown. We'll never hear the end of this now. A true son of Erin, whose forebears were forced to leave, who did them proud. Lighting penny candles, prayers, endless obituaries. Kennedy was going to get rid of the border, or so some said. Well, well he's dead now; it comes to everyone in the end, terribly sad. Jacqueline and the children. I remember reading about Abraham Lincoln's family.

The colour of whiskey was gold in the morning, now it is a paler, dulling liquid, one that calms the edges of reality. On the road to Freshford, everything looks foreign and unfamiliar tonight. With its lights a-blaze and doors open, I pass the Clontibrid church, where I notice figures in dark consternation, secretive going-ons. The very air sighs for the demise of the president..

"They're in church already praying for his soul," says Mary awed by the news. "I was so close to him at New Ross; reaching out and touching him, he stared right into me, taking my hand, seemed an eternity in those few seconds." And the tears in her eyes are going to fall. She was with the president.

"Will you come down to the church with me?" Mary asks demurely.

"For what?"

"I want to say a prayer for him, come on it'll do you no harm."

"Must we?"

The church has about twenty seated people. Jesus in brown and Mary in her blue, life size, on each side of the altar. Curious faces turn towards us. No priest is present; he would be the one, wherever he is. Mary kneels and covers her face. If he comes, what can he say? Probably he'll just give me a stare of disapproval, he's hardly going to make a scene and throw the Protestant heretic out. The low, soft interior light bathes the scene in pathos. They know now who she's seeing, so the priest will soon be aware I was in his church with her. Mary doesn't care a whit!

Later, I'm about to leave the cottage, when at the half door she suddenly calls, "Wait!"

Disappearing inside for a moment, she then runs out with something in her hand. "Here, do you want a good laugh? It's me when I was ten." It is herself, a smiling child in a Fair Isle torn sweater; on the back, in childish letters, is written Mary Malone 1956.

"Can I keep it?"

"Of course you can, silly goose."

Returning to Kilkenny; I discover that I have to stop. By the dim car overhead light, I take out the black and white ragged photograph. It says something about this child of Ireland and that something is pain. Christmas in a cold cottage; skeletal, frosted landscapes, with a few sweets and maybe an orange. Is it any wonder that the warm interest of the handsome President of the United States of America would affect her so much?

* * *

The silver hours are illusory here; heating and shaping my concentration. I'm pursuing a chimera of elusive Irishness, which is never to be found in the fabrication of objects. And is barely ever present in the inadequacy of thoughts and words from outside the stables. Kilkenny again hypnotises me upon a summer's evening. The cracked, square, grey towers; gables, and chimneys, rendered in some parts perfectly golden by the most brilliant orange and yellow lichens and in places festooned with the dark-green drapery of Irish ivy.

The days tumble. The now familiar workmen are immune to the growing fuss. The rabid Scot an irritating fly, with the beautiful Birgitta blown witch-like on a cloud over the same seas her fierce marauding forebears sailed in order to plunder Ireland.

"Stockholm ar varldens vackraste huvudstad," says she.

"Fwaw, she's gorgeous!" says John, gazing after her.

"You'd be a lucky man to get a handle on her John." I'm daring him to try.

"I might just surprise you!"

Always, there are voices calling from Dublin and I feel a shifting wind, enveloping mists and sometimes I hear the warning of a fog horn, telling me to be wary. But the view clears soon enough. Oisin Kelly finally arrives, a cartoonist's caricature of God. He advises me to make the most of Kilkenny while it lasts. He's here from Monday to Tuesday, the most convenient days for him.

Kelly empties a packet of polished, Killiney beached pebbles, maybe with a view to making jewellery from them. He's in for a cup of tea and a smoke, lighting a saved half-cigarette from behind his ear, nonchantly commenting. "You know my life would be perfectly meaningless without a cigarette!"

He shows us designs for theatrical masks; would like us to make them in copper for him. But why not in silver? He suddenly suggests, seeing silver on the bench.

"Whatever you say yourself Mr Kelly, it's not a problem to make."

As a good friend of William Walsh, the rest really doesn't matter. Soon, Oisin Kelly is happily installed in his cosy little nest beside O'Connor's.

CHAPTER 13

A miraculous figure floats towards me from the cottage, ethereal, a faerie princess out of poetry, with harps playing, like a dream, from an ancient race. The colour of water in moonlight. My thoughts the dart of the fox. Mary's dress is ankle length, white, with a red rose sewn to one side. On first sight, she has the purity of new fallen snow, wondrous and so quiet. How did they manage it? Is this an old gown from a wedding long ago now altered? Mary complains on the drive to the Rugby ball though. I should have asked her before an event like this, the way women are about clothes, I was thoughtless to forget.

"The dress has class, it is so different, no matter what you say," I tell her.

"Well, as long as you're happy; it's the best we could do, it's not right though, however." She twitches her shoulders dissatisfied.

"It's never the dress, but the woman wearing it."

"But the dress goes a long way."

"It's perfect," I reassure her. I will have to get serious; I should have bought her a new one.

Out of Ireland, the dress couldn't be bettered. If photographed wearing it by the ruins of Holycross Abbey, the caption would be: *mysterious, bare-footed Irish beauty, standing on a boulder in the shallows of the sun and cloud-dappled Suir, a vein from the heart of old Ireland.* Lord Lichfield never took a better one for *Vogue* or *Harpers Bazaar.*

"You're not to be worrying, you'll be the belle of the ball."

Encouraging her, we walk towards the Metropole Hotel on the corner of James and Parliament Street. Covered with her ragged white coat, in the cold night, those few pedestrians who pass give her much attention.

You never want to come too early to these functions; even an hour after the advertised opening, the bar is nearly empty and we feel ourselves on view. Slowly, more people arrive, greeted with a drink to get them started. I'm surprised indeed to see William Walsh entering, wearing the amazing, crimson poplin dinner jacket, perhaps for the first time. It is beautifully shaped, with subtle differences in the folds and stitchings of collar, cuffs and pockets.

Walsh takes an immediate, keen interest in Mary, upon my introducing them. The youngish, Slavic, ice-blue-eyed blonde he's with is from Finland. There's Eastwood with his motherly wife here from Wexford, and Young with a girl who is arguing with him. He's carrying a full pint of Smithwicks from the bar to the table, smiling happily.

We are seated in the main function room at a round table which is laid out for the guests of honour. Walsh is now with the Lord Mayor, Walter Smithwick and (so Eastwood tells me), Sir William Blunden. No doubt a Baronet, the lowest hereditary title. The honour was invented in the reign of James the First, for those who purchased land to help garrison Ireland. The first Blunden was probably a thief and Cromwellian adventurer, granted lands instead of money for his adventures. And who's the lovely girl no one has ever seen before – they gaze at us - and she sitting right beside me?

"You certainly seem to have captured the heart of this young man," says Eastwood, embarassing Mary by his attention to her. Not to mention Young's leering, "Yeaaa!"

Young's gangly, fair companion digs him with her elbow, and says, "never mind him Mary." She is evidently annoyed.

Lentil soup is eventually served, followed by turkey, ham and apple pie. There is red or white wine, coffee and tea. Mary moves the wine away, despite Young's encouragment. "Go on there girl; a glass of white wine will do you no harm." He gets another dig in the ribs and another, much harder.

The Town Clerk, Farrelly, slaps me on the shoulder out of nowhere, playfully whiskyish in the ear. "You're an awful bloody heretic, get away on back to the North where you belong."

Where did he go?

Mary is staring, disturbed at someone or something...

"What do you see?"

"Oh nothing," she answers, looking down at her plate.

"Is it the man and woman over there?"

"Yes, he's the manager of the Munster and Leinster bank. I worked for them last summer, looked after the children, did cooking and home-work..."

"And. Go on."

"He got at me, when his wife and children were down at Tramore for a week, I was terrified, had to lock the bedroom door. Even when they went to Mass, he'd stay behind and corner me, slobbering over me, opening his trousers and taking it out. All over my clothes, he was a pig!"

"Did you got to the gardaí?"

"God no!" She is blushing angrily. "Do you think they'd believe my word against his, a bank manager?"

"You poor girl."

"I just left and they never paid me. His horrible, holy wife Bridget said I was ungrateful and not to be asking for a reference." Trying not to show her feelings, she has the face of the dispossessed. I squeeze her hand, which is cold. Hateful memories are darkening her mood, as they dance near us. To them, Mary is unrecognised and easily forgotten, what does he care about the pain done to the sixteen-year-old girl? He's a rotund man, in his secure and respected position, a pillar of the community, church-going, golf-playing and a surreptitious libertine whenever the chance arsies to prey on the vulnerable and innocent.

"I want to dance!" Mary exclaims, suddenly standing, watching their every move.

So in quick steps around the floor, we draw towards the happy couple, who are completely unaware of us. Mary catches his attention, leaning towards him.

"Remember me?" We dance alongside them. "I worked for you last summer."

A moment's blank look, then a hesitant, "ah yes, it's Mary, Mary something, I didn't recognise, you look so different." He's getting nervous. Then Mary turns to his astonished, wife, who is big arsed and matronly.

"Your husband is a filthy, fucking pervert; he never left me alone all the time you were out of the house!" Mary speaks with great hatred. It was bravely said.

The bank manager's wife lets out a loud, birdish squawk, turning to him – he looks stunned and pale - before dragging him off. There is a pause in the dancing, heads turn, people wondering what the commotion is about... The band plays on.

"We'll keep on dancing, see if I care. That's a load off my mind; his wife will never forgive the bastard now," says Mary, the dagger dripping blood in her hand still!

The loud music and song reverberates into a familiar rhythmic abstraction, one derived from the sweating, wild Irish bandsmen of the court of the High King Turlough, or Murtagh, whoever. Mary's laughter and movements represent an abandonment of her past, of Kilkenny, and also show her rage at the bank manager and his wife.

It is disturbing and surprising to see the change in her. *Release Me*; *Mean*

Woman Blues; *You Can't Help It*; *Don't Be Cruel*; *You Win Again*; *You're The Only Star In My Blue Heaven*; *What Did I Say?*; *Hound Dog*... ending with, *Save The Last Dance For Me*.

We are seated at the table again, breathless. Walter Smithwick comes over, exuding benevolence and curiosity; I rise to seat him beside us. "Mr Walsh has been telling me all about you, will you come back with us for a bite of late supper perhaps? And who's this lovely young girl you're with?"

"Mary's her name, Mary Malone."

"You can't be from Kilkenny or we'd have surely noticed you before," says Walter to her. Mary looks up, seated now and demure. "And where are you from Mary?"

"Near Urlingford, the Tipperary side."

"Do you know where we live, at Kilcreene Lodge?"

"Yes I do, by Irishtown." Mary answers immediately.

"Well then, we look forward to seeing you," says a smiling Walter, touching Mary lightly on the bare shoulder.

"So you're in with the Smithwicks, well don't be forgetting us now." Eastwood comments when Walter leaves us.

"Sure if it wasn't for me you'd never have met the girl, remember, so bring us back a barrel of Smithwicks!" Raucous, John reminds me yet again of the night I met Mary. I feel sympathy for his exasperated companion.

*   *   *

Quietly, Mary directs me to a crunchy gravel pathway and hotel-sized Victorian residence. It is like mausoleum, white and large windowed, but glowing with a warmth and suggestion of sustenance. Expensive cars are parked outside, we follow the delighted guests inside. Napoleon Bonaparte confronts me, majestic and ornately gilt-framed on one side of the large, high stucco ceiling room, which has an amazing chandelier. Honey shades; antiques; comfortable furniture; a sideboard of assorted drinks; plates of triangular-cut sandwiches filled with cheese, ham and fishy pastes; cake and various nuts. Mary is nervous with the ladies, Walter's wife Eileen, looks her up and down and asks too many questions.

Walter is an assiduous host, quite the county and family historian. His forebears were given grants of land confiscated in the sixteenth century, acres in Carlow, Tipperary and Kilkenny. Accumulating wealth with each generation, they were eventually able to purchase the St Francis Abbey Brewery. He even has letters written by Daniel O'Connell to a great grandparent and...

To my mind, the people here are slowly and grotesquely turning into life size, well-dressed cockroaches, eating and drinking and guffawing. Encircling poor Mary, they become hysterical, poking and pulling her dress with the most hideous and freakish laughter. For them we are a game!

Mary is in fitfully disturbed sleep when arrived at the cottage. She will awaken from the wealth of Kilcreene to this!

"Are you sure you won't change your mind and come back to Kilkenny?"

"You know I promised Mam I'd help her with some chores and messages. Drive safely for you're tired as me, I'll see you..."

"The day after tomorrow then?"

"Yes, I'll be waiting."

Embracing her is like holding a rag doll: all feeling has drained from the day. Dazed and unsteady, from behind the half door, I see her straighten back to life again.

I stop on the way back to relieve and to stay awake. The sky is lightening to golden pink, streaked with turquoise; I can just make out in the far distance towards Thurles, the black zeppelin of my childhood's memory, disappearing from view.

* * *

Cutting a triangular-shaped, silver sheet gauge eleven, rounding over both sides and soldering them hard together, I form a tubular, straight spout. I paint the inside with a mixture of rouge, polishing powder and water, which I let dry with a stop on the small end, then fill with molten lead until it has cooled solid. Using various hammers, I shape it into a graceful, tapering spout. Finished with a tap, the lead falls out in one piece.

With an unsteady hand (the nightmarish encounters still lurking from the other night), I file the wide end to fit the lower body of the curved pot. I borax the joint and attach the spout with binding wire, carefully heating and soldering over the sieved entrance, concentrating on getting this part accurate. Thankfully, it didn't move. So I can put down the blow torch, turning out the flame which had warmed me so pleasantly. Such are the mysteries of flammable gas interacting with the atomic structures of silver when worked and annealed. I let the piece sink into the pale green pickle, satisfied.

"Meet any nice girls yet John?" Ask, relaxing somewhat.

"No, but I tell you, some of those country girls need a good wash!" he answers cruelly.

"You're not serious?"

"I went to my first dance the other night, and I tell you it's a fact!"

"I've never noticed, maybe some just don't have the facilities to bath every day."

"Could be. I'll just have to get used to, go native... if I stay!"

"In a crowded dance hall one's bound to work up a sweat John. Natural body odours do you no harm; they are an enticement in fact."

"I don't think so, it's called personal hygiene."

Is this an English, awakened prejudice? It must be nonsense, to be so finely attuned to detect odour at a dance? Ridiculous, this is an echo instead of the portrayal of the Irish being dirty and Catholic!

I'm stupefied an prolonged silence. Now I must carve a nylon handle to fit and dye it black, sure why not emerald green? Someone's bound to be asking questions about this enterprise eventually. Here comes Kelly, no doubt to instruct us about his theatrical masks.

"This is the one I've decided on, and you might as well make it in silver." He is sheepish as he hands over the sinister-faced drawing: a trophy for a drama award. "Is there still warm tea in the pot?"

"I'll make you a fresh pot Mr Kelly," says John helpfully, getting up. Is this what we're supposed to be doing, a mask for the Commedia Nuova? Kelly discourses on his preference for Michelangelo to Bernini... his time is of no consequence, his commission is in good hands. Satisfied, he leaves.

"Interesting job there John, do you want to make it?"

"I certainly do, can I start right away?" John is studying the drawing carefully.

"Yes of course, what gauge do you need?"

"Better make it twelve."

"We've two full sheets of it, so make up a template and cut it out yourself."

"I'll really enjoy doing this, an unusual challenge, that Kelly's an interesting bloke and this drawing is superb." Full of admiration, John holds the image close to his face, then he looks out of the window. "Your bird Mary is coming this way."

Something's wrong! Letting her in, I feel she has a look of the hunted, now safe from the Earl of Essex's men, who had smeared her with aniseed for fun and given her a head start. They're after her, the dogs barking ever closer, the first man to catch can have her anyway he wants! I take her by the hand and hurry to the end room, ignoring John, and I close the door.

"What are you doing here? I'd be coming out to you this evening anyway?"

"I just had to get away and see you; I got an awful fright walking into Freshford this morning, shopping for Mam." Mary explains, barely holding back the tears. "The curate, Father Cleary, drove up beside me, the one that gave out to us, about me seeing you, a Protestant. He offered a lift, said he was on his way to Freshford and Kilkenny. So I, like a fool, could hardly say no to a priest and got in. But he wasn't going in the right direction, so I asked him but he just laughed, ignoring me. Said he'd make it easy for me if I gave him something in return, putting his hand on my knee and pushing up my skirt. I freaked, opened the car door and was ready to jump out. That made him stop. He tried to grab me, but I was too quick for him, but he followed after me. I was terrified. He was shouting over as he drove past, that I'd never be good enough for you in my circumstances and you couldn't be serious about me and you'd never ask me...," a hesitation, "… to marry you." Now she is sobbing with loud gasps of deep pain.

"Yes, I'll marry you, that's if you'll have me?" I reply automatically, without a second thought. The poor girl, I can't have her suffering so, for I do love her, wanting to be wedded to Ireland forever somehow.

"You are serious?" She is dumbfounded, in laughter and tears now.

"Are you? What about the job in London?"

"Oh fiddlesticks to that. You'll have to get me an engagement ring and arrange a date." She sounds most determined.

"What about the priest, will I get after him? Complain to the Bishop?"

"Don't be daft you can't touch priests here; marrying you will be revenge enough for me, he wouldn't dare try again or complain."

"Well if you're satisfied."

To which reply, she throws her arms around me with an excited kiss.

"Go on up to the flat and I'll see you later." I watch her tripping off, exhilarated, almost able to fly.

"Bird trouble?" asks John, measuring the mask and figuring out how to make it.

"The priest's been after her for seeing me, a Protestant, and a lot more."

"Religion seems to matter a lot in Ireland, Tom Eastwood reckons it's what keep the Irish on the straight and narrow, the fear of Hell! Do you go to church?"

"Hardly ever."

"And with women you can't be too careful."

"What do you mean?"

"Well you know how they can wheedle their way into your affections with body shape, arse and tits. Then it becomes difficult to get out and the sex is over in seconds.

"It's called love John, a natural coming together of the male and female, to create new life."

"Yea well, I'm footloose and fancy free; fuck them and leave them, is what I say!"

"That's brutal John."

"It would be in Ireland without Durex, I agree!" John replies. Kelly's drawing, grinning at us mischievously.

I'm stunned. Mary and marriage. The priest. And this earthy Englishman with Kelly's design, enthusiastically starting to interpret it. What will become of it eventually? Maybe the mask will be stolen, hidden and forgotten. Then found as an Ardagh or Tara in a bog of some future Ireland, damaged and tarnished black as eternity. Taken as being from a distant tribe, the Veneti or Getae, for one is never really in control of one's work.

"Are you not going to answer it?" John turns to me to surprised. The telephone! The telephone. God, yes, I heared it, but never heard. Now alerted, I answer to a voice from where?

"How would you like to stay at Castle Blunden until Rolf Middleboe arrives? You can move in anytime and you might as well, since we're renting it now." This is Michael Clarke of Coras Trachtala, a voice I recognize, a soft and easy man.

"That would be great Michael, kind of you to offer, how do I get in?"

"Robbie Haughton will give you the key, it's a fine big Georgian house on the Waterford road I believe."

Well, well, Castle Blunden will give Mary a surprise. We can live like an Anglo aristocrat. It is just like them to rent a castle for a Dane! I can hardly believe it; I shall live in the house of a real, live Irish hereditary baronet.

CHAPTER 14

"Fully furnished, with everything you need," says Robbie whistling, handing over the key. And John can move into the adjoining flat immediately. I won't say a word to her. On my return, I find her still over the moon. She has tidied the room, has the bed made and is washing the dishes. She can't wait to tell Mam. Getting into the car, we head towards Waterford.

"Where are we going? This isn't the way."

"I want to show you something, it's not far."

"Like what? What?" Her voice is pitched high with impatience; higher than the summer swifts and swallows of the castle.

"We're nearly there." I drive through a wide-gated entrance, the house looms large, sloping slate roofed and solid against the ominous colouring sky. Three stories and eighteen paned windows; a single storey colonnaded Doric portico over the doorway for arrivals.

There is a sudden gush of cold wind, shivering the trees. Mary is like an animal, caught unaware and asks, "what are we doing here? I hope this isn't haunted."

Turning the key, I open the door to a dark hallway, before finding the light switch. There is a door on each side. We enter the first, a well-stocked library: green-shaded lamp over a leather inlaid writing desk; Adam style fire-place; thick, buttoned sofa and matching armchairs. We are surrounded by portraits of the owners male forebears, coated in blues and reds. And of ladies, beautifully dressed in pinks and creams, with the whitest imaginable dead hands and faces. Who are these Blundens with their framed coat-of-arms on the walls? It looks like black bricks quartered with lions, topped with an angry demi-lion, winged and beaked griffon.

"You can be mistress of the house Mary, if you like for a while."

"Are you serious, how so?"

"Kilkenny Designs are renting it, but it can be ours if you like until the Danish designer arrives."

"God I don't know, it's such a lovely room, amazing how some can afford to live in such comfort and style." She speaks with wonderment.

I examine the book titles. *British History in the Nineteenth Century and After; The Peace and the Protestant Succession; Blenheim, Their Finest Hour*, Winston S, Churchill... and there's certainly no Kevin Barry in this house. Unlike Mam's, where I noticed it askew, faded from sunlight, surrounded with shamrocks.

The sitting room is even more sumptuous, with carved and floral patterned chairs, gilt mirrors, more portraits, and a painting of hunting with the Kilkenny Hunt: over the hedges they go, the red sprawled over the green. The interiors are probably late eighteenth century; how age can lend to a house the atmosphere of our predecessors. In the dining room is a fine Heppelwhite table with Ladderback chairs and a tall glass-fronted cabinet of lovely Wedgewood cream-coloured earthenware, with blue and gold edged designs. Upstairs, the master bedroom has a split Serpentine-fronted ladies dressing table with mirrors front and sides, assorted silver enamel matching brushes and combs. Mary sits and begins to brush her long, dark hair, dreamlike. For Mary should have been at this table right from the beginning somehow. I bend beside her, to see us both reflected. We are just passing through, as, long before, at the same dressing table, were the pretty ladies with the dead white hands. The mortality of life and beauty mocks and it is frightening.

Mary reaches up to me like a child seeking an embrace, trusting that she has found love and care. I take her to what must be Lady Blanden's soft, richly embroidered, wide covered bed. It can't be allowed to happen yet, as it wouldn't be fair. Yet inside a thundering waterfall of thrusting passion, I know there'll never be another feeling like this, the sensation of coming all over her naked stomach. I'm relieved, selfishly, on the moon colours created by the dim light: flesh and thick, creamy sperm.

Her eyes are closed in a trance of some strange atavistic Irish female rite, inherited without knowing, where she rubs my sperm as a lotion. It is a kind of bonding, or something I do not understand.

My sleep is disturbed; I can see Mary, Mam and those two girls, wretched and half starved, dressed in rags, tapping and scratching at the windows, in the freezing cold and heavy rain outside. They can't be let into Castle Blunden though, for they're a different class, two worlds: side-by-side but miles apart. I wake to see Mary looking down at me, troubled.

"I don't want to stay, let's go back to the flat, then Freshford," she says, getting off the bed and straightening her clothes.

"Are you sure? There's plenty of wood and coal, as much hot water as we need. You can be the Lady Blunden for a while, live in style." I tempt her to stay.

Her response contains annoyance, "and why would you be thinking I'd want to be Lady Blunden?"

"I mean live in the same comfort, not like her," I reply, corrected.

"I'd burn the place down, wouldn't give it a second thought, an insult all this and you well know the rest." She speaks with fierce conviction, her beautiful, grey eyes blazing!

Locking the door behind us, we step into freezing cold and heavy rain. It's almost as if the big house has had the effect of wiping the excitement of her future marriage away. Mournfully, Mary reminisces over her past unhappiness in a low monotone, on the slow and stormy road to Freshford.

"Imagine what it was like for me to be taken away from my mother at the age of five? Given away to strangers like a stray puppy. My childhood was the saddest and most challenging one for any child to endure. I saw my mother only three times in all that time. She sent me a chicken and a Fair Isle cardigan on the Limerick bus when I was seriously ill at the age of eight. After my post confirmation and wanting to become a nun, I was turned down with, 'God doesn't want the likes of you!' I have always felt I was an object of shame and ridicule, I have never had happiness in my life until hopefully now..."

* * *

I'm late heading for work, experiencing a cutting sadness and apprehension, an ineffable legacy from yesterday. John is busy on Kelly's mask, which is beginning to take shape. From the blackened silver's first annealing, it emerges matt white from the pickle, then is rinsed under running tap water.

"Robbie just told me you can move in beside me anytime John."

"That's just what I wanted to hear, great news!" John does a little dance with the mask over his face, which is freakish. "Three pounds ten shillings a week isn't it?"

"Yes" I watch him dry the mask with a quick blast from the blow torch.

"I'll move in right away." John pauses. "David Reeves was here earlier, curious about Kelly's mask. He said the window catches were a joke, Montgomery should never have used them."

"What does he mean?"

"The catches and long-holed openers with the curly ends."

"Curly ends?"

"Yes."

"They do the job, what's wrong with them?"

"Said they're old fashioned, putting them in windows these days, not draft proof and really tight.'

"I see." Today, everything here is surreal somehow... and I feel even more so answering the phone.

"This water pitcher in gold better be a masterpiece at that price. You may go ahead and make, but keep it under your hat, Walsh was hesitant but thought something might come of it, is that clear?" Paul Hogan is speaking loudly, is he annoyed?

"In twenty carat gold?"

"That's what you said, yes." And now his answer is suspiciously quiet, "but we really shouldn't you know, however you go ahead."

"So I'll order the gold?"

"Oh yes, and may God help you!" And he must have put the phone down abruptly.

What does he mean? Am I skating on thin ice? With Mary's joy now at my side what can go wrong? I must get her the diamond engagement ring.

"We're to make that twenty carat gold pitcher I told you about John."

"You're having me on?" His reply is doubtful, his eyes on the mask, which is still only beginning to take shape.

"That was Hogan on the phone just now with the go ahead."

"Who's it for?"

"Don't know."

"Madness, the gold will cost a fortune!" says John, turning to me, troubled.

"It certainly will." I'm starting to worry, will the metal stand up to so much raising? Perhaps it isn't such a good idea? And what about Kelly's plasticine doddles. I suddenly notice the tin again. Better go see.

Kelly isn't in his room. But Jesus Christ is there, crucified on a large St. Canice's tomb, a rubbing on the facing wall. Kelly is evidently starting to carve two birds out of a block of wood, one probably an owl, the other definitely a dove. On the floor is a thick cover of unswept shavings, two chisels and an open, empty packet of Players. His reason for living!

* * *

Mary's Christmas job in Woolworths is confirmed. She's wearing the blue coat again, selling broken chocolate and assorted sweets in large wooden trays. From their laughter behind long counters, there's a hidden pain and sadness in these Woolworth girls. I can take her home in the evening and maybe she stay the night. She wants to see the priest with me. Getting married to a Protestant, what can they say?

"We can do it in a Registry Office surely?"

"Ah no, it must be done proper." Mary replies adamantly. She's not going to hide away to Dublin or Belfast but wants everyone to know. If that's what she wants, then that's how it will be.

"Is the priest the one that attacked you?"

"No, he's the curate."

"So when do we go?"

* * *

A blighted modern house is cut into a sleeping bare blackthorn hedged field. There's a newish, wrap-around windowed Vauxhall Cresta to one side, marigold and white. The lumpish woman opening the door is suspicious and irritated, casting a stern eye on Mary. She shows us into a cosy, dancing-fire lit room, whose odour of a variety of tobaccos immediately hit us. Cartons of cigarettes are stacked on each side of the fireplace: Carrolls Number One to the left, Sweet Afton to the right. There's even a large box of Montecristo cigars. Beneath my feet is a ghastly, swirling red carpet.

"I've never been in a priest's house before, he certainly lives very well," Mary whispers, warming her hands to the fire, gazing around the room. It's occupant can hardly be into fasting and religious contemplation... Mother always said they lived too well!

As he enters, he clears the remains of supper from around his mouth. I've never been this close to a priest or even spoken to one before. He is in his late middle-age, in a rather shabby, well-worn black suit. Holding out his hand, I feel the keen appraisal of this small blackberry of a man as we shake. Mary, however, only obtains a glancing nod.

"So you want to marry our young girl?" He speaks condescendingly, seating himself on his rug-covered armchair beside the fire. "Have a seat, do sit down."

I'm on the sofa with Mary nervously beside me.

"You're a Protestant, we believe, and as you know the Catholic church does not encourage mixed marriages. There'd be conditions, and I'd need Bishop Birch's permission for this to go ahead." He waits, silent for a minute, for us to digest this. Behind him, on the wall, is a macabre painting of St Agatha's breasts on a silver salver overflowing with her red blood. Like the ghastly, rimed Cardinal's hat he's now wearing, dear God!

"In this case, however, because of her circumstances she'd be doing well by marrying you and the many children — hopefully — of the union would be Catholic. You'd have to give your word and sign to that effect, understand?" He eyes me, waiting for an answer.

"Yes, yes of course."

"Instructions in the Catholic faith as well, we would arrange for you to see one of our priests."

"I'll look forward to that." I'm smiling and I answered rather too quickly. It would be a lark listening to Papish trumpery!

"Will you now? I'm surprised, it's a serious matter. " The priest is somewhat disquieted.

"But of course it is; I fully understand."

"I hope so."

It is unnerving to have a picture like that in one's sitting room, bloody, bleeding breasts... what's he saying?"

"We've got a good man in Kilkenny, a Father Magee on the Ormonde Road, who will be able to see you. And sure maybe you'll even see the light and come over to us, who knows?" He looks at me sideways with an tempting smile.

"You've a lot of cigarettes there, Father." I change the subject, amused to hear myself say Father to this stranger!

"I enjoy my cigarettes yes, usually Carrolls tipped in the mornings and Afton full strength in the afternoons, with a cigar perhaps before bed.

"Would you be worried about your lungs?"

"Not at all, all in God's good hands, whatever will be, would you like a cigar?"

"No thank you Father. Well, so maybe I will, but I'll smoke it later."

"Help yourself." He points to them. "You'll need to cut it with that little yoke inside."

I get up and go over to the cedar wood box, where there is also a large bottle of John Jameson. The cigars are eight inches long and thick, with pretty red and gold bands around them. I clip the covered end.

"I do go to the dogs a lot," he says, "greyhound racing that is, do you ever go yourself?"

"Never."

"Can we arrange a date for the marriage?" Mary, forgotten, asks hopefully, moving to the edge of her seat.

"Well now, Mary isn't it? All these things are to come first and you'll need your mother's permission as you're not yet eighteen." This mention of her mother upsets her. "You're a fine healthy girl Mary, and please God there'll be lots of children."

God almighty, she's no brood mare: do women even exist for these men? Still, I will go along with whatever it takes to make her happy.

"And of course the marriage will not take place in front of the altar, it will be in the vestry, to show the churches disapproval!" The priest informs her, as he shows us to the door.

"I didn't know you smoked." Mary quizzes me on the return to the cottage.

"More of a souvenir really, I'll keep it forever, like Grandfather's cigarettes in a fancy tin Queen Alexandra gave them going off to France to fight the Hun. He never smoked."

"It'll be a while yet before we're through with all this, you don't mind I hope?

"Looking forward to it in a way."

"In a way?"

"An hour and so with a Roman priest could be interesting, who knows, he might even convert me!" I turn to her with a grin.

"I wouldn't want that, the Protestants are a better class than us Catholic mostly.

"What makes you say that?"

"Well they seem to own everything from what I can see."

"The reason for that is mostly historical in Ireland."

"Well then, weren't they the clever ones."

"I suppose you could say that in a way, but things are changing, hopefully."

*   *   *

Mam is pleased it went so well, though little Eileen is a shy and sad presence, lingering silent and ragged, as a ghost from penal times, bewildered and haunted. Nora is doomed; it's written all over her. The breath of Irish history hangs heavy over this cottage.

"Mary has good blood you know, the district nurse from Knocktopher told me she's a Langrishe!" says Mam casually, the bolt hitting the bull-seye, but who owned the crossbow? For I've heard that name before somewhere, was it... the old woman in the village shop? Yes, where ... Knocktopher! The big house. I remember Knocktopher Abbey and the name Langrishe, Sir somebody. It was Terence, Sir Terence Languishe, and what skullduggery went on then and there you'd wonder? The dog! Could her father have been a baronet? Mary is strangely uninterested. This is the first time she's ever heard anything about her father, yet she doesn't ask Mam to elaborate any further. I recall, too, that Mary said her mother does live near Knocktopher!

*   *   *

Does the North exist down here? Or, far beyond Dundalk, is it just as distant a country as Turkmenistan? A letter from home brings back youthful memories of my travels from Ballynahinch to Newcastle. Past the ever burning bush, the windowed, orange hall of gentle Seaforde. I would sight the sea and Slieve Donard, then pass Mount Panther, approaching

Dundrum, becoming one with the first beginnings of light.

I'm looking at father's royal red Elizabethan-stamped, Kilkenny-addressed envelopes, which invariably ending in Eire. Can there really be a country called Eire? Eire, it's a word that should be used for a gas that is lighter than air, rising as ethane, highly unstable and liable to explode if not handled with great care. The preposterous fiction that is Eire; I sometimes feel Eire is an invention of my imagination and my thoughts turn to the name Langrishe, as a summer fly cannot be chased away. It that really her lineage?

Mary comes gaily up from Woolworths, carefree and radiant, accompanied by a laughing friend. Christmas is drawing near. The gold has been ordered from an incredulous Johnson Matthey; they have never made a circle that carat and size before.

Turning the lights out and closing the darkened workshop, I notice that Kelly's mask has a mysterious luminosity now that it has been lightly polished. I lean on John's file rack watching opposite him.

* * *

"Would you like to meet my parents and spend Christmas away? I suggest to her, offering her a break from Kilkenny.

"Oh, God, I don't know, couldn't we just be together in the flat and I'll cook us the dinner? For you'll need to get the ring first to show them we're proper engaged."

"It'll be after Christmas in Dublin for the ring I'm afraid and a whole turkey wouldn't fit in the oven."

"I can wait and sure a chicken will do, they've ready-made plum puddings in the new market on Rose Inn Street, I never had turkey for Christmas before anyway!"

"Never?"

"Never." Mary answers with momentary deep sadness (out of where?).

"It won't upset Mam if you stay for a few days then?"

Mary laughs cheekily. "She thinks you're a gentleman."

"She could be wrong you know."

"I don't think so, will we go to midnight Mass in St Mary's?"

"If I do go to your abominable papish Mass, my tongue will turn black and even fall out!"

"Ah go on, it'll do you no harm."

For Mary's certainly worth a Mass and many more if needs be, for she'll soon drift away out of all that absurdity.

* * *

As we boldly walk united as one, towards St Mary's for Mass, I feel a mischievous thrill that I should dare to trespass. There are a few familiar faces present and they show surprise and curiosity. For who indeed is she? Beneath the altar is a relief showing the Adoration of the Magi in cold, white marble; there is a brass tabernacle; a silver gilt monstrance and silver chalices on display. Lurid, explicit stations of the cross are on each side above, leading to Christ's crucifixion and the red lamp light of whorish sin and temptation.

Mary is a glowing bright star now in the firmament of her past misfortunes. The Dean and his curate will be very disappointed to know I was here: another gone to the Romans side. He need not be worried though.

A slowly growing presence emerges from the distance. I can't quite be sure, my mind is confused and cluttered, midway between fantasy and reality. The old priest is holding up the chalice, gleaming, flaming light reflected on his hands, sipping the blood wine lie of Jesus Christ. I can see him more clearly now and am certain. Yes, the priest is definitely Adolf Hitler!

I join the queue forming for the Host, Mary encouraging me, "come on."

My limbs are frozen, paralysed by this sighting, chilled as from a death sentence. She has to direct me gently — and it still feels painful — to the altar. Adolf Hitler in that most sacred of places, still a Catholic! Kneeling to him, the blackest devil incarnate of all time lets the wafer drop without touching my cupped hands and when I look into those see-through, cruel eyes I know that the Fuhrer is alive and well in Southern Ireland!!

Dipping her fingers in the little font by the main door on the crowded way out, Mary flicks water at me, careless with laughter and the fright dissolves somewhat... but that was him?

The festive decorations on High Street cover the passers-by. An intuition draws me to the unlocked stable yard, which we check. I sense somebody is about; the workshop is lit up on in the early hours of this lovely Christmas morning. And here is a surprise! Obsessed, John is still working to complete Kelly's mask. It has the same luminescence as when clouds part to reveal the moon.

"Will we give him a fright?" I suggest quietly.

"Ah no, it would bring us bad luck to disturb him when he's like this, can't you see the full fool's moon has brought the lunacy on him, working this day and hour on a yoke like that!" Mary refers to the old superstition, but I think the obsession is surely more from Kelly than the moon.

Standing by the entrance to the workshop pathway in the shifting dark, we watch him as John deals a 'ratatattat' here and a 'tattah' there to the silver mask, which is held firmly in the pitch block. Now a fox comes by, which is astonishing. It trots past, calmly assured, glancing torch-eyed at the two of us, as if wondering what we are doing here.

Leaving the devil and the mask and the Mona Lisa moon (smiling now) we return to my flat.

CHAPTER 15

There's virgin blood on the sheets, under a vibrating Mary on this Christmas Day. With her sublime innocence, she's like the rare, wild Irish rose found white and pure by the hedgerows bordering Tipperary and Kilkenny. I had discovered them in journeys from Freshford to Inistioge, and on the slumbering ruins of Kells and Holycross Abbey, sparkling from summer's morning dew. Here comes the sudden, shadowed, cold swoop of the kite. A Langrishe. And a victim's cry of pain, for predatory man must have his damned due. An outrage and violation with everlasting shameful consequences for unwary Catholic girls. I had to explain in the face of her bewilderment the reason for wearing at this stage the awful Protestant sleeve from Blake's surgical supplies! The fumbling poking of my manhood. Maybe, she intuitively questions if we didn't do it the right way. Because immediately after, stupefied, tearful and wet she asks, "when will you be getting my diamond engagement ring?"

"We'll away to Dublin in the New Year and you can pick out one yourself, within reason." I reply, kissing her moist cheeks.

I can hear times footsteps on the landing to the door, follwed by a light knocking. John, ashen and psychotic, but triumphant, has the finished mask in his hand. At first sight, it is a sort of skull, that he now holds up to his face, covering it and chasing all normality to flight here again. What is Oisin Kelly and Kilkenny doing to him, to put him into a state like this? The making of prototypes for Irish industry a distant memory, hidden by the rising mists of the Nore, spreading over the rational explanation and subverting those forgotten words. What we are supposed to be about here

I recall only as far-away lilting tunes. Looking into the face of this beautiful girl, all the rest is of no consequence and doesn't really matter.

*   *   *

Wrapped in golden paper, tied with a red ribbon, are socks and a striped tie with a snowman Christmas card: love and kisses, forever and ever and ever, from Mary. A new herringbone, black-and-white tweed coat, with a fluffy collar has her thrilled. These crystalline, precious minutes tick away and I'm far too aware the clock doesn't stand still. She is so anxious to please and is behind the partition, preparing the plain Christmas dinner.

"Will we invite John over to share this?" I suggest.

"I'd rather you didn't, but if you must." Her reply is hardly enthusiastic.

"He's all on his own."

"I know."

I'm unable to rouse John by knocking, so after quietly opening his door I see him fast asleep on the crumpled bed, not a movement. I leave him well alone. The mask is on the side locker beside him. I could tip-toe over and take it as a joke? No! It would be too cruel.

Back in our flat, the meal is excellent. "This is good. So who taught you to cook so well?"

"Home economics at school."

"In Freshford?"

"No, Kilkenny."

"It is a long journey every day to and from there, you must have been exhausted"

"Don't I know. And for all the cooking I learned, there was never the proper ingredients and stuff in the cottage to cook proper anyway. The butcher in Freshford always gave us the worst cuts of bacon and meat whenever Mam could afford it, on tick when we couldn't. He knew we were dirt poor!"

"Sounds awful."

"You can say that again, and he always looked at me queer!"

"Well your skills won't be wasted when we're married for sure."

"I'll do my best now."

As I'm halfway through the plum pudding she asks can we go to Freshford to see Mam before it gets too dark. She has a few presents to give them.

"You should have told me earlier, for I've nothing." I feel mean now.

"What I have will do from us both," Mary answers carelessly.

*   *   *

The sight is bizarre and weirdly upsetting. In a field near Freshford, there is a nightmare of unnatural goings on, for a litter of brawling pigs are suckling a cow that doesn't seem to mind their greedy, thrusting snouts, which are straining upwards in a feeding frenzy beneath the fat adder. A fearful free-for-all in the mud. I stop to watch.

"What's the problem?"

"Look in the field, did you ever see the likes?"

"Sure I've seen them at that before."

"Isn't it strange though?"

"Milk is milk, they just want to survive."

I suppose she's right, but somehow the sight leaves me disturbed and apprehensive at life around here, below the barely visible moon in the colourless, cold sky.

It is excruciating, entering this cottage. Mendacious, broken Ireland is alive and well in these mean walls of an old woman and the abandoned, illegitimate girls conceived out of wedlock and branded by Catholic sin. This will be their circumstances for ever more. The Langrishe at the big house will have to find out about Mary. A Lord Leitrim in the waiting, maybe, who deserves the same bullet for his black heart!

Do I dare to guess what they had for Christmas dinner? Sliced bread spread thinly with butter and jam, biscuits and tea, lemonade? No, no, there's a small, half-eaten iced cake sprinkled with those awful, hard and tasteless tiny silver balls, with Santa fallen on his face. Cold, cold hearts, morning frost and snow predicted. A snow which will soon cover so much pain. They must share a bed to keep warm, listening to the scratch of mice somewhere near. The wind above the chimney moving ashes in the grate

The parish priest will now be having one of those Montecristo cigars beside the fire, drinking whiskey with St Agatha's breasts above his holy head, an extraordinary sight. His curate, despite the moral demands of his order, is habitual in the stimulation and deliberate use of the body part designed for other purposes, having dared to try the reality with Mary. A journey through nettles and briars. Lives broken before they begin. In the New Year, when I make the golden jug, this great wave of contradictions will be a heavy, dead weight to carry.

They love Mary's new coat, touching it and feeling it. Strangely, they stroke their cheeks upon the fluffy collar. Isn't she the lucky one. Thanking us for the sweets. If only Elijah would come down and take them all up to heaven.

* * *

I am looking in the phone book, for that name is irritably unusual. One of the quality Anglo, no doubt. L,L, Langan; Lanigan; Langrishe. Sir Terence Langrishe, Knocktopher Abbey. Knocktopher yes! It sounds so powerful and grand, a devil-may-care plunger in his youth, probably with some service in the British Army or Royal Air Force. I can ask Mary's mother if I can see her. The district nurse even. It could well be him, the blue beard of Knocktopher, pretty girls in the vicinity beware! The house I saw that day, gazing over from the graveyard, held secrets aplenty. However, it's no one's business but her own.

*   *   *

We are parked near Inistioge beside the Nore, stepping over to the edge of the roaring river, a deluge from winter's heavy rain. The sight and sound of it reminds me that nature eventually sweeps all human endeavour away. For the moment the car is a warm refuge, until a torch is suddenly shined in on us. We hastily pull apart. There is a tap on the window, which I roll down.

"Are you alright there now?" It is a beaming, friendly garda, a comfort somehow, but I do not understand why.

"Ah yes, we were just out for a drive," I reply.

"It'll be dark soon, you do go easy on those wet roads now, I see you're from the North."

"Yes I'll be in Kilkenny for a while, the Design Centre, you might have heard about."

"The making of silver isn't it?" He had heard about the centre, though he sounded as though he was unable to understand it.

"Well, yes, amongst other things."

"Good night then and God bless, you take care." He's gone as quick as he came. Another memorable interlude on life's journey.

Mary laughs as we drive on, drawn ever closer by a magnet force, through Bennettsbridge and Thomastown, until the narrow road leads us to Knocktopher.

"God, how did we arrive here?" I exclaim.

"I think you know very well. You wanted to," answers Mary knowingly.

By the entrance to the graveyard, the last tall remains of the Abbey, narrow and jagged, stands before us.

"Do you know where your mother lives here?"

"No and if I did I wouldn't want to see her, for all the good she ever was to me!" Her answer leaves no doubt.

I spend a moment in contemplation, vapourish airs slowly rise over the gravestones. "Will we walk on up the big house, just for the hell of it, they'd be the Langrishe's Mam mentioned. Terence is the one I looked up, he could be your father!"

"You couldn't be sure and if he was, he'd deny everything, slam the door in my face!"

"Come on trust me, if we're stopped we can say we're looking for our dog, a wee terrier."

"Oh, alright then, but I'd rather not."

The wide high iron gate is shut, but opens easily to a driveway that is pitch black from the high cover of the trees. Slowly and carefully, we approach the house, keeping to the side.

"Let's go back, this is too creepy for me." Mary holds me tight, her eyes those of a wild thing caught in a trap.

"You stay here then, by this tree, and I'll go on just out of curiosity."

"Don't you be long then."

"I'll be back in a jiffy."

In the foggy darkness, the house is like a series of black boxes put together without planning. A few of the pointed windows are lit up, the big green Jaguar I saw earlier is parked outside. Approaching the window, the curtains are not quite closed and I peer through. There's a man wearing a dinner jacket and bow tie seated in an enormous leather-button armchair reading the paper by the fire. Turning the page, he glances towards me momentarily and I can see the resemblance, ever-so-faintly, of Mary. It must be Sir Terence Langrishe. A perfect target from the window.

I can understand where the violence came from in the past. Living in such feudal surroundings, his own flesh and blood an unwanted bastard of no consequence, a girl to be hidden away. The pretty village girl, the mother, glad of a job in the big house and the few shillings. Langrishe, a predatory wolf circling his easy prey, without a second thought, the poor girl's head spinning, for she didn't want to lose her job. Distraught at the consequences of what had happened, she was trapped. And soon enough, she finds out she will be a mother. Who does she turn to? Her father, mother, the priest? She would be terrified to even mention his name. The shame on the poor girl, secreted away to Roscrea. And Mary born as an embarrassment and reminder of her sin. Sir Terence Langrishe took what he wanted and would hardly even remember her, for there would have been more women then, droit duseigneur!

"I'm sure I saw your father just now through the window, in a dinner jacket and bow tie, maybe going somewhere, or perhaps he dresses like that for his dinner here. Handsome enough, in his late sixties I would say." I say this to Mary, who is hiding like one of the hunted, native Irish of Spenser's day. An outlaw and trespasser on her own land, the wrong side of the high stone wall, waiting worried. By birth and right she should be on this side.

"Getaway, how can you be certain?" Her voice is careless, as if unconcerned about a man of his class and behaviour.

"Would you not be curious?"

"No, not now, you can ask my mother whenever, that's if she'll tell you, come on lets go."

* * *

After trying several, Mary chooses a single diamond-and-gold ring from Weirs on Grafton Street that costs thirty-five pounds and she's well pleased, although the diamond is rather small. The weather is unsettled, with sudden gusts and heavy rain, fleeting sunshine and umbrellas blown inside out. I watch one, abandoned on South Anne Street, like a dying Jurassic bird. We turn into Kildare St, towards the Shelbourne for a treat of afternoon tea. In the bustle of this warm and comfortable old hotel, money allows choice foods and drinks in the company of the casual, expensively-dressed. You have to be well off to stay here. Some are countryfied and there is also a harsh, insistent voice of an American. Mary can't get over the ring, glancing and holding it up on her finger; a definite proof of my commitment.

Once more Mary lifts her hand, catching the sunlight, out from the clouds through the high window. It turns the diamond to tiny, flashing colours of the rainbow. Mary moves her hand this way and that, tipping her beautiful, grey eyes and her hair oil-black and golden. Nearby, a grey, green-tweeded lady smiles knowingly over, perhaps remembering her own feelings from long ago.

We eat colourful pastries and drinking tea, her skirt is rather high above her perfect knees. I will have to get up to Belfast and Blake's Surgical Suppliers again soon. It's a shame they are not available this side of the border. That's Rome rule for you!

CHAPTER 16

Oisin Kelly is delighted with his mask and full of praise for John's skill at interpreting his drawing so well. I'm glad to see it away. It has a mocking presence, an indefinable something that's unsettling.

"Am I to charge you for this Oisin? For nobody's mentioned pricing and costs for anything yet?" I ask.

"You leave that to me, I'll mention it to Walsh if I remember, for sure now's the time to use Kilkenny while it's here." There is amusement in his cynical eyes and he smiles wryly.

"Would you like it hallmarked?"

"No, no, it's fine just the way it is." Holding it out at arm's length Kelly contemplates the mask happily, then off he goes.

"Vanders would have charged him big money for that in London," John comments, bewildered.

The postman arrives with a registered Royal Mail parcel from Birmingham. Tearing away the brown paper, corrugated and plastic wrapping, I come to the gold circle and pieces of gold wire. God, it is so heavy! It must be be well over one-and-a-half times the weight of silver. I unfold the invoice: the price is two-thousand-six-hundred and forty-nine pounds, fifteen shillings and sixpence.

"Feel the weight of this John, once in a lifetime and never again, remember these days when you're an old man."

"You can be sure of that, I find it hard to understand this Kilkenny operation most of the time."

"Sure it's not really happening, John, and you'll wake up from the dreaming someday. A very tall tale in the years to come, telling anyone."

"Could well be." He feels the weight of the gold on his hand, amazed, "we'll have to anneal this most carefully, with a lot more care than silver."

"Six hundred and fifty degrees C for thirty seconds and then quench in cold water once the metal has cooled to black heat. That's what it says here in the covering letter." I read some more. "It goes on about oxidization and protection with a concentration of boric acid in alcohol.

"We needn't worry about that, for there'll be very little as I remember with eighteen carat and this being twenty."

"Let's hope it doesn't crack," I say hopefully.

"Or we get the orange peel effect on the surface," continues John.

"There's always a risk with something like this for the first time, something never tried before. Atomic structures have a mind of their own."

He has one more thought. "Metal fatigue."

Oh, no John, God forbid.

"The soldering can be a bugger and eat into the gold if we're not careful." Again, I think this is perhaps not such a good idea. Walsh must have something up his sleeve to give me the go ahead, who knows? Two disparate souls, brought together by chance in the stables of the Marquess of Ormonde, descended from a long line of voracious thieving robbers coming from the Norman invasion and conquest of Ireland.

These thoughts sneak surreptitiously into my mind, always intruding, since I have the key to the estate office and the castle is empty as a drum; my footsteps are the only sound. For they have long departed. I'm hoping this will come right as my first hammer stroke is struck on the gold. And God only knows what Michael Clarke will say when the invoice arrives for him to pay!

* * *

The candle-maker's first candles have images of bishops with croziers, which Kelly obtained from medieval rubbings found about Kilkenny and downsized. Clever, intricate Celtic patterns have been modified from whatever insipiration Kelly has found, such as the devil jumping out of the Book of Kells. The ceramist David Reeves floats back and forth, passing me with a brief nod, preoccupied now, with his assistant Garry Sharpe from Stoke-on-Trent, a friendly and boisterous man.

The Scotsman, David Wilson, is doing something with textiles in a corner of the front loft. Rolf Middleboe is well ensconced in the baronet's castle; he always greets me with a clownish wave and grimace as if Kilkenny Design is a bubble of amusement for him. And surely it must be the same for you? He seems to say. Are we not having a well-paid holiday amongst these simple, trusting people, who are childlike and believe in fairies, holy wells, whatever? Middleboe has some old-forgotten designs found back in

Denmark, which he thinks he might as well use. One is of different circles: sixty-four small brown, grey and black circles, grouped as a square touching four medium circles, squared in grey and black. The pattern is repeated above and sideways on a beige background. It is, in fact, quite nice. Another has two identical, soft-bottomed containers, which are cross sectioned and whose colours alternate in pale shades of blue, with two young Kilkenny boys wearing ill-fitting white coats helping him.

According to Seamus Butler, the builders have been told they'll soon be given the plans from Montgomery for Walsh's new apartment, to be constructed above the Ormonde estate office. I must take another look there before the room is cleared out. I remember the paintings and especially the two books, would they even be missed?

Thankfully, this gold is easy to work. After each annealing, I raise the sides with hammer strokes. Who will ever believe this was made here in the years to come? I feel as though I'm working for some high king, Celtic druid or priest and creating one of those extraordinary gold collars and torcs displayed on the National Museum. A Catholic patron for this jug though, to hold the magic wine that turns supposedly turns into the blood of Jesus Christ. Perhaps Walsh is the friend of a wealthy bishop, for no money is spared for the objects used in their elaborate rituals... As demonstrated by Cross Michael, the Bishop of Galway, and his new cathedral.

Mary is up from the city, carefree, accompanied by a pretty, laughing friend. She has news, "you've to see a Father McGee in a house of priests on the Ormonde road for six weeks."

"Starting when?" I'm none too pleased.

"Thursday week at eight in the evening and don't be getting smart with him; I know, you'll hate going, but the time will fly."

"In a house of priests? Is this really necessary?"

"You promised and it'll do you no harm, you might even find it interesting." Now her tone is encouraging.

"Am I allowed to dispute the Catholic faith with him?"

"No! Best to just listen and go along with what he says and not to be arguing, causing us problems. He could report you to the Bishop, who might stop the church wedding if he thinks you're an out-an-about heretic atheist!" The grip of the church is still with her in spite of their shameful behaviour.

"He would hardly do that."

"Well you make sure that he doesn't." God love her, I'll do whatever she says.

"I'll leave my Protestant doubts behind then and be a good boy." My answer induces her friend to hilarious laughter, which is contagious to the pair. As I watch them run off down the windy Parade, hand-in-hand, I see Peggy Haughton passes them with a cold face.

* * *

As I come out of the Ulster Bank on High Street, the Protestant curate is coming in. He stops with a questioning look and, "what's this we hear about you at Mass with a girl, we thought you were one of us!"

"She's my girlfriend, so I went along with her at Christmas that's all, no harm done." I'm not going to start a row with him here.

"There's not many of us left in the South now and you know what will happen with the children if ever you get married to a Roman Catholic!"

"We're not married and there are no children, so there's nothing for you to worry about." I reply, almost feeling sympathy for him.

"They say she's wearing an engagement ring," he adds.

"Do they now?"

"The mother has a powerful influence, be warned, and sure there's still a few nice Protestant girls left in Kilkenny, have you noticed the lovely wee one behind the counter?" He nods over to the pretty cashier.

The curate's northern voice reminds me again from whence the tribe came. The one I feel part of, something that can't be helped. I remember one time seeing the orange men on the Twelfth of July, marching up the hill from Ballynahinch to the big sloping field on Lord Clanwilliam's estate. The parade was coloured orange, purple and green. Bowler-hated and dark-suited, their leaders addressed the crowd from a raised platform with bright Union flags against a blue sky and lazy summer clouds. Their shouts were of defiance at the Southern state and Catholicism.

* * *

The day continues, to the sound of hammer blows and the odorous smell of sulphuric acid. There is lustre and rouge on the lathe's spinning mops, from John's polishing silver. I'm constantly wondering what Walsh will do with this golden creation when it is finished. I expect it will be fateful and drift off to imagining the slopes of Mount Leinster on a dark night, where two wary figures with long-handled shovels are digging and whispering. What am I to make of all this!

There are few boundaries here anymore, fantasy is fact, dreams the reality. At John's suggestion, I decide his friend Peter Donovan should come on over from London, where he is currently employed at Naylor Brothers. I'm hoping Walsh won't mind, Hogan agreed to the idea anyway! Donovan's name is Irish, his family were probably famine refugees. He's a brilliant silversmith.

* * *

Fortunately, the third flat above Haughton's is available. Peter Donovan is sallow skinned and good looking. He's easy spoken with soft brown eyes, will give Kilkenny a go, for the welcome change. It is well worth a try for him, he's still so young. He arrives somewhat apprehensive at the decision he's made.

"Why are you making that jug in gilding metal?" Asks Peter on his first day at work, rather puzzled.

"It's twenty carat gold, here see for yourself." I hand him the nearly raised jug.

"My goodness so it is; who on earth is it for?"

"Nobody seems to know yet and maybe we'll never find out."

"The gold must have cost a fortune," says Peter amazed, appreciative of the precious metal.

"That's the way it is in Kilkenny Peter. See that old codger out there?" John points to Mountgarret. "He reckons he's a Mountgarret, a relative of the Lord that owns the castle and yesterday when I went up to Seamus to get a bit of wood, he was in a kind of trance with his lips moving, wouldn't answer me, very strange."

This makes me smile. "That's the Angelus at midday John; when the clock strikes twelve a lot of Catholics do that."

"Well I think it's weird to ignore me like that."

"The South's a Catholic country, as you well know John, didn't you get any religion at school or from your parents then?"

"About Jesus and that sort of stuff?"

"Yes"

"Maybe some, I can hardly remember," he replies vaguely.

"Were you baptised even?"

"I haven't a clue. What about you Peter were you?"

"Same as you John, I wouldn't know, we never went to church, although I think my granny was a Catholic!"

John turns to Peter, curious. "Is that right?"

I haven't told anyone about marrying Mary yet and the fact I have to listen to Catholic doctrine.

Watching Peter lay out his tools from an old Gladstone bag – settling into his bench space – I wonder what to ask him to make. For do people even buy domestic silver these days? It's first thing to be stolen as it is easily melted down to an anonymous weight and sold for cash.

Still, we are on a wild goose chase, I must try to enjoy the ride. A silver cigarette box? But I know that smoking causes lung cancer. Candlesticks went out with the electric light switch. With tea bags and instant coffee, what is there left of real use to make? Handmade goblets and bowls, or knives, forks and spoons will be very expensive, what with tax and the retail mark up on. But sure, maybe, as Walsh says, something for the export market.

Something Irish made and Dublin hallmarked would be a dream combination for wealthy, Irish Americans, who will buy anything from the ould sod. Begorah!

Over the next day or so it's an education to watch Peter effortlessly make a condiment set, with a clever four-knuckle hinge. If its owner isn't careful the salt will eventually corrode the silver, leaving nasty black spots... as black as the priest I must go see.

* * *

With Mary anxiously gripping my hand in the fading winter light, we take to the house of the priests. It is past the fateful Club House, a substantial, grey, three-storey building opposite St Kierans College on the Ormonde road. As I'm about to press the bell, Mary turns to me and I can suddenly see in her sad, pleading eyes, all the hurt, pain and sorrow of her life: from the Langrishe to this day. Smiling weakly, she says, "good luck and remember what I said to you before!"

McGee is a ragged and aggressively shaped man and it seems he is ready for a fight. Balding with strands of lank black hair, and a couple of day's stubble on his creased, pale face, I would guess him to be in the mid-forties. He has medium build and gives me the impression of a storm-tossed scarecrow in the desolate field of his Catholic belief.

The priest looks at Mary with thinly disguised dislike: women, the source of all the world's woes since the temptress Eve waylaid poor Adam. He knows fine well she'll soon fall away from the faith by marrying a Protestant and in his mind, this is only a short stop to becoming nothing. McGee shows us both to a gloomy but comfortable sitting room; he is so obviously aware of Mary's beauty, as any normal man would be. She will give him wet dreams, when he addressess the memory of her in the night, to waken cursing her for his weakness and sin!

"I'll leave you now and see you back at the flat," says Mary apologetically. She is uneasy and obviously relieved to be seeing herself out.

"Do sit down and how old is the girl?" McGee asks, drawing the dark curtains, then setting himself opposite.

"My future wife is called Mary and she's seventeen."

He pauses for a while, as if deciding which poisoned arrow to fire from his bow. "I would have thought she was much older than seventeen."

"So, how old do you think she is then?"

"Oh, thirty-eight or so, certainly not seventeen. Are you sure she's not having you on?"

I ignore him and go along with this charade, just as Mary wants. Even though I'm irritated by the cheek of him. He waits for an answer with a taunting, sly smile; failing to get a response he continues in a more mischievous way. And, lo and behold, I see another plate of St Agatha's breasts. Would they be compulsory in every priest's house?

"You're a Protestant from the North aren't you?" He pauses, as if to savour his accusatory words, "and as you well know, we Catholics suffer fierce discrimination up there, but you can be sure it won't last, for someday there'll be a United Ireland, our young men will see to that!" He is aggressive, but I'm determined not to make a stand.

"You could be right, I've never given it much thought."

"Never much thought!" he exclaims.

"Yes, and sure, the Catholics will outbreed us eventually. Without birth control, there'll be no need of the gun."

"That filthy Protestant practice, against moral law, will be your undoing then." McGee grips the sides of his chair and, leaning forward, suddenly proclaims, "without the shedding of blood there's no salvation!"

I'm almost ready to walk out but I must try to keep calm. "I wouldn't have thought so myself. You were to tell me about your religion."

The priest leans back and takes out from his pocket a packet of Sweet Afton. He strikes the match and is about to light one. In his burning eyes is a desire to light the funeral pyre of the heretic. Dear God! Why am I here, in the Middle Ages? McGee's face gradually becomes glazed and as terribly distorted as one of Francis Bacon's meat-red-and-pink twisted figures.

I listen with disbelief to his tirade about the one true and only Catholic church; with obedience to the Pope an utter necessity for salvation. All derived from the biblical saying of Christ to Peter, about being the rock to build his church upon. The first Pope, a disciple of Jesus the Son of God and all his successors to the present Pope Paul possessing the divine gift of infallibility on the basis of support from the Holy Spirit and so forth. On and on he continues, it's hardly credible that in this day and age anyone believes in such nonsense.

"What about Luther? Was he right about the church selling indulgences then?" I just about manage to intrude, without thinking.

"Luther split the church asunder!" McGee explodes.

I am unable to resist continuing the argument. "But wasn't he right? You can hardly buy your way into heaven, can you?"

At this McGee gets up, stumbling, leaving the room. Soon he returns with glasses and a bottle of Paddy whiskey, pouring two large ones. "Here, drink this and begone, you awful Protestant man, seducing our young Catholic girls down here in Kilkenny."

Then the priest sips his whiskey, lights another cigarette and perhaps the the soothing nicotine and alcohol calms his fevered head. A strange evening ends, with all the fight gone out of him. Sighing, he says, "you can see yourself out, and we'll see you next week."

Opening the flat door and turning the light on, I see that Mary's asleep beside the electric bar fire. Waking sleepily, she asks me, "well, how did you manage with McGee?"

"Just fine, you've nothing to worry about, but he's three sheets to the wind if you ask me."

"Well it's only for an hour or so and just a few more to go."

Hurriedly, I seek in the top drawer for a Durex. Then I'm kneeling before her and she is happy to comply. It is all over in seconds. Absurdly, I remember reading about IRA Volunteers after a job, wanting the same.

Mary becomes anxious now and upset. "Now that you're finished, you'll have to take me to Freshford." Why did she have to say that? It was a sharp reminder that her fading Catholicism is not yet gone. I can taste her sweetness on my finger tips and yet smell Magee's Sweet Afton from my jacket sleeves.

CHAPTER 17

Late one evening the golden jug is finished. I ask Mary to be the first to fill it and pour water into my tea-stained mug. For she should be the first to use it. An ephemeral gift, made in sorrow, asking her forgiveness as an avatar of Ireland; a recollation of distant memories me to last long into the future.

The Assay Office has never seen anything like the jug before. I have to carefully instruct them where and how to hallmark the '20', Hibernia, fleur-de-lys and date letter W.

"This is gas, this is really gas." Paul Hogan is intrigued, he picks the jug up from his desk. "Does it pour well with no drips?"

"No drips and it pours well."

"It's very heavy."

"That's gold for you," I reply.

"A magic metal certainly; gas though, really gas this, unbelievable."

"I'll leave it with you then, do you want a note or invoice from the workshop?" I ask.

"Ah, no, we're not into that yet. You just keep sending the bills for Michael to pay." He picks up the jug again and pours thin air a few times. "Incidentally, Walsh was a bit miffed you have another English silversmith there now."

"I did check with you about him." I remind him.

"Oh, I know, I know. Now by September Professor Erik Herlow and Ake Huldt will be over to judge what you're making, so maybe afterwards we'll try selling to Harrods in London.

"Is that right?" I comment warily. *To judge what you're making*, he said, when their ghastly, carved heads hit the shoreline, spreading the word of good design from the small Nordic countries. An example for Ireland to follow some day.

"And you're not to forget something special for the World's Fair in New York." Hogan reminds me again. I had nearly forgotten.

* * *

There comes a strange and hurridly hushed request from Walsh to be available Sunday at midday. So I'm waiting and ready by the stable doors to open them for him and his guests to drive through. It is well before the due hour. In the workshop, I am puzzled as to why no one outside is to know. At least it's not raining. The sun is diffused behind tumbling, grey clouds. Everything as was left on Friday evening, with the unfinished silver pieces on their bench spaces before us. Each of us has his own method of making them, a form of identification on the finished piece. You can tell who made which, from Peter's clear seam soldering and precise planishing marks, to John's signature hammering and polishing, which brings the silver subtly alive.

What is a clay figure of Kelly's doing there? The cones of borax are little obelisks wrapped in blue and white paper, twisted at the top. Glancing at the sky, I see a patch of pearl blue is a way out. The hands of the clock move inexorably to High Noon. Who can be coming? On each side of the stable doors is a large, round stone ball bollard. I sit on one like a sentry. The ivy on the walls opposite is well on its way to reaching the castle battlements high above me. My heartbeat quickens as Walsh's familiar chocolate Triumph 2000 edges cautiously into the Parade.

He is checking the coast is clear, because his car is followed by a large black Humber. Immediately, I open the heavy, folding doors to let them through. William Walsh is on his own and I get a cursory nod from him. There is a man and woman in the rear seat of the Humber. Once it is through, I close the doors behind them and walk to where they have parked, a few yards into the courtyard.

The man who has stepped out of the car is wearing the dark turtle-neck sweater and matching jacket. Incredulous, I recognise him as Tony Armstrong Jones, the Earl of Snowden, and he is holding the door open for his wife, Princess Margaret, whose head is covered in a white scarf. Walsh, beaming like a Cheshire cat, does the introductions: their driver is the Earl of Rosse. Princess Margaret gives a weak smile and doesn't hold out her hand for me to shake like the other two. She's small and very pretty, wearing a lovely, white-belted trench coat. She has the bluest of blue eyes. The Queen of England's sister and two earls at the stables on the same day! Walsh, in his country gentleman tweeds, is most solicitous. As Princess Margaret takes out a Benson and Hedges gold pack and inserts one into a large holder, he hurries to light it for her.

Following them around like a dog, I join in their tour of the stables before we eventually arrive at the workshop. Their plummy voices are peculiar, slow and drifting in the damp Irish air. They praise Walsh for having instigated this unique centre of excellence for design in Kilkenny rather than Dublin. A stroke of extraordinary imagination. Faithful to an unhappy country, now, hopefully, with a brighter future.

I wonder how he got to know them. Snowden is into design and photography certainly, a good contact I suppose. I have read about Rosse in the papers. The Armstrong-Jones' are related on his wife's side; British army; Eton; an ancestor famous for a telescope. The princess is a right little bitch, I would think; she's so obviously bored stiff and trying her best not to show it. She doesn't say much, this great-great-granddaughter of Queen Victoria. She's probably related to Richard II, who was in Kilkenny nearly six hundred years ago, the plaque on the castle wall says 1399. He was trying to sort out the Irish, which went horribly wrong of course, as soon as he left. And didn't he lose his own head on arriving home? And the body was buried in Yorkshire? Yes, Pontefract!

In the workshop, Walsh picks out a small silver bowl and presents it to Princess Margaret. A Walter Mitty tale, people would say in years to come.

"Oh really? How kind." She stands by the door, rocking from foot to foot, impatient to leave. The old stable clock is melting into the abyss of memory and space time. Finally, they return to their transport and leave. Walsh should not have given her that bowl. Rosse and the Royal couple are probably heading back to his castle at Birr, they can't be too open in the Republic. It would cause a commotion. There has been a nasty incident already, with, 'Brits Out', painted on his Lordship's surrounding wall.

The drowsy afternoon dissolves. From Peter's room — he has a girl already — comes laughter, while from across the landing, John fitfully plays his guitar. My pockets are full of heavy change, some has come through the lining. After carefully extracting it all, I spread the coins on the table. Their value is more than a pound and I peruse their unique Irish designs. The harp on silvery and copperish coins, with an assortment of fowls, fish and animals on the reverse. The horse on the big half-crown; hen and chicks the penny; sow and litter the half pence; greyhound on the little silver sixpence; the hare worth three; a silver salmon, two shillings; the bull, one and look, here's a well-worn Queen Victoria penny, nearly black with age, I can barely see 1893. Mixed with these are some English George's and the present Queen, whose awkward sister has just left Kilkenny in a dream, the magnetic connections attracting her or pushing her away.

* * *

Monday morning sunlight is streaming through the window across Haughton's garden from behind the roof of what was once the Marchioness of Ormonde's dowager house. While I am concentrated upon silver making, I'm suddenly aware the shadow of a figure peering clownishly in. It is David Harrington Angus Douglas — the eleventh Marquess of Queensbury — again. He gives me a friendly wave with another funny face, then saunters off towards the candle maker.

"Who's that?" asks Peter.

"The Marquess of Queensbury."

"You're joking," he replies, unconvinced.

At which John interjects. "You better believe it Peter, in Kilkenny there's quite a few."

"Sure, Princess Margaret was here yesterday with William Walsh and the Earl of Rosse," I tell them.

"Now you are having us on, that I don't believe." John speaks determinedly.

"Look the cigarette butt with her lipstick stain." I remember her studding it out on the soldering stand (the cheek of her) and point to it.

"Could have been anyone here over the weekend," John points out.

"I tell you it's true."

"This Kilkenny lark is getting to him, Peter, wouldn't you think so?"

"Could well be." Peter answers smiling, he is undecided.

A lark says he, indeed, this is so far from reality. The heady talk; the theatrical masks for Kelly and Walsh's silver. Then there's the golden jug, which I suggested jokingly, hardly expecting them to agree. And now what to make for the fair? A large, round rose bowl with Ireland on the face should do it. 'I am of Ireland', from the old poem in Irish, is, of course, 'IS D'ÉIRINN ME'.

I confirm the spelling is correct from An Gum: 'the leading Irish language publisher since 1926'. I will make the lettering in square silver wire, a lattice-like fitting over a gilt bowl. Twelve to fifteen inches diameter, a wow from the auld sod for the Americans.

I begin designing the bowl, but my thoughts are invaded by a premonition that this cannot possibly last.

* * *

A turquoise-blue Cortina is parked some way from the stable entrance one morning as I head to work. Two faces are watching me and I sense a trap. No? Yes. Halfway across the courtyard I turn around and go over to the car, approaching it suspiciously. It has Dublin plates. As I almost knew it, inside are Paul Hogan and Michael Clark. Shame on the pair, snooping around to see the time I started work.

"You boys must have been up early this morning, what's brought you down so early?" I confront the pair; I wouldn't have thought this of Hogan.

"Where are the other two silversmiths, are they still in bed?" Hogan asks brusquely.

"They both do their eight hours every day, whether from nine or ten doesn't much matter to me. I don't think Rolf Middleboe's arrived yet either, maybe you should check in on him out at Castle Blunden!"

Clarke starts the car and without another word they move slowly away, turning into Patrick Street. Aiming for the Club House no doubt. Their unpleasant behaviour lingers with me for the rest of the day.

* * *

Mary, being most assiduous, God love her, reminds me not to miss McGee's assault each week. I find it is not a problem being suffused in cigarette smoke and under the effects of an occasional glass of whiskey. It is a strangely unhinging experience, a tug of war, words as bats flapping in and out from the dark places of my mind. Ruined and ivy-choked old words to do with getting married. They come at me disjointed and are connected only abstractly. Built brick by brick on each side of the divide, leading to madness for this tormented priest.

From childhood I had heard stories about (and avidly read about) bad popes living in monstrous luxury, unbridled sensuality and vice.

I have an endless list to throw at him: the veneration of saints, relics, indulgences, the burning of the reformer Jan Hus, Savonarola and hundreds of heretics and witches. McGee replies that none of us are perfect, even Peter denied Christ three times, yet was chosen by Christ to found his church. And he was given the keys of this Kingdom of Heaven, as is clearly stated in the gospels. The sacred flame of faith was handed from pope to pope. Even an unworthy one was a completely legitimate successor to Christ.

Magee explains all this with the devil of religious certainty in his eyes. The Titian portrait of Pope Paul III with his two nephews says it all about the corruption of Catholicism, about the way the popes made their relatives and favourites cardinals. And didn't one Borgia, Pope Alexander VI, after bribing his fellow cardinals to elect him pope, have his illegitimate children recognised and celebrated their marriages with splendour and pomp in the Vatican? TheChurch, switching the blame for Christ's crucifixion onto the Jews, even though He was executed under Roman law for being a revolutionary. The penalty of crucifixion makes that clear, for if he had been executed for blasphemy (as the gospels maintained) he would have been stoned to death, the Jewish penalty.

The bishops cooked the books when Christianity became the religion of Rome. When Constantine made Christianity the state religion, the church did not want to remind him that his Roman predecessors killed Christ. Jesus wouldn't have understood any of this.

McGee brings a contagion of conflicting and violent thoughts, vomiting forth in bloody and burning shape. I have to get a grip and leave well alone. When he brings up Cromwell and the penal laws, I remind him that he would do well to remember Louis XIV's revoking of the Edict of Nantes, which led to a much worse persecution. Or Pius Pope XII, who never once condemned Hitler and was silent about the Holocaust; who was against the founding of the Jewish State in Palestine and who never once protested against the Nazis unleashing of the Second World War.

We turn the barrel organ over and over in the familiar old tunes we both know so well, week after week.

McGee, opening the door one evening, stepping out, and, raising his arms to the lengthening sky light, said, "can't you feel the hand of God about this time of year, when spring is in the air?"

"It's one way of seeing it, I suppose."

"Suppose! How do you think then this whole miraculous creation came into being?"

"Nobody yet knows, but if God was the creator, then who created God?"

"That is the greatest Holy mystery, we can't be expected to know God that intimately, save through the grace and love of Jesus Christ who died on the cross to make us free from sin and the hope of eternal life."

On my last visit, McGee warns me, "I'm not going to listen to any more of your Reformation Protestant nonsense; you come from the awkward brigade, typical of those from our occupied six counties, steeped in all the hoary old chestnuts you so obviously know by heart. The church in those far-off days was living in a different mind-set, crueller. Calvin even had people burnt too, you know? And Luther was no lover of the Jews either, do you hear me?"

Nodding at this, I let his strictures pass. There is a gentle breeze this evening and we are mollified upon parting.

"So listen, you will be married in our church, but you must undertake to raise your children in the Catholic faith, understand?"

"Yes." Meaning, 'no'; an oath taken under duress is no oath.

"You give me your word?"

"Mary will take care of it, I won't interfere." I will make whatever promises he needs. There is a look of scepticism on his face.

"You will sign."

"Yes, I will." Whatever it takes.

"Now, I'd like you to read this, whatever you think of the Catholic Church, you could well find Aquinas interesting." He hands me a paper-back book that he's been holding since I arrived. *Summa Theologiae*, Thomas Aquinas. I have never heard of him, who was he? It is a parting gift from this priest of many moods, from dormant to volcanic.

"Away with you now, you fearful Protestant!" He holds out his hand for me to shake, somehow holding on too long. I can't fathom what is in his expression, perhaps he is caught between the spirit of doubt and that of alcohol. Strangely, he offers me a cigarette for the first time. I will almost miss these weekly encounters, I think, flicking the cigarette into the foot-path and watching as sparking, it rolls to one side.

*   *   *

The rose bowl will be difficult enough. I take the measurement for silver sheet, which needs to be at least gauge fourteen. And the quarter inch square wire can be rolled down if needs be, with plenty to spare. Such extravagance is hard to believe, even here. I have to get an extra-large stake to raise the bowl's shallow sides upright. Since I know there's a firm in Kilkenny that makes farm implements (pig troughs and the likes) I should be able to do this.

From one task to another: those two books in the Ormonde estate office will be cleared out soon, gone forever. And I saw in Haughton's office an interesting book that I borrowed on the gentry and aristocracy of Kilkenny.

The Langrishe were certainly well represented, having accumulated wealth by the many marriages amongst their own kind: the widows and daughters of wealthy landowning lords. They became the owners of Knocktopher's magnificent estate, with its lush countryside and tenants already in situ. A certain Hercules Langrishe was carver-in-ordinary to Queen Henrietta Maria, who prevented the arrest of the 'Five Members' by Charles I. For many years father passed to son the position of MP for Knocktopher in the old Irish Parliament. And they were handsomely rewarded when the time came to voting its demise, receiving in excess of £13,000.

There was a Langrishe who was Commissioner of Revenue and of Excise, a very lucrative post. That, with the rent roll from his Kilkenny estate made him a very wealthy man, with a Baronetcy created as well for the family. The coat-of-arms was quarterly, or and sable, four cov-ered cups counter exchanged with the crest of a rampart lion. Rampant indeed.

They claim descent back to the Middle Ages: came over to England with William the Conqueror, then eventually founded a branch to Ireland. Master of the Kilkenny Hounds, another dashing young Langrishe probably sowed his wild oats with the peasants. He was a Lancer indeed. Then there was the gentleman Usher of the Black Rod in the Irish House of Lords. Pages of the stuff: Eton; High Sheriffs; JPs, a Deputy Lieutenant…

All the way to the present one, whom I saw dressed for his dinner that dark winter evening, eating cottage pie with his last servant and with time running out. His daughter raised in such squalid circumstances of shame and slight, trying to keep warm by Mam's mean fire in Ireland's cold Catholic climate.

* * *

Mary was delighted that my time with McGee was finished and nothing untoward had happened. If only she knew. Collecting her on a Sunday afternoon, I find she has the paper for her mother to sign. Mam has explained to us how to get there.

We arrive at Inistioge in the Spotted Dog. The little waif of a girl I remember from last year is still serving there. I order a beer and bitter lemon.

"Is your Mum and Dad not here?" I ask her.

"Gone to Mass."

"Is that so."

"Gone to Mass." She answers again, louder. This girl has the most disturbing and penetrating green eyes I ever did see in a child. I'm overcome by the strangest of feelings, a sudden explosion of brightness in my head, time infinitesimally warped, leaving a material effect in the form of a stopped clock on the wall. My watch says six but the clock five.

Dizzy, I return to Mary and glancing at the clock again see that it is now at just after six, the same as the watch.

"Did you notice the clock Mary?"

"No."

"It was an hour behind and now it's an hour forward, the correct time."

"That couldn't be, you're having me on."

"No, no, it was … at least I thought so." I find it hard to understand. There is some kind of meaning here. Behind and then forward.

"The girl corrected the time when you weren't looking."

"I'd have seen her, did you?"

"No."

"And anyway, she couldn't have reached that high."

"Might have been something in the clock."

"Hardly possible."

"Well it must have been, if what you say is true, a stuck spring, or wheel suddenly loose."

"Maybe, maybe ..."

"You're very pale." Mary turns to me, concerned.

Inistioge must be the prettiest village in Ireland. This was where Bishop Berkeley wrote his famous *Queries* and I always remembering the one: 'whither a gentleman who hath seen a little of the world and observed how men lived elsewhere, can contentedly sit down in a cold, damp, sordid habitation, in the midst of a bleak country, inhabited by thieves and beggars.'

Well, I certainly wouldn't agree to that this hushed evening. When I'm with Mary, I feel that Ireland is extraordinary.

We watching the wide, flowing Nore below. Dear God, why must this pass? Forgotten on some distant shore. Far into the future, will she even remember us together on the bridge at Inistioge? The book McGee gave me is still here. I take it out and show to her. "The priest gave me this, be said it might be interesting to read, the basis of a lot of the Catholic church's teaching, written by a Dominican saint called Thomas Aquinas, have you heard of him?"

"The only Thomas I know was the apostle," she says, taking the book with a certain amount of distaste and giving it back to me immediately.

"He was tough on heretics and all for the burnings!"

"If he wasn't Jesus Christ it's just another man's opinion; burning people alive, what sort of behaviour is that!"

"You're not interested in it?"

"Certainly not," Mary replies most assuredly.

"Nor am I then." I let Aquinas fall below us into the fast flowing river. We watch it bobbing away towards New Ross. It might even reach An Mhair Cheilteach. Mary then takes out her rosary beads, crumpling them into a ball and hurls them mightily away up into the air, where they seem to remain in shock, swinging out in a last gasp, before falling to the water, floating a second, then disappearing forever to the accompaniment of her laughter. That was courageous, for there's now tears in those sad, grey eyes. She presses herself into me and my arms are tightly around her. I never want to let go.

CHAPTER 18

Returning from Freshford, a grip of excitement suddenly takes hold of me as I think I have an opportunity of rescuing the books. No one will be there at this time of night, so it's now or never. I am concealed by a curtain of darkness on this late moonless night. Entering the stables, I say to myself that there would hardly be a list of the contents kept in the office. Hopefully, no one will ever know the books are gone.

I insert the key to the Marquess of Ormonde's estate office. William Walsh will soon be living above this room, so I'll never get a chance like this again. And why not? Weren't they all thieves at the point of a sword in those days. An odour of dust and musty dampness greets me, it is like opening a mausoleum. The books slowly appear out of the gloom. With trembling hand, I turn the pages. Here are star-shaped drawings in pen and ink, delicately water coloured, the forgotten last possessions from a feudal age.

Who were these long dead men and women, who are falling out from their disintegrating ornate gilt frames? Would there ever be a Rubens or Titian amongst them? The sideways Ormonde lying there in his household cavalry uniform of red: with gleaming breastplate, high boots, and holding his cross-of-St-George, horse-hair plumed helmet in his right hand. The other one clasps the hilt of a sword. Another is perhaps of the marchioness, in flowing blue-and-blood-satin finery. And lying on the bare flagstones is King Charles again, with his look of advice that I remember from last time.

It is these magical two books must have, a gift from Marshal Sebastian Le Preste de Vauban, dedicated to His Grace, James,

Duke of Ormonde, Knight of the Garter, Captain General and Commander-in-Chief of the land forces, Warden of the Cinque Ports and Constable of Dover Castle. All these titles so beautifully written by a joyous swirling hand.

The rooms contents are a tumbled confusion, raided by the wreckage of time. It has the chill of the pantry where the fowl are hung and the butter and milk kept. They'd be worth a good price in years to come. I could say the old Marquess gave them to me, for he'd be lying dead by then. Mary could hide them under her bed for a while. When she floats away, dreaming of the jewels she so richly deserves to have, these dark blue, beautifully bound, books will journey with her.

I will take them out to Freshford tomorrow

Back at my flat, I am unable to sleep, instead I'm pouring over illustrations of extraordinary fortifications by the dim light of the flat. He'd maybe have known Louis XIV, like his grandfather the first Duke, a companion of Charles II when exiled in France. What an extraordinary interweaving of life: from Mam's lowly cottage to the Duke of Ormonde and a Marshal of France!

* * *

The next morning I wake up to an awful frignt. On the footpath in front of the workshop, the portrait of King Charles is moving along under the tattered arm of Seamus, followed by the rest of the contents of the Estate office, as they are carried towards the empty buildings at the rear of the stables. Holy cow! I hope they won't notice the Marshal has gone. It is most upsetting and in a panic, feeling weak, I call from the door to Seamus, "what's going on?"

"We're clearing this lot out from the two rooms they were in, they are going to be made into offices. We've to store them away for the moment, but if I had my way I'd have made a bonfire of this rubbish, for who cares about these people now?" His answer is listened to by John and Peter, who have stopped work and are hypnotized at the moving panorama of Irish history before them.

"Well, go easy on King Charles there Seamus," I say, "those paintings are fragile."

"He's a dirty looking gobshite if you ask me!" Holding the king with both hands at arm's length.

"Defender of the Faith, chosen by God, Seamus."

"Not this fecker surely?" Seamus stares boldly at the King, then, shaking his head, moves on.

"See what I mean, there's even the odd Royal that goes by," John says to Peter.

"I'd certainly like to get my hands on one of those swords," Peter murmurs quietly to himself.

Robbie Haughton appears slowly afterwards and calls into the workshop. God he's noticed. No, no, just a weak wave in the passing, unsteady on his feet at this hour. I was just in time, if he had searched the flat... I will have to get the books away out to Freshford in a hurry this evening.

* * *

As I drive, I'm aware of shifting tides of Kilkenny, pulling me this way and that. And the ever changing, transient verdure on the road to Freshford again. This hauntingly mournful drive is exquisite as a result of the miracle of that first journey. The time I left her by the Clontubrid crossroads. Even now my heart beats faster in memory of it.

All Ireland was there in the sadness of her childhood, the spirit that kept her going, digging for potatoes in Mam's small patch by the hut. Her toilet was a circular, opened board and in her dreams, she would be terrified that her doll would fall in. Raining and hungry days, with little to look forward to. Running out of the cottage, wanting to get away as fast and far as possible.

Tonight, it is only for a drive.

I open the case and show her the books.

"God, where did you get these?" She is as wary as a bird, turning them to and fro.

"I took them out of the Marquess's estate office."

She frowns and her voice is accusing. "You stole them!"

"Well yes, but nobody will know, they've been lying there for ages forgotten. I just had to have them, they're so unique."

"Dedicated to the Duke of Ormonde, Knight of ..."

"He was a Jacobite anyway." I cut in, "who favoured the return of the Catholic, ousted King James' son, the old pretender, they called him. All his possessions and titles were confiscated, if they'd have caught him he'd have suffered the terrible traitors death. There's nothing to worry about, I tell you, they'll never be missed."

"They're not yours though are they?" she persists.

"They are now, sure we're only doing on a minute scale what they did to the likes of you."

"You're a terrible man." She studies a few pages carefully. "What are they?"

"Plans by a famous French military engineer for defences and fortifications in the seventheenth century."

"A mine of information you are, they wouldn't do anything for me." Mary closes the book with a shrug, "but it's not a problem, I'll even put them under Mam's bed with her potty where they really belong, she won't mind at all."

"Are you sure?"

"Oh yes, she'll think it gas and anyway, who'd ever think of looking under her bed!" She smiles now, mischievous, and soon we are embracing outside in the twilight, the car stopped by the roadside. Above, the skies are darkening blue, grey, cloud-shaded violet and faintly yellowy-peach on the horizon. Around us, the ever-changing greens are in flux and drifting.

*   *   *

A walk around the trade in Dublin is of no consequence, although they listen politely and half-heartedly to my attempts to interest them in the wonders of modern design. Too embarrassed to even mention prototypes and the paying of royalties. This tour has to be done: a one-off effort for Kilkenny's sake, to show that I have tried. But I resolve never to do so again. Inwardly, they are mocking. The idea of Kilkenny seems to them to be a preposterous notion and they know, too, the fact that the tax payer is contributing to the experiment. I leave to their amused, furtive whisperings and delightful malice.

They share a wonderful gift of being able to agree, to show an interest, and promise to consider a few designs until the cows come home. They pretend to be interested, but know full well that at the end is a void of silence. And rightly so perhaps, a mystery is better than reality. Saying what we really think would be blasphemy in these encounters. I'll let myself be the source of laughter for this strange and secretive society. Just who does Kilkenny Design Workshops Limited think they're codding?

In the background of the Dublin workshops are a profusion of ecclesiastical and domestic items made in brass and silver. Coming from the Reformed Church, I was never aware such outrageous inventions ever existed. Chased, cast and engraved with Celtic interlacing, the IHS, the PAX sign, the lamb, the dove, the pelican feeding her young with the blood from her pierced breast and a thousand variations of these. Tea sets, trophies and cups made like the Ardagh Chalice, spouts with animal and bird heads. Napkin rings, christening mugs and milk jugs with monster-eating handles wrapped in Johnson Matthey stamped Celtic wire in three different sizes, large silver salvers with Book of Kells-style snakes twisting in an out around the edges. Copies of the De Burgo-O'Malley chalice that was made nearly five hundred years ago. These early Tara Brooch type creations, they say, could only have been made by angels in their complexity and cunning. It's hard to imagine the uncertainty and the difficult conditions of those times. Woven with Christianity, how can anyone escape the legacy of an Irish landscape and history?

* * *

The weaving workshop is experimenting with many different methods of weaving: big bold, thick ,colourful stuff from those Swedish girls. Fair and fresh-faced lovelies, salty aired and perfumed from their wild out-doors, they evoke the sounds of cold, clear running water and narrow pathways of fallen pine cones. The wind gently moaning: "come into our log house, it's warm and built to last a thousand years. We'll tie up our long golden hair into tempting coils and swirls, decked with bright flowers and cook you a meal of moose pie, dessert of gathered wild redcurrants, raspberries, blackberries and strawberries in sour yogurt, the milk from our wonderful Swedish cows." They saunter through Kilkenny oblivious to the many hidden eyes. Theirs is a country that Ireland would do well to emulate.

Here comes a poor boy from Burnchurch on his father's bicycle, looking for a job. Deferential, and utterly quaint, he's like a lad from the last cen-tury, carrying a contagious sadness that affects me deeply. Like birds that notice where others are feeding, there's always someone around willing to learn. Perhaps he hopes for a craft job in textiles, wood, clay or metals. Irish designed and hand made.

I'm glad not to have missed this experience, finding her. An angel-made treasure, shamefully hidden out of sight. These first few years will never be repeated. The metal workshop is a submarine in deep unchartered waters. Strange creatures swim past. The blue cortina has a big mouth and enormous eyes; it could be dangerous. The rarely seen, beautiful Anna Rose Carrigan; the Royal Margaret; the occasional Marquess and Earl.

* * *

Mam sits heavily beside me, dressed in her shabby best black, breath-ing laboriously; she has a faint smell of moth balls and camphor. Mary sits behind me, silent and nervous. She gives a nervous smile to me in the rear view mirror. We drive through Kilkenny's busy Saturday afternoon and I spot Peter there with his girlfriend. It doesn't take long for the races to mix. The story of Ireland is in this journey to Knocktopher.

We pass that forbidding entrance, the private road to the old Blue Beard's home. Mam directs me to a narrow road, which leads eventu-ally to a recently built, ugly bungalow. The front and sides are an untidy display of breeze blocks, sand, buckets, cement mixer, shovels, trailer, and calor and propane gas bottles (yellow and red). A collie dog feverously barks at us, running up to the car.

"I'll go in alone to see first Mary, you're not to be upsetting yourself now, everything's going to be alright," says Mam, getting out with difficulty. She threatens the dog with her stick and it runs away, barking at a safe distance. Faces appear at the window.

"God, how I hate having to see my mother, for all the good or interest she ever showed me. Put away in shame and raised like this. The indignity of having to get her permission to marry." Mary mutters to herself, watching Mam keenly at the bungalow's door, which has been opened by a young girl.

"Would that be your half-sister?" Immediately I realise it was a mistake to ask.

Mary is trying hard not to cry. "See if I care. I never had a family and I'm certainly not interested in her lot now."

Mam returns to the car. "We'll find your mother down at the church, it's only a short drive away."

We arrive at a nondescript, pebble-dashed church with small crosses high on each gable end, where crows sit undisturbed. It has a porch entrance and leaning beside it is a ladies bicycle with a carrier basket leaning. Just inside there's a table with corked bottles of Holy water in various sizes. Oh, how do they believe in such nonsense? For water is water, essential for life, but still only water and not supernatural.

Opening the spring doors, the church is quite dark with two stained glass windows, one on each side (above the altar and the far end opposite), which gives a sombre, disquieting effect. Those funny little birthday-cake size candles are flickering in one corner, lit for special intentions as Mary once explained to me. There's a woman on her knees near the altar, polishing the brass communion rails, that must be her mother. In a position that suggests she is asking the Almighty's forgiveness. She doesn't see us, as the three of us approach her back. When she looks up startled, there's no mistaking Mary's mother. Beneath dark greying hair is a similar face and eyes, with nearly the same nose, though she lacks that something of her daughter's extraordinary vivacity.

"Lord it's you, you gave me a fright!" She addresses Mam at first and then her daughter. "Hello there Mary, how are you?" Standing up, confused, she eyes me keenly, "and who's this tall gentleman you're with?"

"He wants to marry your daughter, Margaret, and they've come to get your permission. There's a paper to sign as Mary's not yet eighteen." Mam explains.

"Is that right? My goodness me Mary you're still so very young to be getting married, you're not in any trouble are you?" Her voice is low and fey, strangely detached, a distant moan coming through the mists that hide long-abandoned places.

"Indeed I am not!" Mary replies annoyed.

"Ah, well now, anyway, we'd better be going back to the house, let me put these away in the vestry first." Wearily resigned, Mary's mother gathers up her cleaning stuff.

Margaret moves off to the vestry, which reminds me that we won't be married at thealtar but in the vesetry, with the Brasso and dirty cloths, buckets and mops. They are experts in their fine art of shaming and belittling the vulnerable innocent.

Mary's mother can't be more than forty, probably younger. She would have been a teenager then, working at the Abbey. It would have been far too easy for him. I imagine deep sighs coming from the vestry, her mournful cry, the rabbit snared, this kaleidoscope of Irish woman trapped inside a country church, a mental prison. Being Catholic here would be hard to escape from.

A mother down on her knees; a priest after Mam and groping Mary. Permission from the Bishop indeed. The sulphurous fumes of childhood's nightmares momentarily engulfing me, Mary is impatient to get this over and be away. She is at the far entrance now, waiting.

I drive slowly behind her mother, who is on the bicycle, pedalling unsteadily from side to side.

The bungalow is sparse and poorly furnished. We are invited to be seated and she calls her children in. Mary shaking her head, whispers to Mam, "we're not here to meet them and play happy families!"

"Never you mind now, this will soon be over." Mam whispers back leaning over, touching her arm, reassuring her.

Shyly, the children are brought to see us, mute and not wanting to stay. There's Patrick, Rory, Bridget, Geraldine and the youngest is Teresa. They are a ragged bunch, from four or five to maybe thirteen.

"This is your eldest sister Mary, who lives far away beyond Kilkenny." Margaret introduces the children to Mary, who visibly freezes, gazing towards them without a word. They leave quickly, apart from little Teresa. Her mother, at the sink, filling the kettle, asks, "will you all have tea?"

"That would be nice Margaret, I could do with a cup." Mam answers. Mary pulls a sulky face at Mam, to indicate she wants to hurry on and not be wasting time drinking tea.

Teresa tugs her mother's skirt to say something. Bending to listen, Margaret replies, "yes of course you can."

The little girl comes over to Mary, so innocent and trusting, I can barely hear her, "the cat's had kittens, would you like to come and see them?" This forces a smile from Mary at last, who can't say no. Turning to me, Teresa adds, "you'll come too."

She takes Mary by the hand and leads us proudly to an open shed at the rear, where there are bales of hay and snuggled behind one — a warm and safe nest — the cat and her tiny kittens.

"Would you like to hold one?" Teresa asks Mary trustingly.

"Oh no, the mammy cat wouldn't like you to take her baby away."

"She really wouldn't mind."

"Are you sure?"

"Yes." Picking up a tiny kitten, Teresa puts it into Mary's shaking hand.

While Teresa delighted with herself, having a new-found friend, Mary is shaken and visibly confused.

"They're mine, would you like to have one?"

"We already have a cat and couldn't manage another one."

There's something happening to Mary, which I can faintly understand. She is grieving for what she has lost until now. Swallowing hard and trying not to cry, Mary is aware that for the first time she has a sister.

The tea is poured and those awful Jacob's fig rolls are produced. Teresa, by Mary's side, a jigsaw piece in life's jumbled complications, grabs a biscuit boldly and laughs naughtily at her mother's frown. For she knows she can't be scolded in front of strangers.

"So you want to get married Mary, well that's not a problem for me, but be warned, life with a man is not always easy, though if you've decided, who am I to say 'no'?"

"He has a good job at this new Kilkenny Design thing," Mam offers.

"Yes, I read about that, by the Castle in the old stables opposite, very nice and all government supported; you're doing nicely there Mary."

"I'm not marrying his job!" Mary retorts.

"Ah, you may say so now, but believe you me it does help, a regular wage."

"You have to sign this then Margaret." Mam produces the form from her bag. Margaret appears now to be wistfully far away.

"He's a Protestant and took lessons from the priest, promising to rear the children Catholics," Mam continues, bringing loud laughter from Margaret in a strange and haunted way.

"So you're a Protestant... well, well!" With more laughter. "You take good care of her, promise me now." She points her finger at me accusatorily.

"Yes, of course," I reply.

"I was never a good..." Suddenly getting up, Margaret holds back her emotions, goes to the next room and returns with a shoe box of photographs, selecting one for us. "This is Mary's First Communion." A wondrous blossom of life; an innocent Holy soul in white; in law, a child of no one, *filius nullis*.

"Such a beauty even then." I say to myself, passing the picture to Mary, who briefly glances at it but does not touch it.

"Ah yes, but beauty can bring so much trouble for women sometimes."
Margaret is sad, beaten by circumstances on the anvil of life.

"I have a pen here Margaret, just put your signature on this. Mam places
the form on the arm of the chair and points to the place. Mary's mother,
unsteadily, signs 'Margaret Malone', as a nine or ten-year-old might.

Then she looks up at me. "You seem a nice man, but then they all do at
first!"

It's now or never. I'm curious to know, but it's no one's affair but hers
and Mary's. Still, I have to ask. This is the only chance I'll get and she can
easily say no. "The district nurse in Knocktopher told Mam that Mary
had good blood, she was a Langrishe. Which one was her father? She has
a right to be told." These words feel like a sentence of death in the long
silence that ensues. Ireland inflating before me, betrayed, in poverty and
suffering abuse from those in power.

"Let's go and see the kittens again Teresa, I just don't want to hear any
of this." Mary, furious, rises abruptly and leaves with a delighted Teresa
beside her.

"Oh God, why did you have to ask? And see how you've upset Mary.
Bringing the past up now is no use; it is best well forgotten." Margaret
chides me, speaking mournfully. She brings her eyes down to the floor
and clasps her head with both hands.

Mam gently encourages her. "Ah, Margaret, he does have a right to
know what blood he's marrying into."

"I'd rather not, you've raised too many ghosts from the past asking me
this."

"Just his name and that'll be the last of it," I say. She's really upset.
There is such pain in her face as she looks up at me.

"Holy Mother of God there'll never be an end of this for me!"

I find myself drawing closer to hear her.

"I suppose you both have a right to know. I was Mary's age, exactly, and
so glad to be getting the job in the big house with the quality folk: helping cook, cleaning and other tasks. Ten shillings for six days a week, with
Sundays off. Coming up from the village, it was like entering a new world.
They had the best of everything and the Lady Joan was very kind. But for
him, the Terence one, well I won't go into details, at first I didn't mind,
though it was strange that he was so familiar with a servant girl. With his
arm around me and kiss on the cheek. I knew nothing about this kind of
behaviour, the way it progressed when she was out and he got me alone.
With him being titled and well thought of in the county. I didn't want to
loose my job, but it was just so awful I had to get away. Too late. I was so
ignorant, in the family way and poor Mary was born in Roscrea where
they put me away. Father went crazy mad, mother acted as if she seen a
ghost and they called the priest. I couldn't tell them it was Langrishe."

"Do you ever see him now?" I ask.

"Very occasionally, in the village, in Kilkenny a few times. He just treated me as if it never happened, that I had his child. Did he even know? And can you believe it, a year or so later, he even attempted to give me a lift in his big fancy car when I was hitching a ride to Kilkenny. I walked on, couldn't bear to look at him. While he slowly followed, before speeding away. He wasn't going to lay his hands on me ever again."

"So Sir Terence Langrishe is her father?"

"Oh yes... but look it, aren't you the lucky one for all my trouble?" She grips my knee and she is crying. "My husband wouldn't have her about the place."

"I'll take good care of her." I say.

"I'm sure you will, you were right to ask me, I'm glad you did now."

"I think we should be leaving." Mary is standing by the door, was she listening?

"We'll leave you in peace now Margaret, thanks and God bless." Mam comforts Mary's mother, putting an arm on her shoulder.

"Good luck for the future Mary and I am so, so sorry, I may never see you again."

"You never saw much of me anyway. Was it even three times in the last seventeen?"

"I know, I know, maybe one day you'll forgive me and understand the way it was." Putting her arms around her daughter, Mary is unresponsively cold. She has no shame about the concept of revenge.

On the narrow road again, not far from the bungalow, I slow to let a van pass the other way, the face of the driver is glaring at me. Margaret's husband?

Returning to Freshford, I find it hard to focus my thoughts on silversmithing in the morning. Instead, the pendulum swings from tragedy to the ridiculous. Out of the blue I ask Mary, "would they be for drinking, those bottles of Holy water?"

"No, silly goose, you bless yourself with them."

"Like with the water in the fonts by the entrance?"

"Yes the way you've seen me do it before."

CHAPTER 19

Bending, cutting, forging and soldering silver wires in different thicknesses and lengths, I shape the curious Celtic script and form in large lettering: *IS D'EIRINN ME*. The words are encircled by a halo to form a covering lid to fit over the bowl. Measuring this exactly is a challenge.

Making sure the base or the underside of the bowl doesn't come through on the inside while I'm carefully soldering, I progress satisfactorily. It is deep beyond comprehension, how the miniscule silver atoms are dancing. How unfathomable and bizarre that nobody really knows what his going on beneath the blows of the hammer.

On Tuesday, Percy le Clerk, inspector of National Monuments at the Office of Public Works, pops in for an interesting chat. The next day Father Donal O'Sullivan, the mysterious Jesuit priest from the Arts Council whom I met before, visits the workshop. Then arrives the gentle Lex and Cecil Hyde to look into candle making and woodturning. Their talk is delightful and as lazy as the drifting clouds above: ever-changing, ephermal and eventually turning to bitter sweet remembrances.

On Thursday comes William Walsh, taciturn and diffident. He watches the construction while in deep thought, a trifle sombre perhaps. His concern is with prototypes for Irish industry and the coming Fair.

The sudden, dark and unhinged figure of Father McGee upsets me. He is just outside the polishing shop, John has let him in. Waving *Apologia Pro Vita Sua* in my face I'm obliged to come out to see him; this is annoying.

He greets me with a far too familiar, "so this is where you're working, how interesting."

John and Peter are wide-eyed at yet another intrusion, wondering what it is about this time.

"I've brought you this book, I think you'll find it interesting. How was Aquinas and his *Summa Theologiae?*" The book is obviously an excuse to come in and nosey out. McGee moves around the workshop, picking up this and that, boldly without asking.

"I threw it in the Nore, from the bridge at Inistioge." I surprise myself with the reply.

"You're joking of course." He spots my drawing for the bowl, "good God man, this surely can't be from you? 'I am of Ireland', if my translation is correct."

"Spot on."

"Are you serious?"

"Why do you ask that?"

"I think you know very well what I mean and where are these young men from?" He confronts John and Peter, who are disdainful and mute.

"They're both from London."

"Two Englishmen; sure with yourself, is there nothing for an Irish man here!"

"You have to understand that Kilkenny Design has a definite international employment policy," I reply.

"Oh dear, is that so? How and ever then, I'd best be on my way, I'll leave you all to continue with whatever it is you're doing, hope you enjoy the book and God bless."

"What's he on about?" John asks perplexed as soon as the priest has gone.

"That's the priest I explained to you about recently and here take this book he gave me." I toss it o to him.

"Written by a Cardinal Newman. Never heard of him. Englishman, his spiritual journey to becoming a Catholic. Came to Dublin..." John reads aloud to himself.

"Did he try to convert you?" Peter asks.

"No, just doing his job, if you can call it that."

John looks up. "What's a Cardinal?"

"Prince of the Catholic church."

"A prince?" he says with surprise.

"Oh yes."

"I'll give this Newman bloke a go then and let you know how I get on." He closes the book and puts it to one side. I would never have thought John had any interest in religion.

"I think we have another visitor coming this way," Peter matter-of-factly informs me from his bench space, looking out of the window.

"My goodness me, it's his Grace, James Arthur Norman Butler, the sixth

Marquess of Ormonde, the current owner of the castle and these stables if I'm correct." I can only hope he hasn't noticed his missing books.

Letting him in, he recognises me with friendly countenance and a warm hand shake.

"This is the Marquess of Ormonde, and this is Peter Donovan and John Blagden, silversmiths from London, working in Kilkenny now." I introduce the old aristocrat, who holds out his hand to each of them with perfect courtesy.

"You must find Kilkenny a big change, a far cry from congested London, what!"

It is John who answers for them both. "It certainly is, it's almost unreal to be only a few minutes walk away from work. But the pay is not the greatest; we could do with a pay rise."

The Marquess is surprised, perhaps by John's boorishness.

"Silver teapots you're making wasn't it? Have you any to show me?"

"Come into the other room and you can see what we're doing."

There, an assortment of silverware is displayed in the two glass show-cases Hogan sent down from his Japanese exhibition.

"All this was made here in the stables? How amazing; I would never have thought it possible." The castle owner studies the contents in silence, somewhat bewildered. The silence of history. Yet again, I experience a dizzying and profound response to the the careless twisting of time.

Quickly recovering, I ask him, "what's going to happen to your castle?"

"Ah, well you may ask, more a millstone on my shoulders these days, who would even want to buy it? I certainly couldn't live in it, but we are working on something, eventually I hope."

"Where do you live now?" I'm curious to know.

"Maidstone in Kent. Kilkenny always takes me back to my youth, before the Great War. Oh yes indeed, how everything has changed, for the better let's hope." He says this without remorse and with a smile. "I better be on my way."

With a salute to Peter and John as he leaves, I let him the marquess out, thinking that he must be near the last of his illustrious line.

"Nice enough old geezer," says John.

"What's a marquess?" Peter asks.

"The title between a duke and an earl. Entitled to wear a silver gilt cornet of alternating strawberry leaves and balls; his coat of arms is above the castle entrance, you can see across from your flat."

"In other words Peter, a load of old cobblers and not to be taken seri-ously!" adds John, mockingly.

* * *

I'm driving north again, with Mary alongside, nervous at meeting the parents for the first time. There's a brand new British customs post dividing the widened road. That of the Free State is still rather shabby in the same old painted greens which I remember from earlier times. I'm almost physically aware of the change as we cross the border into Newry and County Down.

On the road between Hilltown and Kilcoo, a distraught man comes stumbling towards us, waving his arms to slow us down. There's been a dreadful accident, where a car is upturned, with another horrifically damaged, radiator boiling, shattered glass and parts scattered. A screeching wild woman is kneeling over a body, bloody and lifeless, as the upturned car suddenly ignites, to the screams of someone burning alive, someone who finds it impossible to get out!

A foretaste of things to come, the blinding white hot light of eternity, then, 'nothing! thou elder brother even to Shade. Thou hadst a being ere the world was made...' There is little I can do to help. Mary is pale and shocked. The Royal Ulster Constabulary arrive and there is a strange contrast between the horror on the road and the fact that life continues. My attention is drawn to a robin in the hedge. In the distance, the familiar blue Mournes are sharp against an afternoon spring sky that is particularly clear. I am waved on.

Down the steep hill from Castlewellan, the screams still echoing behind us, she casually remarks, "I didn't know they carried guns up here."

"The constabulary?"

"Yes." They always have done, sure the IRA were still fairly active along the border recently remember? But not anymore, hopefully."

The curbstones by the crossroads are painted red, white and blue. We pass Magherahamlet Church of Ireland and approach the old homestead. It is long, low, white washed and blue-grey slated; homely and snug, a woven part of Ulster's planter heritage. Leaving Kilkenny is like experiencing the lowering of a paraffin lamp, with the light dimming around us.

"You're not to be worrying, everything's going to be all right." After driving into the farmyard I take her hand. It must be daunting for her. Father appears, bending boiler-suited from the byre.

"So what have we here?" Father speaks with his direct and clipped RAF speak, which sounds peculiar in this foreign land of Ulster, now his home. He greets Mary with an obvious eye for a pretty wench. I'm spun away to that fearful day the war ended, when he appeared. And even now Father is still somewhat of a stranger to me.

I look up to the sounds of the big Nuffield tractor drawing closer; it sweeps around, pouring blue diesel fumes from the exhaust. My brother glances at us without stopping, nor slowing even. I'm annoyed at the impression Ulster must be having on Mary: Speeding vehicles, hard voices and dreadful accidents. Mother is at the kitchen door, displaying the momentary alarm of the older woman towards one so much younger. It's inevitable and can't be helped.

"This is Mary, Mary Malone, we're getting married." I introduce her boldly.

"Well, let's have a look at you then girl." Father welcomes Mary, coming to her side of the car. Mother is speechless; both closely inspecting Mary as they would a new heifer.

Entering the Aga-warm kitchen, Father is obviously chuffed by this unexpected and glamorous Southern intrusion. He takes her all to himself, to the sitting room, as Mother subtly questions me on Mary's background and religion. Doing the right thing, but she's still so young and I'm to remember there's no birth control. I assure Mother not to worry about that and I tell her too, about Mary's unfortunate circumstances.

"Well, if you're sure, but don't rush into this. She's not in any way, you know what I mean?" Mother goes on.

"No, she's definitely not!"

Father is over the moon with thoughts of a beautiful, young daughter-in-law: a real Irish colleen from Kilkenny and Tipperary too, how romantic. Mother, well, she'll get used to it eventually. For her, it's not so much about the religion, but who Mary's mother and father really were. This is something Mother's not quite convinced about, what are the implications of the blood of unforeseen inheritances? What could this mean for her grandchildren? Even if the story is true, the wretched half-doors and gypsy encampments of the poor, superstitious Irish appear before Mother, along with atavistic fears about peasant beliefs, Holy wells, confession, drunkenness, filth and priests. Can a Catholic ever change?

Probably, these images only arise rarely in my Mother's mind, yet I can tell they are there all the same. It can't be helped. They are like a distant star, invisible at first, then appearing ever so faintly. If you turn away, then look again, it has gone.

My brother faces the sink, washing his hands, I can faintly hear him say, "let's hope you'll have no regrets; were there no nice Protestant girls down in the Free State for you then?"

CHAPTER 20

We spend the night in the end bedroom, floating together... Listening to the old house sounds; it is a wooden ship, sailing to where? The wind moving to us from those mysterious prehistoric places along the coast, from Ardglass to Newcastle, and up the driveway where the ivy-clad trees creak and bunches of spring daffodils stir. But are there ghosts disturbing her dreams of Ulster?

I waken to the sound of hungry pigs squealing at buckets. There is a photograph on the dresser of Father with six airmen; it is grey and fading, with a caption: 'British Military Mission to Russia, Air Section at Archangel 1941'. The stories he told me. Such as meeting Stalin, who was surprisingly small, with a pock-marked face, thinning, short, dark greying hair, wearing a plain mustard-coloured uniform. When Stalin entered everyone froze. The Russian dictator had yellow eyes, the eyes of a wolf that drilled into you. He was suspicious of everyone. Stalin stands quite clearly in my mind. How strange to see him now, good old Uncle Joe from the war years.

Fred Hennan is putting milk churns out to be collected across the fields by the bridge, his brother Bob is starting to plough. Wasn't mother understanding, to let us sleep together. I open *The Home Preacher* and the words spill out, black as a distorted wood louse running for cover. I slam it shut again! The sound wakes Mary, whose frightened head and shoulders rise up from the covers.

"What was the noise? It gave me an awful fright."

"My closing *The Home Preacher*, sorry."

"The what?"

"This silly old book I used to read as a child, scary stuff."

"What's it about?"

"God." Here comes the shadow of a dreadful thought. Mary and Stalin together. It's just a phantom of the myriad connections between memories in the brain, of how they join together somehow, to print a picture. In a panic, I have to hold and kiss her, to reassurem myself. It's stupid with her barely awake.

* * *

"I take it you've never been to Belfast before." I ask Mary as we enter on the Ormeau road.

"God no. Sure, I was only in Dublin once before I met you."

"It's so different from Georgian Dublin, more hard edged, British industrial and Victorian. What did you think of the parents?"

"Your father is nice, not so sure of mother though, I think she's disappointed maybe. You told her everything, I wish you hadn't."

"What did she say?"

"She sort of tiptoed around the subject, but gently, for it must have been a shock, her son going to marry me, a Catholic without a proper family. It could have waited."

"Why there's nothing to be ashamed of, they'd have to know eventually."

"You wouldn't understand."

"Anyway, we'll have to get some Durex, we don't want to start a family yet."

"They're awful yokes."

"There's no alternative."

"Whatever you say." Mary is clearly indifferent.

"I'll show you the City Hall." We walk around Donegal Square holding hands.

"Oh look, I've never actually seen one flying before." She is pointing to the large Union flag above us, "what does it mean?"

"The red cross of England's St George; the blue and red saltires of Scotland and Ireland."

Her gaze seems excited. Suddenly, it is an extraordinary and magic moment. Out of Ireland's tragic past, a mysterious rare butterfly, intrigued at the enormous flag. A bold statement of Ulster's Protestant people in front of the City Hall. Can I really keep her?

"But not really Ireland's."

"Well this part, for most people here certainly. Say hello to Queen Victoria." We are passing her statue, entering the impressive porte-cochère and marble-lined vestibule to the main entrance hall. It is stunning with a red-carpeted grand staircase and landings made with creamy marbles from Italy and Greece. The floor is a black and white chequered tile. "This is over-the-top Edwardian, far too ornate for me. But look up to the dome and John Luke's mural."

It is a depiction of Cave Hill in the distance, with industrious, hard-working, inventive Belfast the foreground, in butter soft yellows and egg shell browns, with touches of red and green, against an aquamarine and grey white sky. I remember trying to draw Julie's Caesar's head in the classical drawing class. There came a low, timid voice behind me and I stood up to let John Luke sit down. He took the HB pencil and with absolute mastery drew a perfect likeness, then cross hatched it with a hard pencil. Imagine. He was a silent, lonely man; ghostly and gliding, with awesome talent.

"It's dreamy and strange; an artist's view of this world." Mary slowly and very deliberately remarks.

"You could be right."

I go to Pottinger's entry and Blake's Surgical Supplies again, to the same charming goon in a white coat, who is admiring Mary.

"And where's this lovely girl from you're with today?"

"Kilkenny."

She shouldn't have answered.

"Aha, I hope not one to enter Blakes risking your immortal soul to eternal damnation and the fires of hell!" He goads her mischievously.

"Why do you say that?" Mary asks him innocently.

"Contraception is a mortal sin for all Catholics, heinous in the eyes of the Pope and God."

"Get away!" There is perhaps the faintest blip of fear at his words; she is still taking a long time to break totally free of the church.

"How and ever, we know better in Belfast, so what'll it be today Sir?"

"Two gross, no three."

"Thirty-six!" Mary glances at me surprised.

"Well yes, might as well; there's John and Peter remember?"

"Can I tempt you to a jar of KY Jelly as well, a wonderful lubricant, the cat's whiskers you might say, combined with the feather light." He moves towards the next room, "I take it you'll have both Sir?"

"Yes."

He returns with the jar and those peculiar violet and pink packets, that I used to wonder about when at the barbers.

"Now you be careful crossing the border with these and remember you're smuggling sinful devices into a Catholic country, with serious consequences if their customs stop and search you!"

"How much?"

"I'll make it thre pound even for the lot."

"There you go." I present three Lady Lavery green punts to him, which he accepts rather disdainfully.

"Safe journey and mind what I say." He winks at Mary.

As we head back to the car, Mary asks, "how did he know I was a Catholic?"

"They just somehow do up here!"

A have a momentary feeling of despair upon leaving the familiar lands of my boyhood and entering the bizarre and surreal surroundings of a foreign place. Subdued in me are lurking fears of the Free State, which arise suddenly in the shape of the cold, black crows, a priestly breed on the roadside. Dreamy enterprises are shrouded in the clouds, where I can occasionally glimpse men making peculiar things in gold and silver. Who is this beautiful Irish girl beside me? Kilkenny is a tall tale, the city in the distance, like in Giorgione's *Tempest*.

* * *

As a terrible loneliness engulfs me, frightening me as I enter into the stables. Peter and John are unusually quiet, there is an atmosphere of something brewing.

"We both need a pay rise to eighteen quid, or we'll be forced to leave." John suddenly asserts.

"I had a feeling you'd soon ask."

"The going rate in London's twenty five." Peter confirms.

John takes over. "We quite like working here, but how does Walsh and Hogan expect us to live on fourteen quid a week? It is ridiculous. Look at Middleboe and Reeves, I'd love to know what they're getting."

"There's a two-tier society developing here now, between the workers and even yourself, what are you earning?" Peter surprises me by asking.

"A hundred a month."

"Are you really any better than us?"

"Well they did hire me to get the workshop up and running, and that's what I was offered to start with. You both came at fourteen, no one forced you."

"Yes but we now know it's not enough to live on in Kilkenny, isn't that so Peter?"

"You said it John."

"Well, all I can do is ask and see what they say..."

Five or six minutes pass without another word being spoken. I'm aware of the mid-morning spring brightness, warming the old stones outside, a wagtail, never still on the footpath, flies away.

"I think that Middleboe's on a well paid holiday in Kilkenny if you ask me." Peter breaks the tense silence.

I wonder aloud, "what about your girlfriend if you leave?"

Peter looks at me coldly, "she'll have to get over it."

When I ring for him Paul Hogan's not available: maybe the after-noon, definitely tomorrow. This is a nuisance, it's always something with Hogan, where is he anyway? I'll still finish the rose bowl soon, even if they go. They are hardly asking for much more really, four quid... London apprentices, always riotous.

*   *   *

I'm still with the keys to the castle. Evening draws over without much intention, a somnambulist dreaming the castle; there are historic and mysterious forces at play here. The great edifice is available to me, the new owner for an hour that can stretch to seven hundred years. I can be the Duke or Marquess, whatever I fancy, wearing a coronet of straw-berry leaves and robe of scarlet cloth lined with taffeta and doubled with ermine.

I ascend the high drum tower overlooking the city and Nore, the moon faintly beginning its journey. Every day ends in ruins here. Shadows grow in length as the sun falls away, life grows old and dies. Am I going to live in Kilkenny? Or, eventually, will I have to flee? I wonder what is behind this door. It is an enormous seated lavatory and from the cistern above hangs a golden, patterned chain with white ornate handle to pull and flush foul excrement away. Thomas Crapper and Co. Walls of blue and white ribbon tiles and a bath children could swim in, which has enormous brass hot and cold taps.

The long Gallery's carved marble fireplace tells the story from the first Theobald Fitzwalter, a knight who accompanied Henry II into Ireland and was made Chief Butler of Ireland in 1177. Entering the high roofed kitchen, half underground, I note the star-shaking bell box, which would have told the servants below the identity of the person demanding atten-tion above. Lord Ossory's bedroom calling, the new servant girl is very pretty, better tread warily going there, for they can take what they want. The blackened cast iron ovens remind me of Auschwitz incinerators. On the shelves are numerous large copper pots and pans and what would that rusty looking yoke be for?

Oh God! I step back. A very large rat comes trundling across the floor, stopping and looking up at me, not in the slightest bit afraid, for he surely knows the castle is really his, now that all the fair ladies and gentlemen have gone. The mind-set of the Design Centre faithful is a far cry from the reality of what's happening outside the stables in Kilkenny.

*   *   *

"I'll ask Hogan about your money now." I tell them first thing next morning. Apprehensively, I dial Coras Trachtala and am put through to Hogan. I get straight to the point.

"Paul it's me, the silversmiths want a pay raise to eighteen pounds a week, they're finding it hard to cope at the fourteen!" He doesn't reply. "Are you still there, did you hear what I said?"

"Yes I heard, it's out of the question, they've only been there a few months and that's what was agreed!"

"They'll be away next week then."

"Sounds like blackmail, if they go so be it!"

"That's your final word?"

"Yes we'll get a couple of Irish next time, shouldn't be too difficult."

"I'll tell them then, it's inconvenient, they're really good and well into the Kilkenny way. It's a shame to let them go for the sake of four quid."

"No one is irreplaceable, they can't be allowed to put a gun to our head, you tell them!" He puts down the phone abruptly.

He hasn't thought this through and finding replacements to come and work in Kilkenny won't be easy. I'm pondering the situation and notice Oisin Kelly through the end window coming out of the lavatory and into the candlemakers next door. Not for long though. Now he's approaching me, what does he want this time? I invite him to the office and as I'm alone with him, explain the situation.

"Leave it with me and I'll have a word with Walsh." Kelly says. For him it seems to be a problem that is easily fixed. He's known William Walsh for a long time, the charioteer in his office, and he respects the silversmiths for having a skill he can use.

"How soon?"

"I'll call him right away if you like. And could you get those sharpened for me?" Kelly empties a folded cloth of chisels on the desk and picks up the office phone. I hope Walsh is available, he's been in Africa recently about Guinness. He should be home by now... yes, yes, he's there, thank God!

I return from the end room to Peter and John, who are waiting for me eagerly.

"So what did he say?" John asks immediately.

"Kelly's talking to Walsh about it now."

"Did Hogan agree?"

"It's up to Walsh."

"And Hogan."

"No, Hogan said no John, but let's see what Kelly can do."

"Doesn't look good Peter."

"We'll be on our way." Peter replies.

Kelly's in there a while, the laughter's a good sign. Who'll remember this anyway? Like his bishop and saint candles, once lit they will melt away to nothing, can't believe in a permanent present all the time. Who cares if they go, maybe Hogan's right, I should just become one with the tides of Kilkenny's fate.

"You'll get the extra four pounds in next week's pay," says Kelly matter-of-factly. He takes out a folded paper from his inside pocket, he is well prepared, not wasting a moment. "This drawing of a dove I have, can you make it in bronze or, even better, silver, like the mask?" Drawn to about quarter size, though realistic (for Kelly's no admirer of the Abstract Expressionists), the bird shows his distinctive hand.

"Take some of this modelling wax and carve it with a sharp blade, you can use heat as well, we can then cast it for you." John, rather obsequiously, hands him a pink square of wax.

"So I could have as many doves as I want?"

John nods. "Unlimited quantities; they are easily mass produced."

"Amazing."

And away he goes with his wax, both problems solved, simple as that. Hogan will hardly be pleased; a shot across his bow, however... I had best sharpen those chisels.

That was good of Walsh, but then again, it's not coming out of his own pocket, it might have been different otherwise.

I don't want to upset the apple cart. These early days in Kilkenny have been a glorious dream but bad feelings and simmering discontent can be infectious. I am making the finishing touches to four mice and a dead cat in silver, which shouldn't be doing, but which I worked on for a little each day. The IS D'ÉIRINN MÉ lettering for the rose bowl is almost complete on Peter's bench. He is a dark horse. He certainly has the skill. and it is a superb example of modern Irish design and workmanship, hah! Should the trade in Dublin ever discover it was English made, the story would be in the papers. Captain Le Bas, he of the hallmarking duty, knows everyone. There would be ructions and acrid jealousies and understandably so. Far away in New York, nobody need know. This is an awful lot of silver mind, which I have not even priced. I was not asked, but maybe I should in case an American wants it.

CHAPTER 21

On the laneway that buds from the cottage, I am unable to wait. I am so excited as she steps into the car. No perfumer could create her scent, such haunted Irish airs of flesh, foliage and landscape.

"I've a present for you Mary."

She is surprised and delighted, taking the little box from me, opening it.

"What is it, what does it mean?" Her voice expresses confusion.

"Four mice at the funeral of a Kilkenny cat, they're carrying it to his grave."

"Is that so?" Slowly, she shakes her head. "Oh yes, I can see their little noses and the cat on their shoulders."

"Do you like it?"

"Well, yes of course, it's so different, but weird about death. Why did you make like this?"

"Something from Kilkenny for you, an act of revenge of the mice on their tormentor."

She looks at me strangely. "Did the mice kill him?"

"They did."

"Good," she says definitively.

Mary studies the piece intrigued. I try to memorize the instant, to store it for a lifetime. Opening the clasp, I pin the brooch on her jacket.

This extraordinary Kilkenny girl says, "I never need to be reminded of Kilkenny though."

She is somewhat spooked, perhaps I shouldn't have given it to her.

"We'll have to see the priest about the wedding; what time would suit you?" I ask earnestly.

"Any day or the evening between seven and eighth would do."

"And the date for the wedding?"

"Say about August, a lovely month in Ireland, and keep it simple, for there'll hardly be anyone from your side."

"There'll be none," I answer most assuredly. "All's we need is a best man and bridesmaid, then maybe we'll go away to say... Portugal."

"Portugal!" she exclaims loudly. "God, I'd love to go there, all that warmth. The bright flowers, palm trees, sand and blue sea: so far away from old Ireland's damp and misery."

"They say it's even more Catholic than here, if that's possible."

"We wouldn't be going to church," she says.

"Will it be that awful Cleary one we have to see?"

"Ah no, he's gone, we have a new curate now, I've only seen him once, he seems OK."

"What happened to Cleary?"

"He was moved to Limerick."

"Any reason?"

"No, but they are moved around."

"So we'll be seeing the new one and married as well by him. Imagine if it was Cleary still, the dog." I have another thought. "Maybe we should be thinking of a house, the flat will be too small for us both."

"But it's cosy and warm. And really enough for us both to be getting on for now with. Are we going to live in Kilkenny for the rest of our lives?"

"I really don't know. So anyway it will be August, they'll be cutting the corn up in County Down then."

"Go way," she says softly and subconsciously.

Floating on a great cloud, I return to Kilkenny, which seems to drift, incomprehensible and impossible to break free from.

Far away, during quiet, dreaming moments, I see the dark Abbey and whispering trees. Herself coming up Patrick Street, surprised to find waiting me by the Club House. Mid-summer evening around Kells, to Kilree by moonlight, a Round Tower suddenly confronting us, awesome and strange. As earth moves and turns to silver, we approach the ancient covered cross, made of pure gold. For the hour glass was full then, but the grains of time are beginning to fall.

* * *

I'm torn over the question of building a house in Kilkenny. The Ulster Bank might give me a loan, a safe investment that could only increase in value if ever I have to sell. And wouldn't she love a new house? All modern, with a proper kitchen, flush toilet, hot and cold water, and proper heating throughout. But there's nothing to say this is permanent here. If I get on the wrong side of Walsh, it could be difficult, or even Hogan. And Kilkenny will change. There is talk of the Finns arriving. They were on Germany's side during the war.

Nothing is set in stone, I could be gone in a flash, to where? To a shop on Upper John Street, where I would never see the light of day, bent and cramped beneath fluorescent light. That way lay madness.

Here is Newman's *Apologia Pro Vita Sua*, which has been tossed on the bench before me, suddenly disrupting my thought. I look up and ask, "well, how did you find the Cardinal, John?"

"Verbal diarrhoea, you said he was a great theologian, my arse!" John is brutal.

"You read it?"

"A few pages was more than enough, how anyone can take such a convoluted mouthful seriously is beyond me."

"I heard he's heading for sainthood."

"Yeah well, just goes to show, lunatics the lot of them."

Well said Englishman, I think, no trumpery for you here.

There's an architect on High Street, Colm O'Coughlan, I shall go and see him this afternoon. He has a modern flat-roofed house, the only one as you come into Kilkenny on the Castlecomer road.

* * *

Colm must be Kilkenny's Mies Van der Rohe, for his office is clinical white upstairs with the latest stainless steel and leather chairs, reproductions of Mondrian. It's as modern as you'll get in Kilkenny and a surprise. This youngish man is effusive at thoughts of getting the go ahead on a house he'd be free to design. It soon surfaces that he is annoyed Montgomery got the job for the stables. It wasn't put out to tender. Colm can draw up plans in no time and there's land for sale on the Glendine road opposite the Golf Links, two hundred and fifty pounds for a good site that can immediately be built on.

Returning to work, I feel I am doing the right thing. There is nothing definite. Will I be charged for the plans? I should have asked; I was too hasty. Should I go back? No, that would look bad. Maybe she's right, it's far too early yet... I should wait and see.

Farrelly is straight ahead and unavoidable.

"The man himself, I heard you were with Father McGee taking instructions, will you be turning?" he asks me eagerly.

"God I will not. That was for her sake only, so we can get married."

"But sure why not? Wouldn't it make life much simpler for the pair of you."

"It's not going to happen."

"Who's the lucky lady anyway? Is she from the city? Do we know her?"

"I wouldn't think so, she lives toward Urlingford way."

A moment's silence in which his inquisitive look, asks, are you not going to name her? But he won't probe any further.

"Anyway, congratulations and good luck for the future." Farrelly holds out his hand to shake. "I've to get pork sausages in Dores for my supper."

He his harmless enough, likeable even. It takes all sorts.

I walk on past the pretty girl polishing Doctor Purcell's brass plate on the big yellow Georgian door. She is the one John mentioned, an eye opener.

The ancient sound of hammering flows through the stables from the workshop, mankind ever-busy from the dawn of history and before, making objects to adorn and use in gold and silver. The methods have hardly changed or been bettered. Yet it's difficult to understand how they achieved so much without gas or electricity.

I notice that turquoise blue cortina again, parked empty outside the candlemakers. It is disturbing, what is it doing there and who was in it

Approaching cautiously, I hear the voices of Hogan and Clarke inside the building and turn to leave them alone.

"That's a great looking yoke they're making in there." Hogan calls after me and emerges with Clarke. Both are carrying a large candle in each hand, which is most peculiar.

"You were in the workshop?"

"Indeed, yes, just what we need for the fair."

Joe the candlemaker is by his open door, he raises his arm with a peculiar gesture behind their backs.

"And getting married we hear," Hogan continues.

"August probably, no fixed date yet."

"So I can be your best man?" He speaks jokingly but is shielding his seriousness.

"Well, yes you can, but it'll be a very simple affair." And why not? It's thanks to him I got the job.

"You should see her Michael. He's a lucky man, I'll hold you to that now."

Words and gestures come effervescently from him today. The candles have the black knights and bishops of Jerpoint around them. Our talk is inconsequential: Kilkenny's lazy, sleep-inducing airs, like the effect of drinking whiskey,with a little soda water.

* * *

More days of indecision follow, raising the money is not a problem with the job at the Design Centre. The Ulster Bank will lend me what I need and plans for the house are ready for me to discuss. The wedding is booked at Clontubrid church on the thirty-first of August, when Mary will be just turned eighteen. The new curate was business like, but rather cold, otherwise he seemed normal, as normal anyone can be of that religion.

I am by the South Cross of Ahenny, which I have come alone to draw and perhaps derive inspiration from, however vague. It must have been made more than fifty generations ago, the blink of an eye. A people easy to convert. These motifs have been copied to distraction in pressed peat, brass and copper, jewellery, postage stamps, gravestones and much more. Obsessive and repellent, deeply carved with spirals and interlacings, its outline a pronounced rope-like ridge of gadrooning. I am suddenly gripped by a desire to find normality and run. The familiar carved wheels holding each arm are weathered roundels, with another one in the middle.

Falling into madness, I examine the Lions Den and what looks like Noah's Ark. This darkening of eternity here, a game of snakes and ladders, hoping to reach heaven and not falling to hell. The long list of every known sin, yet forgiveness for each one. It's getting far too late, and there's nowhere else to run. Here comes the gentle breeze across the fields of April's new grass and bovine quietude, calms me beneath the afternoon's uneasy sky of scattered feathery clouds. I feel I must take the risk.

* * *

A house it shall be then. I go to see Poe and Kiely solicitors on Patrick Street to arrange the purchase of land. I am entering a Dickensian twilight world of legality and ancient disputes, with groaning bookcases of thick law books, piles of folded legal papers tied with black and red ribbons and the clickiticlick of an antique typewriter. The chair I'm sitting on is ready to collapse; there's a daddy-long legs moving across the opposite wall to hide behind *The Monarch of the Glen*. The painting is behind cracked glass, with a flaking gold frame and it has been hung beside last year's Kilkenny Products calendar.

Faint voices faint and nearby traffic. Through the window I can see heads of the passers-by. Time moves in this fashion, as I wait for young David Kiely. Suddenly, I am startled, noticing a large black metal box with 'LANGRISHE ESTATE' written in bold, uneven capitals of white paint. It is right beside, just an arm's length away. Mesmerizing me, I reach out a finger out to touch it and get a static shock! Quickly, I pull back. Kiely would know all about them, I can always ask him. He has arrived, wearing worn green corduroy jacket, cavalry twills, a ropey striped tie and scruffy worn soft shoes. He's no more than twenty five. Lanky and pale, his words shoot out as from a spitting machine gun. Kiely has eyes that don't miss a trick. I'm hardly aware what he says, the sinister black box has upset me.

The transaction is straightforward enough. Just a paper to sign. Now I'm the owner of a small piece of Kilkenny land for two-hundred-and-fifty pounds, a sum that I had already saved.

So near so far. I would just love to know what was inside that box: the rents, many acres, marriages, inherited what from who, got how?

"The name Langrishe." Pointing to the box, "you obviously handle their legal affairs, what sort of people are they?"

"Why do you ask?" Kiely answers suspiciously, alerted.

"Because of a great wrong that happened some years ago at Knocktopher, concerning the..."

"I don't want to know then!" He interrupts me loudly, holding up his arms, a disturbed bird about to take flight. A moment normality returns just as quickly, as though the question had never been asked. The conversation resumes: how is the Design Centre doing? Do I like living in Kilkenny? And so forth. The deed is done now, there can be no turning back.

That was a strange encounter. Of course, there is client confidentiality and also Protestants closing ranks here perhaps? It doesn't matter and yet. What is there to hide? The black box hovers, kite like, above me for the rest of the day and into night. The lid opens to a monstrous black beetle that makes 'ticky-tick' sounds with its wings. A vulture by Knocktopher, nesting, all Kilkenny his by ancient rights. In an open coffin before the altar of an old country church is a beautiful Kilkenny girl, the light of my life, so dead, dead!

*   *   *

Colm O'Coughlan, the architect, recommends a builder on the edge of the city, off the Freshford road. I am let in to a barrel of a man having his cup of tea, eating a large slice of lemon Swiss roll. Confusion reigns, with many children and a large, sulky wife soothing the latest arrival in her arms. He surveys the plans, saying that it should have more than three bedrooms as the family is bound to grow. He looks at me with a sly chuckle. She raises her eyes to the ceiling, the boy — table high — makes a grab for the cake, screaming. He will be delighted to take on the job, and we agree a price at £3,500. He will need some of the money, preferably cash up front, in a couple of weeks when he'll be able to start building.

I question whether I'm doing the right thing all over again, for Mary's hardly over the moon. Her intuitive common sense maybe, is that working in the surreal atmosphere of Kilkenny is skating on thin ice that will soon melt. They'll have to be doing something with all this silver soon and the rose bowl is finally finished. Much to the cynical pleasure of Tom Eastwood and John Young, who come up to mock.

"To be honest, I think it's an awful looking yoke," says Tom, amused disdain on his face, "what's it for?"

"It's a rose bowl Tom, you pick roses and place them between the lettering, the bowl is filled with water for the stems underneath." This serious explanation is met with guffawing laughter.

"Jasus, is this what Kilkenny Design is about? What does the lettering mean?" asks John.

"I am of Ireland, in Irish."

"Cod Irish you mean, Gaelic whoha, the usual Celtic crap and nonsense." Tom tries to be provocative.

John takes the wide bowl with both hands and attempts to place it on his head. The silver is far too heavy and he lets it down with a heavy thud on the bench; I shudder, maybe it is dented.

"You're chancers the lot of you with this Kilkenny Design racket. Making rose bowls, I ask you, all at taxpayers' expense." John's voice betrays drink taken but I experience a momentary panic. What he said could be true. As they depart, John and Peter — who have been listening, silent and wondering — are invited for a jar with them later on. I had the same realization earlier, when I was in Dublin getting the bowl hallmarked. The Assay Master was speechless at first, another extraordinary piece from Kilkenny, what is going on there?

CHAPTER 22

Cattle are still grazing in my field. Even if it is only potato patch sized, they lived on as much before in pre-famine times. It is enclosed by a spring green, blackthorn, bird-song-filled hedge. We are watching himself and a boy with pick and shovel digging foundations along a path laid out in string, from pegs on lines. When a heavy shower starts, they cover head and shoulders with one-sided cut meal bags, becoming cowled from a distance. Like they are digging my grave. It seems a hopeless task, just the pair of them and not a brick, sand or cement in sight. It's going to take ages at this rate of digging. And I wonder do they even have a mechanical cement mixer. Mary turns to me with far away eyes and says, "do you think we'll ever get to live in it?"

* * *

"We don't be using them Johnies down here, we're a Catholic people and you're breaking the law having them." A loud, accusing voice comes at me the next morning heading to work. It is the refuse collection truck. The man who was complaining throws the bin back on the footpath and the lid flips back with a twirling crash.

What's he on about then? The used Durex in the bin must be the Johnies, as he calls them. It is quite extraordinary in this day and age to have someone poking around in one's rubbish, as some kind of moral policeman.

"What's that he said?" John catches up from behind.

"He discovered a Durex in the bin and is giving out, can you believe it?"

"Well you did tell me Ireland's a Catholic country and they're not allowed." He is highly amused.

I have to be more careful in future, putting them inside a Del Monte peach tin, wrapped in paper, the lip pushed tightly over and the tin stamped flat. The Design Centre is getting a bad name and can't be upsetting native susceptibilities too much.

So what more surprises will Kilkenny bring forth today? William Walsh and Anna Rose — smoking those sweet smelling Kent cigarettes — arrive unexpectedly with an artist called Hilary Heron. They want to see the rose bowl, to demonstrate silvermaking for Hilary. It is viewed sphinx-like by these experts of good design and taste. They say little. I can see he's somewhat disturbed and is looking for something unattainable here, Anna agreeing with him and seemingly wary to have an opinion contrary to his. A sense of unease permeates me when they leave. Again it is difficult to know what he's expecting and what to make. The cross currents flow from different directions, impossible to fathom, as the prophets of good design come and go all the time.

Peter is reminiscing to John about how he once soldered a spout on the teapot without cleaning away the fire stain. His old governor was watching, then simply knocked it off with a tap from his hammer, so Peter wouldn't make the same mistake ever again while soldiering silver.

Pink Valerian is growing on top of the wall opposite, with delicate clusters of purple clinging miraculously on the rough sides below. I find Poppey and Columbine around the stables, Scarlet Pimpernel and Forget-Me-Not with Dog Violet and Foxgloves in a corner by the broken drainpipe, all surviving undisturbed. The mysteries of nature are soothing, invisible and airborne, taking hold in the most unlikely of places, flourishing with sunshine and rain, without much, if any soil.

This silver's a ghost's metal, reflected of dreams, so wondrous and malleable and easy to shape. I rarely find satisfaction in it though, just in a few pieces, such as Oisin Kelly's mask, made by John working late by moonlight and kept by his bed when finished. The moment was brief, but for a while the magic glowed, beyond comprehension, but definitely present.

I'm inwardly detached though and I always was really. I should have left silversmithing well alone and never got involved. Silver quickly loses its shine to finger stains and scratches. It was by mere chance that I took it at art school. A lovely wee one from Ballymenna was my real interest then.

I drive into Freshford and stop beside that curious little Romanesque Protestant church (it must have been built before the Normans came). The times she'd have passed here in all weathers; God knows it must have been painful, doing messages for Mam in the village where they would

all have known. Waiting on her own for the J.J. Kavanagh bus from
Urlingford to Kilkenny.

The old door is locked. Inspecting the double recessed doorway and
gable, my fingers touch weathered stone and I think of the many wor-
shippers who passed through here. Who was terrorizing this part of
Ireland then? Vikings? Munster and Leinster men? It got awful bloody
between the Malachy and Brian. We only have the priests to worry about
nowadays.

When I reach the cottage and get out of the car, distraught cries greet
me. An oppressive sense of the hopeless condition of Ireland overwhelms
me. All this tumbledown living, which is made the more bizarre by the
job have in the stables. For there is no modernity, nor hope of anything
better on the way. The pathway from broken gate to cottage is a long
and torturous road of Irish life, strewn with thorns and sharp stones that
pierce and cut one's feet.

Mary opens the wretched half door, changed and barely recognizable
now. Behind her is Nora in fearful state of hysterical upset. Mam's comforting arm is around her, holding her tight. Little Eileen stands frozen, a
lost soul, so pale and confused.

"What's wrong? What happened?"

"Nora was raped!" Mary grabs my arm.

"Raped, raped by who?"

"They're big farmers towards Gathabaun way, he's their eldest. Mam
went to see the new priest who just said he was a good lad misbehaving
and Nora will have to get over it, for that's a woman's misfortune and
life!"

"Did you go to the Gardaí?"

"God no, with Nora so upset and the long walk into Freshford; they're
not there all the time, they'd only be sniggering the way men do, for any
the good would ever come of it. Can you even imagine Nora giving evidence in court?"

"How did this happen and when?"

"He came to the door in his car, asking to see her and Nora foolishly got
in. She arrived home in a terrible state, bloody and bruised. He just threw
her out when he'd done, in broad daylight imagine! To a fourteen-year-
old-girl. It could so easily have been me, God forbid. Men can be swine!"
Mary explodes, her eyes are alight with an Irish woman's echo of ancient
hurt and pain.

"He'd get at least ten years for this in any normal society, let's report
him to the Gardaí in Kilkenny, or Freshford if they're there," I say.

"I don't think Nora will go, she's far too upset." Mary replies. Nora
shakes her head, Mam likewise, silently agreeing. How the law and agents
of the state can intimidate the dispossessed and weak. Three abandoned

girls and an old woman looking after them. It would soon get out and the laneways around Freshford would be dangerous for them alone: fair game to be hunted at will. Outcasts in their own land, 'the Holy lande of Irelande.'

"I'll go and let them know what happened to Freshford first."

Mary is grim. "For alls the good it'll do, you'll see."

"We can't just do nothing, where does this man live?"

"Don't be going there yet, be only more trouble, they'd kill you, looking at me at Mass he was, I know what they're like, knackers the lot of them!"

"Come on into Freshford or Kilkenny if they're not there Mary and we'll see what can be done."

"No, you go on and see them if you will, I'll have to stay with Nora, for the moment at least."

If she gets pregnant over this, her life could be ended before its hardly begun.

* * *

I peer through the hatch to a thick, smoke-filled room. The Garda in Freshford is a big bull of a man, with slow and suspicious Kerry accent. He says, "you're the man from the Design Centre with the red Mini, Northern Ireland registered." His tone is faintly threatening, as if to say, you know we don't miss a trick here, even in sleepy Freshford. The other Garda has his back to a desk, swivelling around, attentive to what could be afoot, why is this owner of the red Mini with Northern Ireland registered plates here?

"I want to report a rape that happened this afternoon."

"Phwaa, do you now?" He arches his eyebrows and narrows his dark eyes. "And who are you to the victim of this rape, if indeed it is so?"

It's like acting in a tragic silver screen film, lost in a treacherous Irish bog covered in mist. Peasant to his bones, purposefully slow, the Garda is enjoying the welcome distraction. It's an opportunity to investigate and question the girl to see what this is about. He'll enjoy the importance of being in charge and his imagination will stir to thoughts of the coupling pair.

He says 'no' means 'yes' and asks how was it done: this way or that? Leg out the window? Or the bonnet? Rear or front seat? Where exactly did it happen, if it was rape at all?

I can feel already how the hidden forces will work. The father talks to the priests, a good word here and there, commenting on the way women are, remembering Eve. Couldn't be helped, auto-drive took over. He's manly and with wild oats to sow. Not his fault, bit of a lad. Some girls, country girls especially, can't help provoke. The devil is in them for it.

There is a plucked turkey on the chair, neck hanging down with bright red combe nearly touching the floor. It looks weird in the electric light, molybdenum coloured, with spot of blood on the beak. I'm asked why couldn't she have come, as she'll be the one making the statement, or is this a fuss over nothing?

"I'll go and see if she will, but I doubt it."

"You do so, for we shall have to investigate her most thoroughly." He says this with a freakish smile, stretching himself tall.

"And you'll call to them?"

"Yes in half an hour or so, we know where they live."

I have to keep reminding myself that I'm not dreaming. And as I drive back it occurs to me that I will have to work again on the silver hinge that doesn't look right. Erik Herlow and Ake Huldt will notice. Silversmithing is inconsequential. For Nora has disappeared. She ran out of the cottage into the night, as if wanting to fly free from the violence that begot to the violence. God forbid no... where has she gone to?

"I followed after and tried to find her; she could be anywhere in the dark out there. She's in such a terrible state, she's capable of anything!" Mary is frantic and almost accusatory towards me. She'll surely return, where else could she go? For Nora is nobody's child.

The same two Garda arrive, stooping into the cottage, seemingly amazed at finding a living like this. They are so big and brutal, a uniformed intrusion on such a wretched, small room, with a fire that is nearly out. They take notes, names and say that there is no point searching for Nora this time of night. She'll have to come back, they'll return to see her in the morning.

Further up the hill, I'm calling, calling, to a field overlooking the county towards the city, a troubled landscape. Cattle are innocently watching. The sky has a faint glow from Kilkenny. Nora could be anywhere.

"Do you want me to stay?"

"No, you may go, I'll put Eileen to bed the poor child. We can only hope and pray Nora returns. I think Mam had a minor heart attack when Nora rushed out. It's happened a few times before. It should be the doctor she wants, but I'll get the priest in case."

"I'll call the Garda in the morning at work and see you tomorrow evening."

With the briefest kiss, she turns away and as I drive off, I'm left with the feeling that humans are always alone in the end.

Parking by the raised footpath slightly down from the stables, I notice the morning is beginning to lighten faintly. Still in the car, a feeling of apprehension grips me as I notice a figure slowly shuffling towards me on the footpath. Now he is above the window, dressed in plus-fours and carpet slippers, wearing a Tyrolean jacket with an iron cross on its button hole, those hypnotic, opaque eyes again. That unmistakeable face staring straight ahead, even older from last time, but instantly recognizable. I hurry fearful up the stairs to bed and hope oblivion will protect me.

* * *

Making silver is a complete absurdity right now. Getting motivated is so hard. It is difficult to concentrate. I work as a programmed automaton, feeling that the stable enclosure is an unreal bubble, disconnected from the events outside. The workshop is foul from a mix of silver polish, sulphuric acid fumes and cigarette smoke. It's suddenly sickening. The Irish handmade design seem a lark, today at least.

We can never reach the Swiss watch and jewellery making standards. Crafts there took years to develop, when French Huguenots fled legally sanctioned persecutions to Geneva. Eventually, a watch was made with twenty-four complications by Patek Philippe for the American banker Henry Graves.

I examine Oisin Kelly's little pink wax Irish pig. It is on the bench, teasing me. I have to start somewhere, so perhaps it should be to make this in silver. Or maybe place it on an Irish charm bracelet, green-eyed, cold enamelled. A hundred years from now this Kilkenny silver will have become curiously dated, the larger pieces causing future generations wondering what on earth were they trying to do? A sort of elegant plumbing in silver.

I can hardly ask Peter and John to smoke outside, nor Kelly. I wouldn't dare.

I phone the Freshford Garda — the Freshford Garda indeed — those two charmers better not make things worse. It is in their hands now. I'll be there this evening soon enough. What a shocking thing to have happened to such an innocent, young girl. She's bound to return, scarred for life, dear God. Would she ever be up to facing a trial? Could the priest be right to drop it? No.

Kilkenny's early summer roads and laneways are hauntingly seductive, leading to the never-ending, somnolent quietude of nature and man's past in stones. It could so easily have been Mary. She wouldn't have stood a chance. I now find out that my rage can make me capable of murder.

There's not a sign of Nora anywhere to be found. The Garda came and searched about for a while, then went to question the big farmer's son and never returned. The distressing cottage scene cruelly reminds me of the Great Hunger I recently read about. The book was illustrated with images of the very same Ireland I find here today; nothing has really changed.

Ragged men are hunched, dark and silent by the ashes of the dead grate, rosary beads in one hand. Mary, haggard, has the suffering Irish peasant face of her mother. She is with little Eileen, the woman holding the child to one side at the rear in the print of, *Clothes Being Disturbed At Kilrush* (1849). Oh, what am I doing here anyway. There comes a sudden urge to flee, which passes quickly. Their semi-roofless, abandoned thatched cottages; skeletal trees shaking in the cold wind before the threatening, leaden heavy sky. They came over the Slieve Mish Mountains, pauperized and wretched, starving people everywhere. All the old ghosts of Catholic Ireland seem to flutter butterfly like on the windows, wanting to get in.

"She must be out there somewhere, let's have another look," I suggest hopefully to Mary. But she shakes her head, far away; I'm an intruder now, from a different time and place.

"Come on, we might as well before it gets too dark, give it another go; she might be afraid to come home after what's happened." I try again.

Mary shoots back annoyed, "and why should she be afraid at what's happened, as if it was all her fault!"

"I know, I know...," I reply chastened.

We walk together over the fields. Under a clear creamy blue sky the hedges and trees are all an extraordinary luminous green this time of year. We look into all the concealed dens and hideouts that Nora could possibly be in. Asking neighbours who stare blankly, shaking their suspicious heads. News of her disappearance is over a wide area now, what's going on? The old lady and three girls living up a forgotten laneway are excluded from the community. Their circumstances are too dubious. There is a touch of fear in passing their cottage perhaps, the shoeless girls gazing up from behind the gate. A devil's brood for the unwary, wouldn't you know? Hurry on. The devil has many disguises

This seems a hopeless task, but she can't just have vanished into thin air.

We are approaching a low-lying boggy area of high bull rushes and silvery water, which glints to the ever so faint new moon. We must have covered a couple of miles to get here. It feels like a landscape that has been undisturbed since the last ice age retreated. A lone mallard duck rises, startled at the sounds of our approach. It rises higher and higher, it is away and no longer earth bound. The ground is unsteady, trembling. It is a layer of weedy, watery peat, covering God only knows what, the bones of rebel Irish fleeing the Militia of 98? Pushing through the thick bull rushes to the water's edge, I see there's something out there, slightly submerged, dappled and ghostly phosphorous-like. I go out in the water to my knees to get a better look. I could well be sinking deeper.

Nora is floating face to the sky, wreathed in strings of wild emerald growth, her eyes wide open in a peculiar way. Metamorphosis, the old Christian belief of a soul leaving the dead. With her final mortal breath she found peace, happiness at last is evident on her pale, ethereal face.

Millais' drowned Ophelia from Hamlet comes to mind.

It is a shocking discovery that I'll have to report. The end of this poor child is the will of their God. Will they ever be made accountable for this? The big farmer; the baronet; the priest. Should I gather her up and bring her out? But Mary might freak. I should say nothing, so she won't have to see the body. I'll leave it for the Gardaí, or whoever's job it is. It is a beautiful enough grave, with the water and reeds... In a week or so she'll be hidden and forgotten.

My clothes cold and sodden to the waist, I return to Mary who is waiting anxiously in the field.

"Well did you find anything?"

"Sad to report yes. Nora's out there in the water, she's..."

Mary rushes past me, into the bog.

"Don't go in there, you could drown too." I grab her and she fights to break free.

"I'll fetch her then; go back, get out of this."

Wading in, my shoes sucked by gripping mud, I feel an awful chill. It was the death of an English King once. With outstretched arm and hand catching a piece of her dress, I'm able to easily draw her towards me. A part of the natural world of the bog almost, a body in gentle decay, which does not want to leave. I am an unwelcome intrusion. I lift her, dripping and so light, an empty shell, smelling of the wild watery bog. Then back through the thick screen of foilage to laying her gently on the grass.

Mary kneels beside me, brave and quietly sobbing, arranging Nora's hair and clothes to look decent.

"We'll have to leave her here for the moment, while I get the Garda, they'll know what to do."

"I'm staying with her, you'll have to go and tell them yourself."

"Are you sure? Here all alone, will I tell Mam?"

"Yes, you might as well, at least she'll know now. Go on hurry up, this is bloody murder!" In Mary's speech I catch the flame of peasant revenge and outrage; her eyes show she is capable of anything.

"If you insist, but I'd rather you come."

"How can I leave? It wouldn't be right, between a stray dog, rats and crows picking about by early morning, anything could happen. Go on."

Climbing the gate from the field and looking back to Mary by the fading light, I see old Ireland in all its tragedy and historic pain. The grieving, distraught picture of the innocent. A scene from Great Famine is there yet again, but this is 1964!

CHAPTER 23

Garda and ambulance arrive and those alerted to the news are gathered in hushed voices at the gate. Walsh wants Kelly's pig and now a wren pepper pot. While Nora is taken to Kilkenny's morgue, where she will be left in refrigerated drawers I believe. The days and dates are askew.

I've noticed a certain ignorance in Walsh. A fine fishing rod is in the back of his car, beside olive green waders, net, gaff and a see-through lidded box of rainbow-coloured flies. For today is Friday and we are travelling to the funeral that Mary insists upon. There's no money for it here, so Nora has to return where she come from in Roscrea.

Woman and girl, a tearful scene on the cold steps of this Celtic-cross tipped nunnery, hospital and maternity ward. Nuns swish by: black, faces floating pale along long corridors. Stopping, haughty and hurried, one of them directs us to the rear, where there is an open, unkempt weedy ground of disturbed plots, which make tidy rows of little graves.

In the furthest corner of this area, a man is bent over, filling what must be Nora's grave.

"We missed everything, look at this, they told us to be here by eleven!" Mary exclaims suddenly. She has been silent and fraught since this morning. In her hand is a single white rose, taken from the cottage garden.

"Was there anyone here for the burial?" I ask him. The man stops and pierces his long-handled shovel for a rest into the soil that has already covered the coffin deeply.

"One of the sisters said a few words, the usual. Poor girl, just another child of shame, to be buried here, if you know what I mean."

"No priest?"

"No, no." He takes out a cigarette from a packet of Woodbine and lights it expertly.

"You'd have buried a lot I can see."

"Nearly every week there's one or two, this will soon be full." I take him in: he's a scarecrow in his worn jacket and torn sleeves (elbows protruding); his baggy trousers are pushed tightly into the turned-down tops of his muddy wellington boots.

"Gave us the wrong time, couldn't even wait. Was there even a Mass?" Mary murmurs low and sad.

"It's nearly always the same, just the sister with a hurried prayer, very rarely do they bother a priest."

"And no headstones."

"God no." The gravedigger looks up to the sky, "Sure in the end it doesn't really matter, carved marble and fine words are soon forgotten with the years and weather." Thus speaks the sage of the graveyard, taking a last inhalation from his cheap cigarette with an unpleasant sucking motion. He flicks the butt away, picks up his shovel, with just a few more spadefulls the burial is complete. Stamping the soil down with his feet he's away. A bold robin is watching, anxious to get at the freshly turned soil. Poor, poor Nora. Mary lays the single white rose upon the grave.

Tipperary and Kilkenny are in bloom as we drive back. I am wondering about what will happen to little Eileen when Mary's gone? It doesn't bear thinking about. This old earth is travelling at 65,000 miles per hour on an ellipsecal path around the atomic furnace of the sun, carrying its crowded load of life. With a diabolical randomness the weirdest, cruellest, things can happen, as the French Marshall knows.

I must not forget the books hiding under Mam's bed. I must do something soon, at her age and condition the situation is dicey. They'd have noticed him missing by now, but not a word. Not from his Grace, living in Maidstone for years. Haughton? Hardly, he whisked everything out without an inventory. Nobody knows, nobody cares what was in the Marquess of Ormonde's Estate office when it was cleared.

It was a moment of history to be alone that night, never to be forgotten, a once-in-a-lifetime experience, as though witnessing the end of a feudal age. But they still cling on. I recall my image of that bad baronet playing billiards by himself, pausing wistfully to gaze over the fair land and village of Knocktopher. Sad that this will soon no longer be his. No doubt he has memories of the hunt that gathered outside when he was a boy; of the tragic, beautiful Irish face of the village serving girl.

* * *

The ancient cement mixer splutters, shaking and turning the Blue Circle cement, sand, gravel and water to concrete, which is let into a wheelbarrow and pored filling the foundations. Mechanization at last, with a load of building blocks in sight too. The day is warm and cloudy with a light breeze; it is just the two of them as before. This whole field will soon be full of houses in a year or so, despite the stasis of Catholic Ireland with the midday Angelus ringing from St John's church and St Mary's cathedral. Both remain standing, muttering words in prayer that I can hardly hear. The dark magic of religion clings to them still. Time pulses, as my own heart beats to annihilation and then unfolds again.

"How are you getting on?"

"Not a bit of bother, we'll be laying the first blocks soon." The stout Kilkenny man evens out the concrete in the ground with a trowel.

"Did you know the Pantheon in Rome was built of concrete, two thousand years ago. It lasted well don't you think? The great dome with the hole at the top."

"Is that so? Well I wouldn't be knowing anything about that, a great invention though, sure, where would we be today without it?"

"Were you ever there?"

"Ah no, I never was, the home of our Holy Father himself."

"That's right, Pope Paul."

"But maybe one day with this young lad, my son Fergal." He touches the boy on his shoulder, smiles shyly at him. I would guessFergal is about fourteen.

"I'm sure you will." Enough of this, I should let them carry on. "Keep up the good work then, I'll be out again in a few days."

"God bless," he says, raising his hand.

"And same to yourself," I reply, turning away. So many God blesses and Holy Fathers indeed. The Angelus hour falls away, these moments are soon forgotten, ballooning far above, fusing with the clouds. Yet my foundations here will last at least two thousands years. It is some consolation for mortality.

We have a visitor at the workshop. Kerry Gunning, one of the metalworking Gunning's of Dublin, is chatting to Peter and John. He won't like what he sees, this state-subsidised silversmithing.

"I'm down to have a look at what all the publicity's about and making sure everything's hallmarked. I'm a warden of the Assay office in case you don't know." Kerry eyes me somewhat mischievously.

"We've only been at this a short while; have they showed you some of the results in the next room?"

"Yes, but from what we've been reading, you'd think Kilkenny's the greatest invention since the wheel!" he speaks forcefully.

"We can't help what the papers write, it's embarrassing I agree."

"The big yoke made for the World's Fair. Who ordered and payed for it?" His tone is accusing.

"A good question, it just somehow mysteriously grew from the day I was at the Export Board. The Fair was mentioned and it came into being: a piece big and bold, knock-them-back, Irish sort of thing. Made for the Board I suppose, we never bothered to price it."

"So this is how it works? Make what you please, money no object. It wasn't even put out to tender. You're not the only silversmiths in Ireland you know. Silver has been made in Ireland for hundreds of years. Ever been to the National Museum in Kildare Street? What do you think Gunning's do? Not to mention Alwright and Marshal or Gills and Smyths do." Kerry speaks loudly; he's a trifle hot under the collar I would say. John and Peter are standing attentively, bemused.

I reply by saying, "but it's nearly all plate for the Catholic Church. This will be domestic silver mainly and jewellery. No reproductions. I mean why keep copying De Burgo chalices and the likes of the Cross of Cong."

"We're here to bring Ireland into the modern world of the nineteen sixties you could say," remarks John, with a smirking grin. He is well aware how English is his voice. But Kerry pointedly ignores the remark.

"Take a trip up to Goldsmith's Hall in London and see what they're making, Gerald Benny and Stuart Devlin, you'd be amazed at what's possible." Peter is more earnest.

"Things are a lot different in Ireland, we're a poor country with a troubled history. We love the Celtic, our cultural identity. What I've seen here, to be honest, is just plain boring. It is well enough made though. Where and when you're going to sell it is beyond me."

His point is discouraging because it is valid, but I do my best. "Someone's going to Nieman Marcus and Tiffany's I've been told, they'd be more our market. There's Weir's and Morton's too."

"I wouldn't be so sure there, tight fisted old Prodys, believe you me."

"This Second Vatican Council could change everything at Gunnings, you could well be forced to change." Kerry doesn't reply to my counter, he is frowning somewhat. "There's a similar enterprise like this in Norway, which works very well..." I add. "I can't remember the name and anyway the Scandinavian design experts think design in Ireland is shite and something drastic has to be done!."

"God is it that bad? We need outsiders to fix us, has nothing changed?" Kerry turns to Oisin Kelly, who is coming in.

"What do you say Oisin? Is this Kilkenny Design a nonsense? Unfair competition to Kerry Gunning here?" I make the introduction.

"Well I wouldn't be worrying if I was you Kerry, it's a grand idea to be doing up the old stables and starting something new. This will be no competition for anyone, there's a big enough world out there for all, I'm

enjoying this immensely, let's hope it lasts!" Kelly accompanies his enthusiastic words with a chuckle. He is enjoying every minute of his working
break from Dublin.

Kerry, is impressed by the lay out and equipment at least. "All payed for
by the tax-paying public, I can see."

"Are you sure we couldn't interest Gunnings on a few prototypes?" I
open the door for him to leave.

"Are you serious?" he answers, though somewhat mollified now with
what he's seen and heard. He disappears through the archway, where
I glimpsed Mountgarret a while earlier. Oisin Kelly is obviously glad
Kerry's gone, the reason for his visit to us is a rolled sheet of paper in his
right hand. It's a design for a silver salmon salver baking trophy that he
wants us to make.

Fredrikstad! That was the name of the place in Norway Walsh and
Hogan went to see, the place where the idea of the Kilkenny Design
workshops was born.

"See you gentlemen tomorrow," I announce. It is half past five, time to
down tools and get away out of this place to the Marble City Bar.

There, the only customer is a man at the counter, smoking, crouched
over a near empty pint glass. With a double whiskey, I sit in the far, darkened corner and once seated watch the barman slicing a lemon. The
other customer and the barman exchange a few words, then the man
raises his glass over to me with a weary smile.

The old bar hasn't changed in a hundred years, it is one of those time-
warped worlds one can so easily find about Kilkenny. My companion
lights a cigarette from the butt of the one about to finish. A full pint is
placed before him, which he contemplates lovingly before tasting. The
Guinness gives him a white lip and the expression of a mad man. He
wipes away the froth with the side of his hand. I promised Mary I would
be out there this evening, it will be a long enough drive either way.

A pale, poorly-dressed woman enters with a baby in her arms and a
young girl clutching her long skirt. She whispers into the man's ear. He,
obviously annoying, shakes his head. The little desperado of a girl comes
over and boldly stares up close at me. The snotty and foul-smelling baby
needs a good wash. The baby starts to cry loudly, the woman begins tug-
ging at the man's arm, but he brushes her away.

"No!" he shouts.

There are tears in the woman's eyes as she calls over to the girl, takes
her hand and leaves. The ghost of Bridget O'Donnell and her children is
there when they've gone. Then I'm offered a gesture of embarrassment
from my fellow customer: that's women for you, what is a man supposed
to do? For old Ireland was here again just now and as so often in the past,
had to quickly leave, heartbroken and tearful. With gracious expertise the

barman pulls another pint for him, there will be forgetfullness in alcohol's deceitful oblivion.

* * *

Passing Poe and Kiely solicitors in the dead of night, my thoughts turn to David Kiely, a Dracula-like keeper of the sinister Langrishe black box. A light is on in David's office and an awful, skeletal silhouette appears behind the drawn curtains. Why did he raise up his hands as though not wanting to know? Awful secrets are hidden there. Unimaginable ones.

I throw myself onto the bed and am awakened from troubled dreams by a knock on the door. Teresa, Peter's girlfriend, is on the landing.

"Have you a cup of milk? Peter's hopeless. We've none?"

"No Teresa, unless you want it sour."

She laughs giddy, a lithesome Kilkenny colleen on fire. "We'll drink it black then, not a bit of bother."

She's for the taking there, I would say: do go carefully Teresa, it could all be over in a minute or two. She saunters back to Peter's flat, with a devil-may-care, hoot of a look and a see-if-I care backward glance. She is crossing her Rubicon.

* * *

I am in the workshop feeling guilty; I should have been with Mary yesterday. I hear voices, a murmuring swarm of bees coming this way, led by Wiliam Walsh and Paul Hogan, who are in lively conversation. I recognise the suave Louis le Brocquy and hedgehog-mannered Montgomery; there's also the lovely Anna Rose; the young Smithwick; Sowersby, dog sad, and someone I've never seen him before who looks German. Like an afterthought Seamus Butler hurrues to catch up with the group. They stop outside, no, not today thank God. But then the foreign one with Walsh now points towards me and, yes, he's coming over.

Bertrand Binggeli is a jeweller from Switzerland, Walsh has brought him along to see what he thinks of the workshop, Bertrand explains to me in stilted English. He seems pleasant enough, about my age. With a faint nodding smile, our visitor acknowledges Peter and John.

"You give small piece silver."

"Whatever you need Bertrand."

"Have three or four millimetre thick, yes?"

What's that now? Say an eighth of an inch? I give it to him.

"Dat is got and piercing saw too, yes."

"There you are." I lay the saw on the empty bench where he has seated himself. Peter and John are watching his every move. Is this a foretaste of the future? Kilkenny is nothing permanent. We are just passing through. The house, the house... Do you think we'll ever get to live in it? said she.

Bertrand soon forges up a simple pendant with the raising hammer, which is clever. Then glancing at his instantly recognizable Patek Philippe watch, "Must go, Walsh take back Dublin." Without another word he's off.

"What was all that about?" Peter asks.

"I suppose they'll hardly leave us like this for long, they'll be looking for a wide variety of talent, with a strong Scandinavian flavour. Maybe they've offered him a job."

"Well I'm not fooled by him, this is his little party piece he's made many times before. He was trying to impress." John says, inspecting the pendant closely.

"I wouldn't be too sure there, these Swiss are perhaps the world's finest craftsmen, did you notice his watch? Swiss made means the highest quality you can get."

"Yeah well..." murmurs John to himself. Here comes that overwhelming disconnect, we are making these otiose creations, but I will enter a very different, stark other world this evening.

Is there any point calling to the Garda at Freshford to see what's happened, for surely the law will take its course and justice be done? Or will it, no harm to ask.

CHAPTER 24

It is the same Garda as before.

"Now boyo, there's no need of you to be concerned, this'll all be taken care of, you can be sure of that." He says this with a frosty look, meaning, 'be gone, this has nothing to do with you, for we'll deal with this in our own special way'.

Once more I am at these crossroads. I will always remember her that first night, disappearing into the darkness, into the black heart of Catholic Ireland.

"I was expecting you yesterday, you promised me, why didn't you come?" Mary's at the cottage gate, annoyed, her distress heightening her beauty.

"I was too tired. After work I had a drink to steady my nerves, then fell exhausted on the bed, I'd have killed myself on the road coming back late."

"Were you too drunk to come out then?"

"God, no Mary, just so awfully dog tired. How's Mam and Eileen?"

"Not good, I'd be worried about Mam."

"So what's happened? Did the Garda get after your man?"

"No they did not. As far as we know. With Nora gone, between the priest, his father and the Garda I doubt if anything will ever be done."

"That's awful."

"Sure, what can we do?"

"Will I go and see him; just to let them know?"

"It'll do no good."

"Will I give it a try?"

"I wouldn't if I was you."

"Show me how to get there then." As I would like to get a look at them.

"Are you really sure?"

"Yes."

* * *

Some miles from Clontubrid, I can see what must be the farm Mary described, across some fields. It looks disturbing; some sense warns me to leave the car by the roadside and approach on foot. Am I doing the right thing? Pausing to pick honeysuckle from the lane's overgrown hedgeway, I inhale the sweet fragrance, subconsciously preparing for the worst. I could easily turn back. No, it's too late as a large mongrel dog on the yard is aroused. He starts to bark, walking slowly towards me, stopping then forward again. There's a rusty hayshed, old outbuildings and breeze-block lean-tos. A large, oozing manure pit to one side of the yard makes an odorous scent, along with that of silage and sour milk

Worn tractor tyres have been split to make feeding troughs. A loud 'cock a doodle do' comes from a fierce black rooster with bright red comb. He is standing on the manure, warning those inside the dull, cement, square two-storey house. A scraggy York sow appears, with a squealing, skittish litter hurrying after her. I'm immediately reminded of Durer's, 'The Prodigal Son Amid the Swine.' The dog is snapping at my heels, this isn't going to be easy. What the hell? At a door, which I presume leads to the kitchen I hear voices, which are suddenly silent. They must be wondering who it can be at this hour.

An apparition from Goya stands before me: a very large woman in a dirty apron with a snake's dangerous eyes. On the table behind her, they're having tea: boiled eggs, bread, butter, jam and cake. The father is a Desperate Dan lookalike, the eldest boy a growing carbon copy, with his two younger siblings much the same. The girl by the sink, looks mischievous and interested in anything for a distraction.

"Do you have a son called Kieran?"

"And who wants to know?" she says, her tightening pie face signalling that she senses trouble.

"I'm a friend of the young girl's guardian. The fourtneen-year-old girl your son brutally raped!"

The daughter having drawn closer to hear, lets out an hysterical laugh. The father stands bolt upright from the table, with a sudden screech from his chair.

"You do get away out of here now, this is none of your business, they're a bad sort those girls anyway, we know well where they're from!" She is shouting.

"She killed herself because of what he did!"

"Begone!" Screams the father, "before we lay a hand on you, or you'll be the dead one if you don't leave!" Standing behind his wife, he must be near eighteen stone. The eldest boy has a stupid grin, as if to say what he did showed he was a real man now. The other two boys rise menacingly, ready for the show to begin. Having disturbed a wasp's nest, I should really run.

"You fucking bastard; my Kieran's a good lad, sowing his wild oats on them bitches who are only sluts. She was asking for it anyway!" The mother is wild and frenzied.

The daughter can't stop her hysterical laughter. Then as if in a preconceived plan, they rush out and grab me, frog marching me helpless to the manure pit and hurling me face forward onto it.

"Get out of that if you can; they'll never ever lay a hand on my son, you can be sure of that." She sneers at me murderously. I'm surrounded by prehistoric savages looking down on, an Irish bog killing from the iron age.

I'm in a ghastly mixture of cattle dung and straw, mixed with pig, and chicken shit. The warm oozing putrid filth will not let me get out. A sinners violent death.

"We see you again, I'll castrate you like we do the pigs, now get the fuck out of here, understand!" This from the violent, ugly, barbarian man whose family is out of an asylum.

"Look at you now," the daughter taunts me. "You're just a piece of shit. Kieran was only having a bit of fun, she didn't have to kill herself, they'd have taken care of her at Roscrea if she got pregnant." She makes psychopathic motions, raising her skirt and showing her arse. All together now, they howl in chorus with the dog.

I stumble out bruised and shaken, spitting out filth; my clothes destroyed. I limp off down the laneway to stones, catcalls and the dog chasing after me... Mary was so right! At least the manure was soft and broke the fall. This thought reminds me of when the Protestants threw two Catholics out of a high window, in sixteenth century Bohemia was it? The dung (or the angels, as the Catholics said) broke their fall, saving them. Plucking grass, I wipe off as best I can; the inside of the car will be destroyed but I can hardly drive naked.

Mary does a good job with warm water and an old towel to clean me, at least well enough to get me back to Kilkenny. Recounting the ordeal only creates more gloom, with Mary casually remembering, "I'd see all six of that family at Mass most Sundays."

Between Freshford and Kilkenny, I weigh the difference between them and Langrishe. I feel shipwrecked, that I've crashed exhausted on a strange shoreline. A letter from mother is waiting for me, with fifty pounds for Mary's wedding dress. This is a nice surprise and takes my mind off everything.

* * *

It is Saturday morning and Mary is excited at the prospect of getting her wedding dress made. I have to post a design to Paul P. Hogan, Irish Export Board... wait, I should say Coras Trachtala, Lower Baggot Street, Dublin. Dublin would be Baile Atha Cliath in the Gaelic and is there a translation for Lower Baggot Street? It would be interesting to find out. I could write both versions; better stick to the Queen's English, as he'll think taking the piss. The first language of the twenty-six counties that I never hear spoken and that Mary hates. I should maybe learn a few words and try asking the way to Tipperary or Freshford. Who knows where I'd be directed to?

The day is dry, dreamy and warm as I walk down to the Post Office. The pretty, little doe-eyed Miss Kilkenny tears off a sheet, lightly, licking it without using the orange sponge in the metal container. Four, three penny stamps of four green shamrocks in each corner of a Celtic cross. She glances at me at coyly, as I hand her a well-worn silver shilling with the crowned head of King George V.

"Will that get to Dublin by Monday?" I ask as she puts it away.

"I'd be surprised if it didn't now." She is smiling, as though to suggest it doesn't really matter. And I suppose it doesn't.

I look out to Parliament Street through the wide parted windows, where a sudden, ghastly apparition upsets me. It is as though a woodcut of Lucas Cranach or Tobias Stimmer's 'Mill of the Papacy' has come alive to haunt me. That same monstrous brood again of mother, father, daughter and sons. They are in laughing and boisterous mood.

Crossing the street behind them, I watch as they go into this shop and that, bold as brass, not a bit of bother. Sure, nobody knows what really happened and it's soon forgotten. That's the way it is.

Mary is sitting on the bench to one side of the castle's high entrance, head back and eyes closed, sunning herself. Her long dark hair is fiery from the hot midday sun directly above us. She is oblivious, at one with the mysterious, moving spheres. *All calm, as it was bright*. It would be a shame to disturb her.

"I've just seen the boyo that raped Nora, with the whole family; I nearly bumped into them." I speak quietly beside her and she blinks awake.

"We might as well forget about them now, nothing will be done." Mary is resigned. She gets up and takes me by the hand. "Come on, the dress-maker's shop is up William Street." She is anxious to be sorted, hurrying us through a gap in the busy traffic onto High Street, then she adds, more to herself, "sure, maybe Nora's in heaven, for aren't we all taught to believe that. Those without sin anyway."

There'll be no fancy lace and long white silk gown for this vestry wedding, the kind with brushes and buckets for the bridesmaids. Mary slowly fingers the cloth samples, eventually deciding on a plain white Donegal tweed suit, with a blue poplin blouse and the same coloured shoes, hat and handbag, which we will get later on.

The dressmaker is a kindly, middle-aged woman, but surreptitiously curious about Mary. She conducts a mild interrogation, with Mary seemingly unaware of it. She's never seen Mary before, is she from the country or city? When and where is the big day? Which school did Mary go to? This is a subtle fencing of words and the two are well matched. Mary is just ahead on points, having given very little away. Yet somehow the dress maker is aware of the true situation. Fussing with tape measure, notebook and pencil (which is in and out of her mouth), she asks Mary to come back in a week for the first fitting. And Mary's over the moon.

We walk through the crowds of the city; all life and lighted day into the parade.

"I've something to show you," I say.

"What?"

"Wait until we get upstairs in the flat, it only works in the dark."

Soon, we are back and I ask her to close her eyes and lie on the bed. "This won't take a minute."

I little nervous, she complies. "What are you up to?"

Drawing the curtains and changing bulbs in the side light, I switch them on again, yes!

"You can open your eyes now."

"God, how did you get that?" She sits up, surprised by the red light.

"I took it from St John's Church."

"That's terrible, if someone finds out, your name will be dirt!"

"The church was empty, I think it's cute, Catholic idolatry supernatural, mumbo jumbo stuff."

"Whatever you say, weird though to want that. You make me wonder sometimes, the Northern Protestant thing in you I suppose." She shakes her head, puzzled.

"Sure the clergy are the supreme thieves and beggars of all time, and anyway it's only worth a few pennies, they probably have boxes of them, cheaper by the dozen! And didn't the Constabulary with the help of a magic lantern on the gable of a house in Knock make the Virgin Mary appear? That was the explanation of the retired RIC Inspector!"

Her face is now becoming a mask, which scares me, then wondrously she shines with Holy light, a Renaissance Madonna.

I try to explain, "the whore of Babylon riding the seven beaded Beast and offering the cup of abominations to humanity, that's how the Reformers portrayed the Catholic church. Look how we have to behave to get married and how you were treated."

"I know, I know, but God I never heard the church described like that."

"The whore was wearing the Pope's triple crown."

"We women seem to get blamed for everything," Mary replies with alacrity.

"I'll get rid of it then, throw it in the Nore with the Aquinas book where it belongs."

"And my rosary beads." She brightens again at the memory.

"When it's on at night I think the Devil sneaks in."

This interests Mary, "what do you mean?"

"I'm not really sure, in dreams maybe... no, no, of course not!"

Opening the curtains, I take out the bulb, which feels strangely cold. Then folding it in the *Kilkenny People*, I crush it underfoot, as I would a woodlouse or poisonous spider.

"Come on into the workshop and I'll make your wedding ring, it won't take long, we might as well use a bit of leftover twenty-carat from the water pitcher; nobody's about on Saturday afternoon."

"But you keep until the day, for to wear it before the wedding would be unlucky." She is excited, but that positive feeling is entwined with caution.

"You'll have to try it on a few times so it fits properly."

"That won't matter and will you get hallmarked?"

"It's hardly necessary, but if you insist."

"Oh yes, for this ring I'll wear forever." God bless her to say so.

"Wouldn't my makers mark be enough?"

"No, it has to be hallmarked like everyone's."

"Whatever you want." She's learning fast, to know about hallmarks. It's nuisance to get up to Dublin for it, but feck she's right.

Doing a nixer as they say down here, I roll the thick, gold wire, which is as soft if it were pure. It does need annealing though. Mary is sitting cheekily on the bench, feet on the three-legged stool, an enticing effervescence of young womanhood in among the less savoury presence of the other two (or three counting Oisin Kelly). She is surrounded by half-finished silver and the debris of their cluttered working lives: cigarette remains are piled three deep in dirty ashtrays a near empty pink and white packet of Siúcra; there are the ever-present stained mugs; a packet of Barry's tea and another of Jacob's fig rolls and between them, the little wax pig. Leather aprons beneath each half-moon bench are covered with silver fillings and scrap. Hammers and files lay where they were left off, ready to start again Monday. All the tools of this mysterious craft of silversmithing and of making whatever Kelly wants.

Returning from the soldering stand with the gold wire annealed, I see that Mary's taken a silver beaker from Peter's bench beside her. It has a wonderful look and feel, though only a beaker. Peter's presence is within it, a ghostly reflection in every hammer mark, which is uniquely his own. The maker's mark in his beaker will have the new KDW logo stamped on. Designed by Louis le Brocquy, and recently arrived from Birmingham, ring size small, medium and large.A clear combination of the K and D in the W standing upright. It's a shame no one will ever know the real makers who tirelessly raised the silver up from the flat.

"What do you call this, and what is it for?" Mary asks me carelessly, holding up the beaker before her.

"It's a beaker... to drink from obviously, water wine, milk."

"And expensive."

"Well yes, handmade, hallmarked Irish silver, would make a nice presentation as gift, don't you think?"

"I suppose so... It seems a lot of effort though to make a simple cup." She puts it down puzzled, "all that hammering and expense."

"Maybe, but that's the way it is here now, silver will always sell."

"Let's hope so." Although she says this softly to herself, I feel a sudden stab at her remark.

"Wrap this binding wire around the finger you'll wear it on, to give me an idea of size."

Mary complies eagerly.

Then, cutting the gold wire a fraction, I bend both ends up until they touch exactly. Borax and solder, then file away the excess and round it up to near finger size. With a smidgen of scrap, so the Assay won't scrape too much or any at all for the assaying. I make out the docket, and hammer my mark on the inside of the ring.

"I'll post this away and have it hallmarked by the end of the week. It will be ready with just one more fitting from you."

"Aren't you the greatest?" She is clearly impressed, admiring the ring on her finger for a while.

"It is the simplest thing a goldsmith can make, so remember this day, when you're old and grey. The day you were in the Ormonde stables watching your wedding ring being made; no one will ever have a memory like it."

"How romantic," Mary says, embracing me. Those willing grey eyes indicate I had better lock the door. I show her into the windowless polishing shop where she exhibits no coyness here. With her arms around me, she presses firmly against my hardness. Turning her back towards me, she grips the motor sprinkles on both sides and leans forward. Lifting her pleated skirt, she presents her wondrous rear, awakened. I unbutton her blouse; a hand on each breast brings low gurgling sounds from her.

Rolling on the cautionary Johnnie, I hear the poet's winged chariot hurrying near, *while we may at once our time devour*. From starry skies I'm finally returned. I take the shrunken Johnny, place it on the soldering stand and torch it to carbon, destroying how many potential souls?

"They say there's a new pill coming that will make these yokes largely redundant."

"And that of course means they'll be banned down here, you can be sure of that." Mary, the wiser of the two of us, straightens her clothes.

"It wouldn't surprise me at all."

"The man in Blakes will have to change over." She remembers her trip north.

"Or go out of business, as you'll probably need a prescription."

"What Catholic doctor would risk his immortal soul, if the bishops say no?" Again this is well said.

"It's beyond understanding."

CHAPTER 25

William Walsh's chocolate triumph 2000 has just shot through the rear archway, driving on over and parking right beside us, Jesus Christ! Then comes Anna Rose's Sunbeam Rapier, with a badly damaged headlight on the front passenger side; she is always in a hurry, far too fast Kelly said, the lift from Dublin she once gave him left scars. And yes, Paul Hogan's Morris Minor follows closely behind. This is a convoy of sorts, all parked together up close to the workshop. Making a point, fencingus in, our escape blocked. The only one who ever parked so close before was Jack Lynch with his Zephr. Another early morning raid, caught in the act, red handed, no, no... what is going on, do they want?

Peter had been singing, *A Hard Day's Night*, but his voice fades and stops at their abrupt arrival. Surely they could have all come down in the one car? Taken unawares, I get up most apprehensively. They've reached the end of their eroding finances maybe? Industry and Commerce are anxious to know where Kilkenny's going. It can't be subsidized for much longer. Several clouds darken my mind.

With the briefest of courtesy, Walsh gets straight to the point. "Take out everything you've made so far, so we can see where we're at."

Hogan is steely eyed, Anna Rose has at least a friendly smile and, if anything, appears rather embarrassed.

"Give me a few minutes then and I'll have it all out in the next room; it won't take long." I sense this is going to be an Inquisition.

Kneeling at the lower drawer, I notice a large black woodlouse hurrying for cover across the orange sisal carpet and know fine well there's a nest of them living underneath. How do they get in? There's a lot of silver here, but not Kelly's and then there was the items for the New York World's Fair, not to mention the golden ephemera and I mustn't forget the lovely Princess Margaret's little silver rose bowl.

"You can come in now, it's all there apart from the silver and gold that was taken." I explain the missing items to them, while watching John nervously preparing for soldering.

The small room is claustrophobic and Anna Rose is going to smoke, the sweet Kent aroma an opium that makes me feel dizzy. We are into absurdity again, having gone behind the curtain of reality on the stage of life to the other side. I'm in two places or even more at the same time. What's going on out in planet Kilkenny is unbelieveable enough, but back here is stranger still. Their unconnected comments arrive as if from a hollow sounding tunnel. The silver is floating weightless, as they take it and put it down (clumsily). In spite of everything, no matter what they say, this is the best we can do.

So what is this and that for?

Do you think it looks right?

Well I'm not sure, for there's an awkwardness in the handle, the point of the spout is a trifle too sharp.

This is very clever, but I've seen something similar before, was it the shop by the Hötorget skyscrapers in Stockholm?

... and they go on and on, perusing the collection, making their speeches about seeking new ideas with distinct characteristics, inspired by Ireland's own rare and unique resources; balancing between the traditional and modern;selling to the most sophisticated and demanding customers

I have to open the window, to let so much hot air out. I was beginning to suffocate.

This is the moment Hogan's been waiting for. He chooses the graceful sauce boat (made from the one piece of silver sheet) and holds it before him, "how much have you priced this for?"

"Sure, none of this is priced yet, you know that."

"Not priced!" he exclaims in shock horror.

"Yes." Is he serious?

There is an uncomfortable silence. Shuffling and with indeterminate mutterings they glance at each other. We have the reason why they are here.

"All workshops will eventually be put on a self-sustaining path, paying their way, the silver as the first, starting from now." Walsh asserts this with slow deliberation. I'm surprised.

"And who'll do the marketing?" I dare to enquire.

"Well, Kilkenny will obviously, isn't that so Paul?" replies Walsh perhaps a shade doubtful, turning for confirmation to Hogan.

"That will be arranged; there'll be a shop in the stables and we're already looking at outlets in London, New York and Dallas, Texas. Anna will be in touch with the buyers of Tiffanys, Harrods and Nieman Marcus, whenever this is correctly priced and approved by Herlow and Ake Huldt. I think we should involve them." Hogan the clever apparatchik now, advises Anna, who nods, but I can tell she's far removed.

"So what overheads are included, beside wages and materials, to work out an hourly rate?" There is a momentary pause, for they haven't considered the question.

"We will supply you with that, it's not a problem." Hogan answers, he is a very different person today.

"What about prototypes?" I ask.

"Any enquiries yet?" Walsh looks up hopefully. For the first time I see a first chink of light.

"None," I answer.

"Well, it's going to take time, we'll jump that hurdle whenever arises and Paul you're right about Herlow and Ake Huldt, get their opinion on this so far." His forefinger motions to the much-handled display. "But you start costing everything now understand!"

This new urgency out of the obfuscating mists, it could have been discussed in a less sudden and heated manner, what is with them suddenly? Is Walsh a Don Quixote character tilting at windmills?

"What was all that about?" John asks downing tools, when they have gone.

"They want us to cost everything; we'll have to make a note of the times spent on each piece. Common sense really, with whatever materials and overheads." I reply in calmer state now I've had time to reflect.

"Kelly's as well?"

"Everything. But it's their job to do the marketing and you'd wonder how they'll manage."

"Time will tell." Peter pipes up with the obvious truth, barely audible.

* * *

Leaving the stables after work, walking down the steps past Haughtons, I see Anna Rose coming in the opposite direction.

She stops. "I really must apologise for this morning, their behaviour was confrontational and unnecessarily rude."

"They were a bit rough all right, what's with them today? Why the emphasis now on paying our way?"

"Don't mind them, Kilkenny is not a place to make any long term commitments. Give yourself two or three years at the most, they'll want everyone to move on except themselves. Would you really want to live in Kilkenny for the rest of your life?"

Mary certainly wouldn't, but then there's the house!

"Maybe not, but the whole Kilkenny Design idea, what do you really think, can it pay its way?"

"No. It will last as long as the Government is prepared to fund it, but will never survive like any normal business."

"Is that what they want, a normal business?" I ask, wanting to really know.

"They may well try, but it won't work without the support. Eventually, it could turn into a sort of agency for design advice. That would camouflage the financial shortcomings, you know, offering training and education to keep the grants coming. You'll never earn much working for them."

This is interesting to hear. "What you say makes a lot of sense; I'll always try to bear it in mind."

"It's what I've figured out listening to them, after all they're civil servants essentially, not entrepreneurs risking their own money. That's two very different worlds."

"Well thanks for the advice; this certainly puts Kilkenny on a much better perspective."

"Enjoy yourself. Enjoy the once-in-a-lifetime experience, working and living in such a place. From what I've seen you're doing all right."

"Do they like what we're doing so far?"

"Oh yes, very much, but remember Walsh is looking for..." She stops in midstream gazing up to the sky, "I really don't know." With a smile and a beautiful, dreamy, careless expression, she shrugs her tailored grey suit and delightful padded shoulders and the moment is gone. She'll soon be away with the summer swallows.

*　*　*

It's the Lord James Arthur Butler, Hereditary Chief Butler of Ireland himself, sixth Marquess and twenty-fourth Earl of Ormonde — to give him his correct title — approaching on Parliament Street. Do the locals know who he is? Or ever care? As a boy, would he have walked the streets of Kilkenny? Taken a carriage to St Canice's on Sundays in the last years of Victoria's reign? The only contact in passing, would be men doffing their hats and women curtseying to his father and mother, the Marquess and Marchioness.

Recognising me, he raises a hand in greeting. "Aha, the silver man, what, and how are things in the stables? Did you make many teapots today? Extraordinary, quite extraordinary, would never have believed it."

Crazy old fool, is he joking or not? I can't help but like him.

"A few, my Lord, a few." I give him his due deference, sure, it's only an act. He'd know the Langrishe; he's about the same age. What's there to loose, they are all from the same dying class, the so called aristocracy of old Kilkenny. Why do I even bother, is this becoming an obsession?

"Did you ever know the Langrishes?"

"The Langrishes, ah yes, Knocktopher way, be ages I last saw him, Terence it is now? The eldest was killed in the Great War you know. In the Royal Army Flying Core, bit of glamour in the air, nice uniform, high above the bloody trenches, they all wanted to join in those days."

"Is that right?" Maybe I should have left well alone.

"Why, why do you ask?" His eyes are alert. Too late. Am I opening the Langrishe black box?

"I'm marrying his daughter."

"Are you now?" He looks puzzled, "I was never aware he had one, just the two boys."

"Her mother worked up in the big house."

"Ahaa, I see what you mean then." He's certainly not annoyed or put out. "By Jove, he certainly did have a reputation all right, I remember. He was once engaged to that awful Barbara Cartland woman, the one who writes those silly love stories, with pink hair and yappy dogs, what. She thought the Shinners would shoot him and broke it off wouldn't you know!"

"I've heard of her alright."

"Terrible shame what you say, for the young girl, I can well imagine. One woman's enough for any man, what, don't you think?"

"Yes I do." Whatever he says, what.

"In my day in the castle there was no messing with the servant girl, and plenty of them were damn pretty enough, strictly out of bounds, what, and rightly so. Langrishe, the old goat, I can well believe it. Damned lucky the Shinners didn't shoot him, that sort of behaviour wouldn't go down well with the natives. I well remember when King Edward came and stayed with us in the Castle, he was supposed to visit them at Knocktopher, but never did in the end ahaa! Extraordinary, you should be marrying his daughter. Bet she's a real beauty, the crossing of the blood can bring it out, dark hair and green eyed ehh."

"Dark hair and grey eyed my Lord."

"Well anyway, good luck and keep the teapots coming haa!"

Then a few seconds later when he's moved on, a loud, "Pingo Pingo!" comes from behind me. I turn to the Marquess. "That was the name they called him, Pingo by God; it came to me just now!" Passers-by are amused at the old man's outburst, looking at him as if he's mad.

Well, well how very interesting, from his lips comes the tumbling dark of the past.

I return to the stables. What will it be this afternoon? Candlesticks or condiment sets; should I fashion a cute little mustard spoon to match the pot? Do people still use them?

Garry Sharpe the potter from Stoke-on-Trent acknowledges me, beaming from the far side of the crescent courtyard. He is a boisterous and friendly man. There is talk of a girl coming from Holland to turn native woods into various size bowls, plates and boxes with lose fitting lids, containers for many things: fruit, salad, sweets, to cut bread on. The poplin weaver is at his window above, floating high with Kilkenny's summer clouds in his lofty nest. There is the constant hummering of Canning's polishing motor, revolving three thousand times per minute. Oisin Kelly is making more angels and owls from clay and wood, just out from the lavatory, advising Peter not to go in for a while. The candle-maker's door is open.

"How's it going, Joe?" I call to him.

"Ah now," he replies, unseen from inside.

There are new designs for tea towels, printed cotton and curtaining, with newspapers reporting on woven bedspreads, textiles, Kelly's birds, silver and the many candles, a Kilkenny speciality, all paving the way ahead for Irish design and manufacturing. The stories are always positive. They must know what they're doing in spite of what Anna Rose said.

The large room where the horse's stalls used to be will have windows put in, facing out towards the castle, to display whatever has been made, for inspiration and for sale. They are advertising for a general manager and Walsh's accommodation will be ready soon.

* * *

Evening at Castle Blunden. Middleboe is dozing in the green shaded library, to a plague of German soldiers, becoming cockroaches at his feet on the carpet of his peaceful little Denmark. He wakes thankfully to the lazy, careless halls of Kilkenny.

* * *

Mam thinks her hour has finally come, sending Mary down to fetch the priest. He is peeved at having to enter her wretched cottage, no doubt thinking it is another false alarm. He is a dark and unsettling presence, as he stoops into Mam's tiny room with his kit of Holy oils. This is where the young Mary would sleep beside Mam in winter to keep warm. Little Eileen is fearful at what's going to happen, making me feel a numbness from head to toe. Mary's thoughts and dreams go far far beyond Freshford and Kilkenny.

* * *

I draw closer to John's room across the landing, listening to those recognisable sounds. Softly, I open the door slowly... no, no. I don't need to
watch.

* * *

I'm at the Kilkenny Club House dining room with Mother and Father,
which they observe as though tourists in a foreign country. Mother holds
up her glass to the light, automatically wiping it with her napkin, the old
prejudices remaining. But not from Father, who is disappointed Mary's
not here. He won't see his lovely Irish colleen until tomorrow.

The bee in Mother's bonnet still irritating her is that Mary is marrying her son. And where is she really from? The cicrumstances, indeed,
are clouding. His mind is made up. Men are so stupied where women
are concerned, it only takes a bit of leg, curve or look, and they lose all
reason. Nature's way. Suppose can't be helped. Some sort of title he said
her father had. Their way in days gone by with the servants. Going on
still here. Most were burned out. The seventy-year old Earl of Bandon
bedded with a young one, surprised by the IRA, who threw him out before
burning his castle down, and not all that long ago. They'll be married in
Kilkenny, at least out of sight. I couldn't attend a vestry wedding, imagine.
The cheek of them. And on her side, who'd be there? Embarrassing. All
their own way or nothing, those priests. Will make sure the children are
brought up the reformed way, the nonsense behind, whatever he signed.
Well, happy days for him anyway, with his future daughter-in-law. Youth
over age every time.

Father has turned to stories of marriages in India, when Mother suddenly grips my arm, "you are sure now aren't you about marrying Mary,
you can still change your mind!"

"Yes, I am!" I answer irritatedly and am then regretful, as it's only natural for a mother to question so.

"Of course he is, she's a lovely girl and you're a lucky man. Leave the
boy alone now, he's made up his mind, me too."

"As long as you're sure, I'm happy for you," she says this to herself,
resigned and lowly.

It's getting late, we are the only ones left in the dining room. The breakfast tables are set, we're holding them up. Mother leaves, weary for bed.
On the stairs together going down to the entrance, Father stops, fasci-
nated by the Spy cartoons, pausing at each one.

Having left him, I'm a little way off on a deserted, dim-lit Patrick Street
and I glance back. Father's a solitary figure underneath the hotel porch,
watching after me, raising an arm to his son. For he is an Englishman and

CHAPTER 26

"Must it be the Club House? Isn't there somewhere else we could meet them?" asks Mary.

"It's where they're staying, and is about the only decent place to eat in Kilkenny."

"There's the Rose Hill on the Callan Road."

"They're happy enough at the Club House and, sure, it's where we first met, remember."

"Oh I know, but I'll always see that miserable little room they gave me on the top floor, with only a sky light to look into a cold night sky. And me wondering was it my life to live like this, a skivvy for others. People will always take advantage of the poor."

"The Club House is quite famous they say, wasn't there a Master of the Kilkenny Hounds that rode his horse up the steps and inside it?"

"Is that why it's famous? For a stupid prank by an eejit like that, showing off. It wouldn't impress me," Mary replies sharply.

"Their sort had it all in those days."

"They certainly did and some of them still do." These words are even more sharply spoken.

They're waiting in the carmine-coloured bar, a place of profundity that magic October evening last year. Mary and I were brought together by a broken promise. The former Lancashire Fusilier, Langrishe, taking the Knocktopher girl, producing a beautiful daughter at exactly the right time to serve behind the Club House bar when I entered the room. Was it by preordained calculation, who knows? Mysterious fates weave a subtle cloth of many Kilkenny colours.

that is no bad thing either. 'Once more into the breach, dear friends, once more ...'

Looking from the flat's window, it is a clear night sky, where a fullish moon has a faint veil of cloud over it. To the bathroom, letting out a line of moonshining urine, making a perfect tinkling curve. I can hear a faint motor sound in the distance, one that is getting nearer. Opening the window, I see a terrifying sight directly overhead. An enormous black, swastika-tailed zeppelin is moving slowly, quite low, casting it's long shadow. I'm paralyzed as it disappears over the Marchioness Dowager's house, growing fainter and fainter. Where was it coming from? Where is it going to? It wasn't hugely loud, the engine was muffled and all the more sinister for being stealthy. Sitting on the bed, my head between my hands, I contemplate the awful predicament of my life.

Father's beaming, "ah, my Irish daughter!" He bear hugs Mary, who is blushing and embarrassed at his loud English voice amidst the crowded (momentary silent) clientele. Mother is calmly accepting of the situation now and gives Mary a gentle kiss on her cheek. Any staff watching the transformation will be bewildered and envious at Mary's new circumstances. In this hotel of dreams, how many have visited by its curious deceits and charms? Here is an inverted world like no other. The laughter of yesteryears, ghosts, smells, sounds of crying in the night and ecstasy too. Carousing huntsmen and good fellowship amongst their class. Memorable wagers laid.

On Mary's third night, she woke up terrified: the doorman who never stopped eyeing her was outside. I slip back to listening to Father's conversation... that de Valera was right to stay neutral during the war. I'm drowning under the lacey ceiling and buttery-walled, dining room. It was warm and cosily confusing. From the far table the cold, insane, blue stare of Adolf Hitler penetrating my thought, it's my imagination and yet...

Mary is so very striking, her beauty enhanced by the gentle shaded light, which is caught and danced with by the silver-plated cutlery.

"And how's the house coming along?" enquires Mother, somewhat dubious of this Kilkenny business, without wanting to say so.

Silversmithing in the abandoned stables of a penniless Irish Marquess, his castle falling into ruin, what is the Free State now?

"A bit slow; you can see tomorrow on your way home," I answer.

"Any trouble getting a loan?" she continues.

"No, the Ulster Bank were most obliging."

"Is the Marquess around?" Father wants to know.

"Oh yes, he was here only the other day, quite a character, very likeable. He lives in England though, was in the eleventh and twenty-first Lancers, their commanding officer. Haughton, his agent here told me, he was awarded the Military Cross during the First World War."

"So he wasn't murdered, chased or burnt out of Ireland?" Mother interjects.

"Oh no, the Ormonde's were well liked from what I've been told."

"Most of the eldest sons of the Irish gentry were wiped out during that first war's awful slaughter," Mother remembers.

"My CO in India and Burma during the last show was the Earl of Bandon, Air vice-Marshall — or was he an Air Commodore? — back then. Another character. One storey goes that on a train coming into the station, the passenger opposite left the compartment, seemingly he'd gotten off, but he left his case behind. So Bandon threw it out of the window onto the platform as the train pulled away, thinking he'd forgotten it. The owner then returned with much abuse for the Earl. He got the Bath at the end of the war for services rendered."

"The Bath, what's that?" Mary asks.

"Companion of the Bath."

"Does he share his bath with someone then?"

"Ah, no my girl," Father answers chuckling, "It's a military and civil award in various grades. Bandon's would be a gold Maltese cross, enamelled white tipped with little gold balls, worn around his neck from a crimson ribbon."

"Tipped with little gold balls," Mary says to herself, with incredulity.

Well may she be amazed at such an award. They cover themselves in such nonsense, tribal stuff with coloured feathers. It is more a kind of jewellery for the well-connected and foolhardy, to give them a feeling of superiority to the rest.

As the evening winds down there is no more to be said. For whatever reason, Mary's not going to stay with me tonight, which is disappointing and frustrating. Locking the car across from the castle, I gaze at the night sky. Astronomers say those stars and galaxies are so far away that what we see now is only how they were when the light from started to travel unimaginable distances, measured in light years.

It is an absorbing thought, so why do we even bother? I travel into the far away space of sleep, for Kilkenny could be the same as those distant shores.

* * *

Mother and Father call around next morning, they seem to be strangers, with the world splitting apart. I show them the silver, creations that have suddenly grown ugly, an absurdity of a fevered imagination. Mother is wearing the silver brooch wings of the RAF; Father a pin of the Royal British Legion. They seem to be impressed, Father especially, but Mother (I can tell) is thinking, is this really the way to be making your living? And now I wish they'd hurry up and leave.

They chat to Peter and John, asking for their thoughts on living here, where the ivy grows on broken walls and an exquisite sadness permeates the long summer evenings.

* * *

It has started to rain heavily, as I lead them to the house on the Glendine road. The site looks awful in the rain, those breeze block half-completed walls, with no builders around and not much for them to see. The story of Ireland; what on earth have I begun? An unfinished folly for years to come? The legacy of the man that worked for that Design Centre, do you even remember him, so many years ago? The words of Mary return to haunt me, *Do you think we'll ever get to live in it?*

"It's far too wet to get out, we'll be drowned, maybe when it's finished we can come and stay." From the half rolled down window of his Vauxhall Velox, Father explains.

Mother leans over from the passenger seat, "you take good care now." She is worried about me working in this strange and dangerous place. From where they sneak over the border to blow up and murder our constabulary; fanatic hearts have no compassion. And there is that fiercely controlled, almost universal, harsh Roman religion.

"Tarrah, tarrah then, away we must go." Light-heartedly, father has seen it all before. Life goes on. He rolls up the window and returns for what to him, perhaps, might be an even stranger corner of their United Kingdom.

* * *

"When's this wedding of yours, I am your best man, am I not?" Paul Hogan's abrupt call comes out of the blue. It suddenly hits me that the wedding is only a few weeks away. It may as well be himself as any other and I can hardly say 'no'.

"August thirty-first at eleven a.m., it's a good half hour drive from Kilkenny to Freshford, so you'd have to be on the Parade no later than ten that morning, where I'll be waiting. It'll be the simplest affair you can imagine, a marriage disapproved of by the Catholic Church, in the tiny room where the priest keeps and puts on his fancy gear, with the brushes and brooms."

"Ah, sure don't be minding them, they have to be showing you northern Prodies who is in charge down here. Sounds really gas; I wouldn't want to miss this for the world, I'll bring a hamper of food and some wine, we can picnic in a field somewhere if the weather's fine."

Hogan sounds lyrical, he really is that intent on wanting to come. A day out from Dublin, travelling expenses paid, to a *Ne Temere* vestry wedding and a promise forced under pressure. Great gas indeed.

"Any ideas for a week away after?" I ask him, "a sort of honeymoon you could say."

"Don't be giving me that honeymoon nonsense, especially from you. What about the Aran Islands? Inishmore, I was there last year, wild and romantic, with plenty of time for you'd know what yourself." He gives a knowing laugh.

"Where did you stay?"

"Kilmurvey House, get in touch with a Bridget Hernan there and she'll sort you out."

"Well, I might just do that, so we'll see you on the last day of August is a

Monday, on the Parade."

"And don't you forget the boys will be over the middle of September to see what you've been up to, let's hope they're impressed at what they find." Suddenly, Hogan is stern.

"The Scandinavians: Herlow, Ake Huldt and others, you mean?"

"Yes!" And the phone has been abruptly put down, without another word. It is strange how his last few words were almost threatening. But that's the way he is; it takes all sorts.

This Kilkenny is a runaway horse caught by the tail: let go and you're finished, hold on for the journey and eventually you will have to let go from mental exhaustion. What does he mean by hoping the Scandinavians are impressed? It's enough to make me want to leave, my mind being filled with such a riot of contradictions. St Agatha's breasts upon a silver salver, dripping blood on the parish priest's head is now a recurring nightmare; Aquinas's book, given to me and now hopefully destroyed by fish and salt water; Nora, floating dead in the green, mysterious sighing bog, under a pale moon, more beautiful, more sublime and more at peace than when living; unlocking the castle with those old iron keys to explore the huge echoing corridors and rooms of the once mighty Butlers, long since departed; guided by the darkest night into their estate office to take the Vauban books, which nobody was aware were even there.

One day I will wake from the dreaming, dreaming Kilkenny and Mary. From making this silvery nonsense, where certain pieces have disappeared.

* * *

Mary is well pleased with her wedding outfit from the dressmaker and with the other accessories we already purchased. She finds it hard to believe how much money I have spent. But the Aran islands turn out not to be such a good idea.

"It'll probably be raining and from what I've read it's a meaner, more barren world than you'd find around Freshford," Mary observes.

"Sure, we'll be together with no interruptions, whatever the weather and surroundings."

"Oh I know, but you did mention Portugal. And I was so believing we'd be going that I was looking at brochures in Des Mannings on High Street. There's the Algarve and the beautiful beaches between Sagros and Lagos with their grottoes and sandy coves. Kilkenny wouldn't exist over there."

"You remember the names."

"It would be a taste of paradise for me, with all their different foods, the warmth, maybe you'll take me next year, buy me a bikini before we go." She has the Devil in her eye.

"How could I refuse."

"You can fly from Dublin in a couple of hours."

"You've been talking to Des."

"Yes, he told me to work on you, they do specials and short breaks."

She really does want to get away, to leave Kilkenny. She's only been out to see the house twice and has a strange indifference towards it, which is disturbing.

There are wedding presents: a ceramic angel from Oisin Kelly; a blue and brown table cloth from Rolf Middleboe; stainless steel knives from Peter and John and a pink cheque drawn on the Ulster Bank, Ballynahinch for £100 from Mother and Father. The day was so far away, and now it rapidly approaches. The river of time is a precipitous waterfall, which I am about to fall over. Soon there'll be just little Eileen and Mam together in that wretched cottage. God protect the child, alone upstairs where once there were three, with only poor Kevin Barry looking down upon them for company. She can sleep with Mam, all heavy and wheezing, the room full of the odour of moth balls and camphor. Outside the dangers are lurking for the dispossessed, where so many children of Ireland are conceived by the power of the Holy Ghost. Like Jesus Christ was, without a living father.

* * *

The day finally arrives, it is photographed by the Nimbus A satellite, showing the British Isles and Europe lying in bright sunshine four hundred miles below its orbit. The picture is relayed to a meteorological station at Lannion in France and you can see Kilkenny and surrounding counties clear of all cloud.

Hogan is early driving into the Parade, looking carefree and ready for the fun to begin. He is wearing a greenish-blue stripped blazer and straw hat, which has an even more colourful band. It would be more suitable for an outdoor summer party than a wedding, but he did say it would be gas and if the church can mock in the vestry, so can we. I only hope Mary doesn't mind his appearance, for this is what she wanted. As proper as it could be in the circumstances.

"See what I've brought you." Hogan stretches across to the rear seat and opens a hinged hamper of little pork pies, rolls, a whole roasted chicken, ham, cheese and wine. "What do you make of this? Very special, my favourite." He hands me an unusually-shaped jar, labelled, *Burgess Genuine Anchovy Paste Laboratory tested*, painted on a red seal. *By Appointment* is written underneath the Royal Coat of Arms.

"My goodness me!" I exclaim.

"You spread it on the biscuits I've brought; it's delicious."

"Have to try it then."

"And an iced cake from the Tea Time Express, specially made for you." Hogan puts the red and gold lettered carton on the passenger seat beside me.

"So where to my friend? If you're ready lead on, can we stop for a jar and to prepare the few words I must say."

"There's a place on the way, so you follow. I'll need my own car as we'll be driving on to Galway after." I'm wondering what he has to say.

"Aha, you're heading for the Aran Islands," Hogan replies knowingly.

"Yes and let's hope the weather stays like this."

We stop at the *Three Castles*. I barely avoided an accident here once, after I almost fell asleep returning to Kilkenny and woke up just before the ditch. The overhanging branches, with their skeletal fingers had smacked the windscreen and woke me just in time. From our farewell embrace at the cottage gate to Rochester's mocking, 'nothing!' Kilkenny was nearly gone forever between the two in seconds.

The *Three Castles* is more a general store at first, than a pub shut too early. He'll give us a drink at the back, in the store room, on upturned beer crates sit waiting for a warming whiskey each.

"Where are you two gentlemen going this early, all dressed up?" The colourless, unshaven, overweight proprietor is in shirt sleeves and braces. He looks curiously at Hogan when he hands over the whiskies.

"This young man is going to be wed," Hogan answers.

"Another lamb for the slaughter then, you have my sympathies." He pointedly turns to me and gravely shakes his head.

"Don't mind him, it's an honourable state. I can highly recommend it," says Hogan as the owner leaves.

The floor is cold concrete, the crates are hard and unsteady, there are two black hens tied by their yellow legs in a corner that cluck low in pain and distress. Hogan takes out his tin of baby Dutch cigars, "here do have one."

I reach for one and bend to his American Zippo lighter; I've never seen him with it before. I must get one for the workshop; there are spent matches everywhere. Hogan rocks on his crate, enjoying his cigar. "I don't inhale, it's for the aroma I enjoy them." He gazes around the cluttered room and gives the poor hens a pained expression. "This is gas, really gas you know." Shoulders leaning against the wall, he sits, legs splayed out in front of an old poster for *Wills Captain Cigarette's*, then downs the last of his whiskey. Holding up his hand, solemn voiced, he intones, "it is my duty as your best man to advise even at this late hour, you can change your mind."

"Are you serious?"

"Yes, you don't have to marry the girl." Suddenly his crate slips and he lands on his arse loudly.

The proprieter comes in carrying a long-handled brush. "Excuse me now, this job I must do, are you alright?" He addresses Hogan, who is shaken and ridiculous on the floor.

Grabbing a hen by the legs, the owner places the brush staff over its neck on the floor, presses down with a foot on each side then pulls the flapping squawky hen towards him with all his strength. Hogan, still on his arse, watches horrified as the same fate is meted out to the other one. It is matter-of-fact and expertly done, the hens' bodily functions still twitch for the last time; the faintest drips of blood trail the executioner as he leaves with his victims.

"The man's a bloody savage!" cries Hogan upset and dusting himself. I help him get up. "Let's get out of here." We hurry out. I'm strangely affected by this reminder of the fragility of life.

We park across from Clontubrid Catholic Church, which is bold in the bright sunlight. No one is around, we haven't met the priest yet. I walk over to Hogan, who is still in his black Morris Minor.

"How much does a priest normally get for a vestry wedding, or does he deserve anything at all?" I ask, leaning on his roof looking down.

"A wedding's a wedding before the altar or in the vestry, a fiver would be about right." I can hear in his answer that Hogan's composure is fully restored.

"I'm giving him two pounds and ten shillings and not a penny more, considering the way they've treated us." I show him the sealed envelope marked Priest.

"Whatever you think. Sure, we'll be away before he can open it."

"Maybe this tarnished and worn Victorian penny I've got would be more like it." I can feel the old coin in the pocket. "When you think about them, they're the world's supreme parasites and infernal beggars. Thieves of the mind you could say."

"You could be right, but sure, it's a lonely old life, celibate with a lot of doubts. They get hooked into it when young and impressionable. Aren't the Prods much the same?"

"No, not to such a degree and at least they're allowed to marry."

"And our priests don't know what they're missing!" With a knowing grin he says, "have you got the ring for me?" I put it on the palm of his right hand, the circle of nearly pure gold."

"You made that yourself." Hogan picks it up and scrutinizes it carefully.

"Yes." What's he looking for?

"I won't ask you where the twenty carat gold came from. And you complaining about our parasite priests!" He glances at me with amused accusation, knowing full well it came from the scrap of the golden jug.

"God, you must have good eyesight to see the hallmark." As if it matters that I've been found out.

"We better be going, the bride will always be last," says he, getting out, crossing over to the church and opening the many-coated, brown painted double doors.

We sit together to the right of the altar that will soon to be denied us. It is familiar from the day I was here after Kennedy was murdered. Suffused by darkening browns and sulphurous yellows, I inhale odours of risen damp. I study the idolatrous statutes of Mary and Jesus and a heavily framed picture of Jesus on his way to be crucified. Slap it to them Jesus, suffering son of God, so you can rise again and your followers can blame it all on the Jews. There is the pulpit, where I can imagine the fox preaching to the fowl, using the power of words to charm his credulous flock, so as to better to pluck and devour them. Cromwell called these mass houses. Turning to a slight sound from behind, I cannot see anyone. Then a peeping head appears and immediately disappears and another, to the surreptitious, gagged laughter of someone hiding on the choir gallery above.

They are mocking Mary's vestry wedding, the child born out of wedlock, in common law *filius nullius*, the child of no one. Word got around then, they could have all known.

"Did you hear that? There's someone up there." I nod my head slightly towards the balcony.

"Don't be minding it, they're only ignorant peasants, culchies beyond the pale," Hogan replies unconcerned.

"Will I chase them out?"

"God no, not a row at this early stage, think of Mary. They're only jealous with nothing better to do, we'll be out of sight in the vestry anyway."

Behind that mean, narrow-pointed door.

Here comes a black-suited, stooping priest, hurrying over, business like with pen and paper. "You never signed this for any children of the union to be reared in the Catholic faith, sign here." He instructs me brusquely, pointing to the place with an adamant finger.

"I nearly got away with it then."

"Nearly, but not, and you did give your word, so I'm told."

I lay the agreement on the ledge before. He's not one for small talk and is clearly anxious to get this over. His intense, inquisitional eyes are boring into me, reflecting the fires of hell. So you're the heretic I have to wed.

Again, if good King Henry of France got Paris for a Mass, I can do the same for Mary. I sign the worthless agreement with a flourishing lie. The priest hasn't shaved and I notice the small piece of Silver Shred gollywog marmalade on his upper lip from breakfast. Will he even bother changing into the proper gear?

As the sun comes out from a threatening priest-black cloud, Mary enters, glorious in white, touched with sapphire blue. She is followed in their shabby best by Mam and little Eileen. The girl is bewildered and smiling nervously, knowing full well that within an hour Mary will be gone.

The unfolding scene encapsulates old Ireland's twilight sadness: broken grey walls, lengthening shadows, superstition and the heart-stopping beauty of Sir Terence Langrishe's daughter, who is getting married today. She has been captured by the miraculous engineering of the human eye and Hogan's, "Jesus Christ look at that!"

Curtseying ever so slightly towards the altar and seating themselves across the aisle, I notice the eye of Jesus Christ shedding an ominous black tear. A fat fly is moving slowly down his pale, plaster cheek. And at least the priest has changed. He beckons to us all from the vestry doorway.

Mouldy, damp and cold, without a single idolatrous image, although the sharp ended fire extinguisher reminds me of a sinister Spanish confraternity mask, the colour of his crucified blood. It would be better to have the service outside, under the natural purity of this rare end-of-August clear sky. Just as I expected, we are sardine tight with the confusion of hedge clippers, a rake, brushes in jars of turpentine, paint, bottles marked Holy water, a special galvanized bucket (twisted mop end inside), a pamphlet about, *Marion Pilgrimages Shrines of Italy San Giovanni and Sorre* and ourselves.

We are a curious gathering of humans, considering Mam's first breath was the famine century, born when Parnell was still alive. Mary is full of excitement to be finally leaving, her future far from Freshford. Little Eileen of the sorrows. Because of her mother's unfortunate circumstances, Eileen has been forced to live in a harsh climate. Paul Hogan is years ahead of this world, pursuing modernity via absurd abstractions, with foreign-sources advising him. Eventually, he hopes that unique Irish creations will emerge from Kilkenny Design. Then there is the priest. Words can never suffice for the priest. All priests; suffering, abnormal men. A sudden faintness takes hold of me, as though I'm watching a bizarre and troubling film in slow motion. All turn towards me; get a grip, I'm getting married!

The priest's mouth is an orifice of rushed and barely concealed contempt for this mixed union. He is a serpent from the depth of iniquity, hatched from the rotten papal-coloured egg of Catholic dogma and superstition. Without any grace or good manners, with ill-concealed feelings, he gabbles the service. Perhaps too, he is overwhelmed by his proximity to Mary's exquisite womanhood, which is overpowering for any man. Is he undressing her, with his tell-tale mocking eyes? The normal solemnization of marriage has meaning and good intent, but not this travesty and insult. Still, all that matters is Mary's sweet Kilkenny-accented voice, wild and fragranced, saying, 'I will.'

We move to another small room on the other side of the altar and sign with two identical surnames, Hogan and Mam being the witnesses. Will I keep his money and give it to Mam maybe? No, I hand the envelop to the priest.

"Thank you father, it's not your fault having to marry us this way." Let's see what he says.

He doesn't answer or thank me, just takes the envelope and strides away down the aisle. Stopping half way, he turns with a fraught look. "You can see yourself out." Imagine.

Taking Mary's hand it is time to end of all this nonsense and walk slowly into the bright midday sunshine, the sky is still cloudless and wonderfully blue.

"If we head towards Durrow in the direction of Galway we should find a place to picnic, then you can be on your way to wedded bliss and earthly delights." Hogan advises us, winking. Here is the middle class Catholic, a la carte or lapsed, standing out amongst these rural Celtic Catholic peasants, holders of the old faith through years of persecution and discrimination. What does he really think? All I know is that he wouldn't have missed this for the world.

We'll be away now Mary and you take good care, I'll pray for you and all the happiness you deserve." Mam embraces Mary, with little Eileen tearful at the parting. I feel a darting pain for this poor child of no one. Mary consoles her, "I'll be back again soon and you're not to be worrying."

No doubt those in the choir gallery will spread the word. There is just the old woman and a growing girl now. Fair game for farmer's sons to hunt.

Watching them slowly and sadly walk towards the enchanted laneway, which is overgrown on late summer's thick greenery. Hogan silent and confused, gazing after them. Outside the church, Mary has left ready a small brown case, tied shut with string as the handle is missing. There's really nothing inside worth stealing.

A sloping field by an old bridge over a tributary of the Nore provides the perfect spot. The Nore, Barrow and Suir all rise on the long Slieve Bloom-Keeper fold that runs south-west down the south central region of Ireland. Eventually these rivers unite to reach the sea at the broad estuary of Waterford. *To ioyne in one, ere to the sea they come, So flowing all from one, all one at last become.* As Spenser eulogized.

I fold out Mother's Royal (or Stewart) red tartan rug, supposedly we are related on her side. Or was it the Appin branch? A clan of considerable importance she once explained, traced to Banquo, Thane of Lochaber, from a Breton. He was therefore Celtic noble. I looked it up and wrote everything down: the marriages, murders and the battle at Hallidon Hill. Scotland is in my blood, skirl of the bagpipes, the, *Road to the Isles*. Nasty fellows those Bruce brothers, though, when they came to Ireland. There were dreadful scenes of plunder and devastation, perhaps even where we are picnicking. Could there be the remains of something choked in ivy the far end of the field?

Our choice repast is laid out by Hogan with almost feminine grace. Mary is seated regally, legs bent behind her and knees uncovered, sun kissed and extraordinary beautiful.

"Aren't you so very good to come and bring all this," declares Mary, wide-eyed at such fare.

"It's my pleasure dear girl, so much more fun and better than dining in Irish country hotels, yuk! This is glorious, fire away, help yourself, I'll open the wine with this yoke." Hogan screws the corkscrew in, the bottle between his knees.

By the river where cattle gather to drink are wet, trampled gutters. A large flesh-pale landrace sow is rolling in the filth, pestered by her litter, who are ever hungry for a raw and tender tit to suck. She gives a sudden exasperated squeal, flicking her head to signal them to go and leave her alone. Enjoy life while you can, for soon enough you'll be turned into one of these delicious pork pies. The air is a warm haze of busy winged life that I can hardly see: dandelion seeds float around us and there must be others, even smaller, from the lone mushrooms there. A red admiral butterfly, bright as an advertised meal, I welcome. But the bothersome wasp in Kilkenny's hurling colours, I shoo away. A lone pigeon is high overhead.

I suppose Hogan is under pressure from Walsh and naturally anxious that we will come up with the goods to satisfy whatever Walsh is looking for. He spreads a biscuit with his special anchovy paste.

"Here try one of these, they're orgasmatic." He presents it to Mary with a flourish; she is surprised. Taking a hesitant bite, she savours it for a while.

"I've never tasted the likes. Oh yes, can I have another one?"

"Good on you girl, of course you can." Hogan spreads the paste even thicker this time. "And yourself, will you try one?" He is most generous today.

"Go easy on the paste." I'm not really a fishy person, apart from the cod, but I take a bite. It is too salty, with a strong, oily, fish taste, which will stay long in the mouth. "An acquired taste you could say." I force the remains down and hope that the flavour will disappear with a sip of the wine.

"We're two to one then," says Hogan, impishly smiling at her. And soon the small jar of anchovy paste is gone. And so with our time here.

Thankfully, this Languedoc garnet-red wine and the pork pies dull my sensibilities away to a delightful lethargy that seems to last forever. I have a life of wonderment in Kilkenny's dreaming silversmithing. Savouring each mouthful, the pie is fulfilling, with its crisp brown pastry and jelly around the meat. Kerrygold butter and strong blue cheese on the biscuits make a wondrous combination. Our conversation is like bubbles that float, rainbow -oloured and transparent, reflecting inconsequential thoughts here and there.

We are booked into the Skeffington Arms Hotel Galway for the night. The feast has just begun. I am admiring Mary, who is finishing the last biscuit, fed dog-like by Hogan in the most unladylike fashion. She is unaware of the submerged undertones, enjoying everything, as she is entitled to today.

"A toast to the bride and bridegroom." Hogan raises his glass, with that sudden, peculiar, searching quick stare of his. It shows a disquiet, as if I shouldn't be here. It contains, too, the unanswered questions about Mary he is too polite to ask. Who was Mam and the strange child? Where did they disappear to? Lighting a cigar and lying on his back, eyes closed, Hogan blows perfect smoke rings. How does he manage that? Mary smiles over at me reassuringly. Then Hogan's voice becomes trance-like, distant and low, officiating at a strange initiation, quirky and weird. "They'll be here on the tenth, the day after you return."

"The day after you return," I repeat, oblivious at first to what he means. The Scandinavians, of course, of course. This wine, food and the fall of Mary's glistening hair makes me forget. "So which ones will be coming?"

"Oh, Erik Herlow, Ake Huldt, Peterson, Sorenson, le Brocquy with Walsh of course and myself and probably Father Donal O'Sullivan."

"The Jesuit priest."

"Director of the Arts Council," Hogan adds.

"Yes, of course, and what will they be actually doing, or looking for, I should say?"

"Well ... if we're on the right path, design wise really and it's good to have such advice from renowned experts. Coming from small countries similar to our own, we should try to emulate them, after seven hundred years of English domination."

"So what do you say yourself, from what you've seen?"

"The silver's fine, yes indeed... but there again I'm no expert, but look it, not to worry, we'll soon know what they think."

Know what they think ...

CHAPTER 27

I notice the sow and her litter have gone, which is disturbing as only animals can sense danger coming. Earthquakes, lighting storms, the Reichstag bombarded and on fire... Adolf Hitler could still be here. Hogan raises a lonely right arm from the car window and leaves towards Portlaoise, the shortest way back to Dublin.

"And this is where you saw the light of day," I remark as we drive through Roscrea.

Mary murmurs pensively, "my earliest memory is of an angry, pale-faced nun cowled in black looking down at me. Then, with the funeral of Nora, it doesn't bear thinking about. The sorrows of Roscrea are born and buried here."

"Wasn't Hogan the good fellow, to bring all that lovely food and drink? A gas man, as they say. You really liked the anchovy paste."

"Oh God I did. And you wouldn't be finding the likes of it in Kilkenny, for sure."

"I'll ask him where he bought it and get some for you. So how does it feel, being married now?"

"Wonderful, just wonderful." She grips my knee turning to me, radiant, giving me a big hug and kiss on the cheek. "Even though the service was a disgrace, but what care I, we're legally married and no one can take that away from me, ever." She says this most purposefully.

Coming into Loughrea, I suddenly realise that I forgot the Durex, God! It is far too risky just yet, I wouldn't be able for any children yet. And I'm not returning to Kilkenny. They certainly wouldn't have them around Eyre Square. Legally forbidden, they may be under the counter, but I will have to go most carefully.

The landscape has changed, there are less trees and those which are visible are blown over from the Atlantic, leaning over bone-coloured boulder walls that fence meaner soils and scraggy sheep. White seagulls above and the faint whiff of sea-salty air. This is Galway. Without Durex on my wedding night. Naturally, she'll have expectations but when we are in our hotel room I confess. "It'll have to be coitus interruptus for the next week, I left the Durex in Kilkenny!"

She continues to undress into a pretty pink nightie and slips without s care under the golden cover of the double bed.

"What nonsense are you talking? Sure we're married now so it doesn't matter, they're disgusting old yokes anyhow." She is so carelessly Catholic, without a thought for the future. An act that is over in seconds but the bawling consequences would continue for long after.

Drawing towards her, I soon forget caution and am as careless as she, greedily inhaling Eire's extraordinary womanly essences. Whatever will be and Blakes Surgical Supplies can go to hell.

* * *

Having forsaken caution in the night, I wake to a feeling of mild anxiety next morning. There's a full Irish breakfast waiting in the easy, welcoming dining room, however, a comforting haven to forget. The other guests seem similarly content. All life is a brief rest from the awesome breath of time ... outside.

"You seemed worried when Hogan mentioned them coming with the peculiar foreign names. Who are they anyway and where are they from?" Mary solicitously pauses, knife and fork at the ready, she could easily devour Dane or Swede any time.

"So-called design experts, which they probably are. From Sweden and Denmark. They sound a bit too academic rather than hands on makers themselves, I really don't know. Hogan and Walsh are certainly enamoured of them."

"Not a bit of bother then, you've done your best and if needs be we can always move on."

"To where?" I asks, as the shadow momentarily passes.

"America," she replies determindely.

"I really wouldn't have a clue about America, although there are some very distant relatives from the ones that left County Down during the early eighteen hundreds, by sailing ship from Newry to New Orleans. Mother looked them up and even writes to some of them."

"There you are, it needn't be a problem with contacts. Do we want to spend the rest of our lives in Kilkenny? As I've said to you before."

"Perhaps not, but I've only been just over a year here."

"All the more reason to be leaving," she remarks, a little bitterly.

"Well, we shall see after the boyos have gone, whatever develops, you could be right. Or we could move north and start like Harron."

"Still Ireland though. And didn't your Blake's man know I was a Catholic immediately? The Prodies up there are a strange and awkward lot, so different from the ones this side of the border.

"Like Mother and Father."

"Of course not, he's English and your mother... well, yes, I'd say yes."

"And myself."

"You know very well the answer to that."

Yet how could she know me? Can we ever know another person that deep inside?

"You could be pregnant after last night."

"Wouldn't that be wonderful!" She sounds delighted, without a care, as though it would be another step towards whatever she's looking for.

The Aran Islands are a dark line on the dismal grey, dipping horizon. It is raining; enormous seagulls wheel and shriek overhead, ready for the boat to capsize and provide an easy meal of floating corpses: with a tasty choice of eye, nose or ear to be plucked out and hurriedly devoured. Suddenly, as struck by forked lightning, I can clearly see the absolute absurdity of life in the raw. Human endeavours are devoid of any purpose or meaning.

Her breakfast goes over the side. She is pale and distraught. I should never have come to a place only fit for monks seeking illusionary salvation.

Finally, we disembark at Kilronan pier, where strange and sly men are waiting to take us by pony and trap over the protruding bones of another corpse-like landscape of petrified green. Clippity clop, cold words and a biting, heavier rain. To Kilmurvey House and a boney hand held out for a full ten shillings.

Large and made of dull cement, this must Bridget opening the door. She silently stares at us and for I moment I feel like an intruder. The house is shabby, but homely, with a sense that nature wants to tear it down. We are shown to an upstairs room, where Bridget explains the meal times and where we can find a shop. Atlantic vapours encircle the house outside, visibility is no more than a few yards, the recognizable world has gone.

No romance here, and yet, herself undresses calmly. She combs her wet hair, seated at the old dresser, the mirror reflecting her. I feel a quickening, wanting her. And I'm unable to resist; it's too late now anyway since last night. Protection and restraint are long gone with the wind and rain. In my head is an exploding, flawless blue-white diamond refracting and reflecting light from bright sunshine. The colours of the rainbow are in my head.

Exhausted, we fall asleep as one to a chorus of creaks, a shuddering wind, spitting and gusting on the loose window panes, to the sound of slates loosening, Inishmore sinking, seagulls gathering. I'm drowning in a fearful sleep with an angry sea covering me.

* * *

Solemn words are being recited somewhere. I listen, as though to a burial and I am lying six feet under, while a scarecrow of a priest looks down upon me. Startled, unsure whether I'm alive, or it is morning or night, I ask Mary, "what's going on, do you hear it?"

"It's a Mass."

"A Mass, a Mass where?"

"On the landing."

"With a priest?"

"Of course, there has to be."

"The cheek of them, waking us up to that!"

"It is a Catholic country you know."

"Let them be in church then and not outside our bedroom of all places."

Downstairs, *The Destruction of Pharaoh's Host* hangs over the mantelpiece and a cosy turf fire is burning beneath it. In the dining cum-sitting room are also images of God's terrible destruction of man and beast. *The Fall of Man*, is on one side and the other has, *By Babel's Streams We Sat and Wept*. The opposite wall holds, *Joshua Commanding the Sun to Stand Still*, and *Belshazzar's Feast*. I study each ink black framed print briefly and find upon returning to the hallway that there are more. *The Fall of Nineveh* and *The Triumph of Mordecai*. That latter event I am unable to remember from Divinity. Well, well, waking to Mass; there must be a priest still in the house somewhere.

There's a photographer here at the table with his wife; he's from the *Irish Times*. They spend their holidays most years on Inishmore. He is fluent in the native tongue and keen to show it, with a few Irish words tossed to Mary now and then. He is most knowledgeable on the history and sights of Inishmore, Inishman and Inisheer, but with a tasty breakfast before him, his conversation grows more and more disgusting with every open mouthful. The wonders of Dun Aengus, a huge dry stone semi-circular fort standing on the edge of a three-hundred feet cliff, dropping sheer into the sea. There's a well-preserved oratory built of enormous stones. There are gravestones; cross slab stones; the stones remains of a fifth century monastery; ring-fort stones; promontory fort stones. I soon realize it's really all about the stones, stones, stones and more stones, upright, slanting, spiked, defensive and prone, laid together large and small.

In fact, the whole island's a huge carboniferous limestone he explains, thrown up from fearful pressure below, broken off from the mainland by retreating ice and rising sea. Mary rolls her eyes and even the photographer's patient wife is becoming uneasy. I notice a small patch of blue in the sky out the window, which is nearly overhead.

There are hidden forces at work. I sense a mysterious substance moving in her now, becoming two, becomes four, becomes eight, becomes...

We venture out warily, like woodlouse under a threatening cloud, heavy as stone. To Dun Aengus, which we were told we must visit. Entering the huge, half semi-circular drystone wall I go over to the sharp edge, cautiously glimpsing the boiling sea far below. A feel a restlessness and sense the people who carefully laid these countless stones. Each was touched by a ghostly hand, protecting themselves with such effort from who? Fearful of mainland tribes? Did invading continental people come even this far? In my own way, I'm building walls of futile security: a house; a routine; money. Gold and silver walls made in Kilkenny.

Enormous herring gulls glide so effortlessly overhead, missing nothing. I read that they will eat anything, including the young of their own kind.

"Strange place this, maybe we shouldn't have come?" I say.

"Weird all right, but we are together so the rest really doesn't matter." She draws into me, not caring that anyone might watch, a kind of thumbing of fate. We find meaningless and complete oblivion as well as ecstasy, despite our diverse upbringing.

"We'll catch pneumonia, let's go." I break away.

"I don't care, I could stay all day here, forever." Her appearance is ethereal, sublime but it is now raining again and around us are the yelping wails of the herring gulls.

CHAPTER 28

Mary sleeps beside me, the gold wedding ring encircling her finger (alongside the little diamond engagement ring bought in Weirs), catching the morning sunlight in Kilkenny. We have returned from the island where the priest said Mass on the landing every other morning; I should have asked who he was and where he came from. There had only been a few other guests there and we never spoke much, just sighted one another at a distance during the day, like driftwood floating far across the sea. I recall the bewildered young man at Kilronan coming over to Mary, to touch her on the arm, as if to see was she real. 'The little gobshite', said Mary, startled. The question came to me then, as to whether there would there be lunacy about, what with inbreeding among such a small island population. The other islanders watched, grimacing at the awkward moment, their faces could have been from Goya's, *A Pilgrimage to San Isidroe*.

I suddenly realise I must get up. They will be here tomorrow. I get away on down to the workshop. There's someone talking to John, someone with the silver coffee pot in his hands. He doesn't move but flickers his eyes up sharply towards me on entering.

"And what time do you start work?" There's a threat in those words. He is youngish, in a sharply pressed suit with slanting pockets, made of salt and pepper Donegal tweed. Plenty of dark hair, parted to one side. "We can't have silver with a mark like this," he continues, pointing to the centre mark on the base. Staring at me boldly, he hands the coffee pot brusquely to me, without introducing himself or offering his hand. Then rudely, he turns and leaves, without giving me the time to refute his ignorance.

"Jesus Christ, who is he?" I exclaim, taken aback.

"We suspect he could be the new manager, by the way he was talking, Jim King is his name." Peter laconically informs me.

"Bit of a bullshitter, if you ask me, you'd think he was an expert on silver, listening to him before you came in." John speaks up loudly from the sink, where he is filling the kettle. "The centre point, what's his problem there? Imagine trying to polish it out? It would weaken the silver, ridiculous." When John puts the lighted match to the gas ring, it makes a loud pop.

"If he's the manager, then what's Walsh?" ask Peter.

"Chairman, I suppose," I reply.

"Then who is really in charge?"

"Your guess is as good as mine Peter."

There has to be a centre point when raising or spinning silver circles. Returning to this new development and a workshop of stale, familiar smells, I feel a sense of drift. Where am I going?

"What have you got there Peter?" I ask him.

"A medal."

"A medal for who?"

"Oisin Kelly. He wanted it in a hurry, just after you left, in silver, and there he is now." I glance at the St Columba School something medal, before Oisin arrives.

"Aha, our newly married man returns," says Kelly, raising a long arm in greeting.

"He knows what it's all about now," remarks John slyly, promoting Kelly to smile a little to himself. Coming over to Peter without further ado, Kelly takes the medal and examines it for a while.

"Truly amazing Peter, you've done a marvellous job. Maybe just a fraction more detail in the hands say and we're done; so any chance you'll have finished this afternoon?" This is plaintively said, with an expression you could hardly refuse.

"Come back around three." Peter is clearly warmed by his praise and wants to please.

Kelly replies delighted, "you have the humour on me now."

I go to the next room checking and laying out the silver for tomorrow; it's the best we can do. Behind me, their broken conversation and laughter drifts through as they drink tea and light cigarettes. Kelly is away to Italy next week, to the Marinelli Foundry Florence, to cast his enormous Children of Lir sculpture, weighing eight tons of bronze, twenty-five feet high, ready for 1966, and the Garden of Remembrance, Parnell Square. Eventually it will turn green. That's a nice commission. The mythological story is one I haven't read, but I know the children were transformed into swans. I haven't read anything by William Butler Yeats, not, *Easter 1916*, nor anything else of his.

Thinking of the Easter Rising reminds of the Assay Master with the Huguenot name. He was asked to design a commemorative mark for the fiftietch anniversary. I have a feeling of deflation. A nervousness when I look to the future.

A bowl of soup with Mary is all there is for lunch. She has tidied the flat nicely and we hear on the one o'clock news that Winston Churchill, approaching ninety, isn't well. I see her off down the Parade, where she walks gayly, shopping for dinner this evening.

"You'll be ready tomorrow when we call? And how was the Aran Islands for you?" asks Hogan on the phone.

"Rained most of the time, but an experience never to forget."

"We'll be down about eleven."

"With all the experts from Sweden and Denmark."

"Yes, there'll be at least ten."

"That many? Are you reviewing the other workshops as well?"

"Cursory only, as they have hardly started apart from poplin. Mostly the metalwork, as you were the first and there'll be a young German goldsmith coming in a few weeks says Walsh."

"A German, to work here?"

"I really couldn't say, nothing definite."

"And German."

"Yes, a German, Walsh said he was most talented. Where they met I don't know. So, we'll see you in the morning then, happy days." Hogan puts down the phone.

"There's a German goldsmith coming to work here, maybe."

"A German!" Peter and John chorus loudly together, alerted like dogs hearing a whistle.

* * *

A dish of Shepherds Pie flies from Mary, who has tripped on the carpet. It is splayed out before and she cries out with anguished for the destruction of the pie. This was her first cooking effort since being married.

"I so wanted this to be just right." Shaken, she cries and I kneel down to her.

"It's not important; a cup of tea and toast will do."

"There's a dessert of trifle and cream." Mary brighten a little, getting up.

"Wonderful, all's we need is toast and trifle."

"I'm so disappointed; let me clear this mess away first." On her knees, Mary works to quickly erase her mishap.

"When we've done I'll need to go out to the house, it's been a while, will you come?"

"I will," she answers deadpan.

The fading light of day dulls the old city into one of those awful dreams I get about Germans. Faces are a lemony pale, hiding of secrets. An old woman wearing a Nazi brassard has an enormous rat on a lead; bird-sized moths flutter at windows and lamp lights. A giant snail glides with sinister intent over John's Bridge, it's eyes on stalks constantly moving left to right; it doesn't miss a thing. Mary stares pensively ahead, her beauty dimmed, witch-like in this nightmare. Entering the Glendine road I park near my rash and mistaken decision.

"Well at least he's got the roof on."

"You've a flat roof!" Mary says critically. I should never have agreed to it. It will leak all too soon. There's an awful cement dampness to the building, as I wander silently from empty room to room. It feels haunted.

"We'll need to get furniture and all sorts of things. Wouldn't it have been better to wait before starting this?" Her remarks are a warning shot. Subconsciously, she wants to flee from her past wretchedness in Ireland. And I have my own growing doubts about Kilkenny Design.

* * *

They will arrive any minute. My work slows in anticipation and our chat become intermittent as we listen out for them. Peter is recalling how he fixed up a blind date for John Young with the lovely Danish girl who works in the loft with Middleboe (whenever he's there). Blew his socks off she did, but John was too afraid to ask her out himself. Apparently, this Danish pastry was a game ball, laughing at the idea of a night out with an Irish man. It turned out the date was a disaster, due to the drink of course. John fell asleep on his bed and was snoring; the poor girl was sitting with her coat on by the electric bar fire, looking at his hand-washed underwear on the railing beside her, in a state of bewildered consternation. Then Tom Eastwood arrived.

"Irish manhood my dear girl, there you have a fine example." Tom looked derisively at John and attempted to get him up. But he was completely out of it, the fool. Heading for the exit again at an early age. So Peter walked her back to Maudlin Street and he now thinks he is in with a chance there, maybe. Both Peter and my John are contemplating the Scandinavian girls.

Only now do I notice an orange that has been on the far window sill for days. A mysterious planet, out of nowhere. On one side is a beautiful olive-green mould, with a halo of white around it. "Who's orange was this?" I ask.

John looks up. "Must have been Kelly's he mentioned something about Vitamin C in his diet and brought it one day."

"Let's leave well alone, then, see how it rots for a bit longer." I gaze closely at the eerie beauty of decomposition.

Waiting, waiting. Listening to the light tap of the planishing hammer, of a blow torch lit for quick annealing. The Canning polishing motor is turned on, off, the mop changed and it is on again. John is a bent-over figure behind the glass partition, wearing a long white coat and mask, bringing silver to life by his polishing.

Peter fetches a heavy T-stake and tightens it in the long leg vice, taking the so-familiar packet of twenty Sweet Afton from bench, he empties one, tapping both ends of the cigarette and lights it with a Friendly match. Inhaling deeply, he places cigarette on overflowing ashtray where the smoke rises lazily, diffusing with that he exhales. Peter starts work, unaware that his is demonstrating to me his amazing ability at shaping silver. It is a joy to watch and learn from. Hammering, annealing, soldering and fitting, polishing and (Irish) hallmarking: silver, silver everywhere at the Irish Antique Dealers' Fair for future antiquarians, who will spin tall stories. "Now this is a fine example from the old Kilkenny Design workshops of the last century. You can see by the hallmarks, the letter W for 1964, not a lot was made there you know, and..."

A tall, fair-haired, well-dressed man is walking slowly along, searching toward us. With the murmur of the Inquisitors of Kilkenny silver some way behind him. They are so many! William Walsh is to the fore, then Hogan, le Brocquy, Anna Rose and the Jesuit priest amidst the Norsemen they talk so much about. Here they are, made flesh and blood, descendants of their fearful marauding ancestors. Walsh introduces me to each Sverige-sounding name, forgetting Peter's and John's. I sense a barely concealed amusement from them towards those they see as a generous, simple volk. They have been rceived with such kindness and limitless hospitality in a land where, of course, the Guinness stout is great. There must be a dozen visitors all told.

"This was the first workshop we established and this is where we're at so far." Walsh points to the two full showcases. I hope he will not want me to open them. No, twisting his fingers impatiently at the lock, I insert the key for him, turning it. Walsh slides the glass front to one side abruptly, "help yourselves gentlemen, see what we've made."

I suppose, being experts, they must take and handle the silver, but not everyone of them. Yet each item is inspected closely twelve times and half again, with twenty-four hands and a hundred-and-twenty finger prints all over the items. I suddenly notice the Viscount Mountgarret, nose squashed flat on the window pane, watching, his innocence and peculiar madness is intrusive. He's not going away. Noticed by everyone, it is hard to ignore the bizarre presence, which though irritating Walsh and Hogan, brings barely concealed laughter and smiles to the other visitors.

It is mostly rheumy-eyed Erik Herlow, despite coughing a lot, who does the talking. Ake Huldt joins in, a large unlit cigar in his hand, which he uses as a conductor's baton, to emphasise every word. They are rather academically spoken. The presence of Mountgarret, who is determined to stay as a ragged reminder of the other Ireland, takes the raw edge off the seriousness. It's a kind of, 'Begorah, we're Irish you know and things are never quite what they seem here.' I think it strange that Walsh doesn't get one of us to ask Mountgarret to leave.

The comments of the experts are dizzying. Do they want something more in keeping with nature's subtle curves? Nature, the supreme designer. Observe the branches of a tree joining it's trunk. Give full expression to the softness and malleability of silver, let it lead to sympathetic forms of growth, including the correct properties of balance and just the right amount of decoration, if any. It seems to me that they are speaking from ivory towers and have a general lack of understanding of the craft, as practised in Ireland. They continue, talking about the need to use strong indigenous shapes, organic structures whose genesis comes from good draughtsmanship, which is an important factor. Silver being an important contributor of excellence among the traditional crafts.

Walsh and Hogan on fire, glancing at me as if to say: are you listening? I feel a strong impulse to walk out, never to return.

McCarthy from Industry and Commerce, along with the priest, the painter, (Walsh and Hogan of course), all effusively agree with whatever is said. In other words, everyone but Anna Rose.

As they begin to leave, Ake Huldt, the professor with a string of qualifications after his name, stops beside me. "You know a good cigar twisted at arms-length should sound like a naked native girl, rolling in long hot grass. He does likewise with his. "You're doing just fine." He gives me a wink and friendly smile, touching me on the shoulder.

Hogan is the last out, "And who was that fucking eejit at the window? A friend of yours?" Hogan picks up a silver letter opener and pulls it across his throat in a weird and threatening gesture toward Mountgarret. Our Viscount pulls back startled. Hogan laughs. "It's only a joke!" He throws the silver back on the bench, hurrying away to catch up with the rest. He is wearing a very different hat on today than on our wedding day.

"Crazy man that Hogan," John remarks shaking his head. "What does he actually do?"

"He's an apparatchik, John."

"A what?"

"An apparatchik."

"What does it mean?"

"Some sort of communist administrator, I think."

"How do you spell it?"

"Probably just the way it sounds."

"An interesting word, never heard before, must look it up. Now we know Peter, Hogan's an apparatchik." John calls over to his friend, rising slightly from his stool with a perfectly timed fart.

"So what do you say to all that Scandinavian verbiage then gentlemen?" I begin to put the silver away, which has been scattered everywhere.

"Makes a lot sense design-wise, but it would be expensive to produce if they're going to pay silversmiths decent wages. And is there really a market for it here? Or even abroad, with the hand-made in Ireland malarkey?" asks John.

"Sure, in time we could even be selling silver to Sweden, rather than just beer and crabs." Peter is amused, remembering Huldt's remarks about Guiness.

"You'd wonder though, if they've actually done any silversmithing themselves," John muses to himself.

Peter looks at me. "So, where do we go after this?"

"Carry on as before Peter and be sure to keep time on each piece you make, Hogan did mention that a buyer was coming from Harrods."

CHAPTER 29

In the evening, Mary and I discuss the events of the day. The names of the visitors from across the sea and their names. Mary remembers the few lines she learnt at school:

"Bitter and wild is the wind to-night. Tossing the tresses of the sea to white. On such a night as this I feel at ease; Fierce Northmen only course quiet seas."

"Goodness me, where did you learn that?"

"Gill and Macmillan, *Celts and Normans*. It might even be still there with Mam."

"You've a great memory."

"I remember far too much."

* * *

Jesus Christ, who the hell is this, striding most purposefully towards us next morning? Gestapo clothed, he is wearing one of those beautiful steel-grey leather coats, the kind Hitler, Himmler, Heydr and the others wore. It must be the German already. Tall, Teutonic, with the features of the master race; reddish hair and the most amazing blue, blue eyes.

He introduces himself as Hans Hasselbach, "your mister Walsh ask me to see what I think, make something small maybe."

"You're a silversmith then?"

"And goldsmith, mostly jewels, no so much larger silver."

"Where are you from Hans?"

"Schleissheim."

"Where's that?"

"Near Munchen, Bavaria."

Peter and John freeze at their work, his accent having alerted them to the fact our newcomer is German.

It will be like this from now on. Fair enough, what can I expect? I can't complain, it is what they want, a variety of talent for a year or two, always moving on. I'll never be fully in control again, but will be told what to do. As if they'll ever really know themselves. How could they? And I might even be told to go. I couldn't have expected anything else. They are feeling their way in the darkness of an idea. Whatever it takes. They are a decent enough crowd and mean well. I was largely left alone for the start-up, the chosen one, which was intoxicating both inside and out the old stable walls. The stuff of dreams. Is she really waiting up above?

"This is Peter and John." I indicate to each and he greets them with his raised right arm. A bit higher, it would be the Nazi salute!

"So what are you doing in Ireland Hans? How long will you be staying?" I ask.

"Three day, go back Germany then, maybe to work Kilkenny soon, next year?"

"Well, have a good look around Hans, the workshop is all yours. And what would you like to make?" Sure, maybe he'll never return, like the Binggeliane one; from Switzerland wasn't he?

"Where can I put this?" Taking off his coat.

"Just leave it on the bench Hans."

He lowers his proud Aryan head towards the bench and blows, a puff of dust stirs.

"Dirty!" He glances accusatorily at me, "Not good, for will hammer small into silver, difficult get out, microscopic, like polishing comet tails." He trails his finger over the bench, with a darkened mask on now.

"Here, give to me Hans, I'll make sure it won't get dirty."

I feel a distinct reluctance in him to part with the coat, but he does and I take it into the end room, my hands savouring the long, soft leather. I wonder how could a nation that made coats such as this ever really be defeated.

Returning to the workshop I see our new arrival has entered the polishing shop.

John, clearly disturbed, leans in close to me. "Did you notice his eyes, they're really weird, frightened the living daylights out of me."

"Bloody Germans." Growls Peter.

A sudden startled cry comes from Hans, who we discover transfixed by the rotten orange on the window ledge. "What is that?" His finger points, he is horror struck.

"It's only a rotting orange Hans, aren't the colours extraordinary? They change every few days, what do you think?"

"Nien, nien ... nien!" He mutters to himself, bending closely over the orange, contemplating it.

"Do you want to make something Hans?" I ask, as he leaves the orange perplexed.

"Yes! Have thick silver wire, make bangle; there will do." He points to the roll of quarter-inch square wire.

"Let me cut you a length, how long?"

"Twelve centimetres enough."

I offer it to him. "We only use inches here Hans, so mark where you want it cut."

"No centimetres? Most peculiar."

"Even more so, if you decide to work here Hans."

"Why you say that?"

"Come and find out Hans, it's hard to explain."

With a shrug, he tightens his shoulders, raises his eyebrows and gets to work most earnestly. Selecting hammers and stakes, he starts to forge the wire, stretching it from both ends. I show him how to use the various sievert brass torch heads and where to quench the silver in water or sulphuric acid.

We slyly watch this live shell fired from the Fatherland across the trenches, our heads kept low beneath the parapet. German thoroughness on display. He certainly knows what he's doing. September draws to an end, we are like the autumn leaves that soon will fall and blow about the Parade, blow by those whispering mournful gusts that swirl and toss us continually away.

* * *

What will the results of the Scandinavians' inspection be? And are they still in Kilkenny? It must be an interesting break for them. No doubt they will have amusing stories to take home, of how they were shown around the old city, to drink in dark and quirky pubs, listening to Walsh's ambition to have the castle renovated to provide accommodation for young designers. Up the high, ninth century Round Tower, the delighted Sexton opening the safe to the silver communion plate, laboriously explaining their eighteenth century Dublin hallmarks. Taken to St Canice's and those dull grey mail and armour clad Butler gangster tombs, thankfully forever quietened now. Parliament and High Street shop fronts of the last century with their Celtic lettering, found nowhere else but Ireland. Filing into the Club House and more drinks, warm and atmospheric. Upstairs wafts the scent of cooking, where they are brought to the newly painted primrose dining room. Lunch is served amongst a myriad of pleasurable sensations. Hotel proprietor Florence

Lee beaming at them. Everything as it should be, with a pretty young waitress serving them.

Hans' bangle takes shape, a clever design that will soon be ready for easing into an elliptical wrist size. As he nears Peter (who has been irritable since Hans' arrival), Peter, evidently bursting to confront him, matter of factly says, "you fucking Germans murdered my Grandmother during the blitz."

Jesus, Peter, what are you saying? Hans will walk out in a huff and snitch to Walsh, who's obviously impressed by him. Hans wouldn't have been more than a child when the war ended, but there again, he'd have grown up to be a good Nazi had Hitler won. Well said Londoner, he can't be allowed to goose step around Kilkenny. Walsh is well enough in with the Germans I suppose. The war wasn't Ireland's quarrel, the country was neutral anyway and we all remember how de Valera behaved then. Kilkenny Design is international and we had all better get used to this German. My thoughts are lively during the stunned silence of Peter's brutal remark.

"No, no Peter; I'm five years old war ending." Hans replies deeply offended, "The war was terrible. RAF bomb our cities flat. Mother dead, father in Russia."

"Germany's a disgrace, with those dreadful concentration camps where six million Jews were gassed, what sort of a people could do that?" Peter is not going to let up.

"Ah no, all this unfair at me. Look, I sometimes shamed be German, past heavy burden to bear, want me inherit their crimes?"

"You Germans worshiped Hitler." Peter is adamant.

"Er war ein schechter mensch." Hans resumes is work. A tortoise withdrawn to his protective shell, silent and hurt, no longer the arrogant Hun.

I put my finger to my lips and catch Peter's eye. Enough is enough. Peter's face contorts to a final, hushed, "fuck him!" And I hope no more will be said about the war. Then, as if by magic, out of thin air (I mustn't have noticed somehow), Walsh and Hogan appear in the workshop, which seems uncanny.

"Well Hans, how are you getting on?" William Walsh enquires expansively, beaming at Hans.

"Yes, yes, good."

"So what are you making?"

"Bangle see." He hands it to Walsh.

"Very good Hans, very good I like this indeed," says Walsh, with Hogan nodding effusively.

"And the workshop Hans, what do you think?"

"Could make better; wooden floor not like, needs hard, continual grey or black." What's he on about there? We only put that down last year; I much prefer natural wood.

"Well we can change that easily enough," says Walsh, eyeing the floor with some puzzlement. "Have you had a look at our silver?"

"No."

"Well do so before you leave, and let me know what you think."

"Yes sir." Hans replies obediently, although without clicking his heels or raising his arm.

Hogan meanwhile has picked up a large file and starts to poke at the sandbag, somehow staring at me mischievously, maliciously. What is he trying to say?

Walsh comes to the reason why he's here. "Our esteemed visitors have found the silver well-made and a good start, but personally I'd like to see..." He stops. Showing the palms of his empty hands, with a searching expression, as if not knowing what he's really after.

A solo performance of great expectations begins, mostly repeating ideas I've heard before. He's searching for silver that reflects Ireland's unique ethos.

I feel that by living in Kilkenny I've surely found a little by now, that will-o-the-wisp-the-wisp elusiveness. It needs only a brief sighting to be on the way, like a fox running for cover across the Freshford laneways. I've ransacked Kilkenny's past, including that night in the Ormonde estate office, stealing the French Marshal's star fortifications. I've taken note of the cupola on the front of the stables and of the Tholsel; of the floating, grotesque roof beams of the Long Gallery; of Kilkenny cats and the witch that was burnt alive. I've heard the *Rose of Mooncoin* sung softly by Mary and I've listened to those rasping crows making commotion above old Blue Beard's Knocktopher demesne. I've imagined St Canice's Round Tower lifting off for distant stars and galaxies. The rasping crows making commotion above all of Blue Beard's Knocktopher demesne.

My musings are ended when Walsh makes the relevant point that important buyers will soon be calling. Hogan has hardly spoken and by way of ending their visit, taps his foot repeatedly and pointedly on the wooden floor. As with his prodding of the sandbag, this action is most disconcerting.

Hans finishes his bangle without polishing it, then dutifully asks to see the silver we have made before he leaves. So together with John, we stand before the silver displayed in the two glass cases, waiting for his reaction. You'd think he'd at least have something to say, but no, Hans just stares for what seems ages, until I have to ask, "what's your opinion then Hans?"

His countenace is inscrutable and rudely, he does not reply. Instead, he pickps up his coat, with only the briefest of farewells.

"Do you know what I reckon?" says John, as we both watch him march off wearing that amazing coat (it must have been Wehrmacht surplus

after the war, or even his father's in the SS. God no, it doesn't bear thinking about).

"He's an arrogant Hun," I suggest.

"Well yes, but he's only a jeweller, the silver holloware left him completely flummoxed, as if he wouldn't have a clue about how to make it."

"You could be right there John," I reply.

"And like the Swiss bloke, he's made this bangle many times before."
John has the bracelet in his hand and is examining it closely.

From behind us, Peter calls out, "I certainly wouldn't want to work with
him, a German!"

* * *

Returning with Mary from the ill-fated house on the Glendine Road,
I drive through heavy rain. Over John's Bridge and slowed to a stand-
still on Canal Square, where the drowning, drunken face of John Young
suddenly appears at the window screen. Banging on the roof with desperation, he asys, 'will yez give us a lift out of this shite?"

Mary is irritated at having to let him in. John stumbles into the back
seat. He is a large man and reeks of beer and cigarettes.

"You're a decent fella." John leans forward with his unwelcome hand on
her shoulder. "Is he treatin' yez right? A good man yez have there, Mary
isn't it? Hammerin' away there every day, in them ould stables makin'
the quarest lookin yokes I ever did see. Jasus you'd be hard to know what
they are. Silversmitten thes call it, but, sure, it doesn't matter one way
or thother we're all fecked anyway, dya know what I mean? What dya
say yerself Mary? The light of this young boyo's life, yar Mary, what dya
say?"

I stop on the corner of James's Street, where he's hardly able to get out
and up the steps. John sways there for a while, searching for the key. "The
feckin key, the feckin key won't go in!" He shouts, turning towards us. He
can't manage the key because of how much his hands shake.

Hurriedly — getting soaked — I open the door for him.

John staggers in, with a, "good on yez boyo, well done."

Thankfully, he disappears into the corridor of his darkened consciousness. It would have been so much better for him to have started something
with the Danish girl instead of with drink. And that would have been
especially good for his liver!

"Isn't he an awful brute of a man, coarse and so ignorant," says Mary
disgusted. I don't reply, for there's maybe a grain of truth in John's
drunken ramble. The goings on in them ould stables, who knows?

In the small, dark hours madness enters my thoughts. Figures from
the last few days. I am bizarrely dressed as Punch and am surrounded

by gibbering conversation and drunken revelry (farting, belching and vomit filled with those intricate lies found in the books of Durrow, Dimna and Kells). I discover gold and silver by chance out of bogs, along with leathery, shrunken, half-human remains. As always, the lurking spectre of Hitler is nearby, only it turns out to be Hans.

Then I dream of Mary, begging for sustenance, drenched and fearful in thunderstorm and lightning. She is found the next day dead by the roadside dead, a mile or so from Knocktopher toward Kilkenny. A have a fearful sense of Irish wretchedness, poverty and Catholic superstition until I arrive once more at morning, to where she's lying right beside me, alive.

"I'm beginning to think we should leave." I say this to myself, awakening from the nightmares.

"What are you saying, leave where?" murmers Mary, eyes closed, hardly awake.

"Leave Kilkenny and move to Australia or Canada. America even, where we still have distant relatives down New Orleans way. God's Frontiersmen, George Washington called them."

"God's Frontiersmen, who on earth were they?"

"The early Irish Presbyterian settlers, with the Bible in one hand and a gun in the other."

"Sounds dreadful."

"Washington always maintained he could never have won the war of independence against the British without them."

"Is that so? Well, I wouldn't know anything about that," she says, still sleepily insouciant.

"Soon, I'll just be another employee on a fixed wage and told what to do by Walsh and Hogan, who mean well enough I suppose, but they don't really understand silversmithing. There's a manager, fellow called King, rude as hell here now. And then there's this German coming too, flavour of the month sort of thing, which is going to happen every so often. I can see it all coming and they're entitled to do it that way."

"A German," Mary lifts up her head, curious.

"Yes, a full strength blue-eyed one; he gave John and Peter a fright."

"You don't like them do you?" She is a trifle amused.

"Definitely not."

"I'm sure they're not all bad."

"Anyway, working here's short term; we should plan to leave."

"When?" Mary replies without hesitation.

"Oh as soon as we work it all out. There's no hurry, we have to sell the house first and keep quiet about it. I wouldn't want that to get out yet."

"Well I can't wait to be away from Kilkenny, I've no regrets at all." Mary sits up, full of energy now.

CHAPTER 30

Alone in the flat, I have a feeling the coming days will reveal all the answers. I'm on a careful path leading to an unknown destination. Not that I am acting rashly. I know this will be a big upheaval. Kilkenny is a virus which will have infected my consciousness forever. Outside, I can hear the sounds of the silvery, flowing river nearby. Do I want to leave? Definitely after King and the German. Walsh and Hogan I can live with. But there's Mary. I can certainly leave for Mary.

Where will we go? What shall we be? Am I an Ulsterman still? Well yes. I remember the old, defiant words, archaic, but still rousing.

'Twas the hand who gave the word when
His people drew the sword.

For the freedom of the present, for the future
That awaits.
O child! Thou must remember that bleak
Day in December.

When the Prentice Boys of Derry rose up
And shut the gates.
There was tumult in the street, and a rush
Of many feet.

There was discord in the Council, and
Lundy turned to fly.

For the man had no assurance of
Ulstermen's endurance.
Nor the strength of him who trusted in
The arm of God most High.

* * *

She's gone to see Doctor Purcell, but Mary's morning sickness can mean only one thing, I think, as sunlight intermittently floods the little room, warming and gilding a cold Saturday morning. I'm slouched on the armchair, my mind a whirlwind of possibilities about where we will go after Kilkenny. A worm has turned and it irritates my thoughts. Not a sound from Peter or John, the two Englishmen abed in this foreign land. There's a light covering of frost on the gardens and rooftops behind me. And yes, I can hear her purposeful footsteps on the passageway of this fiendishly complicated universe of time, space and matter (for what purpose does it all exist?).

I watch for the door handle to turn. Mary enters, glorious in her prime. I inhale that womanly breeze. She has a certain look, as if to say, *I have a surprise for you.* Seating herself opposite me, coy in the moment, she lingers. Perhaps her news won't be greeted well.

"I'm pregnant, you're going to be a father!" Apprehensively, she waits for my reply. It was inevitable after Galway and Inishmore; I knew all along. It is awesome though.

"God love you, that's wonderful news; let's hope it's a girl like her mother." I pull her to me and sitting her on my knees, embrace her.

"I'd prefer a boy any day."

I gaze into those amazing grey eyes as Mary starts to cry. She is happy, yet sad. Bitter uncontrollable tears from the source that is Old Ireland. I recall the near naked girl-child from a travelling family, boldly eyeing me accusatoryily, on the road leaving Kilkenny. What century was this? I've experienced so many brief sightings of Old Irelad, strange and disturbing, coming and going out of nowhere. This constant awareness wraps around me as an Inistioge winter fog spreading from the Nore.

A growing foetus now approaches through the same fogs. Floating ghostly white, pinhead eyes faintly emerge, tadpole-like, a mammal yes, but it could be anything yet. The dog, cat or pig on the margins of those weird illuminated manuscripts are all related, said Darwin. Her Kilkenny forebears though, are a sorcerers brew.

"Did he give you anything to take?"

"Ah no, he said it was natural and would pass in a month or so. I don't really mind now that I know." This is bravely, softly spoken.

"We'll soon be in the new house, for this room is far too small for the three of us then."

"I'm well used to it and, sure, we're much better here in the middle of town than way out in the Glendine without neighbours, fine house and all I'm sure it will be."

"Peggy Haughton mightn't like a family of three with a screaming child."

"Wouldn't you think your Design people would have thought about this accommodation problem long before." She speaks rather sharply. The worm turns another few degrees.

* * *

One evening, I take a peek at Walsh's new living quarters, as the builders are finished. It's as well for him, very nice, all spacious white walls and modern furniture, bold, colourful thick carpets on wide-plank wooden polished floors. Is that one of those famous reclining chairs by Charles Eames, if that was his name? Half hidden spotlights make a diffused and comforting light, abstract paintings are on the walls and on a table is a Kelly sculpture in copper green. I've got to hand it to him, William Walsh is the very model of a very modern Irishman.

The view from the windows are of the crescent at the rear and the castle at the front. I'm told Strongbow's wooden fort would have been there originally, after he conquered Kilkenny. Clad in sinister chain mail, his men would have been a plague, spreading with brute force and no quarter given. Settling, with dodgy grants of land given to them from Popes and Kings. Or simply taken by any means they could. Not that they were worse than the Irish chieftains though, the MacMurrow boyo who invited them in. They were always at each other's throats and I see now how murder and thefts have turned into respectability for their descendants: the jolly old Marquess and Baronet of Knocktopher.

In the Wilton Diptych a kneeling King Richard II is presented to the Virgin and Child, all celestial golds and blues, which come to us, floating across the swirling mists of time to. Richard stayed in that (much altered) castle nearly six hundred years ago and he must have known those original drum towers. There have to be some people still living here whose direct ancestors would have been alive then and who would have talked about Richard, just like Mam well remembers the visit of King Edward VII to Kilkenny and the castle as it is today. Likewise with the Design Centre, will it be a footnote of Irish history six hundred years hence?

* * *

Peggy Haughton is carrying a cardboard box under her arm, walking past the windows to the door, politely knocking and entering. "Mr Walsh asked me to show you these old candlesticks, to see if you can repair them?"

Did he now? I open the box to a pair of Doric style silver candle-sticks, which are dented and lean over. Made in the middle of the last century, they have barely visible Sheffield hallmarks of Lion and crown. Inside, they are filled with a brownish sort of pitch for strength and weight. They will have to be gently heated from outside so that the melted pitch can be drained, then straightened and the dents taken out. Probably, there is a metal rod up inside the columns. Then the collected pitch re-heated (it would have hardened in the meantime) and carefully poured back again. This is a difficult and dirty job. Peggy, feigning reluctance, suggests it is hardly worth bothering with. But quite aside from the force of such a demure female, I can hardly refuse a request from Walsh.

"When do you want them?"

"No hurry; before Christmas if you can." She smiles helplessly.

"We'll let you know then. They shouldn't be a problem."

"You're a gentleman," she says sweetly, touching me lightly on the wrist as she leaves.

"You shouldn't have taken those on; repairs are shit work, I had enough trouble with them at Vanders!" John speaks up abruptly, eyeing the candlesticks malevolently.

"I could hardly say 'no' if Walsh wanted Peggy to get them repaired by us."

"Well I'd have said 'no', you never can tell what sort of trouble you'll find with repairs, always beware of the lead."

"What do you mean John?" I am interested.

"Someone's been at them before. I once repaired a beautiful Victorian Crozier that was soldered together with lead without my knowing. The whole thing started to move when I began to hard solder."

"There's no lead on these."

"You never can tell," replies John knowingly.

Peter comes over, curious. He rests his file and carefully inspects them. "I'll do them, let's have a look."

John shakes his head. "You're mad Peter, leave well alone."

"These are Sheffield's finest, pressed and mass produced," says Peter, reading the hallmarks, taking the candlesticks over to his bench.

John shrugs, but we ignore him. Is this an important moment? One that conspires to finish my presence here?

CHAPTER 31

It is a leaden, wet, sombre, late autumn evening and I am driving out to Freshford with Mary, having not seen Mam and little Eileen since the wedding and wanting to let them know her news. How time flies. As I drive I consider how nothing is as it seems. Kilkenny is a deceit played upon my mind. I must try to cultivate a vacancy of purpose and value freedom from preoccupation if I want to survive. We drive into this Catholic crippled countryside and those horny old images of de Valera's Eire arise from my subconscious once more: the brief sightings of Hitler; the litter of pigs sucking a horned cow under a naked flesh moon; a strange sexuality that so disturbs me, somehow. Ragged boys and girls with no shoes on their feet; Dundalk just after the war; the smell of too many babies; turf fires and that sickly, sweet incense lingering in the dark corners of their churches. Churches whose interiors are lit with those tiny votive candles in red plastic containers. As voodoo and pagan as you would see around Haiti. Civil laws approved by God's one and only representative on earth, the steely-eyed, monstrous Pope Pius XII.

"What are you thinking? You're miles away and haven't said a word?" Mary asks somewhat perplexed, turning to me.

"Oh ... Ireland, you know. It comes and goes down here in so many ways."

"Ireland's the one place I'd never want to think about." Mary says this forcefully, looking straight ahead and far, far away, wherever that will be.

"How do you feel going back to the cottage?"

"I'd much rather not, only for Mam and Eileen and even they seem distant now that I've left. Mam was paid for looking after us, as you know, but even so she was kind and did her best."

"What will happen to Eileen?"

"She'll leave school next year when she's twelve, then God only knows what'll become of her around these forsaken parts. Pub, newsagent, butcher's shop and yer man there doesn't miss a trick, sharpening his knives for young fresh meat, you can see what he's thinking about. You could hardly count Mam to interfere, she always owes him ten shillings and more on tick. He's glad to get rid of his worst bacon on her. Then the wife goes to Kilkenny with the children on Thursdays, if you know what I mean."

"And Mam, eventually?"

"I think she'll be buried Tipperary, Kilenanle, where she comes from."

"God, you paint a dismal picture." I murmur this to myself, pulling up at the cottage, which is just visible in the gloom, with one window dimly lit, a million miles from fine silver design and Walsh's hopes for sustainable, highly skilled, small-scale craft production. I have mistakenly fallen into an alien landscape which I can never properly understand.

Mary taps lightly; there is not a sound. Are they wary of a young boyo outside wanting to see Eileen? The top half of the door opens hesitantly and I'm looking down to the terrified face of suffering young Ireland. Eileen's holding the bread knife, as if that would be defence against anyone.

"Why Mary, you gave us a fright, after what happened to Nora, praise the Lord it's you." Mam greets us. She is crouched, leaning to the fire. Eileen is still holding the knife, pathetic and far too thin. In this instant nothing has changed since the Famine. The knife falls on the cold stone floor and with relief, Eileen buries herself into Mary.

As Mary imparts her news, Eileen is so excited. I can clearly see the little mother in her. The sparse room fragments, flooded with Jesus and the Virgin. Time warping to peculiar dimensions. I have the feeling of falling down a bottomless well. It is an effort to listen and I see things that aren't there: the phantasmagoria that is Kilkenny, seducing me.

"Ah, God love you child, you're so young, but no matter that's wonderful news." Mam is delighted, yet her pleasure is tempered by her own memories of years ago.

"Is it a boy or girl you'll be wanting Mary?" comes a voice from afar, that of the innocent Eileen.

"A boy, but I really don't mind." Mary is not so much a part of their world now but hopefully our warm glow of happy expectations, gives them something to look forward to. Certainly, for Eileen.

"How you been keeping then Mam?" Mary asks.

"Not a bit of bother, just the usual aches and pains, comes to us all eventually."

"And Eileen how are you?"

"I'm all right, but I miss you so, can I come and stay with you when your house is built?"

"Of course you can." Mary glances at me, knowing fine well it'll never happen. Eileen's so terribly thin and Mam has a bad cough and there's an air of impending finality and hopelessness. I'm helpless to intervene.

Suddenly, I feel the need to flee from the ghosts of old Ireland that are gathering inside my thoughts and outside, here.

All the way back to Kilkenny, I'm fearful of the dark; skeletal riders laugh beside me before overtaking. Are the scratchings and tapings on the car in my mind or reality? For the Devil himself once appeared on the Parade, wearing his Tyrolean jacket and iron cross. I could hardly believe it. But it happened on the exact same spot where I'm parked now, at about this time. There's a light on in Walsh's rooms above, has he finally arrived?

* * *

As winter draws near, the sun, dropping lower, beams now and then into the workshop, giving rise to infinitesimal lines the colours of the rainbow from the polished silver. It is an aureole of radiance and splendour, a symbol of divinity and supreme power. No wonder it is drawn around the head of Jesus Christ and appears in much religious iconography. These little instances of transcendental beauty are of no consequences, yet are really most profound.

Planishing to a smoother finish, I make the scales of an enormous cod, which are the sequins of a glittering gown. This, I solder on to an overhanging base without melting the rim. Corking back the edge, to thicken each time the silver's raised. The image is, 'Hibernia Chased' and I have her on a chariot drawn by four galloping horses. It is inspired by the Decadrachm of Agrigentum, a masterpiece of Ancient art, the most riveting creation I ever did see. This is for Walsh, in the hope it is what he's looking for. Thus far, we have not had a single enquiry for prototypes, which is not surprising really, knowing what the Irish trade thinks we are, a bunch of overrated chancers and gobshites.

"Has Walsh moved in yet John?"

"Not that I know of." John replies absentmindedly, fitting a handle before soldering.

"I noticed there was a light in his rooms last night."

"I did see Seamus moving furniture up there recently."

"Walsh certainly knows how to look after himself, I had a nosey around the other day, it's a fabulous set up."

"He'll be right on top of us now." An omniscient observation from Peter, who is dishing a circle of silver on the tree trunk.

* * *

Clocks are turned back, another year and Kilkenny's slowly dying. I sense I will soon be gone and have only the memory of a surrealistic episode. It is like being drugged, a figure in Bruegel's' Tower of Babel, absurdly reaching for the Heavens. Once upon a time, long, long ago, in the County of Kilkenny, beside an ancient castle owned by a real live Marquess (entitled to wear his cap of crimson velvet, gold tussle topped, enclosed within a silver gilt coronet of silver balls and golden strawberry leaves), a silversmith came to work. He had a once-in-a lifetime's chance to fool the naïve and unwary, who were patient and willing to let him make whatever he wanted. So he made a rose bowl; candle sticks; a toast rack of most unusual design and, most extraordinary of all, a golden jug.

It seemed a great idea, breathtakingly ambitious, until eventually the party had to stop. Finance began to smell a very large, well-designed rat.

For December at least, I can carry on without anyone disturbing me. But soon Walsh will be here with that manager King, probably in the first week of the year. Definitely some time in January.

The heat in the workshop can become overpowering with all three of us repeatedly using the blow torch. And we feel no need to economise on the electricity, someone else is paying for it. Between the torch and their smoking, a clinging, sweetish acidic odour permeates the workshop. This smell, combined with the constant hammering, induces headaches and I have to surface outside occasionally to escape, pacing a few yards, around to the crescent courtyard, always acknowledging the owl-like candle maker through the window or by his open door.

"How's the candle making then Joe?"

"Not a bit of bother, can't complain now."

"Anything startling?"

"These round yokes from Kelly." Joe points bemusedly to the floor, at candles in a variety of sizes and colours. Indomitable, wary and all seeing, he doesn't miss a trick. You can't fool Joe. His is a manner developed over centuries, a means by which the poor overcome the vagaries of Irish life.

Moving on, I look up to the turbulent threatening sky and take a deep breath. I could hardly ask them to smoke outside, they wouldn't anyway. And the house is nearly finished: without a stick of furniture to go in. Mary was so right, not least because she doesn't want to live in Kilkenny. The monthly payments are much more than I bargained for. It was the stupidest burden to take on at this stage, I would need another seven or eight pound a week at least.

Returning to the workshop fog, with the added fumes now of Peter (an alchemist) melting the bubbling, smoking pitch, pouring it back into

Peggy's candlesticks without charge in time for Christmas.

Christmas. A welcome break away.

* * *

Approaching Dundalk, I can just make out the hazy, diesel blue mountains of the North rising faintly on the horizon. Crossing the border, I drive past squalid lines of muddy livestock lorries waiting, forms filled and stamped. The customs of both jurisdictions occasionally stop a car but most they wave through. Through the dreary villages of Mayobridge, Hilltown and Kilcoo towards Ballynahinch.

Would they have fled on these very same roads as I'm now driving on? The past dead are never far away; they rise quickly in remembrances. Handed down through families, in overheard whisperings, via the same hedgerows and trees, the same roofless abodes, the same air we breathe and of course by written word. 'Whole towns,' wrote Lord Macaulay, 'the seats of the Protestant population, were left in ruins without one habitation. The people of Omagh destroyed their own dwellings so utterly that no roof was left to shelter the enemy from the rain and wind. The people of Cavan migrated in one body to Enniskillen. The day was wet and stormy. The road was deep in mire. It was a piteous sight to see, mingled with the armed men, women and children weeping, famished, and toiling through the mud up to their knees. All Lisbon fled to Antrim; and, as the foes drew nearer, all Lisburn and Antrim together came pouring into Londonderry. Thirty Thousand Protestants of both sexes and every age, were crowded behind the bulwarks of the City of Refuge. There at length, on the verge of the ocean, hunted to the last asylum, and baited into a mood in which men may be destroyed, but will not easily be subjugated, the imperial race turned desperately at bay.'

There's a biting wind and bitter history outside, as I notice a peculiar crystalline and luminous sky, utterly without warmth, over the Mournes. Banks of ominous and freezing cloud will soon bring snow. At least the Mini is warmed from the firey strokes of Austin's internal combustion engine.

"Wasn't Newry an awful dirty sort of nondescript typical Irish town. Imagine having to live there," observes Mary disdainfully.

"I've never liked the place myself and always felt uneasy driving through it. For whatever reason; it's largely Nationalist you know." Momentarily, I wonder how I deduced this, as I never read anything or was told anything to that effect.

"Well you would, wouldn't you, being a Prody of sorts." Her comment is perhaps a shade cursory.

"Of sorts, that's about it. A Prody of sorts, well said." I'm a trifle annoyed but she's right really. I am a Prody, *of sorts*.

The red poppy wreath to the fallen of two world wars is on the Castlewellan memorial, where we go down the steep hill and take a sharp left turn at the bottom. Man and boy sit on the mudguard of the ubiquitous, grey Ferguson tractor, with a buck rake of hay and collie dog behind them. They wave to me.

Nearing Slieve Croob, where the three Laverty brothers live, we travel through a sparse mountainous land without much grazing. Their yard reminds me of a kind of Hieronymus Bosch scene, shades of *The Garden of Earthly Delights*, with their wandering pigs, fowl, barking dogs, and the Pope, yes the Pope, floating in the gloom of their kitchen. The family is always together, gypsy-like in their long tattered coats and brightly coloured neckerchiefs. The old mother is waxy and skeletal and nearly three hundred years old, still alive, still remembering that 1668 and 9 were terrible years that she will never forget.

The Laverty brothers are herding their sheep down to our fields, which they have rented for a couple of years. Jimmy Laverty one could never get over Father coming to Ulster: a Group Captain raising pigs was a matter of wonderment.

The familiar old homestead comes into view, hopefully, a secure and permanent Protestant refuge. *The Lord is my Shephard; therefore I lack nothing. Yea, though I walk through the valley of the shadow of death, I will fear no evil: for thou art with me; thy rod and thy staff comfort me.*

Two moorhens scutter across a disused lint-hole. Growing flax is a thing of the past now; it was back breaking work, Mother used to say. Old ways and lives are always changing imperceptibly and always speeding profoundly. It won't be so awkward for Mary this time, with them both having met the strange Roman girl from the deep South of Ireland. Mary was never quite understood by mother. What was it? Resentment? Wariness?

The pipeline from the Silent Valley runs beneath these fields bringing water to us and to Belfast. On one of the hills opposite was a ringfort once, which is covered with ash trees now. The other has great views of County Down, way over to Slieve Donard and the Irish sea at Tyrrella. I used to go there in sunshine and rain, aware of my mortality. Once, a hare ran up to me and sat beside me motionless, transfixing that late evening by moonlight into a my memory: it felt like I was in a sorcerer's tale of Irish life. In the distance flies the Union flag flying and as it is early July, I can hear the sounds of the Lambeg drums drumming, practising for the Twelfth.

"Well, here we are back in Ulster," I say, stopping in the yard. Mary, non-committal, smiles weakly.

The mongrel, white-whiskered old dog sniffs around the Mini without barking. There is a strong smell of silage. The back door is unlocked and nobody is inside: they must be shopping in Ballynahinch. An opened envelope on the kitchen table has a stamp with stars and stripes, postmarked New Orleans. I put the big, flat-bottomed aluminium kettle on the Aga hot plate to make tea.

Christmas cards cover the sitting room mantelpiece, some ex RAF, a few still serving I notice, from the little mulberry, the dark and pale blue coloured ribbons of the force tied on the fold of the card. My brother is building his new house the far end of the farm. He'll be married soon to a Rourke from Bishopscourt. The RAF took most of her father's land at the beginning of the war. Early one morning, he noticed men measuring his land, it was sinister that they had not even asked. His world was overturned when they confiscated it and eventually compensated him at only £20 an acre. Then it was concreted over and made ready for war. He did get honoary membership of the officers' mess though and all the slops of the whole camp for his pigs, which was pure gold in those dark days.

I put back the cards when Mary calls, "tea's ready."

The kitchen cupboard always has a large tin of various biscuits and cakes. I cut her a slice of the chocolate cake that I know she'd prefer, when I hear someone driving into the yard. The Royal Mail van's engine is still running, the postman's head is down sorting his mail. My fingers touch the golden letters underneath the Imperial Crown on the side of the red Morris Minor van.

"Letters for the Captain, there you go." He hands them to me, *Time Magazine* and another letter stamped with the stars and stripes. This one is marked St Louis Missouri. Who does he know there? Returning with the dog — he was waiting knowingly by the door to get in — I let him settle by the Aga. A warm hearth or stove is one of the few kindnesses an animal can get from humanity.

"I hope you don't mind spending Christmas up here do you?" I ask Mary, who looks somewhat confused as she sips her tea. The whole slice of cake has quickly gone. She gazes out the window, across Ulster's winter landscape.

"Why should I mind? They're your parents and your home." She speaks as if she really doesn't belong, as if she feels herself the wrong side of the iron gates leading to Knocktopher.

"My home is wherever you are." I try to reassure her, but Mary doesn't reply. Catching the dog's brown eye instead, he gives a few flicks of his tail and I go over to pat his head. Silence: man, woman and dog. Hopefully, her mood and lack of conversation is a result of her pregnancy. Somehow there's a sadness radiating from the kitchen of the old homestead.

* * *

Mother wants the child to be born in the North, as most Southern hospitals are run by the Catholic church and she doesn't trust them. For the life of the unborn is the same as the mother's: if complications arise they'd both be let die. The priest on hand, conjuring Acts of Contrition, Extreme Unction and anointing both with Holy Oils. Cowled nurses gesticulating around the death bed. A flock of malicious crows.

"Are they as bad as that?" I ask, having half-consciously listened and having let my imagination run on.

"I wouldn't trust them, Mary will be much safer having the child on the National Health."

I look over to Mary, who is having a boiled egg and toast for breakfast and who has been listening shyly, unused to such considerate deliberations on her behalf. "So what do you say then?"

"Well... I'm not really sure, but maybe your mother's right." Mary wants to be ageeable.

"But is that possible, with Mary being from the South?"

"Of course it is, you're still resident and Mary's your lawful wife, and she must come and stay with us at least a month before the due date." Mother is determined to have her way.

Father calls out from the next room, where he's been listening. "Best to be on the safe side, we'd be delighted to have Mary here."

Mary is hesitant to be away from the world she knows and seems bewildered at the choice being made for her.

"And you can clean the pigs out for me, if you're nothing better to do," adds Father, rather brusquely.

I would much rather not.

Donning a blue boiler suit and wellington boots, carrying the yard brush, I raise a leg in over the first pen. This one is empty and open to the weather. There's a little bowl near the floor where the pigs can easily press a leaver with their snouts for water. The moist, consistent excrement is of a uniform pale brown. They are fed from the mixed dry meal sliding container inside the piggery's eight enclosures. So unlike humans, who being fed from a wide variety of foods, produce the vilest excrement of all. I sweep it all into an open gully under the metal pen door, that leads to an enormous septic tank. When full, this will be hoovered into a muck spreader and spread over the fields. It is a great fertilizer. Each pen contains a growing litter of at least twenty pigs, their mother already pregnant again and gone from them. A strange pig put suddenly in with them would cause trouble, eventually it would be killed. The fist snout cautiously appears from inside, sniffing to check who it is.

Another pig's day. Always the same, in concrete and excrement, the only variety being the sky above. Nothing green or wooded to poke about in or to run joyously through. They are just waiting for slaughter and to provide Homo Sapiens with something to eat. This area is clean, as they hardly ever foul where they eat and sleep. They huddle together for warmth and the safety of numbers. By the time I reach the last pen, faint snowflakes start to fall. This will be a new experience for them, but not for long though The snow dissolves with their excrement, producing a more watery effect.

The cattle stand innocent and patient in sheds eating the face of the silage pit slowly away. Steamy breathed, gentle eyed, a variety of reddish, and black whites, they produce a creamy olive green dung, as consistent as that of the pigs. Mixed with straw for bedding, it becomes heavy and more solid, it has to be lifted with a grape and spread differently. A deal must have been struck between humans and cows, aeons ago. Look after us and protect us for a number of years, then you can kill us, finding our delicious joints to roast. Your ingenuity will made the inedible parts useful. Life will be short and sweet for us, but yours (mostly) will go on into the shipwreck of old age.

The corrugated, red-lead hayshed is stacked high with bales of hay and straw. It is occupied by a big, orange Nuffield tractor as well as various implements of only recent invention, miraculous and welcome changes from the horse and single furrow plough, which I remember Uncle using. Over the mountains, into the deep South, the making of silver hasn't changed at all.

CHAPTER 32

"God you stink, that smell is disgusting, get away from me!" Mary exclaims scolding as I approach. Disconcerted, I retreat back in the kitchen.

"Well I can't help that can I? It was a job he asked me to do. That's the way it is with pigs I'm afraid."

"It smells as if you've been with the dead; you'll have to have a bath."

"That won't make any difference, for it only sticks to your clothes." I take off the boiler suit and boots, leaving them in the porch.

"There's still the awful smell on your hair though." She sniffs me and I'm strangely disturbed by this for some reason.

"If you're bothered that much I'll wash it then, but's it's far too cold for a bath." So, what does she know about the smell of death, Nora, yes, no, well maybe, I can't remember. She was floating, submerged in boggy water, the tall reeds waving and tangled wreathed weeds about her pale face. Mary might well have detected a scent, women are more sensitive than men. In Berlin just after the war, where Father was following the surrender, the smell of death permeated everywhere. Hardly the same as pigs, although decomposition is much the same process.

* * *

In the morning, I wake to a pristine new landscape of brilliant white snow. Touched by the pale, golden rays of the sun they fuse under a silvery blue sky. The view from the dormer window is breath taking. Father and my brother are feeding hay and meal nuts to the sheep, who in this weather need assistance coming into the lambing season. Sheep have been on the sloping fields since time immemorial. I look at Father and think of how this life is a far cry from his airborne efforts to obliterate Germans.

"Come on, get up, it's a glorious winter's day, let's go for a walk after breakfast, what do you say?" Mary is still in bed, rising slowly on one arm, blinking at the reflected light. The bedroom cold.

"I'd rather not." She falls back on the pillow again.

"You can't stay in bed all morning; come on, get up will you?" I want to experience the new world outside.

"I'm pregnant you know, there's two of us now. Here, you can feel it moving, put your hand on my stomach." She takes my hand and guides it to the baby.

"God yes, that's amazing, the little kicks now and then."

"So don't be telling me to get up. What's the hurry anyway, I can tell it's been snowing, so why would you want to go out?"

"Sorry." I'm somewhat startled by the touch, thinking about the wizardry and stealth of nature. From fleeting ecstasy to another human being. Seemingly out of nowhere come responsibilities.

They're all down in the kitchen discussing the latest pig check, delighted the runt of the littler did so well, considering. Brother John gives a weak smile at Mary, with barely a nod of his head. The Hardy Greer maternity unit Downpatrick is the only sensible option for Mary, without a doubt, as I entered the world there. Whether it was a boy or girl was irrelevant then, but the number of Germans shot down that day was. That was the first thing Mother wanted to know and rightly so. She'd seen a Messerschmitt 109 turn around and machine gun a man descending by parachute, turning him into an explosion of blood and guts.

The Royal Mail van has barely managed in the snow, leaving deep tyre marks on the steep driveway. Taking the narrow road, Mary and I walk about quarter of a mile towards Hennan's entrance. It is an extraordinary transformation of the landscape. Out of all the trillions of intricate patterns of snowflake, there's not two the same.

"I don't think your brother likes me." Mary grips me tightly by the arm so as not to fall. She is wearing mother's boots, which are too big for her.

"Why do you think that?"

"He looks at me in a funny sort of way and has never once spoken to me yet."

"I wouldn't be worried, sure at boarding school we never spoke much to each other and even now he is much the same. He's probably gobsmacked by you, an exotic creature, Catholic and Tipperary born. The romantic Irishness of you, so different from the girls up here. Sure what man wouldn't look at you?"

"But you're his brother."

"All the more reason, he's four years older and born in India you know."

Nearing Hennan's, Fred appears on his Ferguson to collect the empty churns, left on the roadside by the Ulster Milk Marketing Board. Crouched low on the hard metal, holed sprung seat, a cap sharp over his foxy alert face, his animal eyes are mighty curious. I know his suspiscions. The Captain's son with a woman indeed and him working down South. Could she even be Catholic. An alert is sounding in his old Presbyterian, weathered head. He will have to find out who is she and are they getting (or are they already) married?

"Hi Fred, how are you keeping? Long time no see." His gaze fixes upon Mary, without replying.

"This is my wife Mary, we were married in Kilkenny last August." I introduce her with an arm around her shoulder.

"Boys a boy, I didn't know." Over the rattle of the unusual fitted Perkins diesel, I can hear surprise in his voice. Fred gets down from his seat, which was covered with a folded over meal bag. "You must be up for Christmas then and with this awful weather, it's a Christmas you'll never forget." He lifts the silvery churns onto the hydraulic buckboard attached on the back.

"So you're from Kilkenny, my goodness me." Fred confronts Mary closely, truly amazed, as if she's from some dark, forbidden place. "Well you know, I'm never been across the border once. They say Dublin's a fine city, that the lakes of Killarney, with Blarney Castle are well worth a visit. But I'd much prefer Blackpool most years around the Twelfth, when brother Bob looks after the farm."

"Ah, you must come then." Mary speaks so softly and sweetly, with a beautiful smile that would melt the heart of any old Ulster Prody farmer, bachelor man.

"Yes you should Fred, there's more to Ireland that just the six counties."

He ignores me, momentarily transfixed by her. A woman, the other half of the human race.

"Must away now." Turning abruptly, he gets up onto the tractor, puts his boot down on the familiar right-angled rod clutch. Into gear, pulling the little chrome plated throttle stick towards, his actions prompt the upright exhaust pipe to spew forth a burst of dirty thick carbon dioxide into the cold Ulster atmosphere.

"So what do you think of our Fred then?" We continue on, past McAuley's lake and the solid wee Magerhamlet C of I with the Union flag (fallen, twisted and wet) above the surrounding graveyard.

"I think he's weird, the way he suddenly turned and left. Did we say something to upset him?"

"He probably guessed you're a Catholic, coming from Kilkenny, and he thinks you've corrupted a good Protestant boy with your devilish good looks, with all that entails." I explain laughing, "that's the sort most of them are up here, I'm afraid."

"Why should he care?" Mary is none too pleased.

"Well I did have to sign that agreement, promising to rear any children as Catholics. He might be concerned about that, though it's a nonsense and meaningless for me. The awful *Ne temere* decree still haunts many Irish Protestants today."

"Why?"

"It means a gradual depletion of the Protestant population and a United Ireland by numbers. Rome rule — which you well know from experience — spreading North."

"That's ridiculous."

"I know, but it swirls around everywhere up here, a sort of hidden but constant worrying wind, low and moaning, a storm brewing somehow. It is inevitable, with their much higher birth rate and contraceptives a venial sin, or is it mortal?"

"The man from Blake's would certainly agree." Mary remembers.

"Well yes, but hopefully things are changing and Fred's really a very good neighbour, lending us whatever we need and giving a hand. Remember, it took nearly four hundred years to bake him into this creation, with many diverse ingredients, some of which you might even enjoy someday.

Screwing her mouth distastefully, Mary says, "I don't think so."

"Mother's uncle Robert was in the Ulster Volunteers of nineteen fourteen, when he met the *Clydebank* in Belfast Lough. That's where three thousand, five hundred rifles were unloaded and distributed for the fight to keep Ulster out of Home Rule for all Ireland. The top gentry were the leaders she told me. But his two were soon stolen by the IRA. And I've never told you this before, but my uncle George gave out to Father about marrying you. He said Father's influence was the cause and it was letting down the side. When the whole family came over from Downpatrick one Sunday for afternoon tea, an awful row erupted. Father threw them all out, calling George an orange bigot; mother was in tears. Father had to promise her not to argue politics and religion in the extended family ever again."

"All because of me. Will I ever be wanted anywhere on this awful island of Ireland?" This bitter lament seemed to come from the innermost depths of her being.

"Don't be silly, he should never have risen to the bait, you can't change people and history overnight."

"Well good for your dad, I think he was right." Mary speaks loudly and forcefully. I'm somewhat abashed; I shouldn't have mentioned the story. She's right. Snowflakes are starting to fall.

"Let's go back, I shouldn't be out here in my condition, this weather."

Folding her arms, Mary shivers and hunches her shoulders together. This was once an ice age valley. From the flint-hearted North Pole, the weather comes as a reminder that ice once covered the whole island, thousands of years ago. No life stirred, or was heard, but the cracking movement of the ice that created our landscape. It will come again some-day, submerging everything, along with the Protestant dead.

We warm out by the log fire that mother has lit in the end sitting-room. There's an Indian fakir made of pale wood, begging on the far wall. Here also is an ivory inlaid table, with a brightly painted, round lidded box. Which when opened reveals another boxes fitted into inside and so on, down to the smallest one, the fourth. On the bookcase are three black elephants in different sizes and two green ceramic horses from China. Among the many books is, *Mother India*. An enormous brass plate, intri-cately engraved with a peacock, stands beside a cow bell which hangs on a leather strap studded with teeth. The beautiful carpet underfoot comes from India or Turkey (or even Iraq, where both have served) and there is a heavy brass bell, clapper missing. Here too is a strange little box, holding grandfather's silver cuff-links, with a palm tree and pyramid on one, ini-tials on the other, each chain linked together. There is a sepia photograph of him in the Grenadier Guards, long-whiskered, wearing the tall bear-skin, standing beside Father who is desplaying his first medal, the India General Service, 1937.

Father's brother was a Commander in the Royal Navy, a lowly midship-man then, his best time afloat was on the China Station. Hong Kong and Shanghai were great fun, I once heard him say, it was a pity World War II had to spoil it all. He was attacked by kamikaze while on the *Victorious*.

"Are you all right Mary?" She is in the chair opposite and doesn't answer, slumped asleep. The stellar little stranger is forming inside her. Stealing over to her, I rest my head on her legs.

"What passes for religion here is a mockery!" I'm woken to father's harsh words from the corridor, on his way to the bathroom upstairs.

Why do women's legs in the dark turn me on so? Mary's skirt is way above her knees, so I can't resist kneeling down to the altar of old Ireland made flesh and she careless and drowsily wanting me inside her. No painted breasts or a silver salver fit only for priests here, but the real thing, with those Southern eyes open and wide.

Hurriedly, I stand up afterward; Mother's footsteps are approaching and she's no fool. Indeed, she was on the train from Lahore to Peshawar with the handsome young officer of the sixteenth Hyberdad Regiment, with tropical nights at Ambala in the Punjab where the Maharajah's palace was near.

* * *

"Who do you know in America?" Father is at his writing desk and this is an opportunity to ask him.

"We discovered that your mother has distant relatives."

"How did you manage that?"

"I wrote to the Mayor of New Orleans, a man with the Stewart name. One thing led to another and to this Dorothy one in St. Louis Missouri. Works for an exclusive jewellers and a pretty wench she is too; she sent me her photograph, here have a look." Inside an envelope that he passes to me is the picture of a generous smiling, glamorous middle-aged lady, standing by a paddle steamer called the *Mississippi Queen*.

"Could she get me a job? For I doubt Kilkenny will last." This comes out of the blue, without me even thinking about it.

"Why do you say that?" Father looks at me over his glasses, surprised, "I thought you were content working in Kilkenny."

"Yes, but it's hard to understand what they're about a lot of the time. For sure, no one's interested in silver prototypes outside the stable walls. The whole trade — what there is of it — thinks Kilkenny's one big joke. William Walsh and Paul Hogan come and go and then there's the Scandinavians as well. To be honest, I just feel uncomfortable with so many people looking over my shoulder and with wondering what they really want, as if they really know themselves."

"But it's a radical new venture for Ireland, something never attempted before and you were lucky to get the job. Give them more time and don't do anything rash, there's nothing for you here if you want to make silver in this Orange Free State." His last two words are most emphatic.

"America would be good experience, who knows where it could lead? I can always come back."

"You've a wife and child coming soon and that house you're building."

"Yes, I know, no harm asking her though."

"If that's what you want then. I'll sound her out with this letter I'm writing to her now."

* * *

Opening the coal shed door slightly, I can see the turkey, wary and worried, as if aware Christmas is approaching. It was suddenly taken from the diminishing flock, delivered at night, and put in the windowless gloom. That would put the frighteners on anyone. Head flicking sideways at the slightest sound, she is thinking that she was always so well fed, never alone, but what's happening now?

The executioner is coming out of the old byre, carrying the long-handled axe. I have to help catch and try holding the terrified, wing thrashing, struggling bird, which is no easy task.

"Put the potato basket over her, with the head sticking out so I can whack it off." Irritably, brother John instructs me in this ghastly business. All because of the Jews. Jesus Christ, born in a stable two thousand years ago. Otherwise I wouldn't be doing this.

* * *

On the cover of *Time Magazine* is Graham Sutherland's 'Risen Christ'; an enormous tapestry in the new Coventry Cathedral. Christ is seated on a throne, pierced hands held up, crucifix behind him. It is coloured mostly greens, with traches of white, yellow, purple and blood red. Coffin shaped, the symbols of the four evangelists are on each quarter. It is star-tlingly original. A slap in the face. I throw it back on the table. I look out over the now ominous Ulster landscape, a night as black as it was in the coalshed for the turkey.

Dreaming under the old rafters and slate roof, everyone is asleep. Even during this short break Kilkenny is fast receding into the mists of the Nore. I'm astride two worlds, which are side by side, yet far apart. I'm reminded of how it was the first time I was in Dublin, outside the GPO, where the Shinner fanatics harangued me in passing. There was a gor-geous young one, with wild red hair, long skirted and lace booted. I'll always remember her, the unknown Ireland she was then. The shocking moment when our eyes met: I felt she was stealing me greedily to herself. "For the love of Ireland!" she shouted loudly as I passed, her mad laugh-ter following me long after. Was this a joke? Anarchy and cruelty for the sake of nothing better to do. I shudder, momentarily awake.

* * *

Ours is not a family for Christmas trees and decorations. Presents were only given to us when we were children and now our efforts are lim-ited to just a few branches of holly if we can find some over the fields. Alcohol is definitely taboo, for some unmentioned reason to do with the past. Mother perhaps takes a small glass in the company of certain visitors, from the one bottle of Sandman Port kept in the dining room cupboard. Instead, in a large jug of water, float slices of lemon. It is placed a crisp white linen tablecloth, embroidered with tiny red roses by Aunt May. The cutlery was a wedding present: Atkin Bros, Truro Works, Sheffield; silver plated king's pattern. Not even the Scandinavians could make better. Blue dragons chase around china-white plates, which are gold edged. I had never really noticed the rose pink decoration on the big creamy tureen, whih has a ruined castle above a deep wooded cliff.

'Berry Pomeroy 1792' is written on the lid. 'Ruby Castle', set amidst fine park land and grazing deer, is on the main dish. The have rococo surroundings and festoons of flowers. It is a display of quite extraordinary manufacturing skill, yet Kilkenny Design would never consider something so Victorian.

"Welcome into our family Mary." Father embraces her and kissing her heartily on the cheek, embarrassing us all as we sit down to the feast.

From Mother comes the faintest look of regret at his gesture, she has lost her youth to the new, blooming springtime colleen and summer is still to come. A surprising competition from the deep South. Could she really be jealous though? Mother serves the now succulent coalshed turkey from the kitchen, accompanied by a wide variety of steaming vegetables which we passing from one to the other. I'm aware of the fragility of these hours, these minutes that are impossible to hold.

Disturbing thoughts intrude on my comforts. Freshford will be covered in snow, the cottage cut off. Mam and Eileen are frozen, forgotten by Kilkenny. The old phantoms arising. Mary... Mary Malone enjoying every bite. A Christmas dinner like she has never had before. She pauses guiltily, as if caught at a pleasure past circumstances would never have allowed her. The child of Ireland, sensing that wherever she goes she is unwanted.

"You've a little sister now, pretty as they come don't you think?" Father addresses John, who fills his mouth, so as to avoid comment. Undaunted, Father continues, "and I've a real Irish daughter at last, how did he ever find you and where did you meet?"

"By chance, at the Club House where you stayed," Mary replies, glancing at me, unwilling to elaborate.

"And we'll have our first grandchild born here soon." Mother is adamant.

This provokes a boorish declaration from John. "Are they not up to scratch down there, that you have to come up North on our National Health."

"We're agreed she'd be much better in the Hardy Greer, where your brother was born during the war, isn't that so Mary?"

"Yes, if that's what you think's best for me, I don't mind." Mary is softly spoken, with a voice Spenser would have known, one that is not of this time: broken and distant. I sense a nervousness in it, that she wants to flee. Whatever it is, I will never understand.

"Will your baby be baptized Catholic or Protestant?" John asks. He should leave this well alone.

"He or she can decide for themselves, if at all, when they're much older." I answer without hesitation, an answer which annoys him.

"And quite rightly so," Father responds. "The sprinkling of water on a child's head doesn't necessarily make them Christian. Remember Stalin, and Hitler were baptized Catholics, I do believe."

"But Christ was baptized by St John."

I am determined to end this. "Christ was indeed baptized by St John, from what I remember, but Christ never baptized anyone. And Christians follow Christ not John. So maybe the church has got it wrong. Anyway John, who cares?"

"Then why does the church baptize anyone?" But John will not let it go.

"Wasn't it something the old Popes dreamed up to get money for their luxury living. The indulgences, Peter's pence, Mass money for the dead, having to pay a priest for their prayers to get relatives out of Purgatory." Mother gives this explanation, she is a true daughter of the Reformation. "A lot of those Popes were very bad men, I'd rather confess my sins direct to God than through a Roman priest."

Mary is uneasy. I can understand her not wanting to listen, for they 've their job well. And even though the flames have nearly been put out, the embers of her religion are still smouldering.

There is silence for a while, as each of us looks to our own ample plates, but discord hovers as John wants to continue down that road. "Sure the South is run by the Catholic Church, remember the Protestant woman from Wexford that had to leave when the priests started interfering, everyone was boycotting all the other Protestants there for some stupid reason."

"Yes that's right, it was Fethard-on-Sea, where the Protestant wife of a Catholic refused to send her daughter to the Catholic school. I remember it well, it must be seven or eight years ago now." How could Mother forget?

"They're emigrating in droves down there, the disappearing Irish they say. The Free State's on its knees." John adds this as an afterthought, chuckling to himself.

"Well look at the mess we British made here, turning democracy on its head. Is it any wonder they wanted us out? Even in Ulster today. And reading about the Famine makes one think." Father raises his voice. Beside his armchair is the recently published book, *The Great Hunger*.

"But they should never have been neutral during the war." Mother will never change on that.

"Oh, I don't know, enough of them joined up to fight. De Valera was right to stay out of the war, there wasn't much little Eire could have done anyway." This is a view Father has always maintained.

"But the Royal Navy was denied Irish harbours. And to give his condolences on Hitler's death was absolutely unforgiveable!"

I'd agree with her there and the real story they'll never believe.

"It demonstrated their independence, that they were not going to be pushed around by us anymore. And look, didn't Eire produce my lovely daughter?" Father reaches over and squeezes Mary's hand. She smiles weakly, confused.

John raises his glass. "To the pious, glorious and immortal memory of King William the third, who saved us from rogues and roguery, slaves and slavery, Popes and popery and should any man or woman deny this..." This toast ends abruptly as Father brings down his fist hard on the table, the Gurkha knife on the wall falling (coincidence or not).

"That's enough of such bigoted hatred. No more!"

Reciting the old Orange toast indeed, as if Mary cares, one side or the other... he's some shit. Mary is hardly enamoured about having the baby born here.

We turn to eating plum pudding and what goes for normal conversation resumes. Normality is rarely found South or North for her

CHAPTER 33

"I've mentioned about you working in St Louis to this Dorothy wench, so we shall soon see." It is late afternoon, Father is licking and folding down the pale blue lightweight aerogramme, saw-edged red and dark blue. A pinkish postage stamp of parliament and Queen Elizabeth, costing six-pence, six D is printed on it. Modern communications are truly amazing; she'll get it within a week of the day it is posted. This is so unlike the early eighteenth century, when our relations emigrated. Then, most were never heard from again.

I hold out my hand. "I'll walk down to the crossroads and post it for some exercise; it will help digest my Christmas dinner."

"Well, this is only an enquiry anyway."

Patting the letter inside my pocket, I think that whatever will be will be. Like when Father just missed a flying bomb by a few minutes on his way to the Air Ministry.

"I hope your brother didn't upset Mary with his stupid behaviour, where is she?"

"Upstairs, having a lie down, she'll be alright, this part of Ireland takes getting used to."

"You can say that again."

Mary is under the golden eiderdown, far away, perhaps dreaming of the forsaken lands on the road again from Knocktopher via Kilkenny to Freshford.

"Will you come for a walk with me, posting this letter to America?"

"No, I'm tired and in my condition; you'll have to go on your own." The last four words feel like a knife in the stomach.

"And will you start the pump on your way?" Father calls after me.

As I head towards the crossroads, I observe that the snow is beginning to melt. A little red post box is fixed to the fence near a telephone kiosk and tattered flag on a flag pole. An island belonging to dear old England, bold and immutable. I suddenly feel I'm in a strange and foreign land. This feeling is reinforced by the sight of Pope Patterson coming home drunk from Ballynahinch's market day, as his swaying bicycle passes me for a moment, Patterson curses the pope. This is the same road the Lisburn linen-draper, Henry Munro, saw his men of Ninety-eight fleeing down from the battle nearby, totally defeated. They are all ardent Unionists today, Father once explained to me, his voice heavily sarcastic. Conscious this might be a life changing moment, I drop the letter into the post box.

The pump house is at the end of a narrow laneway near the rushing stream from Slieve Croob. A single cylinder Lister pump starts with a few turns and the silent valley water from the main pipe is pumped up to the old ship's water tank, high off the ground by the hayshed. The tank was made with hot rivets and bent round steel from Harland and Wolf; it sailed many seas. The engine sounds a heartbeat, the heart beat of Ulster that I've known since I was born, courtesy of the Devil's most enthusiastic disciple, Adolf Hitler.

* * *

Early in New Year's week, we return to Kilkenny. The surrounding countryside is the colour of spilt milk; it is depressing entering Newry. We stop by the Brass Monkey, where the open door reveals a filthy, soaking smoke-filled Hogarthian scene of Ulster's manhood beginning another year. It doesn't look good. Dundalk was only ever shopping for Peggy's leg, chocolate and Sweet Afton, all in demand due to Northern rationing just after the war. Drogheda, according to Wilde, was, '... one of the dirtiest, worst sewered and most ill ventilated town in Ireland.' I recall too, on sighting St Laurence's gate and the Magdalen Steeple, that these landmarks are, 'generally speaking, scarcely approachable, owing to the quantity of filth by which they are surrounded.' Dirty narrow and tortuous streets, 'surrounded by the most miserable portion of the population, and not only is the adjoining locality a disgrace to the town, but the very site itself stands more in need of the Sanitary Commission than any other place we know of.'

Driving through the town now, it seems nothing much has changed since then. Crows, always about those ancient broken stone heights, fly off dead creatures on the road as we approach and, as I see in the rear view mirror, as quickly return.

There is no joy in Dorset Street. Turning into Parnell Square by the big

Guinness advertisement, I'm a stranger here again. I look up to a large seagull perched on the head of Daniel O'Connell, the pale shite from the birds sliding down his face, as if expressing nature's contempt for Irish nationhood and patriots. A great spot to keep watch over Dublin, with Admiral Lord Nelson just passed. I notice treasonable bullet marks from 1916 on the four winged victories below the statue. Amidst the sound of slow moving traffic I hear the occasional phrase in Dublinesque. The Mansion House pediment on Dawson Street has the Lord Mayor's coat of arms: three white, double-towered flaming castles on blue.

"Can we get something to eat, I'm starving?" Mary's coming to from being half asleep, slumped within herself on the far side of the Mini, eyes opening and closing.

The Naas pub has a discontenting atmosphere of existence without purpose: few customers and a road to nowhere. I order wholemeal salmon sandwiches and orange juice, with coffee. Coffee which Mary now drinks for the first time.

"So tell me, did you enjoy your Northern Christmas?" The sandwiches arrive with a glum girl. Fed up, no doubt, to find herself at this time of year in the same old job.

"It was nice to get away from Kilkenny, but between your mother and that peculiar farmer friend of yours, I felt under suspicion for being a Catholic from Kilkenny. It was like some sort of stigma attached to me. Although your mother means well and of course your father too. It's the same South and North for me in this wretched country. Beneath the surface, one way or another, however, well disguised. There's a feeling against me. We must try to emigrate while we're still young. Free me from Ireland, that's what I really want!"

"You are serious".

"Of course, I am." She eyes me most assuredly.

At Crettyard the sign welcomes us into Kilkenny. The county still has fields of snow. A rising moon looks silver, reminding me there's more silver waiting behind glass, wrapped in acid-free tissue paper, slowly turning to the same colour as the landscape bathed by the light from the mysteries sphere before us.

Driving into the Parade, I always experience the same feelings of time running backwards, especially when I park in front of that dear old castle. The flat now seems squalid and pokey, hardly warmed by an electric fire, of which two bars are broken. The bed sheets so cold as to be damp; we are without milk to make tea; the bread is mouldy and the builder has to be paid five hundred pounds to finish what I no know will be a building I will never inhabit.

Taking down the Irish Life calendar for last year, I see Peter Brennan over his potter's wheel for December. Turning back the months to July,

I look at myself, supposedly soldering an Irish made jug, that was actually made in London. The picture was taken the year before by a Dutch photographer from Stillorgan, who remembered the Germans rounding up the Jews of Amsterdam to be gassed, men, women and children. It is early morning before we both fall away to restless sleep, tossing and turning, swimming in the absurd, cinematic-like images that appear and disappear from the North.

The stables are deserted, the workshop desk drawers are difficult to open. Whatever Kilkenny's weather does to them involves tightening. And those nasty little woodlice will take over the world eventually. Above the polishing motor, a fairly large spider dangles mid-air. Lightly touching it with a file, it shoots up to its web on the ceiling, extraordinary. The rotten orange that so distressed Haselbach the German, now has a hard shell of peel. Through the window, I notice a rat slowly advancing on one side of the pathway. Dear God what does this foretell? Picking up the big hammer, I wonder where the rat has gone.

Taking out the silver, I appraise each piece. It is far too precious, and, sadly, made for a bygone age. Peter has been carving a rosewood handle to fit and peg two sockets on a teapot that the Marquess of Ormonde would be delighted to see on his bench. He's gone to London with John for Christmas. My own set of six, twisted wire napkins record Newgrange, which is a dangerous influence once you are infected by it. And difficult to forget, I would imagine. I haven't the heart to continue with them just now, as woeful negativity overshadows me, dripping with the melting snow on the roof. It is everywhere in this dirty old Irish town, today anyway. In comes the sudden shaft of bright sunlight, Mary arrives, having been shopping in the new enterprise on Rose Inn Street, which seems to stock everything.

"Will you ever get out of here, you're still on holidays until next week." She scolds me softy as I open the door for her to come in. "I've some nice fresh bread, beans, tomatoes, sausages and eggs for our tea."

"Make sure you grill the bacon and sausages, don't fry them in the pan."

"Ah go on with you, a bit of animal fat will do you no harm, but I will. Do you mind if we go out to Freshford this evening?"

"No I don't mind." Not that I really want to enter that unnerving Irish wretchedness and superstition again. The historic otherness distresses my sensibilities, with their Hail Marys, crossings, confessions and Holy waters. And the abandonment and object poverty that she's still a part of, wanting to escape, but forever haunted by it. Her circumstances are a stigma stamped on the innocent from birth. The dog Langrishe, casting his own child into that purgatory, would he even know she existed? The mother in her expectant condition, failing to turn up at the big house for her chores. Plenty more girls in the village and surrounds.

"What are these queer looking yokes for?" Mary asks, taking one of the napkins I'm working on.

"They'll be napkin rings when finished."

"Napkin rings, do people still use them?" She sounds surprised.

"I certainly hope so and don't you think a set of six, Irish made and hallmarked, will make a nice gift?"

"Well yes, maybe. They never had them in the Club House, even for special dinners." Her eyes are doubtful and puzzled, as she puts them back with the others.

"And that's a teapot." She notices Peter's bench.

"With the rosewood handle soon ready to be fitted to it." I hold both up for her, touching them together.

"How much will it cost?"

"The three pieces, when finished, will be well over a hundred, I would say."

"As much as that?"

"Oh yes, easily."

"Well, they must know what they're doing to be making silver teapots in Kilkenny."

"You'd think so. Do you want to go out to the house?"

"No, no, not today, don't you think we should sell it soon, if we're going to leave?"

Her negativity is even more disturbing now, as I watch her disappear through the near-crescent archway. Abandoned by her mother, she does not want to be constantly reminded of her shame.

CHAPTER 34

Mysterious and eerie old Kilkenny. It feels a bit disquieting tonight as we drive towards Freshford. Once entered, it will always bewitch. I hear the siren calls of Irish memory. At first it is as if the cottage was never there at first, only for the fact Mary is beside me do I believe it to be real. The constant tricks and illusions of Irish reality and time yet again. There is not a sound or light as the cottage comes slowly into view; is there anyone inside at all?

"Have they left?" I ask apprehensively.

"Sure, where would they go?" Replies.

"Mam's son is from Tipperary."

"God, no, they never got on, an awful gobshite he is too."

"Why do you say that?"

"Never mind." Eyeing the cottage distastefully, Mary clutches my arm. It is very cold, with the snow still quite deep in places. Something's not right, I feel, after giving a few knocks on the door.

"We may go in, it's probably not locked," Mary says fearfully, opening the door.

We release the most dreadful smell. Turning the light on, a mouse quickly darts across the floor. Dear God, did she come out of this? The fire hasn't been lit for ages; there are the remains of bread and cake, a tiny Father Christmas still on them.

"Oh, Jesus, Mary and Joseph they're dead!" shrieks Mary, ashen-faced, coming from the other room. "They're beginning to…"

"You're not serious."

"Oh yes I am, both together in the bed. The poor child with an old woman for warmth, hypothermia is what they call it, I think. Mam, her heart first, then Eileen must have just given up the ghost, half-starved beside her. You don't have to go in."

I can't help myself and see two faces from the top of the covers, strangely careless and far away, decomposing to the colour of putty. Better get them a decent burial, for much longer like this and they will become unbearable.

Mary pulls me away bitterly. "We'll have to let the Gardaí know, it's nothing to do with me anymore and never was."

For this is the famine all over again and not for the first time visited here with its full, awful horror. Let's hope there'll be no enactment of the funeral scenes at Skibbereen, when coffins were unprocurable. This is now 1965.

"Let's get out of this, I'm going to be sick if we stay for any longer." Mary errupts with the look of distraught, suffering Irish womanhood that seems immemorial. Her hand is on the latch.

"Is there anything that belongs to you here?"

"Nothing," she is surprised that I even asked.

"I'm having this, if you don't mind." I take the peculiar blue milk of magnesia bottle marked 'Holy water' from the dresser. A kind of macabre talisman of the occasion for some unknown reason. It is the same colour blue as the Virgin statues beside the country roads that I saw when I first came to Kilkenny, that fateful summer before last.

"Are you out of your mind, surely the last thing you'd want?" Mary is nearly shouting.

"I'm not going to drink it."

"You better not, come on hurry up." Opening the door, she is anxious to get away, far far away!

Gazing around the foetid, desolate room, at the bric-a-brac of Catholicism, I'm disturbed by the thought that the other Ireland is hidden but still there. The Garda Station in Freshford is deserted, so Kilkenny it must be. Then lighting strikes suddenly, how could I have forgotten? The Marshal Sabastian le Prestre Vauban is lying under the death bed. "Those books, those books, we'll have to go back for them."

"Well you know where they are, you'll have to go in by yourself, for I'll never set foot there again. Luckily the station was closed, can you imagine the trouble we'd have, if they'd found them? It wouldn't have taken them long to put two and two together with you at the Design Centre, silly goose!

"I know, I know." It doesn't bear thinking about. I turn the car around.

Collecting the stolen books that once belonged to the mighty from under the death bed of Ireland's poorest is a strange dichotomy. Their author was an ardent soldier and supporter of Louis the Fourteenth, the

Sun King of France. The monarch was a right bastard by most accounts, a warmonger who revoked the Edict of Nantes, persecuting Protestants and his own overtaxed people. A protector of the nobility and, of course, the Catholic clergy. The book's first owner was the second Duke of Ormonde, who had to flee to France, being a Catholic sympathizer and Jacobite. Everything turns full circle, Louis body was exhumed by revolutionaries and destroyed. It is no more now than Mam and Eileen will be soon. Sun King and peasants alike.

"Mam wrapped them up in an old shawl, they're right under her bed. Go on, in you go and don't be long." Mary is impatient to be out of this forever, as I hesitate a while. Inside is a nightmare of filth and vermin; outside, the extraordinary loveliness of Mary.

My eyes having become accustomed to the darkness, I don't want to turn the light on. Deliberately letting the cottage remain veiled, I hope this is a bad dream that will wake from in the morning. Entering Mam's bedroom, I see the two faces, pale as before, then momentarily a passing cloud uncovers the moon and they seem to wake. Mysterious forces are at work, things move and change, bodies swell and at a microscopic level, organisms begin their necessary work. I'm afraid to pull back the covers. Cremation surely the most hygienic for dealing with human remains, no need for coffins, priests and headstones.

I'm down on my knees suffocating, now where are they? Something wet, very wet. Dear God, I have a hand in her potty. Never mind, they have to be found, get a move on. What more surprises could there be underneath? At the top of the bed, by the wall is a hard bundle, carefully covered and tied with string. The dear old thing.

The cold water tap in the other room rumbles and spits running water at last, it must have been frozen, there's pee on my shirt cuff as well. Gazing back at them for the last time, I am reminded that death comes to us all eventually. The poignant scene is fossilized in amber in my mind; the poor child never stood a chance.

I put the books in the boot; they won't be missed at all.

"I have them thank God. Isn't it so awfully sad, freezing to death at Christmas and we're the only ones that know."

"Who's to care anyway, it was always like this for us here." Mary does not say another word, until we near Kilkenny."

"Give me that bottle of Holy water you took."

"What for?"

"Just give it to me." Mary demands sternly, taking and rolling down the window. Then she hurls it away.

* * *

Two laughing Londoners approach the workshop, disturbing me. They sound rudely Shakespearian: Tudor English or Plantagenet even, an echo of ancestral adenoidal cockney in their voices. Even before they enter I feel that they lack seriousness and hold within themselves a hidden scorn. Whether I'm imagining this or not, I find that I am not as happy to greet my returning friends as I should be.

"Has old Walsh moved in yet?" asks John, placing his Gladstone bag on the bench. There is a mocking smile and a 'couldn't care less' attitude in his colourless eyes.

"Not that I'm aware John, but his luxury pad is certainly ready for him."

"Lucky sod, he certainly does himself proud, money no object, fully furnished and rent free no doubt!"

Peter grumbles cynically as he sits down. "He's the driving force behind Ireland's rebirth of good design and manufacturing, what do you expect John?" Peter looks tired, his eyes are glazed and unfocused from his Christmas and New Year's festivities across the water. I watch him light a cigarette and lower his head.

"Or whatever you can get away with," John adds, with a note of despair.

"He's all right John.," I say, "sure, none of us would be here if it wasn't for him, do you really want to be living and working in London all your life? This is an unique experience, when you're an old man, you'll remember it fondly."

I wonder, I really do sometimes, living in the sticks over here, what's there to do on the money we earn? I can't exist on ruined castles, Celtic Crosses, the views and country girls expecting you to marry them." John takes off his duffle coat and attunes himself to the vase he was making before Christmas.

A disquieting, silver-making day begins, with little by way of conversation and an angry, unsettled sky of intermittent heavy rain, which changes swiftly from solid black to fleeting blue. Sudden shafts of sunshine, spin about me as I cross the courtyard, leaving me bewildered and fearfully on edge.

Out of nowhere seems, shocking me at first, I see Walsh and the general manager sheltering under the outer archway entrance from the Parade. King, isn't it? Yes, the boyo I briefly met in that distastefully earlier encounter. Jim King is the new general manager of the Kilkenny Design Workshops and Walsh is, well, Chief Executive and Chairman I suppose. Both are glaring conspiratorially at me, offering me barely a hint of recognition.

Guiding this influential and — for many — controversial enterprise into the future, these eagle-eyed amateurs know best. Taking a more strategic, hands off and broader view is only common sense really. No need for them to get bogged down in the practicalities of manufacture.

They can develop excellent ideas over a good red Bordeaux at the Club House, making reference to Walter Gropius and the Scandinavians of course. Then there was an Oskar Schlemmer and George Mache. And a Mies van der Rohe suggested a sky reflecting glass and steel box for the Phoenix Park. There was no essential difference between the artist and the craftsman, I am told. Both have a strong desire to bring honesty and parity to materials, all these things being intermeshed. The artist is an exalted craftsman. Expertise in craft is essential to every artist. It all makes terrific sense and will result in beautiful artefacts being placed into the hands of ordinary people.

Then they were gone and I was back on Patrick Street and the real Ireland waylaid me again. For the tragic, grotesque and ragged appearance of Kevin Traynor, the enormous newspaper vendor, comes before me shouting, "Evenin Herald!"

* * *

"Did you go to the Gardaí?" Mary greets me at the flat door.

"Yes, they'll sort it out and inform Mam's son, I think Eileen might have to be buried in Roscrea with Nora. Will you go their funerals?"

"Definitely not this time, I'm finished with all that there, it'll make no difference anyway, I'm not related to them and the dead are dead, there's only ever silence from the departed." Mary's tone is resolute.

There is a young man coming towards us on the stable's side footpath; he is dressed in Donegal tweed and grey flannel and introduces himself as Pat Henderson. He will be the accountant, he explains, along with whatever else Kilkenny Design has in mind for him. He has an important message from Paul Hogan, to bring all the silver up to Dublin, for a meeting at two p.m. in the foyer of the Intercontinental Hotel, Ballsbridge, this Thursday fortnight. There will be a buyer from Harrods to see it. And I've to make sure it's priced right, with delivery dates and descriptions of each piece. Henderson has a handful of intimidating yellow job cards for us to start using: time spent on every job, date of arrival, date of departure. The cheek of them, without even discussing this with us. And with us already logging this information.

"So tell me Pat, as you're the accountant and bookkeeper, how do you want me to price this? I can give you the weights of silver, wages and time roughly spent on it — when you consider the many interruptions we have — what other overheads should I include, do you think?"

Pat smiles benignly, "God, I wouldn't know, whatever you think yourself."

"What about the other workshops, have they discussed pricing yet? How much is O'Connor's poplin by the yard? And who had the idea for the job cards, did you give them to Middleboe?"

"Ah, God, no, not Middleboe, he's away in Denmark still. It was King's idea and nothing to do with me." Pat answers defensively.

"Is he really here full time with Walsh?"

"I think it'll be a few more weeks, maybe even a month or two before they're both finally settled. They'd have loose ends to tie up in Dublin first, it takes a while you know."

"Is that so Pat? It's all a bit vague, but you can take these cards back to where they came from."

Pat holds up the palms of his hands, refusing to take the cards back. "He did say you were to use to start using them and he'll be the boss now." Obviously, Pat does not want to get on the wrong side of the general manager.

"All right then, I'll keep them and price the silver as best I can." It's impossible to keep the annoyance out of my voice.

"Game ball, sure you can only do your best."

Whatever he means by that.

The goal of assisting and developing Irish metal enterprise somehow doesn't fit selling silver to Harrods. Still, it's only a start and the sales have to begin one way or the other. And it really doesn't matter to me, for it's a lovely hotel and I can stay the night with a meal. For now, it's on the house, although I know this won't last much longer.

* * *

"Let's go and see McCreery the Auctioneer and Estate Agent and put the house up for sale, as it's nearly finished now and you've paid the final amount." Suggests Mary.

"Maybe we should wait a bit longer and see if there's any word from America. I didn't want to be suddenly out of a job and with no money." I am wary, uncomfortable with thoughts about an uncertain future and abrupt dislocation.

"You won't be, we're still living in the flat and the house will be no loss; we'll have plenty of time to get your money back, even make a profit."

"But I don't want anyone to know." It would be all over town and the stables.

"I'm sure they can do it in the quiet," she encourages me.

"And just keep on the way we are for the moment?"

Mary stands up and holds out her hand, indicating we should go right away. "Yes, it's not a problem and won't take long. You can do it before you go back to work this afternoon."

On High Street there's a persistent and malignant voice behind us, calling to Mary. I turn to be confronted by the English working man's burden, straight out of Punch.

"We didn't see yez at me mother's funeral Mary, where were yez?" says he.

Mary is shocked and angry. "You do fuck off Paddy, you're dirt, I never want to see you again!"

"Ah go on with ye girl, who do you think you are? I knows alls about yez, wasn't me mam so very good to look after you, married I hear now, does yer man really know where you came from?" He looks at me directly, laughing maliciously. Then he's away, melted into the midday crowd. An assassination in broad daylight, the assailant gone before cognisance is regained.

Mary runs into the Post Office, tearfully upset, turning against the windows to avoid onlookers, where she explains. "The times he'd come up, supposedly to see Mam, but trying to touch me, were terrifying. Mam didn't seem to notice and I'd be scared to mention it to her. And he'd know when she'd be at Mass and we were alone. It all started when I was much younger, just eight or nine, he once very nearly had me, but I only just managed to run out when he was, well, you know. He was never interested in the others. God, when you think about it, both dead and buried and hardly into their teens!"

"Come on then, remember we're on our way to put the house up for sale." It doesn't bear thinking about; the poor child.

"Yes, of course." Mary brightens somewhat, wiping away her tears.

And, surreptitiously, the house is up for sale.

* * *

I'm on the early morning road to Dublin with a borrowed suitcase full of silver. I stop to relieve myself by the great mote of Ardscull around which the road from Naas to Athy pivots. Here are shades of an ancient massacre, of medieval murders and strife: as if the many bare winter trees that surround me are sighing for the long departed beneath them. How long did it take to travel from Kilkenny to Dublin before the railway was built? When riding a horse was the only means of making the journey? Would the first baronet, Sir Terence's ancestor, have been in a swaying coach, rattling through Castlecomer, Carlow, Athy? A whole day, perhaps, or even two, hurrying past the dispossessed at their cabin doors to his safe seat in the Irish Protestant Parliament, with his titled friends and ample refreshments.

I'm reminded of Dickens's, *Tale of Two Cities*, the Marquis's coach running down the impoverished, unfortunate child. The fuss a tiresome bother and they few coins tossed to the distraught father, whose revenge came within hours. Sir Terence, however, did not even give a few pounds to Mary's mother. He just wiped his hands of the matter and easily forgot about them both.

Lying in his hot bath, soaking up the heat, a familiar figure appears, not quite forgotten. As he is dreamy and half asleep, Sir Terence is lulled by visions of Ireland's steamy vapours and only recognises the mother of his child as she runs a kitchen knife across his throat. The breath of Charlotte Corday is upon him. He has awakened too late! This half-rising, coughing, gasping bloody mess, was once a haughty baronet, officer and gentleman.

My imagination brings forth nightmares, past and present. It is time to drive on.

The car park is full of expensive cars. Entering the Intercontinental Hotel, I see a new world of dazzling modernity that contrasts dramatically with old Kilkenny. The well-dressed people and bold abstractions on the walls. A warm and efficient service and tempting odors from the busy restaurant.

In the hotel shop are Aran sweaters; the varied greens of numerous scenic postcards; jewellery and Waterford Glass. Lyndon B Johnson is on the cover of *Time Magazine*, the man of the year just past. There's a hum of contentment and of people doing business. Here too are obvious Americans, voices loud and harsh, so different from the soft and gentle accents of Kilkenny. I feel conspicuous in the foyer as though under an unwelcome and harsh light.

There's Paul Hogan, beckoning towards the Dubliner bar, smoking an unusually long fat cigar. He seems effusive and expansive today. Pointing to the corner seats, I see a large pinkish man is there already. He is about fifty, with a smoker's watery eyes and receding fair, greying hair. Hogan introduces him as David Pritchett, the buyer from Harrods.

"So where can we lay all this silver out then Paul?" I ask, feeling totally disconnected, wanting to run.

"Sure, here will do fine, and what'll you have?"

Is he serious?

"Just an orange, it's a long drive back."

"Stay tonight for goodness sake, have a proper drink. And your good self David."

"The same again, as I'm here in Dublin," replies Pritchett, the Home Counties reflected in his accent.

"A glass of Smithwicks then Paul, will do."

"Good man yourself." Hogan is away to the bar counter, tripping left to right. I'm thinking that this is not the place to be showing my selection of our best work. A bar, a crowded table of tall and empty glasses, beer mats and ashtrays.

"Paul's been telling me all about your work in Kilkenny. It sounds like a most interesting project; I'm dying to see what you've made there." Pritchett is leaning over towards me.

Hogan returns, holding up his arms. "Let the show begin."

The large battered suitcase looks incongruous in these surroundings, but I lift it up onto the chair beside me. The waiter arrives with a pint of overflowing Guinness; a glass of something clear with lemon; the Smithwicks and a bowl of salted peanuts. Pritchett offers me a cigarette, lighting one for himself. Now this is becoming truly bizarre.

I open the case and immediately, other customers glance over. The silver is wrapped in tissue paper and towels to prevent bruising. Now what will the first piece be? The teapot of course, as this is fast becoming Alice in Wonderland and the Madhatter's tea party (with the shadow of the Marquess of Ormonde). As a noisy little boy and girl ran across to see, staring boldly at what's going on, their mother comes over, smiling: children will be children you know, we'll keep an eye on them but leave them with you.

"If David's staying here, we could go up to his room and view this in more privacy," I suggest to Hogan.

"I'll fetch another table over there; it will give us more room." Hogan ignores my suggestion and points at the table's surface, as if to say, get on with it.

"Everything on the tables you mean?"

"Yes, isn't that ok for you, David?"

Pritchett doesn't seem to mind one way or the other, as he slides the empty glasses to one side. He holds the teapot in one hand, picking up his Guinness with the other.

Well, if that's what they want, so it shall be. *The Dubliner*. An asylum of surrealistic imagery, with many voices and the two persistent and annoying imps. I feel disconnected, as though a somnambulist. I'll never see the likes of this again. He'll take this and he likes that, the set of napkins is interesting as well and another Guinness? Why not. He doesn't like the way the lid closes on coffee pot with the green nylon handle, he will, however, try the large fruit bowl, candlesticks, cigarette box and salad servers. He takes out his order book, with the price list laid before him and so far he hasn't demurred. Silver is overflowing on tables, chairs and even the floor. Those passing by are curious, what is going on here?

Each piece of silver speaks of an hallucinating moment, half remembered, a kaleidoscope of imagery. The silver he's holding was so awkward to make. It came right, eventually, thanks to Peter. Mary was sitting on a bench with that very beaker Hogan's fiddling with. The reminders of Kilkenny seem like a fiction of the imagination.

It seems my life is a constant journey into the darkness of an Irish country road. I am returning to Kilkenny. I should have stayed the night, in a bubble bath of whiskey, good food and dreams. But I knew Mary would be waiting. As I left, Hogan's mood changed abruptly: "You're a lot of work to do now, so get cracking and make sure you deliver as promised!"

CHAPTER 35

I have to order a delivery of silver circles, sheet and wire from Johnson Matthey in London. Then break down the Harrods order to some kind of method: the time it will take for each piece and a schedule of work to methodically reach the promised delivery date. Is this Kilkenny Design, or is this Walsh's first steps in the silver manufacturing business? Who knows? The three of us are hammering under passing clouds, the sun crosses the sky, the moon rises and each clear day we are greeted by the morning star. These are ephemeral, amorphous days never to be repeated.

I sense a pressure building, yet old Kilkenny cautions me not to try too hard to please. Stand back a while from the high breaking walls around the tall, sighing, crow-infested trees and take each hour as it comes. Throw them to the wind: Walsh, Hogan, the Harrods man and especially this King fellow. The general manager won't make a blind bit of difference, for Peter and John know their rights. They talk of joining the trade union and are not going to hurry unnecessarily, especially at the money they're earning.

McCreevy thinks he has a buyer for the house on the Glendine road, with rumours abounding about the stable yard about who might be arriving. There's a Bertil Gardberg from Finland coming and that German of the amazing steel grey Waffen SS coat.

The making of silver and life in Kilkenny is a conundrum. Still, make hay while the sun shines, says Oisin Kelly, and I agree with him. Soon enough I'll be working under a cold-hearted Finn, or the German. It's only been a few short years since the Germans carried out the most horrifying and inexcusable kind of voilence. And Adolf Hitler is occasionally sighted in my dreams (or reality, as there's really no difference here). For my future, it will be better to take risks as an entrepreneur than to take a salary. For then one must necessarily occupy a narrow field and be at the beck and call of others.

* * *

There are faces peering through the windows, which is unnerving. They are mighty curious at this mysterious silversmithing caper and come from newspapers, radio and even television. The bolder even enter and standing rudely over us, complete strangers. They demand an explanation of what their taxes are doing for them, wasting our time, and some are non-too pleased, no doubt they are from the Dublin trade.

The days fold away in a quick succession of workshops sounds and the full range of moods in both humans and materials. The wind rattling our peculiar, old, black, curly window stoppers. Montgomery put those in and Reeves, the English ceramist, has never liked them.

With each season comes different slants of the sun, casting shadows that change imperceptibly each week. There's a languid nervousness here; we are floating, implausible, Marc Chagal-like.

When I take a break and sit outside, I look out onto the rubble wall, built of quarried stone of all difference sizes. I go to the rear of the crescent building, where it is never quite silent in the early hours of the morning. Ever so faintly, I can hear a moaning and strange frail echoes of distant vehicles.

The poplin weaver creates wonderful, finely-ribbed cotton fabric of many colours such as the red of Walsh's amazing dinner jacket, a red like that of Jacob's bloody coat, the momentary colour of the evening sky. He works beside Oisin Kelly wherever the sculpter is with us, nesting with his many carved birds.

As a heavy downpour sweeps across the roof, distant thunder alerts all three to stop, momentarily fearful a divine intrusion. It easies off to reveal sharp shafts of bright sunlight on the silver surfaces of our pieces, the colours of the rainbow spliting the light like a rhapsody.

* * *

Looking down from the flat on Haughton's cherry tree (soon to be blooming pink), over the dull rooftops towards the Club House, Kilkenny spins in my thoughts, stretching in and out, mystifying me. The drowning waters, the bog where Nora was found floating. The old woman and child touched by the glancing moonlight, hauntingly dead. Kilkenny, a contagious disease I have caught without knowing it. That first evening; the morning breaking over Cashel and those joyous Tipperary birds; ascending into the valley of Inistioge, where the green-eyed child behind the bar counter had the whole world in her hands, she was the centre of the entire cosmos.

"What do you see out there? You've been watching for so long," asks Mary coming up from behind.

"Oh, nothing really, just day dreaming about the last few years of life in Kilkenny." I turn around to enfold her in my arms.

"Get away." She looks up at me with ridicule, "sure what's there to day dream about, it's just a dirty old Irish town. A dirty whole country for that matter. There was always trouble in the very air I breathed."

"A dirty old Irish town; nothing good, you say... no. Never mind the people, what about the landscape, the history, rivers and views?"

"You can't live on the view. Kilkenny's only cold misery and damp and there's never enough of anything. The way the nuns would look at us, as if we were dirt, for we were born out of sin. Remember what happened to Nora? And that awful Kieran, the rapist, free as a bird still."

"A difficult case to prove I suppose, since Nora was dead."

"He's a murderer!" Mary's voice rises loudly. "Even if she'd lived, nothing would have been done to him, with the priest, big farmers and Gardaí all conspiring against poor Nora. Believe you me, her being only a woman. And didn't you say according to Irish law she and I were children of no one, without parents or relatives? What chance would we ever have living here?"

"Yes, I know, but surely Kilkenny has a certain... well, charm, acharacter that's unique. I'll always remember the night I met you coming up Patrick Street under lamplight to the Club House."

"I was certainly never expecting to see you, a very different sort from the boys you'd meet around here. I was amazed you'd even consider waiting for me. When I saw you at first with that awful Eastwood character, I thought it was some kind of trap. A rough sport and that I'd have to be ever so careful. Then I learned you were working up at that Design Centre. It was just crazy that I'd be spending the night with you, instead of going to my miserable little room. A was woken at five thirty sharp next morning; some surprise indeed. For some reason I must have trusted you." She gazes past, out the window, as thoughtful as I had been.

Seeing Mary walk towards on Patrick Street that night will be the very last memory I have on leaving this world. Words are not enough to ever to explain this to her.

"So without Kilkenny we'd never have met," I point out.

"Well yes, but you'd have met someone else, like the Mary Brennan one you told me about." Somehow, she knows this. Her words make me feel this is a world of diabolical chance.

"I don't think so, she being a strong Catholic. That's why she left me at first. But since she changed her mind later on, I could be wrong."

"She came back to you?" Mary is surprised.

"She wanted me to take her to the Rugby Ball."

"The time you took me?"

"Yes, she didn't know I'd met you by then. She's left Haughton's now, by the way. I pass her very occasionally, never stopping. She's from Stoneyford."

"Is that right? Well, I never knew her." Mary's reply is wistful, strange and far, far away. She is sorrowful within when reflection and I feel she is approaching a fork in the road.

I put an arm around her shoulder. "Have you decided about the North yet? You know how Mother feels about Southern hospitals and their Catholic ethos. She was onto me only yesterday, insisting you must go."

"Insisting? Well I never, someone apart from you who actually cares. Not trusting the Catholic ethos? Well, good for her."

"You are carrying her grandson or daughter and she is your Mother-in-law."

"Of course I'll go, if you're sure you won't miss me, it will be something to be looked after as part of a family, even if your brother and that old Fred the Presbyterian see me as Catholic Southerner.

"I'll miss you all right, but it's for the best, would you like me to drive you out to Knocktopher before you go?"

"For what?"

"To say goodbye to your Mother and, well, confront Langrishe."

"You must be joking, for I'll be leaving all that far behind now. She was nothing to me, ever, not the way I was abandoned and treated. As for Langrishe, he'd only be denying me anyway."

"But your mother, surely it wasn't her fault that Langrishe... well you know what I mean."

"No, I would have always been there to remind of her shame, that's why she got rid of me, to get married I'd say. And you don't intimidate men like Langrishe, it's bred into them to take what they want. Weren't they all of Norman stock originally, you once told me, coming over to Ireland behaving like hungry wolves, enslaving the inhabitants. Guarded behind high walls in his big house, living apart from the mere Irish. It's a shame the IRA didn't burn him out, and, God forgive me for saying so, shoot him dead." Mary, Mary Malone out of Ireland, like a lit torch in her anger, as exhilarated as the one I passed at the GPO.

* * *

I'm driving down the Parade for the last time, when, lo and behold, I see him striding, no, goose stepping with ruthless teutonic confidence and determination. With those handsome, blue-eyed, aryan features, I can easily visualize our German colleague with a coal-scuttle helmet on. He's wearing the sinister, steel-grey overcoat again, concealing whatever abominations it must have witnessed. He's walking towards the stables where, no doubt, the gold and silver Gauleiter has arrived.

CHAPTER 36

My first St Louis sweating summer night, I listen to the sounds of crickets and the air conditioner humming full blast. Outside, a Texaco sign illuminates the room with a wierd red colour from the gas station across the road. It is as surreal and traumatizing as it would have been for my forebears on their first night down in New Orleans, having arrived by sailing ship from the cool green shores of County Down.

America throbs with power and the enormous harmonica-fronted cars they drive indicate great resources are present here. Fighter jets overhead come from the nearby McDonald Douglas factory, reminding me that this is a nation at war.

I'm working on the platinum setting for an emerald-cut diamond, weighing five point seven carats, D colour, internally flawless, type two A. It takes some getting used to. Miss Carlene Goddard, gets out of her white Cadillac Eldorado on the street below, throwing the keys to the obsequious black doorman to park for her.

When she comes up, I try the ring on a slim, manicured, pink, long-nailed finger. Her blonde hair is freshly washed and blow dried; she is immaculately dressed and has a revealing décolletage as she bends over. We are above the five showrooms of Elleard B Heffern, Inc. One each for diamonds; emeralds; rubies; sapphires and pearls. The jewellers hold the results of nature's cataclysmic subterranean events, which creaed beautiful stones, save for the gentle, slow-forming pearls found in molasses at the bottom of the sea.

I'm working with an old American-born German called Hugo Hauptmann. It's not a problem; he's easy going, semi-retired and does the messages and simpler jobs, as his doctor advised him to keep active, so he will stay alive beyond his seventy-two years. Hauptmann bought his business cheap as a young man, when his boss drank the cyanide cleaner. It was after the stock market crash of twenty-nine and distraught businessmen were committing suicide for days after.

Silversmithing here is crude and heavy compared to a platinum diamond bracelet that glides over the wrist like a ribbon of silk. The jewellers magic trick is to show only the diamonds, without the metal that holds them together. An ever-dancing band of fire and ice comes alive to the lights, splitting colours. Diamonds found at great depths are amazing when cut and polished. When the men start to sweat a little at the cost of the women they love, Elleard, the boss, can tell what they're going to buy: say, a large canary diamond ring; or the emerald and diamond one; the enamelled Harlequin brooch; or the ruby, square-faced eighteen carat gold Piaget watch. For there is so much to choose from.

I've been remined that the business has a reputation to keep and of the value of the long-term relationships behind the jewellery they sell. All are members of the prestigious American Gem Society and Gemological Institute of America, alongside salesmen who survived Omaha Beach and Guadalcanal.

"That Miss Carlene Goddard is the hottest piece of arse I ever did see on two white legs," says Moses, the elevator operator on the building on four-o-seven, North Eighth Street, where the business is located. Then gazing at me for a moment, he falls silent and curious, "where you from then?"

"Ireland".

"So why you come to St. Louis?" He replies puzzled, "Ireland's a beautiful country. I read about in National Geographic recently, you do go back there, I tell you, before it's too late, and while you're still young." The old black man is suddenly bent and weary, a warning.

"But I've only just arrived."

"To tell you the truth, and don't you be saying this to anyone, understand, as I don't want to lose my job," Moses puts a finger to his lips, "the very idea of America gives me nightmares. The things I've seen and felt, living here all my life."

"It's not that bad surely?" A feel a flicker of darkness within.

"Maybe for you white folks just fine, but they killed my Daddy in East St Louis when I was only a child, beat his brains out with an iron bar. I remember it well."

"Why?"

"Because we only black niggers and still are. They killed a couple of hundred us that night. Fifty years ago, but only yesterday for me still."

"Are things no better today?"

But Moses doesn't answer. Closing the lattice iron gate, shaking his head, he disappears swiftly upwards. After a moment of reflection, I leave the cool air-conditioning to an oven heat outside. Heading towards the wide Mississippi river front, I walk under the St Louis archway's soaring steel shape, gleaming in the burning midday sun against a cloudless, harsh, silvery-blue sky. I order coke and hot dog on the steamboat, *River Queen*.

Dorothy, the distant relative, couldn't have been nicer, making us feel so welcome. She was delighted to be taking Mary and baby under her wing. For we have a bonny wee girl called Lucy, born in Downpatrick at her Grandmother's insistence. Dorothy is an unashamedly patriotic American, in her mid-sixties, with silver blue-hair and creole brown eyes. Her husband, Garland Brown, is older, a real old-time Southern gentleman. In summer he mostly dresses in a white linen suit, with stripped tie and a red, white and blue ribbon straw hat. Garland has to be called Mr B at the Green Parrot restaurant and the exclusive St Louis Country Club, where Dorothy likes to show off Mary, this lovely Irish colleen, to whom she is now related by marriage. They're intrigued by Mary, believing whatever she tells them about herself. When one waspy lady asks Mary, 'Anglo, of course?" she replies "Yes!"

The war is a taboo subject and Martin Luther King is a communist, of course, sowing high hopes amongst his troublesome followers. Grace is said before meals, the new world Jerusalem, King James version. And Annie, their maid, is a good nigger according to Garland, because she knows her place. For that's just the way it is with them and I'm certainly not going to argue one way or the other, whatever I may think.

America: love or leave is attached on the rear of many cars. The 1958 Buick is almost a giveaway so I buy one and immediately feel like an American, driving with the radio on and listening to Hank Williams' words stretching out as spoonfuls of bitter honey. His many hearts. Crazy, Cold, Cheatin; Chains; Love Sick Blues; Honky Tonk; Moanin' and Long Gone Lonesome. America appears disturbing through the wrap around windscreen. The Buick has automatic gears, power brakes, power steering and eight, very thirsty, cylinders.

* * *

The underground car park of the apartment building is a disquieting fluorescent chamber of futuristic metal shapes called Chevrolets, Pontiacs, Mustangs, Cougars and a Lincoln Continental even. I find myself breathing oily odours amongst them. Parking beside a turquoise and cream coloured Ford Thunderbird, I feel at first that I'm no longer of this world but have landed from distant space. I can't help but admire its exciting new 1965 design. Perusing inside, I see what could be the cockpit of a fearsome fighter jet: ivory shaped seats; chrome surrounds; a three-spoked, dished steering wheel; Bunny Club disc hanging from the rear view mirror; an expensive pair of (unusual-shaped) sunglasses carelessly tossed on the dashboard. This would be some car to own. It probably is a vehicle for a man about town, a womanizer.

The thought causes me to pause, with an unwelcome foreboding; a gust out of nowhere extinguishing a candle flame. Now I feel the car is ominous. For who is the owner of this Ford Thunderbird?

The apartment is empty. Hungry, I take out a cold Budweiser. I am weary-eyed from repairing jewellery. I had been given a free hand to alter and redesign an eighteen carat gold lapis lazuli bracelet and matching brooch. Everyone must be at the pool, considering the heat of evening. Is this is the life want to live? For the moment anyway it is only an experience.

Stopping a slight distance from them, I watch from under the dappled shade of the rain tree. Mary is near yet far away, surrounded by laughing neighbours. She does seem to so like America. She is lightly tanned now, with long dark hair cascading over her bare shoulders. Wearing a bust high plain white summer dress, Mary is in full bloom and the centre of attention. Here, she's a different person, uncannily aware of Lady Lucy's needs and moods.

On introducing myself, I feel her look towards me ever so faintly expresses annoyance. Did I disturb something? Or maybe I'm only imagining this? Their conversation dies, as she introduces her new friends. I want to leave and get a bite to eat. Mary reluctantly rises from the table of cool drinks and returns slowly the apartment. Lucy stares sulky at me and starts bawling.

"You've upset Lucy, taking her away from the pool," Mary complains, bending over to lower the hood and block the from the sun from Lucy's eyes.

"And what about you? Did I upset you too?"

"Well... no, it doesn't matter, time for her bed anyway."

The little dictator continues her racket, she was born on the Glorious Twelfth of July, which must have made her Grandmother happy.

"I'm starving," I say; somewhat irritated.

"Couldn't we go out to eat? I don't feel like cooking now."

"If that's what you want, then OK. What about Lucy though?"

"She'll be all right."

"I think Dorothy Brown must be spoiling you."

"Well she does parade me around as if I'm the daughter she never had and it's nice to be someone. I was treated as nobody in Kilkenny."

"You like it here?"

"So far yes; I'd never want to go back to Ireland again." Mary is beauti-ful than ever in this climate, which for some reason I find disturbing.

"Even for a holiday?"

"No. Dorothy was telling me about Garland, I mean Mr B of course, we mustn't forget to call him that. Mr B, indeed, how silly can you get?"

"America for you, deference for age."

"Anyway, she was saying the Browns were one of America's oldest fami-lies, came over from England in the sixteen hundreds and his grandfather had a plantation near little Rock Arkansas before the Civil War destroyed everything for them, 'Damn Yankees' she called the Northerners."

"Mother's great uncle had slaves too; I remember reading that in an old letter. Dorothy's maiden name would have been Stewart. Her great grandfather from County Down married a Frenchwoman in New Orleans, where they made a fortune out of building. But like the Browns, they lost out after the war, which is how some of them ended up here."

"But God, isn't it dreadful when you think about it, owning slaves." The words are no sooner from her lips and she's that very same Scarlett O'Hara, well suited to this southern American life and hopefully not gone with the wind.

* * *

There is a continuous flow of little yellow packets of jewellery with instructions on each for me to get through. Elleard checks each finished article with a large magnifier to make sure the high standards of the busi-ness are maintained. He takes a special interest in rare sapphires, as does Mae West, who even bought one from him. Now wouldn't that be some-thing? Placing a ring on her finger or a broach on her bosom.

The Swiss watches Elleard's an agent for are an eye opener, a marvel of minute engineering and accuracy, especially the Patek Philippe. I must have one eventually, but at the price it won't be anytime soon. According to Hugo, diamond inclusions that can be seen by the naked eye are 'God damn niggers'. Standing up from his desk in a hurry, he has suddenly realized the time. He puts on his Prussian blue jacket and matching soft brimmed hat. "I'm away to Hummel the watchmaker if Elleard's looking for me." Closing the door behind him, he opens it again with an after-thought, saying, "in St Louis we call the Irish, niggers turned inside out!"

Hugo leaves me with no time to reply and really what could I say? For he means no harm. For the time being I need this job. It's not for me long term, because it is hardly creative, but I have to accept the reality of what they're prepared to pay. I'm working late on to make a difficult ring a size larger, as it is promised for next morning.

Returning mindful and slowly to the car, I see the evening's sky has turned an inky blue. I notice a dangerous air and accusatory menace in the dark faces of the black people whom I pass by. It doesn't seem impossible that I might be waylaid. When I stop at the traffic lights, an exotic choice of women with black, brown and pale shades of skin tap on my window. The black woman with a blonde wig looks most extraordinary. Clear of this suburb, my consciousness drifts dreamily to solicitous old Ireland.

* * *

Driving to work next morning, I see the Thunderbird fast approaching in the rear view mirror, it comes close behind for a few seconds as if taunting me, before overtaking and cutting in dangerously before me. I can't make out the driver, but the ginger-headed woman's face is an unpleasant mask of dark sunglasses and a pouty red, red-lipped look. She expression seems to say, 'get out of our way, you're driving far too slowly'. She even turns around so I can continue to see her. They must be talking about me, for they would recognize this car. It is a most disquieting thought.

"Morning Moses," I say, getting into the elevator.

"Remember: what I did say now?" His reply is quiet and sad and almost to himself. I will have to take the stairs if he keeps reminding me to get out.

* * *

The Thunderbird is there in the evening as it usually is and I have to park beside it again. There's a *Playboy* magazine in the passenger seat, showing centrefold playmate of the month, Kelli Burke from Los Angeles, thirty-four, twenty-two, thirty-three. She is certainly some dish. I wouldn't be able to purchase this back in Ireland, not south of the border.

Mary's left a covered salad, nicely laid out on the kitchen table, with a note saying they're at the pool. There's a letter from Father, who is tedious in his discussions of Irish history, politics and Paisley. His letters are a kind of safety valve for him to let off steam. 'Paisley is peddler of a debased form of Protestantism learned at the Bob Jones University of South Carolina, a forcing house of bigots in the US bible belt, and the moderates are helpless in this hate-torn neck of the fag end of the British Empire. For 800 years the British presence has meant bloodshed and rebellion. There's only one way to end it, clear out and leave it to the Irish to sort themselves.' Page after page of this, with a letter most weeks. It falls to the floor and I leave it there.

Can it be that bad?

Here in St Louis, I feel they shouldn't be this late and decide I will have to go on down to the pool.

The Missouri evening glow on her skin makes Mary particularly lovely. Laughing, her eyes are on fire and excited. This is certainly not the same girl who waited on the Parade for the J.J. Kavanagh bus to Freshford. A man is with her. He is smallish with an open, colourful shirt and gold chain around his neck. He wears tight white trousers and – my God – that must be a snakeskin jacket he's wearing. I've never seen the likes before. It wouldn't come cheap, the many snakes sewn together, scaley grey-blue with tinges of yellow and I look hard. Because it is hard to believe he has matching snakeskin shoes, long and pointed. Ridiculous, yet I feel a sort of apprehension.

It's natural enough, how one thing can lead to another between man and woman, can hardly expect her to stay in the apartment all day and not go out. Whatever it was between them, it quickly evaporates on seeing me. Just that little something, without me knowing what it is, if it's even there.

"This is Neil, he's a photographer." Mary, apparently surprised to see me introduces us. He holds out his hand, and his eyes, his mischievous dark eyes have a kind of smiling lasciviousness along with a message: beware, I'll take you on over her!

"Your lovely wife's been telling me about you, working in Kilkenny by an old castle, and now with Elleard Heffern. He's well known all over the Midwest and has a great reputation."

"Is that so?" I reply cautiously.

"And Mary's the prettiest girl I ever did see." He glances at her and then adds. "Maybe I'll see you at the pool tomorrow Irish."

Heading off, he turns to wave offers a smile to her, as if sharing a secret.

"He's a right cheeky sod, you'd want to be careful with him."

"Ah, he means no harm, he's great fun, says he'd love to photograph me. To have me model for magazines, wouldn't it be great?"

"It depends what sort of magazine."

"And the money I'd get; I wouldn't have to be asking you for any."

"Has he made you an offer?"

"No, but told me to think about it, I can't be cooped up in the apartment all day."

"You've obviously met him a few times." This could get out of hand. I touch Mary momentarily.

"He comes down to the pool."

"And how did you get on with Dorothy?" I ask, not wanting to hear.

"She took us to see a friend of hers and we spent the whole afternoon looking at slides of their holiday in Ireland last year."

"Were you homesick?"

"Indeed I was not," she replies emphatically. "Dorothy gave me some of her childhood books for Lucy to read later on. They're unbelievable, with this naughtily little nigger and that one deserving a smack, eating water melon slices, I couldn't get over them, I'll show you when we get back. Lucy certainly won't be seeing them."

* * *

We are locked together into the night, the pill is a wonderful invention. But then she says: "you're hurting me!"

I'm unable to sleep when I suddenly realise, he must be the owner of the Thunderbird, with the *Playboy* magazine. Surely he does not want her to pose for that!

* * *

Repairing this late Victorian diamond bracelet is a tedious and difficult job. At least the diamonds can take heat if boraxed and not quenched as they are so hard. But each worn gold setting has to be checked and strengthened, which is a painstaking task. I have to get it right, for she's Mrs Golda Werner the Third, and Elleard says she wears the bracelet every day. Ireland seems hazy and distant most of the time, but suddenly present with me now and again.

The Snakeskin-jacket-man got into his Thunderbird this morning and cheekily waved to me on overtaking. Is that what he's doing? In more ways than one? Maybe.

I phone Mary at lunchtime, but she's not there. Well she's a life to lead too, with Dorothy or... no, she's probably making new friends at the pool. I go out on the crowded streets of St Louis, to get a Budweiser and a beef and pickle sandwich. Why do I feel so lonely here? How she's taken to this life? Mary is transforming, turning away from her Irish upbringing.

Mary's turning a corner and here's America, unfolding the way she always imagined would be and in a way she must have without hesitation.

The 1959 Cadillac convertible in the garage lot is for sale.

Oh yes, what the heck, and it's far too easy to arrange credit. I'll give her a big surprise. Those pointed rear tail lights are like spears, for there's madness in a car this size. The next day, I park it by the apartment and turn off the engine. A tribute to America's unbridled excess, with nearly six litres of power it could drive forever heading west.

Their beautiful earth will never run dry, not with those hauntingly weired oil pumping donkeys amidst acres of corn. Motel to motel, ever stranger are the people, who are as one with the moon's never-ending rotation. Never satisfied unless in motion. I'm told the desert stars here are particularly bright, especially for those not wanting to think of tomorrow.

Hallucinating and fearful, slumped back from the wheel, I return to focus. Is this really happening? It is Mary and Lucy and Snakeskin-jacket-man. I crouch lower in my seat, for they'll not recognise me in this vehicle. She's not doing anything wrong, but all the same I have the feeling some-thing's going on. However absurd I think he is, there's nothing I can make a stand on. For he's one of the tenants, with every right to make friends with Mary, and, if he wants, to photograph her too. Who knows? Perhaps this is a great opportunity for her.

Then Mary sees the new car. The way they are walking, slow and easy together, is most alarming. Straightening up I call over.

"God it's you, and what are you doing in that car?" ask Mary.

Snakeskinjacket man eyes me with a definite smirk.

"It's ours, I bought it, what do you think?"

"Well, the Buick was big, but..." Mary is clearly aghast, gazing from tailfin to headlights, "this is ridiculous!"

And he's obviously enjoying her reaction as well as my obvious disap-pointment. "You'll be needing your own oil well to be driving that, it'll do no more than ten to twelve miles to the gallon if you're lucky, in town maybe six. And it's really rather old now." He speaks disparagingly.

"Who wants to be sensible all the time?" I reply.

"Well, certainly, if you can afford it." His knowing retort is mocking.

"Come on, get in Mary and we'll go for a drive."

She turns to me sharply, "indeed I will not, not now anyway."

She shouldn't have spoken like that. Turning the ignition on, I reverse feverishly and the squealing tyres accelerate... to where?

CHAPTER 37

After a great row between Mary and I, disquieting days follow. She is determined to get into modelling and photography, whatever that means. And she's doing so with this Snakeskin-jacket-man, whom I can't stand. She's not going to hang around all day and on this point I admit she's absolutely right. She hints he's even gay, the way that gay men do like women friends; he's harmless enough. There again, I would be the last to know.

At her age there is a whole life to look forward to and she is only just out of her teens. I have no right to keep her in a cage.

* * *

We have driven from St. Louis to Kansas City to Topeka, Abilene.

"Hadn't we better turn back; we don't want to end up as far as Denver Colorado, do we?" Mary is struggling with the awkward, unfolded map. The rush of warm wind is exhilarating. I feel careless and free, happy we are together. Forever hopeful on American's endless highways, and indifferent to wherever the road ahead leads.

"Did you know that Denver Colorado has a connection with Denvir's Hotel Downpatrick? A Denvir emigrated from County Down and I think his grandson went on to found the city of Denver in Colorado."

"How on earth would I know that?" She turns incredulously to me.

"It's the oldest hotel in Ireland, dating from the reign of Charles first; don't you remember? On the hill up English Street to the Cathedral?"

"No I do not and anyway, why would I want to, you're still back in

Ireland. And I wonder sometimes did you ever leave?"

"Well, it's only a short walk from where Lucy was born and I thought of it with you mentioning Denver Colorado. No need to worry we'll never get there. Talking of Lucy, she's beginning to smell."

I have to stop the car for Mary to change her, beside a hedgeless sea of golden wheat, that rolls away from me in great undulating waves, to a fleet of pea-green John Deere combine harvesters on the horizon. It is strange and other worldly, to be under a cloudless, brazen blue sky, so different from Ireland's ever-changing clouds.

"You're Sir Terence Langrishe's beautiful granddaughter, one he'll never know about." I say this, cupping Lucy's tiny pink feet, which are kicking in my hands.

"I wish you wouldn't mention that name, hopefully he's dead by now, the old goat!" Mary replies, cleaning Lucy's bottom with wipes. The baby is gurgling. I feel a rush of adoration at the little innocent being: the big bad world's all ahead of you and, alas, will come far too soon.

"What a change from driving between Kilkenny and Freshford and just look at those combine harvesters." I point across the fields.

"There you go again." This monster would be like a circus in the village. I still can't understand why you had to buy it, it's far too big and expensive to run."

"But the whole excess, that's what I like experiencing, for a while anyway, before we decide one way or the other about staying in America."

"You can forget about me ever returning to Ireland; of that you can be sure."

"We might have to go."

"You'll be on your own!"

Here comes the siren sounds of the Highway Patrol approaching fast and a large black Cadillac sedan, much older than this, slows down. The patrol car stops behind it, lights still flashing. Dressed in a sharp, broad-brimmed hat, wearing sinister reflecting sunglasses, a policeman in a chocolate and yellow striped uniform, strides up to the sedan. He is armed. A black man is at the wheel; I wonder what he's done wrong.

The questioning is over quickly, I can see the policeman throw back the license into the car, rudely, before gesturing them on. And I hear him call over to his companion, "hard to believe an old Jew having a nigger to drive for her." Then he's right beside me, "anything wrong here?" The policeman is big and intimidating; he ignores me but is transfixed by Mary.

"Just changing baby's nappy; you know how it is." Mary replies disarmingly, smiling and pushing her sunglasses onto her forehead. The policeman is confused for what seems an ages, as if he has never seen the like. Then, without another word, he returns to his luminous, patched patrolled car. He's in deep conversation with his companion; they are both seated together. Then very slowly, the patrol car drives past, with both staring intently at Mary. It is disturbing.

Later, I'm powerless to resist my desire for her. I remember how in Ireland I wanted her constantly. There was a time by a near roofless cottage, which smelt of old cattle dung and now doubt full of bitter memories. Another on the car seat. Again, from behind a rotten window frame, looking towards Slieve Croob and Mam's Queen's county. There was magic in Mary then, as the Nore's morning mist rose by Kilkenny and she was underneath me. And now here, with Lucy asleep on the rear seat.

"God, my face, sunburnt." Mary straightens herself, touching her cheeks, dismayed and irritated.

"I'll put the hood up so we can have a nap."

"Whatever you say."

Now we are out of Ireland, we are pulling apart. I fall in and out of a fitful sleep and wake to the sounds of angry wasps. There are cars passing. And that distant hum coming closer, louder and louder, is John Deere coming upon me to devour me along with the ripe wheat. The driver's face looking down upon me, is masked and goggled. He is wearing a skull, the Horseman of the Apocalypse, raising his hand in warning.

"Let's get away back to St. Louis, I've had more than enough of this few days away." When Mary says this, I'm startled into wakefulness, to see her in the rear view mirror, brushing her hair, slipping on her shoes. I reach for Lucy, who is hysterical.

* * *

Mary is asleep beside me, her pale face lit on and off in the colours of the neon signs outside. These motels are transient spaces to rest for the night, then move on quickly. Impermanence is the mystery of time. If I stare at the enormous Missouri moon long enough I can actually see it move. We so avidly cling to this little minute of life, without appreciating that death could be a welcoming friend, returning us to the womb of sweet nothing. Like the words out of the Gideon Bible in the drawer. 'They that be wise shall shine as the brightness of the firmament and they that turn righteousness as the stars for ever and ever.'

* * *

Another one of those disturbing letters from father is waiting in the mail box on my return: an Englishman in a foreign land of England's own creation. This preacher Paisley is a fiery comet across the Ulster sky, who seems to grow out of all proportion to reason. To think this letter was so recently dropped into the little red post box under the Union flag by the crossroads, in the heart of County Down.

'Paisley is phoney from the heels up, a maverick Presbyterian who formed a sect thirty years ago called the Free Presbyterians. He has churches all over Northern Ireland and they are very wealthy. It is surprising, the well-heeled people who attend his services which are packed. He doesn't preach, he bellows. He was ordained by his father, a renegade Baptist, and Paisley ordains his own ministers, a disgusting ragbag of rabble rousers all heavily involved in politics and all RC haters. To them the Pope is the whore of Babylon, they would be more at home in the seventeenth century.

'The big mistake was to divide Ireland against seventy percent of the people in all Ireland in 1920. The British turned democracy on its head.'

No matter what father writes, Paisley is probably spot on about the Catholic Church. Father's letter triggers an hour of soul-searching, numb and inconclusive thoughts about everything.

* * *

"There's an old man called Mississippi that's the old man I'd like to be. What does he care if the world's got troubles? What does he care if the land ain't free?" Moses's words are hardly audible, he's murmuring to himself, miles away, as we go up to the fourth floor. I've been doing far too many repairs these last few weeks. It's not the kind of work I should be doing. We shall see one way or the other: America or Ireland before it's too late. Mary will just have to come, for it won't take a lot to start on my own somewhere, these distractions will have to end.

It's a shame that they don't have proper hallmarking here. I recall the dilapidated office in Dublin castle, where there was always that mad eegit at the gate, with his, "Are yez all right?" The reminiscence brings feelings I can't explain, recalling the embracing, warm, infusing magic that was everywhere. Especially at Thomastown and its surroundings. But I can't go back without her, can I? And would Adolf Hitler come to haunt me again if I did?

"Hi, is Hugo not in? I'm Lorna Lee." A curvaceous blonde enters without knocking, she is something else indeed.

"He'll be back shortly, can I help you?"

"My ring, it's too tight, can you help me get it off and make it larger?" Lorna Lee asks with her slow southern accent from down Mississippi way. She holds out a finger, which has a gold engraved band. It will certainly not be easy to remove the ring and I'm distracted by our visitor's amazing nails.

"Let's try a bit of oil; it might do the trick," I suggest, as she sits down on Hugo's swivel chair, folding her lovely legs, her pencil skirt above her knee.

"Nothing like a bit of oil to help a girl in distress," she says suggestively, squirting a small amount of three-in-one oil on her knuckle. It does the trick, with difficulty and we are standing close together as Hugo comes in, surprised.

"Hugo my dear, your friend is going to size my ring."

"Is he now?" Hugo removes his jacket and hat, "he's from Ireland you know."

"Little old Ireland, land of leprechauns and shamrocks, how cute." This thirtyish, well-endowed lady has a scent that will linger long after she's gone.

"It might crack if I stretch it on the ring sizer, shall I risk it?" I ask.

"What the heck, live dangerously." Her eyes light mischievously.

"Anneal it just to be on the safe side, if you won't mind the colour changing slightly. It's marked fourteen carat." Hugo inspects the ring, with his Opti Visor on. It is always on, he wouldn't be Hugo without it on.

"Will I wait?" she says glancing flirtatiously at me.

"No Lorna, come back in the morning, we'll have it for you then." Hugo seems a touch exasperated at Lorna, but she, in turn, pulls a sour face at him, then winks over to me before leaving.

"She's over the top that one Hugo."

"You can say that again: not long before you came, one evening, I was doing urgent work for Elleard. I went to the gents and she was getting laid, her two red stilettos under the lavatory door and they were hard at it."

"And who was the lucky man?"

"I didn't hang around to find out."

The thought of Lorna getting fucked in the toilet lingers with me for some time afterwards.

*   *   *

I can tell that someone has been smoking in the apartment, a familiar, sweet-toasted, American flavour. I have returned in the middle of the day, with my head splitting from repairs, feeling suffocated. Turning the television on, I see news about Vietnam, Martin Luther King, and even little old Ulster. With civil rights for black people, Irish Catholics are on the march as well. Lying on the bed, I wonder who it was that was smoking here this morning. I have a good idea. Apprehensively, I go to the kitchen bin, rooting through it, then pour it all out on the floor. Would she be trying to hide it? The butt is of a Camel cigarette, which must have been at the bottom. It could only have been Snakeskin-jacket-man, since he smokes them. I feel sick.

Mary tells me about his glamorous life style, how he photographs beautiful models in Barbados and St. Lucia, Antiqua and Montserrat too were mentioned, places of amazing sunsets and palm trees, where people walk bare footed on golden beaches. Bikini clad, black-eyed pirates drinking rum, that sort of thing. There again, after the life she had in Ireland, I can hardly complain if she wants to escape. And perhaps she can, with her natural good looks

Yesterday, Snakeskin-jacket-man drove up close behind again in his Thunderbird, as if urging me to get out of the way. But I wasn't going to let him pass this time, for the old Cadillac can really go. So I got involved in a dangerous game. Although I couldn't be bothered after a short while. Mary would do anything with Lucy anyway, would she? Maybe it was harmless enough. It was such a waste of her natural talent. I should let her do whatever she wants.

"Was Snakeskin here this morning?" I ask as Mary and Lucy return. She colours somewhat in answering, unable to fib.

"Yes he was and I'm definitely going to do modelling for him whatever you say and I wish you wouldn't call him by that name." Mary speaks defiantly and I feel that even little Lucy feels sour towards me.

I know that modelling for him will lead to his becoming fatally attractive to her. With no regular hours and lots of excitement between them. She is that rare butterfly I saw in a summer field by the Nore, beautiful but ephemeral. My head is full of images and recurring thoughts that I can never shake free. I sense of displacement is enveloping me here. I have to get ahead of this somehow, she's not going to be at my beck and call and I can't complain if she takes flight.

"You're seeing a lot of him aren't you?"

"No not really and only because he's so keen for me to do modelling, he came this morning with an album of his latest photographs, and they're amazing, I'd get lots of new clothes to model, he said, and could probably keep them."

"There's something about that man I just don't like."

"Don't be silly, he's very nice and only wants to help me get ahead."

"Do you really know anything about him? And what you'd be getting into?"

"You've nothing to worry about and anyway think of the money he'll pay me, so much an hour when I'm away."

"How much?"

"We haven't discussed that yet, but I'm sure it'll be more than enough."

"More than when you worked in Woolworths that Christmas anyway."

"Ah get away, don't be ridiculous: Woolworths Kilkenny indeed." She raises her eyes and head scornfully.

"And what about Lucy, will she go with you?"

"Yes of course, it won't be for another few years she'll be going to school."

"I see. You seem to have worked it all out without consulting me."

"I knew you wouldn't agree at first, but you have to look at this from my point of view. I'd go mad hanging around here all day, going out with your old aunt. This is an opportunity, one not to be missed, I have to take it while I'm still young enough," she continues defiantly.

"Dorothy's been very good to us since we came, they're of a different generation, and we should make allowances for them."

"How they see black people you mean?"

"That's the way they are and there's no point getting into a row about civil rights and race with them, what good will it do?"

"They'd leave us alone." She speaks as though she doesn't care about falling out with the people who have been so good to us.

"That's not very nice now is it?"

"Well I wouldn't mind."

"So when are you going to start then?" I ask, resigned.

"In a few days, I knew you wouldn't mind in the end." She comes over and kisses me ever-so-lightly on the forehead. There is a definite whiff of the Camel cigarette in her hair.

CHAPTER 38

Am I just a jobbing jeweller now? With the first few weeks of interesting work having faded, it's all alterations and repairs. I'm reading William Shirer's, *The Rise and Fall of the Third German Reich*, which is in hand as I lie on the bed. It depicts Satanic, real-life monsters. Some of them are still alive. I feel a piercing headache. The open book slips to one side of the bed.

I'll be as old as Hugo one day, far from Ireland. I'm filled with inexplicable, majestic desolation and pain. Maybe I have to let go of Mary. I picture her as a little girl, no more than eight or nine, laughing and running bare feet along a Kilkenny country lane. Her playground the nettle covered fallen walls, choked with ivy. Angel carved headstones and forgotten names behind the graveyard gate. We were married by the crossroads and her dream was to get so far, far away.

"Where have you been, coming home so late?" I challenge her as she tries to slip quietly into bed.

"Go back to sleep, I'm exhausted; it's been a long day, I'll tell you in the morning." She bundles Lucy in her arms; the child is cranky, half asleep.

On returning from the next room, she becomes a ghostly figure. She changes quickly and moves in beside me. I get up and turn the light on.

"What's going on? Returning this hour of the morning, it's nearly three o'clock." I point to the bedside alarm, angry and confused.

"Will you please let me go to sleep." She shields her eyes, "come on to bed."

"I want to know what's going on between you and Snakeskin."

"Nothing! Absolutely nothing!" She shouts at me, bolt upright now,

"I'll go and sleep with Lucy if you continue like this." Covering herself with the sheets, shroud like, Mary turns and faces to the wall. I turn the light off and get back into bed. There is a long silence, then, when I reach across to touch her, she moves away.

* * *

Like a fool, I ignore this. Maybe it will fade away. For there is no point continually resisting whatever she's doing. America is intoxicating and I hope that her infatuations will run their course then die. But it is becoming most painful to watch.

Often, she leaves notes saying that Lucy is with the baby-sitter at number twenty-six.

I walk along corridors of doors with those awful peep holes, as if a murder is lurking outside and I press the angry buzzer. It is unbearable, having to live like this. The door opens. The baby-sitter has gleaming, straightened black hair. She wears a tight, short lavender dress, over a body whose colour is a mix of black and white. The lavender captures the African side of her sex, diluting the darker colour to an exotic, easy-going, delightful mix. I've certainly noticed her before, but never spoke to her

"I'm Mary's husband; sorry I'm late. When did she leave Lucy with you?"

With an ebullient gesture, she invites me to enter. "Oh, they left her here about ten this morning."

"They?"

"The man she was with, Neil I think she called him."

"And I suppose he was wearing a snakeskin jacket?"

"Well yes, do you know him?" I am unable to answer; my stomach is churning.

"Did she say when they'd be back?"

"This evening, around nine."

"That's a long day for you."

"Nor a problem, he paid me real well and Lucy's a delight to have."

"And he paid you?"

"Yes, he did." She has a pitying and sad look in those big, dark brown eyes.

"He's a photographer and Mary's doing some kind of modelling work with him," I explain hopefully.

"Well I wouldn't know much about that now." Yet her voice suggests that she does. "Your daughter is such a beautiful child and no trouble at all. She goes out like a light whenever's her bedtime and she is fast asleep now. So you stay a while and I'll bring you some comfort."

"Comfort?"

"Yes, Southern Comfort, a drink like sweet whiskey, you do sit down and relax, you gonna like this."

"Sounds very nice." She goes in the next room, returning with two heavy tumbler glasses of the golden liquid.

"Now you try this." The baby-sitter hands the glass over. She's a fine, tall, well-proportioned lady of forty or so. Sinking back on the couch, close beside me, we clink our glasses together. Sipping the fiery sweetness, a taste a touch of apples and pears. I will have to go easy with such stuff.

"I don't even know your name."

"My name is Idelette Rich."

"That's a most unusual name, I've never heard it before."

"My late father was deeply religious and named me after Calvin's wife Idelette and Martin Luther's wife, Katharina von Boras. Katharina is my second name." As she explains this, I'm aware of an unusual scent, she uses a powerful perfume, which is a most pleasant bouquet to go with the Comfort.

"That's very interesting, two lovely sounding names." Her Comfort relaxes me. I no longer feel as though anything really matters in this old world and I finish the glass.

"Here, I'll get you another." Rising, her dress is nearly up to her arse, and she has to wriggling it down.

"I should be on my way."

"What's your hurry, they could be much later than you think."

"Well, whatever you say." Let's hope not, whatever is going on.

"Good man."

I've been told that black women are the very devil for sex. And isn't all life a game of chance? As Idelette brings in another Comfort, she gives me a little dance, smiling naughtily. Whatever was going to happen, if anything, ends with Lucy waking up and calling out loudly.

Lucy recognizes me, her little face (so like Mary's) contracts to an angry, screaming eruption. She's unhappy that I'm not Idelette, or her mother, or, God forbid, Snakeskin-jacket-man. I think about how Lucy would not be here, but for the fact I forgot the Durex for our journey to Galway. All that fuss about which side of Ireland's divide you'd be born into and now you'll never be contaminated by either. For your mother was so desperate to leave and will never return.

Lucy does not want to be lifted up, her cries become even louder. I feel like I hardly know her, behaving like this. The world is complex and we are nothing, so I had better not try to kiss her. I remain stupidly hopeful. Maybe I am only dreaming that Mary and Lucy are leaving me. This is a dark comet that will quickly pass.

I remember the golden jug I made for Hogan and Walsh in those early days of Kilkenny, the one that disappeared. Was it even made? I recall setting up the silver workshop and those ridiculous coffee and tea sets. It is a fixation in my head again. Whereas, here I am, driving an enormous white Cadillac, which could float over the wide seas of Kansas wheat, perhaps with Mary Malone in the passenger seat, driving towards that big old mysterious Missouri moon (yet the same moon as wanders over Kilkenny and County Down). In this daydream, I'm holding a sixty carat, emerald and diamond brooch that Elleard has on sale or return that once belonged to Catherine the Great of Russia.

My thoughts are driven back to the present by the return of Idelette, who has another glass of Comfort in her hand. I admire her sublimely rounded rear, athletic legs and muscular thighs. Thighs that are a fraction too thick, but strong enough to lock over a man's back tight.

"Where's Riviera Beach Idelette?"

"Riviera Beach see now, that name... Florida of course, Florida."

"That's where they're going next, Florida." I suddenly remember Mary once vaguely mentioned Snakeskin's parents lived there. Well, well she'll be meeting them. Everything's so easy now with the pill. The sleeping arrangements will be interesting there with Lucy. "That's where his parents live, I'm really sure it was Riviera Beach. God!"

"Now you do listen to me and I gotta be careful what I say about this. She's gone; they're a pair; you gotta get your head around it so and move on; it happens all the time as I do well know. So try not to get upset what I say to you, understand?" She pauses for a moment to let her words sink in and to see if I want to continue.

"Yes, go on."

"Just the other day I went down to get a pair of shoes I'd left in that lemon of a car of mine and they were wrapped around each other for anyone to see, Mary pushed up against his T-Bird. Never even noticed me pass by."

"In the underground car park?"

"Yes."

"So explain to me what they were exactly doing Idelette."

"Ah, sure, man, you know, the usual deep throated stuff, with his hands all over her, moanin' and lovin' it and she so young and good looking. But not fuckin, but you can be sure they are so."

"Jesus Idelette, I never thought it was that bad."

"You've been in a daze with that girl for far too long. I tell you now, you just gotta move on, there's plenty more out there, put yourself first, and try not to look back. I know it's hard, but that's life."

"I would never have imagined it coming to this."

"Ah, God, man, love can be bitter, but there's always the sex, an itch you just gotta scratch, something up your nose you just gotta blow out. That's all it is, man, and we can do it together." She stands up and holding out her many ringed hand, takes me to her bedroom.

"This'll do you a lotta good, so lie down and wait a while." Drawing the curtains she turns the low table light on. My thoughts are revolving around what she's just told me. Returning as a red hot oven door that is opening, Idellete's a sexually charged shooting star, which landing upon me obliterates all other thoughts.

"I'm all yours baby, you just take me anyway you want, this is all about you forgetting that Irish Molly O. Let her go, I say to you, let her go."

Idelette the Minister who delivers the Bread and Cup, as touched by the celestial lightning, which is a most profound mystery, crossing the fragile line separating the living from the dead. On both sides is now infidelity. I'm hurting dreadfully, on an emotional see-saw. I really had never believed it would come to this.

* * *

The day before St Valentine's, I'm somehow aware she's bought him a Valentine card and hidden it somewhere. It shouldn't be hard to find in the apartment. After they've gone out I look under the mattress, the most obvious place. There it is. Hidden like a caterpillar, waiting to change into a dragonfly with amazing, rainbow-coloured gossamer wings. Mary is ready to fly away from wet and boggy places where came from. With trembling fingers I open the large, unsealed pink envelope. The card of purple, pink and blue black, has a bold sheep staring suggestively at me and a line: 'Do not wanta go astray?' Turning the folded card out, she has written, 'Little Bo-Peep is waiting!"

* * *

I enter a period of unsound mind.

* * *

I've cracked an emerald and Elleard is non-too pleased. My nights are sleepless and now I definitely know, America was never to be. Mary so wanted this though. It's not the life I could possibly give her. I've the judgemental mind of the Northern tribe, and she has a Langrishe side that always wants the very best, however she was born and reared. Florida is where they're gone to live it seems. Who could blame her, driving towards Denver in an old open top Cadillac? No thanks.

Mary has disappeared into the glamour and excitement of a new life far away from her Ireland. Whatever she can see in him? A snakeskin jacket and a Thunderbird are not cheap. And what was I offering her instead? A return to Ireland as the wife of what? Someone who made silver teapots in this modern age. How ridiculous. From cold Clontubrid cottage to Riviera Beach, well there you go. And she was never aware or noticed or cared about Hitler. How any normal person could think of anything else. In Tipperary town it was, when I saw him. And that dark time he walked past me on the Parade.

* * *

What will it be like at home just now? From Downpatrick on the Vianstown road, I imagine driving over the old disused railway crossing, up the hill to the crossroads, turning left past my earliest childhood and continuing to where sea, shore and land meet. There is a roadside sign to Ballynoe Stone Circle, which you reach through little, circular, caged gates and can enter via a mysterious sunken narrow tunnel, made from low stone walls and overhanging blooming blackthorn and gorse. There someone has placed a pair of tubular tinkling bells on the branches above, and a bold robin leads me ahead to an open pathway leading out to a wide circle of large grey stones of different natural shapes, spaced around the low central mound. Standing on it, I would be able to see the familiar shape of the Mournes rising up from Tyrella Beach, across fields of tall rippling, shinning grass, ready to be cut for silage or hay.

It is an early afternoon in June, with the molten silvery circle sun radiating to celestial blue and only the occasional puffed white cloud obscuring the sky, as if the brief shadow of someone long departed, now risen and approaching me from behind. My fingers could touch rough lichen patches of beautiful yellow, green and blue grey. It is a place of strange, thought-provoking otherness, moving and separate from the rest of the country in its own disturbing way.

My thoughts return to the fact I am repairing yet another gold safety chain for Elleard B Heffern, Inc., Four O Seven, North Eighth Street, Suite Three O Three, St Louis, Missouri.

At least there's Idelette and Lorna Lee at work on the same floor, available to me almost any day. And we spend a week together travelling through Memphis, Vicksburg, Natchez, Baton Rouge to New Orleans, which is a cleansing of memory.

I defile myself, as the Written Word would say, with its stern warnings about impurity and libidinous excess. But I'm trying to bandage wounds that might never be closed or healed.

The fragment of a poem. In a Kilkenny woodland thick with ferns, primroses and bluebells, I briefly a fox, blackbird and hare. And then they are gone. I could never have held Langrishe's daughter, for who knows the reasons for another person's nightmares? Her Ireland was a dung heap. Odorous, with a sickly, sweet incense. She married me, in the subconsciously hope it would enable her to leave. Now she can find whatever she is looking for in Snakeskin. For I am going to cross deep waters wide enough to wipe away my tears. I shall never return, even for little Lucy, whom I never got to know.

* * *

Father's letters are beginning to paint an ever-more dire picture, as the old quarrel between the two sides – only briefly asleep – has wakened again. How lucky he thinks I am to be living away from it. Well, we shall have to see. Hummel, the watchmaker, will take the Cadillac for eight hundred dollars. That is all I will have to return with.

CHAPTER 39

It comes as a shock when the Italian-looking peasants at the John F Kennedy airport in their dowdy, dark clothes are, in fact, Irish. It alarms me with foreoboding as to what I might be returning to. The Pan Am 707 is less than half full, taking off into a night of the darkest blue, with a scattering of faintly dancing stars. This amazing experience has developed in less than a lifetime. The pretty air hostess approaching me in her pale blue, tight-fitting uniform smiles as she passes. If only we could be forever and forever together in the heavens and never nearing Ireland.

Regrettably, the engine sounds change and, as dawn breaks, we land at Shannon. Outside is a bitter spot of rain. On the steps down from the aircraft it is cold; old Ireland has a wet, rugged welcoming coat to put on.

The Aer Lingus girls seem weirdly old-fashioned in their powdery make-up, very red lipstick, and too green uniforms. We are flying across to Dublin. I will never see the Pan Am lovely again, her appearance still remaining in my thoughts. The clouds are torn and threatening, unusually low, as we fly into Dublin.

In town, the people are furtive and hurried. It is though I see Dublin for the first time and it could be the capital of Albania or Montenegro, so foreign and strange is it. On the *Enterprise*, I travel over autumn's partly flooded fields, through dreary Drogheda and Dundalk, where newspaper headlines shout 'murder', until I reach Belfast.

On the last Ulster bus, leaving by the old, red-bricked gas works, the passengers seem like people from those Balkan states again. Voices that once were familiar are now painfully hard to understand.

Alighting in the Square at Ballynahinch, my clothes reek of Gallagher

Blue and Greens. I walk around by the Orange hall and the grand entrance to Montalto, Lord Clanwilliam's estate. His uncle was an admiral who commanded *HMS Renown* and was present at the battles of Heligoland, Dogger and Jutland. For no reason, I suddenly remember father telling me this and he would know. It is an awfully long walk from Ballynahinch to home, if ever there is such a place. At last I sight the post box that started this unfortunate interlude. And I can't help wondering would Mary still be with me if hadn't let the fateful letter drop that Christmas Day?

My brother's new house is an ugly intrusion; it cuts brutally into the side of a virgin field. The faded, whitewashed, fat, round, sloping-topped gate pillars are a reminder from an earlier age. I enter cautiously into the yard. There are no lights on, I'm not going to disturb anyone. The doors are probably locked this late, in these changed and dangerous times. Father took his military rank off the latest telephone directory entry.

I hear the faint tweaks and squeaks of sleeping pigs. In my nightmares I recall weighing them and painting a red spot upon them. What do the pigs think when they watch as their heavier siblings are taken, never to return?

Treading ever so lightly, as dogs can very easily waken, I climb up to the highest straw bales in the corrugated iron hayshed, which makes a comfortable enough space to try and sleep on. I am without a job; a tramp. Where can I find a place to beg and hideaway. I feel myself to be a failure and am full of foreboding about the future.

Sailing in and out of troubled consciousness, I contemplate on how I am here after billions of years of evolution. Simple cells that lived in warm seas became fish-like before sliding ashore with fins becoming limbs. Eventually, creatures were enabled to climb trees, with some coming down to go walkabout in utter confusion: the brain growing larger as they tried to figure out their environments. They were without answers and had to invent gods to explain their existence. It took four billion years for me to come into existence and here I am, under a rusty old Ulster hayshed, watching the dawn slowly lighting over the familiar fields of county Down

I am startled by furious barking from a golden Labrador below me; they have such a great sense of smell. The moment it was let out, it detected me. The dog is in a sweat at finding me, but is wary to advance further: am I friend or foe? Father follows up some way behind, calling the dog off.

"Whoever is up there, come down immediately!"

I rise furtively to expose myself.

"Good God man what are you doing back here. where's Mary and Lucy?" Father is angry and dismayed.

Have I done something wrong, he's hardly pleased to see me. How can returning to Ireland be a crime? The dog bounds over the bales to me, tail wagging, as if this is some sort of a game now.

"You look like a criminal on the run, is this yours?" Father points disparagingly to the suitcase, which holds my entire worldly possessions.

"Yes, it is." As he knows fine well.

"Well come on down out of that, you've a lot of explaining to do." Father speaks as though addressing some unfortunate aircraftsman — with a commanding officer voice, that he sometimes adopts — I'm minded of poor Edge, Father's old batman, whom I witnessed being addressed in the same way over some minor infraction.

I'm brought into a perfect storm between the two parents, with mybrother refusing to say a word. Somehow I know he is thinking that he knew it would come to this, with Mary being from the South. His Protestant, puritan certainties are to the fore; an invisible and silent atmosphere emanating from him speaks volumes, as does the very air I breathe. I'm sitting at the kitchen table drinking coffee and eating cake, surrounded by the odour of silage and pigs.

Out the kitchen window I notice three speeding, olive-green army Land Rovers on the narrow road, disappearing behind Hennan's sloping field. Ulster is beginning to boil. A freeze of reason is becoming endemic here, the warring tribes are gathering and remembering too much of their opposing histories and religions.

* * *

"So, what are you going to do now? There's never been much silversmithing done in Ulster if any." My brother asks, unconcerned. As he speaks, the sliding door is slid open brusquely to allow Father to enter. He throws last Sunday's *Irish Independent* on the table, are they reading that southern paper up here now?

"There's an article about a Dublin jeweller in this, so give him a call and see what he says about getting you started again." Father is still directing the war effort.

The photograph is of Vincent Meehan, busy in his Dublin studio, making copper enamelled jewellery. It has been encircled by father's bold red biro. I will give him a call, but tonight I am early to bed. I've so much to forget, from St Louis to Ballynahinch. Below, I can hear them discussing me.

"He's going to have to get a job, for he can't be hanging around the farm all day doing nothing for long. There's really no future for him in this Godforsaken last imperial wreck of the woods."

"I'll never see my granddaughter again and I was fond of Mary, yes I was." Mother laments, convincing herself.

"This silversmithing lark is a nonsense in this day and age, if you ask me, it went the way of candlelight. Has he even any money with him now?"

"Eight hundred dollars he said," replies mother.

"Humph, that won't get him far, he should have stayed in America, even without Mary and made a go of it."

And so they continue, on and on. I had almost forgotten. Opening the bottom dressing table drawer, I wonder are they still there? No, yes, yes, carefully folded in pillow slips under towels and sheets: the French Marshal, Sebastian Le Prestre de Vauban's two books. I will never forget that name, he's like a faithful old friend coming to the rescue. I hope Lord Ormonde, is well... dead, so I can sell them.

* * *

It is vaguely comforting to hear Vincent's voice on the other end of the phone. That easy-going southern tone emanates recognition when he remembers my name from the Kilkenny Design. It is still going strong, annoying the many, he says, still a mystery to anyone outside the hallowed stable walls. Maliciously, he mentions this perons and that and suggests I maybe call a Father McDyer, who he knows is looking for someone to come and work in Glencolumbkille, Donegal.

On the map, Glencolumbkille is falling into the sea, at the farthest extremity of the county. I could be going from one extreme to another? And a Roman priest as well. Still, it is as good a place as any I suppose, considering my present situation.

"Yes, do come over, there's a couple of empty rooms in the village if you're interested you can start right away." Father McDyer explains and welcomes me with few questions asked. I am amazed and somewhat taken aback. Now the pressures is on. How will I get the necessary equipment and a car? Where will I live? Will there be rent to pay and will eight hundred dollars be enough to get started? Best to go over there and find out. There is an old, faded-green Morris Oxford in Jim Brown's garage Ballynahinch, which I can have for a hundred and fifty-pounds.

* * *

On leaving home, the weather is fairish, above me are clouds of grey-white, with edges of gold, moving lazily in the early morning sunshine, turning to a whisp of rain, becoming a heavy shower, which is quickly over. I had nearly forgotten how green Ireland is. What would Mary and Lucy be doing now? She wouldn't have enjoyed returning to her childhood, which in all probability Glencolumbkille will be. In the landscape of my mind, my thoughts running ahead, oblivious to my passing surroundings until I reach Pettigoe, where the border runs through part of the town. Having a business split by two different jurisdiction's might be most beneficial. Here, long ago, there had been some sort of a quarrel with the B Specials in a priest's house, with the British shelling the town, which was held by the Free State troops. Some were killed and captured, the rest fled with the civilian population.

The uneven road leads to Laghy and Donegal and a wake up call in the astonishing, weird, unreal surroundings. In the boggy water on either side of me are small, mirrored lakes, which reflect the sky with touches of waving, wild flowers and acres of blue and pink rhododendrons. Everything is damp, mysterious and transcendental. The only sign of life is an occasional solitary sheep, a few crows. As the car stutters to a worrying stop, I'm brought back to harsh reality. Without sign or sight of human habitation, there comes a feeling of hopeless desolation. I'm on the way to God knows where. Fearful and frozen, I wonder whether to turn back or go on? I'm marooned and isolated, halfway between Pettigoe and Laghy, Donegal town.

Who is this priest McDyer, anyway?

I can't keep turning the key or the battery will die, so I'll give it a attempt with the starting handle. Would there even be a garage in Laghy? There should be and Donegal's a long walk away. Well here goes. On the third try, after a "dear God make it start," I am delivered miraculously from the crisis, the devil escaping as a cloud of dirty-black exhaust from the rear.

The stoppage makes me wary and I am thankful on reaching Donegal. I press on through towns and villages the colour of boiled sweets. From Mountcharles to Killybegs, where I can recognise Benbulben across Donegal Bay. Kilcar, then Carrick on winding, rain-eroded, pot-holed, narrowing roads, which are becoming ever more difficult to navigate. At last I arrive at a vast bog desert of lunar-like desolation. To my far left, peaks covered in ominous clouds rise high. Treeless and sombre, with every shade of layered, flat browns, the occasional reality intrudes in the form of a stacked pile of cut turf. Scattered sheep are sometimes on the road, whose surface has been eaten away in parts by rust-coloured rushing streams. Nature has used a mighty trowel to sweep and shape the landscape in great strokes, plastering and embalming this empty, bounding wilderness. Without a doubt, I am entering Spaghetti Western territory. I am the lone driver approaching his doom or deliverance, I am stoney-faced and a man of few words. The gawking locals wondering about me and worried why I've come. My daydream is broken by the sight of a faint vapour trail high in a clear patch of the otherwise turbulent sky, the silver glint of a jet plane heading west with the Pan Am stewardess on board perhaps.

There is a definite time warp here, a quantum event, where principles of reality and probabilities interact, another dimension that I clearly feel closing around me. One that only an Einstein could understand, but one which would be truly outrageous if he attempted to explain it. I feel like a door has opened to let me through and then closed behind me. Descending the valley I reach the village of Glencolumbkille —which barely deserves the title village — it has just a few mean dwellings, a pub at each end, an ugly, pebble-dashed church and a graveyard with a short distance between them. The house I'm looking for is beyond a bend, just outside the village, on a raised well-tended grass lawn. It is a large square, two-storey house, slate roofed, brilliant white, situated seemingly so as to keep an eye over the whole valley and whatever might be going on. This must be where Father McDyer lives.

The front door opens to his housekeeper, with an enormous Irish wolf-hound by her side. Nicely dressed and quite attractive, I would guess she was in her mid-thirties, there are just the first touches of grey in her dark hair. Ever vigilant and protective of her charge, she gives me the brief confrontational gaze that asks: who are you and what do you want from the Holy Father? Shown into the sitting room, arising from my subconscious come queasy, irrational feelings, as always on these rare occasions that I encounter churchmen.

"Father's gone to Kilcar and shouldn't be too long," says she in that fey, far-away, Donegal speak, observing me closely. I bet she doesn't miss a trick. "I'm Bernadette McGinley, Father's housekeeper by the way, can I get you a cup of tea?"

"Would you have coffee?"

"Ah no, it's only tea we have, sorry." Her appearance noticeably softens, but she still seems to be searching for something from me.

"That would be just fine." I can't help notice as she leaves, that she has a pair of fine shapely legs.

Standing before the north facing window, I can see over the valley to the tower-topped, high cliff, that falls sheer into the sea. There is a sandy beach, a widening river inlet and scant sign of much habitation. There is what I assume to be the wee Protestant church, rather cute and very lonely against the blackish rock-faced, browns and greens that rise steeply behind the building. It looks like a fragile boat, momentarily becalmed amidst a sea of hard rock.

Turning towards the fireplace, I notice the walls are without the usual iconographic images one would normally find in a priest's house. There are numerous blue-and-white packets of Rothman's cigarettes and the clinging tarry scents of a heavy smoker. The wolfhound, checking on me, comes over for a friendly sniff and a pat, before hurriedly turning to some sound that only a dog could hear.

The similarities with the time I was waiting with Mary for the Kilkenny parish priest come to mind. I can still see her sitting there, nervous and anxious to be gone: it certainly turned out to be as far as possible. From Kilkenny to Florida in less than a couple of short years. A leaden weight of dumb sadness and remorse takes hold of me. The room is without St Agatha's bleeding breasts, but has the same amount of cigarettes. And Bernadette's legs are no antidote for such melancholy thoughts.

Returning with a pot of tea and biscuits on a tray, she lays them before me; I detect a fresh whiff of perfume. She takes the overflowing ashtray and says, "I wish Father wouldn't smoke so much, I think it's a terrible habit, do you smoke yourself?" Then she bends to empty the ashtray into the grate, which is still powdery warm from burnt turf. She has a nice, full, tight arse to go with those legs and, after all, nothing in this old world can stand still.

"An occasional cigar now and then, maybe." Despite my interest in her figure, I reply without enthusiasm. I feel a sense of purposeless, close to despair. I am waiting for a priest; my future is on hold. Oh yes..., she's definitely put on a touch of makeup, rearranged her hair and made her lips redder when making the tea.

Minutes pass, Bernadette hovers on display, fixing cushions, emptying ashtrays, straightening and folding yesterday's *Irish Press*, opening and shutting the sideboard. Whatever she's looking for is not there.

"Isn't it terrible what's going on in Belfast," she says, turning around, her brown eyes fixed to mine all of a sudden. I hear the sound of a car of coming fast up the driveway. "That's Father now, I'll go see to him."

Father indeed, what a nonsense, that's the last thing they'd want to be. He must get that every day from Bernadette. More minutes pass as I listen to their inaudible conversation in the hallway. It is only a short interval before the wheel of fortune starts turning again. I am in the most unlikely of places, yet a fuse could be lit; out of chaos atoms were formed.

"Ah, the man from County Down, I hope I haven't kept you waiting too long." The greeting comes from Father James McDyer, who on first appearance resembles a sort of Joseph Stalin. He is of solid build and medium height; plenty of still-dark, brushed back, cut-short hair; bushy eyebrows and matching dark eyes, a touch of yellowish and a handsome, serious demeanour. About middle fifties to sixty, with an upper lip which is visibly nicotine stained. He shakes my hand with his own, whose fingers are similarly stained. Taking off his coat (a glimpse of torn lining), he tosses it carelessly onto a chair. McDyer wears the usual, well-worn priestly suit. He has the little, shield-shaped pioneer badge on the lapel.

"Could we have a fresh pot of tea Bernie?" His voice has a deep throated Donegal accent, but not completely so. Seating himself before me, he grips the front sides of the armchair with both hands. Subserviently, Bernadette takes the teapot away.

"Is there much trouble in your part of the North?" He asks, more to get the conversation started than through genuine concern.

"No, but we're in the countryside." McDyer's sympathies would be pretty obvious and I'm certainly not going down that road today. So I tread warily.

"It's going to get much worse, once these killings start, there's no knowing where it will end." It is as if he's trying to size up which side of the divide I belong to. Would he even care if I were a Catholic or Protestant? And what sort of a man stays celibate for years in a location as remote as Glencolumbkille. Wed to his infallible church, is he without doubts? His is community of the true faith; guided by the mysterious ways of their impenetrable God.

The priest continues, "so you want to start a business making gold and silver jewellery in Glencolumbkille?" A pause, then, with emphasis, "you'll take on a couple of lads as apprentices, won't you?" He's seeking a definite commitment here.

"Well, yes, Father, but not immediately, not until I get started." I'll agree to whatever he wants; without necessarily ever doing so.

"We have a Mr James here since last year, already with two apprentices, Joe O'Rourke and Connie Francis."

"What do they do?"

"Connemara marble mostly. Bit of an odd fish our Mr James, came over from England just after the war to work in Dublin. A genius some say, but there again I'm no expert on this." McDyer shrugs, raising his eyebrows and displaying the palms of his big hands.

"Where do you sell the jewellery?" It sounds awful, but I have to ask.

"In our craft shop and holiday makers can purchase after watching them at work. I'm opening a Glencolumbkille shop in Dublin soon." I can't help thinking that all this is a far cry from Kilkenny.

Bernadette returns with the tea, which has a green, white and orange knitted cosy covering the pot. She is so physically near me again, my senses lead to a stirring below in response to her scents and slight movements. A mother pouring Father's tea, knowing exactly how he likes it, with plenty of sugar.

"We desperately need new blood in these parts. Any blood, German, English, Chinese even, whatever it takes to impregnate our female population. An invading army of virile young men, to end — dare I say it —generations of inbreeding. I sometimes wish my parishioners were Protestants, who just seem to have that much more get up and go. We've lost our most enterprising young people to the curse of emigration." McDyer speaks slowly and seriously before picking up and sipping his cup of tea. Momentarily, I can see the burden on his shoulders.

Taking out his flip top packet of Rothmans (the airline pilot's choice), McDyer caresses the exquisite cigarette out, lighting and inhaling to the very depth of his soul. He relaxes backwards for a while in silence, enjoying the lovely, calming effect of nicotine. Bernadette is standing frozen by the door, startled and wide eyed: mass rape, wishing his parishioners were Protestants, what is this priest about? He's all by himself and not with either of us in the room.

The stormy sky beyond is constantly changing into different configurations of fleeting blues, covering greys, purple blacks, whites, lemons and bursts of plum. There is a restless sound on the window pane; it is now raining. Coming out of his state suddenly, McDyer throws the cigarette thrown angrily onto the grate; his expression says, why am slave to this disgusting habit?

"To business then." He gets up, "to begin you can have one of the folk village cottages, which are empty this time of year and I can arrange a few hours teaching in Carrick if you're interested." At his desk now, McDyer pulls out a drawer.

"This is for the old Gaeltacht Eireann building opposite the church, you can't miss it, it is in good condition, empty, and ready for you to get started. Are we agreed?" He hands the key over and when I take it, I feel that I have sealed a bargain.

"Go have a look, keep the key, I have another and give us a week's notice before returning." There is no messing with Father McDyer and I accept this job for the sake of my sanity.

"It's David O'Connell, Father, he needs to see you," calls Bernadette from the hallway.

"Well, show him in, this man is just leaving."

"Thank you Father and ..." He interrupts me with a gesture: you need not say another word.

On the way out I pass a long-belted, grey-coated man. Somehow, I've seen him recently before, that face and name, the name David O'Connell... yes! He was on the television news the other day, Daithi O'Connell, Chief of Staff of the Provisional IRA. God almighty, what is he doing visiting Father McDyer of all people? He must be living nearby. Daithi... David O'Connell; I remember now something I heard in Kilkenny. Hogan, mentioned that O'Connell still has constabulary lead in his gut from the IRA's fifties border campaign.

Opposite the church is a solid one up, one down, building. It has a good roof with two new skylights that give plenty of light. The wooden floor upstairs makes a pleasant, creaky sound. The walls and ceilings are made of old, cream-fitted strips of wood and I don't mind the pile of prayer books and pictures of Mary and Jesus. The faintest rhymic sounds of metal digging into stoney ground come from the graveyard. Through the rear window, I see boulders and scraggy ground that rises quickly. A few sheep are concentrating on whatever they can find.

I won't need much equipment, two tables and a single work bench to make only silver. Jewellery, I suppose, there is hardly call for much else around Glencolumbkille. I'm mindful of the golden jug days and much more. I will have to forget Kilkenny, it's not what I'll make any more. Now I have to concentrate on how best to survive in a hostile environment. And with this thought, I spot David O'Connell walking below.

He moves in slow motion, a page out of Irish history and, oh, how he looks the part, walking by the graveyard's Celtic crosses. These intertwined memorials are at one with the dead and those who are dying for old Ireland. The patriot gunman, ever ready, and the skeletal gravedigger who acknowledges him. O'Connell is on a sacred mission to free the Six Counties. He is instinctively aware that I'm watching. As he stands beside a parked car, he glances up, raising his hand to me, a greeting from the Republican Brotherhood. His long, pale face is a mask. He has dark hair, receding at the temples and is thin-lipped, long-limbed, and there are his eyes. Eyes that have in their depths the joys of murderous self-righteousness.

At least there'll be no one looking over my shoulder, but it will be some challenge, making a living at this in Glencolumbkille. I have no alternative. The priest didn't mention rent, time will tell, but the apprentices will eventually become a problem. McDyer was pressurizing me to take them or else. I sink into a reverie full of peasant peculiarities, where I am cunning and slightly mad, making touristy jewellery with local flavours. Trying to capture their stoney lives and the sorry remembrance of a wet, miserable holiday.

The myriad problems this job will entail queue up in my thoughts, as I watch a man, timeless, medieval and dishevelled, wheeling his wheelbarrow of manure through the village, past Doherty's tiny hardware shop, to where a battered black Zephr has a coffin roped on the roof.

Looking back on the road as I depart the village, I see that a thick fog from the sea has mischievously covered the whole valley, so that it might never have existed and was only a dream from which I am now awakening.

CHAPTER 40

Back at home, hallucinating at the bedroom window, I believe I see the opposition to David O'Connell. Three British soldiers, in a long line across the field, slowly approaching our farm. The chequered red and white of their caps against the green. There seems nothing sinister or displeasing in their presence. I reassure myself that they could, in fact, be picking mushrooms. Quickly dressing, by the time I'm downstairs to the kitchen, they're just outside in the yard.

"Would you boys like a cup of tea and some apple pie with fresh cream?" calls mother from the door to them. They are wary at first on entering, perhaps this is some ghastly ambush, of the kind they have been warned about.

They can't be more than eighteen or nineteen, sitting down sheepishly, boy shy, accompanied by scents of uniforms, wet boots and oily metal parts. They are holding their automatic rifles. O'Connell would have them executed without hesitation. Germans during the last war I could accept, but not this ever. I am unable to understand their Scottish accents, as father appears.

"You men are from the Royal Scots Fusiliers, I can tell by the Glengarry you're wearing." Father points weirdly to his head, before starting a long tirade about the Ulster situation. That they don't understand a word of it and glance at each after bewildered, at this bizarre performance from an old Englishman. An officer type out of nowhere. Mother is weary, having heard it so many times before. She slicies into the pie and pours the cream over each portion. For these boys are soldiers of the Queen. Elizabeth II Regina, by tenuous descent from that first Plantagenet in Ireland, King

Henry II, whose son John supposedly camped outside Downpatrick, just below the Bonecastle road, the field ever after known by his name, remembered and handed down for how many years? As this one too could be the Fusiliers' field, for does anything really change. The lads enjoy their apple pie.

"God help the poor boys on the streets of Belfast, so hate filled these days," says mother, maternal and quiet when they have gone.

Father, clearly irritated by his unemployed son hanging about, tells me I should get a move on back to Donegal. With a workshop and a few hours teaching I should be able to survive. I peruse a catalogue from HS Walsh and Sons on the Clerkenwell road, for equipment to purchase: a fiftteen inch square of silver guage II, a few feet of one eight inch round wire, hard and easy solder from Johnson Mattley, and a little gold. The cornucopia of ordering as much equipment, gold and silver as I wanted, (and much more to be on the safe side) for Kilkenny, was a very different experience.

* * *

Wasn't Mary the clever one? She'd be wearing big, round sunglasses, a very different woman now, hair streaming in the wind, speeding beside Snakeskin, learning to drive Thunderbirds and Mustangs as they drive to sunny Florida, Lucy strapped behind. She will grow up little Miss Americano. Thoughts of Mary are a far cry from the priest's house-keeper and the wilds of Glencolumbkille, where I drive a dodgey old Morris Oxford, which is damp and liable to break down.

Father's waving and calling to me from the bottom of the hill; what does he want? So vulnerable, small and inconsequential, an Englishman adrift in Ulster from Slieve Croob to this hill. If only I could take off, free as a bird. I hurry down to him, helpless as he. My brother is even smaller on the opposite hill with the dog, walking by the faintest remains of human endeavour from the ancient past.

"You know I showed our local historian, Colin Ross, your books from Kilkenny? Well he phoned me just now to say he'll give you four hundred pounds for them. When I told him the story, he said no need to worry, for establishing ownership in Ireland was a game of snakes and ladders and he's not going to sell them on. So what shall I tell him?" Father is excited for me.

This news brings me a moment of painful indecision. It is hard to part with the Marshal of France, my old friend, loyal soldier of the Sun King. I remember Mary holding them; Mam hiding them under her bed. Mary, angrily throwing the holy water away, for he wasn't going to drink it. Anyways, it is time to move on. That's always a struggle in Ireland, to leave the past behind. Together with the Cadillac dollars, this should be more than enough for any eventuality.

"Yes, he can have them, I don't mind," I reply reluctantly.

* * *

I have sent two bankers drafts drawn on the Ulster Bank, Ballynahinch, for the gold and silver and equipment. I'm loading the car, ready to leave. Winters has come early to Ulster and I'm cold and wet; the cattle are inside. I have the feeling that father has given up on his youngest son somehow, while mother is still grieving over what wasn't to be.

Entering the dirty green-greys of Armagh and Tyrone, the towns seem abstracted and without shape in this weather. On the road approaching Lack, an intermittent snow becomes a blizzard, with the car coming to a sickly stop. Trying to start it again, I run the battery down.

Once more I am lost and stranded, assailed on all sides, fearful as those distant forebears must have been. I recal the words, 'on the road deep in mire, famished and toiling through the mud up to their knees'. Inside my cold steel vehicle, I know only too well that hypothermia can kill. Unable to find help, I imaging struggling through hedges, my flesh tearing on barbed wire and thorns, staggering over long reed grasses, into a bog where I drown, my body found years later, leathery brown, badly disfigured preserved, pressed flat, with a cut throat! I sit here, immobilized and traumatized... when there comes a tapping on the window screen. It is a capped, pale face that comes to me across the Mesolithic, Neolithic, Middle and Late Bronze Age to Iron and Celtic. Two constables were gunned down the other day from the Presbyterian graveyard in Ballynahinch.

"Are you all right do ye need a hand?" the apparition asks.

"The engine just went dead." I roll down the window to him.

"Let the bonnet up then, I'll take a look." Out of the wilds came Homo sapiens, the wise man. He crouches over the mysteries of the internal combustion engine, how the years have flown: from flintstone axes and arrow heads to this.

"Could be just a bit dirt you have in the carburettor; give her a turn now," he instructs me.

Dead as a doornail. Has it come to this, the beggar in Berkeley's Ireland.

"I'll have to give you a push and you know what to do?"

"Yes, of course." Gathering speed with the ignition on, I let the clutch up and the engine splutters to life, thank God.

"I can't thank you enough."

"Ah, sure. And don't be turning the engine off for a while until the battery's fully charged. Safe journey now." It is all in the day's work for him.

Whatever he can do to help.

Waving to nameless man behind, he's soon gone forever, dissolving into the winter gloom of Tyrone (or is this Fermanagh now?), another quickly forgotten incident on the journey of life; yet most profound and it does give me the heart to go on and not just along this road.

There's an inviting glow from each pub I pass on entering and leaving villages, encouraging me to come inside and forget the delusional dismal world of Glencolumbkille along with the false hope of eerie light from McDyer's church. I'm apprehensive but there is no escape, this has to be it, wherever will lead. What should I make? I haven't a clue.

As I arrive at the village, I'm concious of those earliest metal workers, who had to laboriously mined their own gold and silver, with no ready-made tools to purchase, no gas or electricity available to them. In places as wild as this, all over Ireland, it was much the same then. Am I entering the time zone of a prehistoric age? Cut off by bogs and mountains from the present... who knows?

Bernadette is illuminated by my car lights, standing in McDyer's open door, the wolf hound running over as I park.

"I heard the car, come on and I'll get you something to eat, Father won't be back until late."

"Ah, no, Bernadette, you're most kind, I'll just go to bed, if you'll show me where I'm staying."

"Are you sure?" She sounds disappointed.

"Yes, it's been a long day with this awful weather."

"I'll put my coat on and get the key for the cottage, it's only a short walk away."

"We'll go in the car."

The closeness of a feminine presence stirs me, without turning to her I'm tempted to put a hand on her knee. Not yet, never, someday... maybe.

McDyer has built a number of holiday cottages for visitors to rent, thatched and whitewashed as of old, yet with all modern conveniences. I have the use of one for the moment, Bernadette turns the key to the door and I enjoy a feeling that I'm being welcomed to sustenance and shelter.

"There's bread and milk, butter, bacon and eggs, so you won't go hungry." She opens the little fridge to explain.

"How much do I owe you?"

"It's nothing until you get started; I'll show you how to make a turf fire." Expertly, she rolls and pokes, laying the turf. I am imagining such inappropriate thoughts about a priest's housekeeper, as she lights the fire. "There's plenty more turf at the back for you to help yourself, the bed is made, with extra blankets if you need there. Do you need a hand with anything from the car?"

"You've done more than enough Bernadette, I can manage."

"So I'll leave now and let you go to bed; if you need anything in the morning let me know." She speaks almost reluctantly, smiling to me, then filling the kettle.

"Let me drive you back."

"Ah no, you'll be needin' your rest and the fresh air will do me good." I'm given a rather strange look. Opening the door, I watch her skip down the pathway. She pauses for a moment to wave, beneath a sky that miraculously is clearing. From a primordial pallor on land and rough sea comes the birth of a new time. Along the unknown shoreline, the waves break ceaselessly.

* * *

I imagine Mary and Lucy as Bridget O'Donnell and daughter, in the boggy wilderness between Carrick and Glencolumbkille, famine ragged, barefooted and crazed, waking into the blinding mist and rain, their figures obscured, their wailing sounds difficult to distinguish from those of seagulls.

Laying the equipment out on what will be the workshop floor, I take stock. The little half horsepower Gem polishing motor, two hundred and forty volts at three thousands revs per minute; one hundred and eighty thousand an hour; running to millions a week; a lifetime. And there's the carpenter at Carrick I must go see, has he the benches made from the drawings I sent him? He said it would be a couple of weeks; with no phone this is not going to be easy.

McDyer's Volkswagen four one one is parked just across to the side of the church. He will be at their morning Mass, are rats present too? From the hole at the bottom of the folding door, it certainly looks like they could have made such an entrance, attending the chief of all abominations, the Popish Mass. Rats at the altar rail. McDyer's no fool, I wonder if, deep down, he believes in his religion. He's a decent man …

My thoughts are interrputed by the sight of him coming on over.

"Are you settling in all right? sorry I missed you last night." He follows me up the narrow stairs.

"Yes Bernadette's been most helpful."

"Ah, yes, Bernadette." There is a hushed and pitiful tone in his words. Surveying the equipment at his feet, McDyer says, "you'll be starting soon I can see."

"I'll need to get the work benches delivered first."

"And an apprentice by then, maybe?"

"Far too early Father."

"Well, let me know as soon as you can."

I'm hoping he won't keep on about the apprentice every time I encounter him.

"I'm sure you'll find lots of inspiration in Glencolumbkille, one way or another. Have a look at the angels in the Protestant graveyard," he suggests on his way out.

"Indeed, I will Father." Protestant angels!

I can phone the carpenter from the minuscule post office. I go to investigate; it will be the only contact with the outside world. It is crowded there and I have to call from a corner booth, with everyone listening. The postmistress and her daughter will know everything. Inserting the coins and dialling, dear God, I press the chrome button to hear the faintest of voices, promising he'll deliver the benches by the end of the week, without a definite time or day. No doubt it will take another phone call or two to find out.

Now, what was McDyer' on about, angels. Entering the low-walled Protestant graveyard, the church appears ghostly out of the mist, weightless, a balloon, Noah's ark. It must be his idea of a joke, the last thing I would expect to find here would be angels. I inspect each ashen gravestone. They are mostly flat but yes, yes that must be what he means, and another, there's quite a few. Carved into thick, lichen-covered slabs, are two-dimensional, circular, full, round faces on rectangular bodies with wavy line wings on each side. They immediately remind me of the artist Paul Klee.

They are imaginative and insanely original. The deceased were mostly buried during the famine period. A wet wind whips the tall uncut grass over the stone, vainly attempting to hide the angels. I could develop some interesting designs from these, or anything really. McDyer was right, this is some find. Of all places, imagine finding inspiration from the coverings of the Protestant dead. I could well be joining them here eventually; the place where Glencolumbkille angels miraculously appeared.

Walking on, I notice an upright solitary carved stone, rising by the sunken road. I can barely make out the markings, which are different from the wider, flattish leaning one in the gorse that I saw on the way to the post office. This has a simple, circular, lightly carved cross, which appears more of an afterthought, to convert it from a pagan function perhaps.

In a hollow is the old rectory of the long departed rector, their diminished flock distributed over an ever wider area of Donegal. A substantial and empty building, whisperingly sad, behind a screen of bent, barely surviving trees; this is a Belfast doctor's holiday home now.

My sight is obscured by the even thicker mist now, but I draw closer to a tiny breeze block and corrugated asbestos-type roofed shed. Could this be the workshop of James? The triumph of hope here maybe, valiant and praiseworthy, here they make cheap jewellery, with two fingers to the desolation of their surroundings. Nature's unguided evolutionary processes have been replaced with goal and purpose today. Peeping through the window, I see an old man, seated, wearing broken glasses taped together, reading the *Donegal Democrat*. Behind him are two mischievous adolescents. The table and benches are strewn with coloured glass stones; fragments of the pale green Connemara marble; a sprinkling of silver shamrocks and the usual jewellery-making clutter. A single bar electric fire stands on the concrete floor close to Mr James. His is a cranky looking presence, is this what my life has come to? One of the boys, cute as a fox, doesn't miss a trick, is aware of me at the window. He gives the word to the other, then James, who downs his paper. He looks at me sideways, like a coop of alerted hens. I had better go introduce myself.

"We've been expecting you, you're the man Father McDyer's been telling us about." James sounds cynical; he has something of an English accent and gazes at me unperturbed over his slipped glasses. "This is Connie and Joe, unfortunately." James wings his arm carelessly towards his apprentices and both nod to me. They are obviously glad of the interruption. I sense from James, too, that there's really only a bit of a joke going on here. "So you've come all the way to Glencolumbkille to make gold and silver jewellery, well, well, you must be as big a fool as myself. Are you aware what you're getting into?"

"How do you mean?"

"Oh, you'll soon find out; I couldn't even begin to explain." Bending, James fans his hands to the fire. There are long planks of wood on the floor, to keep their feet warm, no doubt. The place is a shambles, barely fit to work in Glencolumbkille or no. "I suppose it could be a lot worse, you'll get used to it eventually, to the whole of Ireland for that matter, judged guilty but insane." James continues bitterly and momentarily looks faraway. From the look on their faces, his two boyos have heard much of the same many times before. "I originally came over to manage Smith's Ecclesiastical on Wicklow Lane Dublin, do you know the place?"

"Yes, I think so."

"We had a shop on Clarendon Street."

"What did you make, mostly?"

"The name speaks for itself; the church was a great patron, but that all changed with the election of Pope John. We made other things as well, like the model of the Ardnacrusha power station in silver for the E.S.B. We employed as talented men as the Irish can be, that is, whenever they're sober. It was a badly run business, managed in typical Irish fashion, cash under the table. Went into something else and folded eventually.

"I'd been too long in Dublin to ever go back to England and look at me now in Glencolumbkille. They're misfits in normal times; take to violence as a duck to water. They are starting it all over again in the North, revelling in the power of the gun and violence. Everyone is joining the IRA.

And lookit, the head instigator is living a stone's throw from where you're standing right now."

"David O'Connell, you mean, he lives here?"

"The lighthouse keeper's house, you maybe just passed it, down from the Protestant church."

"So that's where he lives."

"One of them even carried a loaded revolver to work."

"Who?"

"The chaser, brilliant at his work but still fearful someone was out to get him, over what I never found out. Those days, remember, the Rising and Civil War weren't that long ago. He was obviously haunted by what he'd done, murder, execution. The Irish can be pretty cruel to one another." James shakes his head mournfully, "he went mad in the end and wanted to die, yet was afraid to let go and meet his maker be cast into Hell." Evidently, this old Englishman doesn't care what he says about Ireland or anyone. "Let me show you something." James takes out from a drawer the dull photograph of some sort of a... metal arm.

"What is it?"

"Well you might ask. It's an exact copy of The Shrine of St Lachtin's arm of Freshford," James explains proudly. "The National Museum let us take measurement from the original."

"Was the arm still inside the original?"

"It was empty. Fine piece of work don't you think?"

"It certainly looks well made." A heavy deluge of rain sweeps noisily over the roof, like the angry spirit of the long dead saint (minus his arm). Connie, and especially Joe, come across as troublesome brats from the margins of *The Book of Kells* or the *Book of the Dun Cow*.

For the rest of the dismal day I wonder what dreadful deed had the Chaser done? Like the pregnant constable who was murdered recently; that was two for the price of one. It is a morbid thing, that shrine, and the mention of Freshford starts my memory bells sounding again. I'm trying to remember where I saw it before and then, as a splinter of glass shot into the brain, I recall the shop James said was on Clarendon Street. There was indeed a window display of The Shrine of St Lachtin.

CHAPTER 41

I must decide whether to stay or go home for Christmas, both options are as bleak as each other. I toss a coin and depart for the painful brooding stillness and malice that hangs over Ulster. The Hennan brothers are forking manure into the yellow muck spreader, furious at the latest outrage, their points murderously impaling the Catholic perpetuators: *Hoc est corpus meam*! And father is fraught over my return.

Christmas is a most solemn affair, even the pigs are muted and slow. They stay well inside, huddled and wary, sensing, as only animals can, that something dreadful is afoot, both in respect to their own fate and that of those living in Ulster. Another is cousin away and my brother is talking of selling up and emigrating to Australia. Paralyzed with foreboding, I return to Glencolumbkille on the only (dodgy) transport available, the fateful hour has arrived when I can't delay anymore. I have to start work.

* * *

The work benches have been made and delivered, the polishing motor and vice are bolted down. Snow streaks the high ground; the streams are torrents of reddish brown. I am about to put pencil to paper. I am fortunate to work upstairs where I can observe the whole village scene but not be part of it. The Sacred Heart of Jesus, in a nice gold frame, hangs on the far wall. There is a small, transparent, blue-ribboned plastic dusty container of Holy water, which has been left long ago on the windowsill. Without thinking, in a devil-may-care humour, playing a game of Russian roulette, I wipe the top and unscrew it, then drink the lot. It should be sure poison for Protestants, heretic and Jews, those that dare mock the church. It would be an extraordinary exit, cause of death unknown, found dead clutching an empty container of Holy water. Warm and tasteless, it settles in the stomach like a moth or two, wanting to get out.

The Glencolumbkille angels it shall be then, just as Michelangelo's God touched the outstretched hand of Adam on the ceiling of the Sistine Chapel. I begin to draw them, it feels natural and comes easy, they are made for jewellery. Those ethereal faces, waving wings, joining this way and that, from the mysterious ether of Glencolumbkille; they have come from high above, seemingly out of nowhere.

Then there is O'Connell, the patriot gunman; McDyer the Roman priest and Bernadette his loyal, yet dissatisfied housekeeper. I could make something out of all three of them. For how can O'Connell take Ireland seriously? McDyer his calling? And Bernadette… well, we shall see. She still lithe and wide-eyed; life's too short not to push on that open door. And I think too, about old Mr James's lament. There's always the odd Englishman living in Ireland somewhere, Kilkenny, Down and now Donegal. It shouldn't be too difficult to construct these silver angels. Inserting the piercing blade in the saw, I spend all morning in concentration.

In the afternoon I see the apprentice called Joe, hands looking up to the window, motioning to be let in.

"It's Joe, isn't it?" I call down.

"Joe O'Rourke it is. Would you mind if I came up to see what you're making?"

"Of course not." Going down, I open the door and point up the stairs. "I've only just started today, going to have a go at silver angels." I indicate the drawings.

"Is that so?" Joe eyes them curiously.

"They are from the graveyard; you know where I mean."

"I've heard talk of them, but never had a look."

"In the Protestant graveyard."

"Ah, sure, James wouldn't be interested in those if that's what they're like, quare lookin' yokes all right; they'll make interesting jewellery no doubt." He sounds as though he may be appreciative.

"I'm sort of inspired by them, as one idea leads to another."

Joe gazes at my work. "Boys a boy, you've got me thinking now."

"How are you getting on with Mr James?"

"Ah, God, James is with the birds, I'm only filling in time before I'm eighteen, then I'll be away to Templemore."

"Templemore."

"The Gardaí, I'll be joining the Gardaí."

"So you're not interested what you're doing?"

"Not the slightest; it's all rubbish anyway, any fool can see that. McDyer's all talk you know, and the grants he can get, don't believe the half of what you hear around Glencolumbkille."

"What about Connie then?"

"Ah Connie Francis is all right, a quiet sort of one, doesn't say much."

"And David O'Connell, what's the story there?"

With a sharp intake of breath, Joe raises his head most cautiously. "He's well in with McDyer, that man, you know, whatever's going on between the two and O'Connell in the IRA; the things I've heard."

"Like what?"

"Ah, now." The young man pauses to emphasize his answer, "the storing of dynamite in the Folk Village!"

"Get away, you're not serious!"

"That's what I understand, but don't be telling McDyer or anyone I told you so."

"I did see him up at McDyer's last year."

"A lot of the time," replies Joe, who is a mine of information, old before his years, no innocent. And he's a veteran smoker, lighting up an Afton Major. I decline his offer of one.

"The other lads can be seen here sometimes with O'Connell."

"The other lads?"

"Rory O'Brady, Martin Meehan and the likes."

"God is that right?"

"Have you seen the De Vere girls yet?" Joe changes the subject abruptly.

"The De Vere girls?"

"De Vere's daughters; they're only gorgeous, would hardly give me a look in though. He's on a bender at the moment."

"Who?"

"Their father, the doctor."

"On a bender."

"Yes, hits the bottle now and then, can just disappear without trace, maybe to Glenties or Ardara, sure, only a place like Glencolumbkille would have him. But they say he's a very good doctor, has a cancer detecting machine invented himself, I was told."

"I'll keep a lookout for his daughters then."

"You really should, I tell you now," says Joe with an all knowing grin.

"So you'll be away when you're eighteen."

"Another six months and that'll be me and a year or two of this you'll be the same too."

"We shall see." Joe finishes his cigarette and leaves, giving me plenty to think about.

* * *

I spend Sunday morning with the silver angels, treading softly on the floor boards, slightly back from the windows, as McDyer's congregation enters into his church opposite. It is mostly women at first, the men chatting a while and those who arrive late gather near the door on bended knee. Somehow managing to follow the service. McDyer must have warned everyone, no interruptions once he's started. It is a peasant scene. One or two suspicious glances are sent my way, as though they are aware of being watched from above.

I can hear the repetitious hum of prayers and seagulls on the gable cross and roof. Their gah gahing noise reminds me of the crows at Knocktopher when we went to find Mary's mother. Unwelcome, big, rain heavy clouds announce themselves from over the wild Atlantic, soon obscuring the brief sunshine that had been firing the angels.

Quite a few cars line the street. As the best-Sunday-suited men emerge to head to either of the pubs, the women sit in the cars reading the day's newspapers. And that man again, this time with a handsome blonde beside him, lighting his cigarette, inhaling deeply, as if glad to be away rather than face the crucified Jesus Christ, who died for his sins in accordance with the Scriptures that this man is impervious to. The Chief of Staff of the Provisional IRA, Daithi O'Connell. I catch those incredible eyes again, which reflect his very being and that perverted sense of Ireland I will never understand, McDyer would know O'connell well, taking his confession, absolving his many murderous deeds, behind the dark lattice screen, so softly spoken.

I certainly never thought would be making the likes of these Angels, but they have emerged so easily from the strange otherness of Glencolumbkille. There are lots of ideas to be found here, on those weathered lines abstracted on fallen and leaning stones. Such as the one with the hole through it, where a fearless robin perches motionless. The mysterious De Vere girls are out of bounds, the nymphets of Joe's frustrated attention. I wonder whether the angels will sell or not; only time will tell for these quare yokes.

* * *

Following s precipitous path, I can see Rathlin O'Beirne island, bleak and forbidding on the horizon. Steep steps take me down to the enclosed sandy beach, aptly called The Silver Strand. The towering dark rocks enclose me. They are ready to thrust up even higher, from the molten movement pushing far below; shapes that were once writhing red hot, speak of menace and foreboding for the world to come. Sheep tenuously graze on the sheer sides wherever grass can be found, their small black, clustered shit is under foot everywhere.

I pause to watch a golden dog running joyously in and out of the incoming waves, constantly returning to his mistress. I envy the simple canine creature, for it gives no thought for the morrow. I can hear her laughter at the crazy dog; her clothes are blowing in the wind, nicely revealing. Did she purposefully let them blow out behind her? As she climbs the steep steps, I'm presented with a wondrous sight of the motions of the most perfect female rear. They torture me to lie behind her, as with Langrishe's daughter, for now the sins of impurity as they call it, do no harm. Reaching the last step she stops, turning breathlessly and content.

"Amazing place, don't you think?" She has an American accent and her face more than compliments the rest of her.

"It certainly is," I reply, hoping more maybe, but no, she's over to a waiting car with someone inside. Her legs, as she slides in, are all the longer than when she climbed the path.

* * *

The months pass and I haven't been asked for the rent yet; it will be a large lump sum. I'm hoping McDyer is just glad I'm here and the question won't arise. But as the holiday season is approaching, he'll be wanting the cottage and I'll have to find somewhere else to live. And indeed, the day finally arrives when I open the door to the priest and as I follow him up the stairs, I sense the time has come.

"My goodness me, is this what you're about?" he asks startled at the jewellery that he finds ready for the assay. Picking up an angel in each hand, he weighs them up and down, perplexed. What does he mean with such a look and remark? Nor any further comment. "There's a small cottage Garda McCabe owns, you can have it as we've bookings coming now for Easter and earlier, so we'll need the one you're in I'm afraid." He is somewhat apologetic.

Homeless in Donegal, on a wild bog road going where? It was bound to come to this nevertheless. He's a good priest, nor is he after past rent, even with all the turf and electricity I've used. And he never even mentioned the workshop.

"You can just see the place over on the far side of the valley; take the road immediately right past the lighthouse keeper's, it will bring you up to a laneway to the right again, opposite O'Gara's gate entrance." He pointing to a slate roof just visible behind some fuchsia.

"No problem, Father, you've been so helpful letting me get started here. I'll go and check it out and move in a day or two."

"You've got to the end of the week if you don't mind. We can try some of your jewellery in the craft shop we'll be opening again soon." McDyer sounds relieved that the cottage will be available again. "This is the key." He clicks it down on the table, hard. "McCabe let me keep it, in case I'd have a tenant for him. I didn't want you to move there when you first came, as needs a good bit of tidying up, if you know what I mean." There is a painful emphasis in his last few words.

CHAPTER 42

I am sad, listening to the sighing sounds of Glencolumbkille, which brush the roof and window panes. Meditative and silent I prepare myself for the tragic squalor know is waiting across the valley. Then I set out.

I'm entering an even earlier century than the nineteenth here. The rusty, broken gate opens to a pathway of hard earth and sharp stones that I can feel underfoot, as Christ felt on his way to be crucified. This leads to what is more a cabin than a cottage, smaller even than Mam's. Mary would freak coming back to this, I imagine, she was right to never want to return. Perhaps her objection was more the thought of Ireland than to me, I tell myself hopefully. Who knows?

I open the stiff door and an awful smell of damp decay hits me hard. Three tiny rooms. The kitchen has a Stanley cast-iron stove, kettle, sink without running water, and, yes, there's a pump outside. I peep hesitantly into what must be the lavatory shed, it has a single-holed wooden board to sit on. Such corruption. I will need to buy lime. Back inside, I pick up pieces of cutlery and crockery. There is enough furniture to sit and put my things on. The iron bed and torn mattress will have to do. I check underneath for mice and their large brethren. At least there's electricity, although I will need to get it switched on.

Jesus is here. This time a Russian icon painted in darkest Prussian blues, black, touches of yellow and red. A sullen emptiness invades me. This is the reversal of my fortunes. Mary became a butterfly and flew, flying from Irish misery. Whereas I am returning to live in a situation worse than perhaps hers once were. Will I just have to get on with it? And make it liveable? I'll need a small refrigerator eventually and much more.

"Hello dog, where have you come from?" I greet the black and white collie dog sitting at the open door. He curious and unafraid of the stranger. Head down, he comes slowly to me, tail between his legs, letting me touch his cold wet nose; sniffing to confirm I'm ok; tail starting to wag. And now he is up on his hind legs, glad to have found a new friend. Likewise dog, I say to those trusting yellow-brown eyes, stroking and rubbing his head and coat. Strangely, this brings tears. The collie runs off a short way and looks back, wanting to play. So I take the small plastic Virgin Mary from the mantelpiece, which won't harm his fine, sharp, white teeth. Impatient and excited, the dog is a catapult ready to fetch. I throw the icon as far as I can and he's away finding it and quickly returning, dropping it before me. I throw it over his head this time and he leaps in the air catching it with perfect timing. Again and again, he'd do this all day. Putting Mary back on the mantelpiece, the collie follows me disappointed and tries to coax me out again.

"Go home now, you have to go home." I point outside for him to be gone. Turning abruptly, the dog runs away at the command.

* * *

Potatoes keep. Eggs, cheese and butter last a week or two at most. The rest must be tinned goods, dried milk, cereals, bread, coffee, tea with plenty of soup. I hope I can buy the soup in bulk from Donegal town. The pile of turf beside the cabin I can use. I have two sets of clothes and will be wearing one, washing the other. The stove will take time to heat morning or evening. But I'm getting used to the bare necessities. Opening a drawer I find used candles, string, nails, a dirty mousetrap and rosary beads, just like the ones that went into the Nore. By now they will be tangled in reeds, having sunk to the bottom, rotted apart, separated and dispersed. It all comes back to me and I clasp these as though they were Mary's, before letting them fall back into the drawer again, which I close.

Passing the stone steps outside, I see five or six little Protestant boys and girls are coming down from their one room school. This is where Lucy would have gone to school, cursing the day she was born in Ireland.

I will need to get more silver soon and a little gold even. And I should be trying to sell some of these angels. A trip to Dublin is going to be necessary, where I shall have to enter as a beggar to Weirs or Mortons, perish the thought. Still, there are plenty of ideas to explore here. I'm leaving Kilkenny's severe lines well behind; I wonder what they'd make of these new creations that are tumbling out of my head?

Images from the Old Testament and New are inescapable in Ireland. So too the symbols of the Apostles. Then there are faces, such as those on the doorway of Clonfert Cathedral. I remember a cow I saw on a mound underneath a luxurious wide spreading ash tree. The cross on the grave of St Patrick, then at Saul, with his mitre and crozier banishing the snakes. Round Towers and Celtic Crosses are everywhere. I have to survive, as the customer is always right, although the academics that came to Kilkenny certainly wouldn't agree. For there is no shame in plundering the past, sources of simple drawings that are quite natural and almost modern.

Columcille sailing to Scotland. I twist long ribbons of silver, as they once did long ago in pure gold, cutting it into chain links, bending it into bangles and chokers.

I notice the few Protestants who come to their lovely church every other sad Sunday, or is it only once a month now here? For this is the life it's going to have to be for me. When the crows begin building their nest up the chimney, it is a comfort knowing not alone. We are making a home together; they are busy in and out with twigs and pieces of sheep's wool and don't seem to mind if there's a turf fire burning beneath them.

The dog belongs to the widow McGinley, who lives a short distance behind the cottage. Her dog is nearly always waiting when I return, wanting to play go catch the Virgin Mary. McGinley never says much and can silently and suddenly appear across the window with a luminous sense of otherness, a free floating apparition, ghostly and darkly dressed, blown in from a sorrowful place, lost and careless of her appearance.

She sits in the kitchen with me one evening, wanting only the company of another human being. Her two sons are working in Dublin. For some time she is staring at her dog. I should have known better than to let him chew the little Virgin Mary, which he's become rather fond of. For he's not superstitious like his mistress. She frowns abruptly towards me and then to the dog.

"Aren't you the dreadful heathen animal." Standing up, McGinley crosses herself, calls the dog after her and without another word walks into the lonely night on her own.

* * *

One morning I spot McDyer, driving up the steep hill towards the cottage, just as I'm about to leave for work. He's turned into the rutted track now. The car should have been left at the entrance, it could easily be damaged here. And, yes, there is a fresh scrape on the driver's side. You'd want to be Sterling Moss to drive like he does. A little more over and the accident could have been fatal. The priest is dicing with death, the speed he drives, he's only milliseconds away from introducing his soul to his maker. Again, I wonder if there's a constant, irritating doubt? He's not stupid and it takes seven years to study for the priesthood. Yet if you were brought up in the dysfunctional atmosphere of Catholicism from early childhood, maybe they can pull the wool over your eyes.

The road from Glencolumbkille to Carrick is a lonely one, as priests lives essentially are. As my life is now too.

Getting out of his newly dented car, smoking, ash flecked down his coat, the priest's bloodshot eyes look exhausted. "You certainly have a great view up here." McDyer points over Glencolumbkille, letting the cigarette fall, foot vigorously twisting it out.

"Yes, Father, indeed. Will you come in and I'll make you a cup of tea?"

"Just for a few minutes, but don't bother making tea." His is a very black and oversized presence, seated in the tiny room. He has a strong smell of nicotine now. McGinley's dog sneaks in as I'm about to shut the door, but on seeing McDyer immediately turns and runs off.

Why has he come?

Looming large, this Roman priest is an important a part of my precarious existence. Of all people and places, my wildest of dreams would not have created McDyer and Glencolumbkille. I presume he's faithful to the present Pope Paul, who's predecessors include many monstrous popes. Innocent VIII, Alexander Borgia VI, Sixtus IV, and so many more, not forgetting the recent disgraceful Pius XII who never spoke out against Adolf Hitler and his murder of six million Jews. I remind myself that McDyer's ultimate allegiance lies in Rome and the shameless hypocrisy of the Vatican: a blood sucking den of mafioso bats.

I remember hearing on the wireless and later reading about the war. The fireboming of Hamburg and Dresden. Dark and dreadful happenings far from the fields of peaceful County Down. This big awkward man is sitting on the wobbly chair that could so easily break and cause him to fall.

"This must be a big change from America for you." His gaze contemplates the cramped room and sparse means of living as if it is his fault.

"Not really Father, life's much the same wherever you are. One can get used to anything and it's a challenge to make this work."

"Giving your life some kind of meaning you could say..." His voice drifts into silence and the ticking of the old alarm clock. In another one of those little pauses when life seems to stop, but the seconds hand keeps moving inexorably, I am unable to reply to him.

"I've advertised for a development officer and I'm hoping to get the right man."

"To do what Father?"

"Co-ordinate activities and get more investment into Glencolumbkille, give me more time for other things. There are plenty of Government grants for start-ups and we need to make more use of them."

"You're doing very well as it is, with vegetables, knitting and the Folk Village."

"But I want to do so much more. What I'd really like is a farming co-operative, bringing all the small farms into one large viable holding, but the people, too set in their ways, are afraid to let go of the miserable few acres they own. They could be so much better off and self-sufficient."

"That would be something." I wonder why he bothers. Shouldn't a priest be preparing them for the next world and not be caught up with the material one? Stick to the baptisms, weddings and the time when the little girls are all dressed in their best white dresses. Confirmation? Or is it what they call First Communion? I recall Mary's mother taking the photograph out of the biscuit tin to show Mary on the day of her First Communion. It was heart breaking then; is so again now; will be always. There's the funerals of course and the Mass money. Old dears leaving lots to the parish, his comfortable house and live-in house keeper and who's to know what goes on there.

It must be easy enough to memorize books of sermons. And easy too, to take up drinking whiskey and smoking cigarettes, activities that seem to be common to all priests. Up in Dublin, incognito, driving around Fitzwilliam Square, they can do whatever they want. They don't have the problem of conscience and guilt. One confession and the slate is wiped clean, so they can start all over again. The life of Riley is available to the priest who doesn't bother about the material welfare of his community, which is up to the elected government anyway, so he should just stick to the spiritual.

"But look, why I'm here, if you want a bit of teaching in Carrick they'll be able to fill you in for a couple of classes each week; if you're inter-ested?"

"That's very thoughtful of you Father, the money would be handy all right. Teaching what?"

"Oh, crafts, art, that sort of thing. Go see David O'Connell who teaches there, mechanical drawing I think, he'll take you along. Do you know where he lives?"

"Yes, isn't he in the Provisional IRA?"

"Ah sure, a decent enough man though." Obviously McDyer does not wanting to talk about O'Connell. "Can I give you a lift down to the vil-lage? He might even be there now."

I regret the decision to join the company of this wolf in disguise, a scourge of the good Protestants of Ulster and the RUC. I didn't have time to think the teaching offer over.

A momentary mixture of fear and excitement quickly subsides as I am about to knock on his door. After all, he's only a young man with a gun, in a secret society, romantic brave and daring. A mysterious indi-vidual for some to look up to. Take away his gun though, he's just anyone, maybe on the dole or teaching mechanical drawing. He knows that if he's ever caught for murdering the dog catcher or bread delivery man, he'll become a martyr for the cause of Irish freedom (whatever that means). After time as a privileged political prisoner, he'll enter old age looking back on the thrills and fun. For that's what it's really all about.

Without his gun, O'Connell wouldn't impress me in the least. I hear his footsteps approaching as shots hitting the flagstone hallway. From the time of Strongbow and across the subsequent centuries of conquest, internecine conflict, famine, rebellion, there have been those waiting to ambush and murder the Earl of Leitrim and Viscount Mountmorres. And why not the Langrishe for good measure. The six little Protestants coming down from their one room school, the story of Mary and her mother, so many images bombarding my head, waiting for David O'Connell to open the door.

"Aha, McDyer's silversmith from the County Down it is." O'Connell is shirt sleeved and friendly. I am drowning in those mad, killer's hypnotic eyes as he stands squarely before me, holding out his trigger hand for me to shake.

"Indeed I am," I reply, softening somewhat at his vulnerability in the flesh now. I remain on guard, however. "McDyer's told me to see you about teaching in Carrick for a few hours each week." We are two people, poles apart, but the supreme Irish patriot doesn't know his caller couldn't care less who governs Ireland.

"Of course, I'm off there now, come along with me if you like, hold on there and I'll be with you in a minute." He returns with his tie and jacket on and the car keys for a clapped-out looking wine-coloured Ford Cortina.

You wouldn't put a pig in this car, it's so dirty, with a door open it becomes a coop for hens to roost in at night. Cigarette in mouth, boney fingers on the bloody wheel, he's attempting to steer Ireland. I'm in the care of this republican coachman who is careering far too fast; do the brakes even work? What a way to end, both dead, entwined together in a crumpled, overturned Cortina, on the rocky road of Irish history from Glencolumbkille to Carrick. Has he a hidden gun? Or does he even bother to hide it, as the guards this side of the border don't seem to mind. The sombre landscape flys past.

"Awful weather we're having." I have to make the remark loudly, above the noise of a broken exhaust, which is trailing underneath us.

"That's Glencolumbkille for you, we always get the first downpour coming in from the Atlantic." O'Connell's reply is hardly audible. He changes down a few gears quickly on approaching a corner. I was right about those brakes and wanting to get out fast. O'Connell spares me a glance, "so what brought you to Glencolumbkille?"

"Coincidence really. One phone call was all it took for McDyer to invite me over, what with a room and the chance to begin right away, he couldn't have been more helpful." I'm gripping the seat sides, feet pressing down hard.

"He's an amazing man, doing all he can for the area."

"Yes he is. So what's the teaching in Carrick like?"

"Oh, sad, sad; once they've finished there's nothing for them here, so most leave, or the few that stay are on their father's small farms, collecting the dole."

"What's the solution then?"

"Get the Brits out, they've been holding Ireland back for years."

"As simple as that."

"Yes!" The sound is more that of a guillotine drop than a reply. He looks at me, his skull suddenly visible beneath a pale skin. The abstractions he adheres to seem absurd to me; as if it matters. Who knows, the strangest things can happen, maybe Germany could be running Ireland in the years to come. Then the IRA would have to take their fight all the way to Berlin.

O'Connell shows me to the staff room to wait for the principal. Soon it empties of teachers, who push past loud, odorous boys and girls. I sense I shouldn't be here, for a lot of art teaching can be a waste of time. Silence falls as classes begin. I am left together with nondescript man who is seated at the table, reading the *Irish Times*.

"Are you a teacher here yourself?" I ask him. He looks up with the weakest of smiles and returns to his paper without replying. How very strange and rude, what's the matter with him, is he deaf? I try again. "Do you know David O'Connell?"

Not even a movement this time, totally ignoring me as the silence is prolonged and uneasy. This is embarrassing. A man who I realise must be the principal enters and my companion gets up and speaks to in Irish for a short while. That provides me with my answer.

"So you're the man Father McDyer told me about." The principal approaches, "come into my office and we'll see what we can do for you."

Following this comfortable, rotund and slow-talking Donegal man, my mind is made up. I couldn't possibly teach here; annoyed, I give a glance back at the true Gael.

The Principal is somewhat surprised that I am no longer interested in teaching, but nevertheless understands it would be too much of a distraction from getting on with my business. He regrets that there will not be a little art in the curriculum. He does, however, agree to pass on my message to O'Connell, not to worry about providing me with a lift home.

I'm glad to be gone. It suddenly comes over me that a drop of whiskey would help before I start the long walk. Home is a good six or seven miles away, but that's better done on foot than in the Republican runaway train. I settle in the bar and listen to the hostelry owner's long diatribe against Father McDyer for preferring the lamplight to the day.

When I'm sure O'Connell would have left the school, so I needn't fear another lift, exhilarated, I begin walking alone on the lonely road through the desert of empty bogland. I am without encumbrances, or any possessions but a Cadillac of daydreams, which comes to me as the pale moon laughs above the blue, high towards Slieve League. My needs are limited really, the rest is just playing with our short time on earth. We are without purpose and nothing but smoke in the end. There is a definite style coming out of my work on silver angels and grave men.

The light is fading as I approach Glencolumbkille and go wearily into the workshop. My environment is becoming structured, safe and familiar. I turn on the tap for a cold glass of bog-flavoured water. And there's someone below; who can it be at this hour?

A young red-headed girl of the most desirable appearance is at the door, "can I come in?" Her accent is very English.

I gesture that she should enter and follow her up the stairs. She has a rucksack on her back, which she drops carelessly on the floor. Her presence miraculously transforms the room. I had almost forgotten the scents and moist breath of a woman.

"I saw your name and sign on the wall, what's it supposed to be?"

"It's an angel."

"An angel." She looks surprised.

"Yes, it's based on the ones we have in the graveyard here."

"Then you'll have to show them to me, so this is what you are, a jeweller." Spotting some silver pieces on the table by the scales, she picks them up and inspects them carefully. She's wearing black stockings and high laced boots, a short raincoat and a red beret over her long hair. Her alarming watery-blue eyes are affecting and she has deft, little, inquisitive hands. "I really like this one, he's cute." She holds up a silver chain with the smallest, swinging it hypnotizingly before her. Everything about her is mischievous. "Do you know where I can stay here?"

"For how long?"

"Oh, just for a day or two. I don't have much money. I hitched from Donegal, after coming on the bus from Dublin. I'm studying modern history at Oxford."

"Isn't that a bit risky for a young woman like you?"

She shrugs her shoulders carelessly.

"So why are you here?" I ask.

"I just felt I needed to see Ireland, what all the trouble is about, we English are behaving so badly again."

"The Irish can be just as bad."

"But at least it's their country."

I'm not going to go down that route; this is an opportunity not to be missed, albeit disturbing to my equilibrium. "There's a hotel further out the road if you can call it that, but I think it's closed and there's the place where old James's staying, but I would hardly recommend it. So that's about it really." Now or never. "You can stay up in my humble abode if you like, you'll be safe enough and will have nothing to worry about, if you don't mind sleeping in a hard bed."

"Sounds like an experience not to be missed," she replies impishly.

"If you're hungry all I have at the moment is bread and hard cheese, tins of peaches and powdered milk for the tea." To which she doesn't reply.

Walking to the cottage, I feel ashamed that I have such meagre offerings; will there ever be an escape from poverty? But I can tell she's strangely excited; enjoying the daring and unexpected encounter with a stranger in the mystical Irish twilight, shadowed memories to cherish. She takes my hand. How extraordinary.

"And, oh yes, there's half a bottle of whiskey, I nearly forgot."

On empty stomachs the whiskey makes us both dizzy. She's obviously one of those English girls attracted to Irish rebellion and adventure. I'm unable to remember the name of the present one in the news, another Maud Gonne or Countess Markievicz, who, mother said, was thrilled when she shot dead an unarmed Irish policeman in Dublin, screaming, "I killed him, I killed him!"

Talking about Irish grievances is of no relevance; I simply agree with whatever she says. Kneeling before her as at prayer is the only religious experience worth having, if I can call it that. And she wants this, inviting me further. It has been a long time. I taste the juicy, ripe fruit between those black stockinged legs, now wide apart. Then I am a burning arrow entering her and a rhythmic feasting takes place as we move as one.

"Oh, God I needed that," she says.

I have regained my senses somewhat, "I should have pulled out."

"Don't be silly, sperm is good for a woman, the best medicine there is. And in any case, haven't you heard of the pill." She laughs and I wonder is she a little mad to be doing this with a complete stranger.

The next morning I drive the Oxford girl down to the village. She'll be able to get a lift to Carrick and Donegal if she walks up the hill thumbing. And sure enough, just what she was looking for, she gets in with David O'Connell. I can well imagine that'll be some adventure, perhaps going off together to buy guns somewhere, for the strangest coincidences do happen.

CHAPTER 43

"Remember you've just another feather in McDyer's hat." A cynical voice dissolves into laughter that already has the sound of tobacco lungs in it. Despite his young age, Joe O'Rourke is on his bicycle behind me, stopping at the graveyard entrance, with a large, knowing grin on his face. "Who was the bird you were with last night?"

Now how would he know about that? I never saw him anywhere.

"She was my sister Joe."

"Go on with yez; ye needn't be codding me there. A fine looking bird she was too."

"She's studying history at Oxford and came to see what I'm doing here, nothing untoward. I can assure you. How are you getting on with Mr James?"

"Don't be changing the subject now; did you have any luck with her?"

"With my sister Joe!"

"You're a gas man, getting away with a bird like her."

"How are the De Vere girls, have you managed a date with any of them yet?"

"Ah, now, don't be talkin; they think I'm hilarious, wouldn't you know and them having to live in the Glen with that mad eejit father of theirs. Who do they think they are? All three of them, right little bitches." He says this bitterly.

"I'm sure there'll be plenty of girls for you when you're in uniform at Templemore."

"I can't wait for the day. It will be messing around here among McDyer's crackpot ideas, without hope of a decent future."

"He's only a priest doing his best Joe."

"I wonder sometimes, I really do." Joes tosses his head disdainfully, "so I'll be away to old James now, good luck."

He cycles off, raising his right arm.

Standing alone by the graveyard for a moment, I eventually walk ever-so-slowly to the workshop, where the grave men and angels are waiting. A sorrowful day passes without interruption, just the faintest murmur of the sea, the occasional car passing. It's shame she had to go; I never even knew her name.

There is a grey Ford Anglia blocking the open gate of the lane, as if a signal to say all this is mine. A pink, porcine, Nikita Kruschev lookalike is approaching from the cottage. McGinley's dog is watching cautiously from some distance behind.

"I was just about to leave; I'm Patrick McCabe your landlord." He speaks boldly. I wonder what will the rent be. "You've a cosy enough little home here, nice and quiet with fresh well water and those old Stanley yokes have never been bettered; it was my late grandparent's cottage you know."

"Is that so?" I do not like the look of this.

"McDyer told me you're a goldsmith, nicely set up in the village and soon to be takin a few apprentices on."

"Did he say that?" Well, it's not going to happen yet, if ever.

"When I went to fetch the other key this morning, he set great hopes on you, so don't be disappointing him." McCabe speaks with a cynical chuckle. "So I was thinkin a fair rent would be two pounds ten shillings a week and as for the turf you've been using, I'll not charge you for that, though there was a fair pile there."

"Thirty shillings a week would be more like it, when you look at the condition it's in. There's no lavatory and the end room is stuffed with useless bric-a-brac."

"That can be sorted anytime, you'll not get a better offer in Glencolumbkille."

"Couldn't we make it two pounds and we'll have a deal." I make this offer, in the hope I won't be staying here for long, but no, McCabe is shaking his head.

"Look it, you've been here for some time as it is, so I'll not charge you for that, but starting from today I'll make it ten pounds a month, with one in advance, take it or leave."

At least McDyer's not charging for the workshop, so far. So I'm a wretched tenant now, paying rent for a hovel to live in, how the wheel of fortune can turn. I'm living as Mary was in Freshford.

"So ten pounds will take me up to the end of next month?"

"Ah, ye'r slippin another week in there, but no matter, you Northerners drive a hard bargain."

"I don't think so, wait there and I'll get you your money. It's in the house." But he follows me inside; a landlord's right, I suppose.

In the end room, up the chimney, is an envelope with all the money I have. At least McCabe stayed in the kitchen and didn't see me take it down. I return to him and count out lovely, Lady Lavery green and honey, Free State single pound notes into his dirty, nailed hand. He should be thankful he's not letting his cottage go to rack and ruin. I can well understand what the peasants felt in those past days, degraded and debased, living in a pig sty like this.

Lighting the Stanley, the dog makes himself at home. He only has to see the little Mary and he's at the door ready to play. There is one of the Oxford girl's hair pins on the floor.

* * *

I have a client. An old man who left Glencolumbkille nearly fifty years ago for New York and who wants a square gold angel ring, size V. When he comes to pay me, he takes out an extraordinary, large ten pound blue note, which has a lone lean ploughman turning his graceful bladed plough, the plough handled drawn by two heavy horses ready to cut the next furrow, facing toward the far hills and fading light. I remember my uncle in a scene such as this. I've never seen the likes before, but it must be all right, for it says, 'Currency Commission, Consolidated Bank Note, Payable at the Principal Office, Dublin', and the same in Irish beside.

"Where on earth did you get this from?" I ask, for it is extraordinarily beautiful.

"My father gave it to me the day I left Ireland and I never had to spent it, so I might as well now before I'm dead."

"How did you manage not to?"

"I got a job as a janitor, living in a large apartment block right away. This is my first visit home and at my age, you might as well have it as they're still legal tender anyway."

"It is a collector's item surely, it seems a shame to use it. I'd love to keep the note, if only I could afford to."

"Could you get Father McDyer to bless the ring before you send it to this address, as I'll be leaving in a couple of days. It'll be nice to have something unusual to wear from Glencolumbkille; those little angels are a lovely idea." He leaves a card with me, his tired, rheumy, old eyes meeting mine. There is something terribly sad and forlorn in them.

"Do you miss Ireland over there?"

"Of course I do, New York's an exhausting place, the continual noise, the sirens, the summer heat and apartment living. That's why the Sunday newspapers are so thick, for to read all weekend inside your wretched box called home. You can't get out to the real countryside unless you have plenty of money."

"I can well imagine, I've lived in St. Louis for a while."

"In the small hours of the morning when you wake for a piss and try to sleep, you think of Ireland, the ever changing sky, soft rain and a countryside that is always near, cool and refreshing. But de Valera's Ireland was not a country for the young then." The old emigrant speaks wearily, living in two parallel worlds.

"You could collect this in two days, but it wouldn't be hallmarked."

"No need to rush, take your time and have it properly done, you look like a man I can trust. You have my address." He taps the card. Seeing himself out, he calls up from the bottom of the stairs. "Good luck and I hope you make it here." Then the door shuts.

It is uplifting to get an order and for it to be paid for in advance. This will be easy to make, using some of the gold. It is sad to think of the old man dreaming of Ireland in the early mornings. So maybe I was right to come home, I had to be in Ireland somehow, whatever about living in Glencolumbkille.

Goldsmithing is a mysterious craft, obsessional, intricate and tortuous. It goes back to those who made it for beads and bones. My book opens at the gold pendant of hornets from the necropolis of Chrysolakkos Mycenae, which was made nearly four thousand years ago. It's unbelievable.

I score three deep lines on a half inch wide strip of the nine carat gold sheet cut, filing at an angle the two ends so they meet snugly, bending them up to a four-sided box. I borax the bends and keep them tight with bending wire, before soldering each corner with hard solder. Cleaning away the hardened borax with sulphuric acid diluted in water, I hammer each side flat, cut out the angel and easily solder on one of the sides, then cleaning again as before. File and polish, texturing the body, wings, feet and face with a burr to make it unique. I stamp the maker's mark on the ring, now it's ready for the assay's.

What an awful nuisance to get there from here. There's some of the silver jewellery, however, that is ready to go. I have the joy of paid work at last. This will be posted to Jackson Heights, New York. I can well imagine it to be an awful place.

The hours can slip away when I am working. I realize it is dark outside, in the forgotten street below. The light on the church wall illuminates the many gravestones, casting their shadows seaward, an occasional car drives hesitantly through as if appalled and afraid to stop. The old girl from the house beside me shuffles past, bent and with head covered by a shawl. She is from another age, crossing herself as she passes the church. It is time to go.

Approaching the lighthouse keeper's and O'Connell's dwelling, a sense of foreboding takes hold of me without reason. There's a light on from one window with the curtains only half drawn. So his silhouetted figure appears black, moving back and forth, gestalating to someone. Dracula-like, a spider, weaving a fearful web from the putrescent glow of the dim light. I feel a cold shiver for the grieving widows and orphans in funeral processions. Is he planning plain murder? To land a shipment of arms? Or a semtex spectacular? I walk on and headlights come on from behind me. The car passes at speed. Was that McDyer, coming from O'Connells? It was hard to tell; there was a car parked outside, the number plates were too far ahead for me to read. It could mean anything, just a friendly call. And yet. Bernadette would be waiting for McDyer; well, we shall maybe have to see about her.

The cottage is cold, filled with the all pervasive Irish damp. Lighting the Stanley is an awful chore, the matches are dead, I'm unable to ignite one. The little happiness I felt over having paid work is beginning to evaporate, as I sit in a vulnerable position over my own defecation beneath me. McGinley's dog is patiently waiting by the rotten open door, despite the hour, rudely watching me.

*   *   *

Waking to a morning of continual rain on a mountainside in a rack-rented cabin to the dying heat of the Stanley, I feel grateful I can at least boil the electric kettle to make tea. Waves of depression pounding my head; will there be no escape?

I have to walk down to the village as the car won't start; the elements seem determined to make my life ever more difficult. Entering the work-shop drenched, I do up the parcel for the Assay. They require money for payment and return any lose change with the parcel, which is most peculiar.

At the Post Office, which is croweded with survivors of the weather, I wait in the queue, when, would you believe it, David O'Connell turns to me with a friendly smile.

"I think you were right not to take the teaching job, it's a slow death and too easy an option. Entrepreneurs are what's needed here, I'm sure you'll survive." With this encouragement, he goes over to the telephone booth, which is now free. Getting through to someone — and momentarily turn-ing to the rest of the shop to send a look around that they should not to be listening to his conversation, arranging another murder or two.

With the rain easing off, I walk towards the workshop when an old, matt-black Ford Consul slowly overtakes me, stopping at the workshop door before I get there. A tall man gets out and introduces himself as

Peter Pringle. He has wavy brown-greying hair, blue eyes and a strong, determined, handsome face. He holds out his hand for me to shake.

"This is my wife Clarrie and our three children." He points to them in the car.

From the Ford comes a tired wave of acknowledgment and I can see a pale face, drowning and sorrowful. Suddenly, all of old Ireland is there again, from time immemorial. I'm falling into a vortex; my life is on hold. This encounter is somehow reality, past and present colliding in wretched madness and heartbreak on the mean village street opposite the Catholic church (of course). Without knowing why, I feel the dark shadow of Irish history on this man, his long-suffering wife and children. Yet also, there is something else in his presence, enlightening.

"I'm looking for the job as development officer and it was Father McDyer who told me about you. I'm a Republican and Socialist and what McDyer's doing here interests me enormously. My old friend David O'Connell lives here too." Pringle explains.

"David O'Connell, you know him then?"

"We were in the same hut together at the Curragh in the fifties. We helped him and Rory Brady escape." He meets my eyes without shame or remorse.

"So you were in the IRA?"

"The Official IRA and Official Sinn Fein, but I'm hardly active these days, in my present situation."

"Not the Provisionals?"

"No, but I can well understand where they're coming from."

Can he indeed? "Is that right? So, where will you be living?"

"McDyer's organised a house for us to rent in a week or two, when we'll be back."

"Well good luck, Glencolumbkille's an out-of-the way place, all bog, mountains and sea."

"That's what I like about it," Pringle says enthusiastically.

"Where have you come from today?" The '98 Rebellion, maybe ... ?

"Dublin."

"Will you be stopping tonight?"

"No, we'll be returning to Dublin."

"That's an awful lot of driving for one day."

"We left early this morning in the dark; we'll be seeing you then."

"Safe journey." I raise a hand to them.

What is it about him? Enigmatic and shabbily dressed, his wife continually watching, a child crying in her arms. There's heartbreak here and collapse. His grey flannel trousers are stained and he needs a new jacket, shirt and shoes. He came to be interviewed dressed like that? I don't know what it is, I'm still in the swirling vortex, but I sense that a tragedy is

unfolding. What was it? Her wounded, crucified-looking eyes perhaps?
The children, seemingly asphyxiated, gasping for air? The baby stuff?
Discarded wrappings and mess? Whatever it is, historical greivances are
without much foundation now. For this excitement, Rebellion and God-
only-knows-what, everything about Ireland is here in this encounter. I
reel out of the vortex, stumbling away from them as they disappear from
Glencolumbkille.

A letter is an event. One is pushed through the bottom of the door by
the ragged scarecrow of a postman. I can see him coming sometimes,
like a broken and wounded bird. He leaves a letter from Father this time,
I can tell from the familiar, no nonsense handwriting. There was a bomb
blast in Ballynahinch that wrecked many shops, but a warning was given.
Yet he can see where they're coming from!

Father's Royal Navy brother has retired to the strange-sounding Bishop's
Caundle and wants a chalice and paten made for the local church in
remembrance of his young daughter who died of a rare disease. I can
well imagine a sleepy little village in glorious countryside, not much disturbed in the hundreds of years since Roman, Saxon and Norman times,
feeling hardly a ripple from the civil war. I'm thinking of the amazing
watercolours of Rowland Hilder; Constable's oils depicting hazy weather
and delicate shades. There will be a medieval church nearby and welcoming pub signs. Still, it is an interesting order and easy to raise by hand.
Once again I can get lost in the magic of proper silversmithing.

CHAPTER 44

This is a bitter land and bitter words blow out from the radio: who killed who and whether they were Protestants or Catholics. Every figure that passes below the workshop is familiar now: the McGinleys and Gillespie's, McDyer (never on foot), the all-seeing Joe and old James with his peculiar gait, moving through the village for lunch at his digs. James never came to see me. The odd time we meet, he usually growls with hostility and his high-pitched, exasperated voice churns with grudges against the nation, whom he considers a Hottentot race, guilty but insane.

McDyer is always the first to leave a funeral, hurriedly zooming off in his four wheels while the mourners slowly depart. Tommy, the gravedigger, shovels the wet earth over the coffin on his own and he's usually very late. Stamping the last shovelfulls down with his nobnailed boots, he conducts a macabre sort of dance that says that this is all there is in this old world. You'll never get out of that, whatever the Bible says.

As night falls and I take the lonely walk back, under a near-full moon, I rest on the leaning standing stone and stop. That faintly mocking noise is the sound of running water, which is accompanied by the unfathomable whisper of sea. My cottage comes into view and appears magical under the peek-a-bo moonlight. I wonder a lot about Pringle. There is no dog waiting for me tonight.

I will have to borrow a few stakes from Graham at Castleward. He is so far ahead of me, with plenty of interesting, well-paid work. That was evident the time I saw him, when I returned to tell him about America and Mary. Despite his splendid isolation, they seek him out. After all, Castleward is a lot nearer Belfast, and even Dublin, than I am. But what southerner would cross the border these days? It is a very alien country to them now. Graham can even get the Irish hallmark, for the very few of his customers who would want it. Nearly all of them require London's Leopards and Lions. Orange Lodges and county councils in particular, are averse to Harps and Hibernia.

* * *

Arriving at the lovely, old Castle Ward farmyard, after a nervous drive from Glencolumbkille, one interrupted by several army checkpoints, I'm looking forward to a welcome and necessary distraction for a few days. But harsh northern voices signal there's a fierce confrontation going outside his workshop. I see two constables, another man and Graham, who nods briefly at me. I keep a short distance from them all. The loud argument concerns rights and wrongs of Graham having smashed the gamekeeper's shot gun to pieces and knocking the man flat out, in a rage for the gamekeeper having shot his cat. I know Graham is not one to lie down and let anyone get away with such behaviour.

Stern warnings resound in the hot air on both sides of the argument. The constables issue cautions and question whether the gamekeeper had a licence for that particular gun (it would be a serious offence not to have one in these fraught times). Graham is told to be more careful; it was only a cat, he could have killed the poor man with such a blow. And the game-keeper was simply doing his duty, the cat was killing rare birds for fun. Graham should consider himself lucky not charged with actual bodily harm or far worse. But they are going to let the matter lie..

I suddenly pity the smartly uniformed, armed, and bullet-proof-jacketed young constables, who are an easy target for the IRA. Out of nowhere, they could be killed. And he knows where they're coming from!

After they have gone, in the workshop, Graham explains his side of the affair, slowly returning back to normality. He wasn't going to let the bastard escape his just retribution, that served him bloody well right.

"Jesus Christ, Graham, that's some yoke you're making there." I have spotted an amazing silver and amethyst crozier head of St Patrick and a snake. "Who is it for?"

"The Bishop of Connor no less." Graham replies with a well-deserved grin replies.

"Can I ask how much?" For it's such a fine piece of work.

"One thousand, four hundred pounds. Not bad, eh?"

"And I've had only two orders since I've returned."

"Give it time," he says reassuringly.

"Can I take the few stakes I phoned you about?"

"Whatever you need. You can even have that one as I've two." Graham points to the cow's tongue.

"I'll return these as soon as I've finished." I pick up five in all, which should be enough.

"No need to hurry and before I forget, I've something to show you." Going over to a pile of old copies of the *Daily Mail*, *Playboy* and a glossy, thick *Harpers Bazaar* magazine, he flicks through the pages, stopping at a section on American fashion, handing it over to me.

"Do you recognise anyone?" Graham asks.

I'm overwhelmed by a sense of utter desolation as I look at the photographs of Mary. It is quite clearly her, without a doubt, in various poses, wearing beautifully tailored clothes, looking absolutely stunning. My God, hasn't she done well? Despite her past misfortunes and the vagaries of Catholic Kilkenny's harsh upbringing and regardless of the mysterious black box at Poe and Kiely's and Langrishe's behaviour, she has escaped to a far better life. How one thing can lead to another: a glance; a word; a promise of a free meal and a chance meeting. I remember Tom Eastwood at the fateful Club House hotel, it would have been better for me not to have gone to meet him. A corrosive sense of grief overwhelms me at the loss of Mary. Strangely, I could never let go of Old Ireland. It had to be one or the other.

"She'd be earning big money now, those models are stars in their own right these days," explains Graham, mindless of my inner turmoil.

My reply sounds faint, even to my own ears. "Yes, so I believe."

"But there's plenty more women out there, don't you be forgetting that." Now more alert to my feelings, Graham is light-heartedly supportive.

"You can keep that if you like; by coincidence a woman gave it to me. She wanted a ring like the one advertised here." I take the magazine and examine Mary's lovely red ruby and diamond platinum ring.

"Another nice order for you Graham."

"But of course, only the best for me." His reply is mockingly self-satisfied. "So what really happened to the pair of you in the end?"

"Ah, Graham, it just wasn't meant to be. She went off with Snakeskinjacket man. It was her chance to escape. She's well out of Ireland and me. Too far gone. She'd have freaked coming back."

* * *

Approaching the Quoile bridge leading into Downpatrick, I stop the car. From the middle of the bridge, I gaze down to the muddy water beneath. With a last look at Mary in the magazine, I let her go; she floats away towards Strangford Lough and maybe out to the Irish sea. I recall a similar moment once with her and Thomas Aquinas on the bridge at Inistioge.

These are difficult days.

Slowly driving towards Ballynahinch via Clough I pass the familiar remains of De Courcy's motte and bailey castle again, with its bright red white and blue union flag as always, flying defiantly above. The Protestants of Northern Ireland are determined that nothing will ever change.

At the crossroads towards Dundrum, with Newcastle to the left, I take the right to Ballynahinch and Belfast, entering shaded Seaforde by an old manse that I always fancied living in. Mary was with me last time I was here. Turning into the narrower backroad, I drive by Forde's tall trees, set back from the road behind a high stone wall that is broken in parts. This is the journey of a lifetime. I have to be around this green land always; it couldn't have been otherwise. Whatever my fortune, I have to feel Ulster's beating heart.

Entering the farmyard expectantly, I notice something that I definitely should not be seeing by my brother's open shed door. It is himself and Sam McCauley. His car boot is being loaded with what looks like bicycle parts at first — I only had a momentary glance – but no, they're disassembled guns of some sort. Shit they're not into that are they? Both look over, surprised at the sudden intrusion, McCauley quickly finishes and closing the boot of his black Saab. What ghastly criminality have I uncovered. I had better remain in the car for a while, pretending I didn't see a thing, but listening.

My brother says, "never again. And just this once. If word ever gets out about this bloody nonsense you're involved in Sam, you'll have us all in jail for aiding and abetting. Now go!"

"Sure, John, if we Protestants don't make a stand, they'll be doing away with the border in no time."

"Promise me you'll never come up here again with the likes of this. Now go. As far as I'm concerned, this never happened, I know nothing about your activities."

"I have your word on that then?" demands McCauley.

"Yes, yes, now go."

"And your brother too?" Obviously McCauley has recognized me, he nods towards still in the car, while I pretend to search for something on the back seat.

"Yes!" shouts John.

"Doesn't he live down there now?"

"Look, Sam, will you please go."

"All right, all right. I'm away." Catching my eye, he puts a long, warning finger to his lips sternly before driving away. And that stubborn, awkward, Presbyterian-Scottish-lowland face can look very stern indeed.

John comes over with an emphatic warning. "Don't you ever say a word about this to anyone, especially Mum and Dad, or we'll all get a bullet in the head, understand!"

"What did he want anyway?"

"Don't be pretending you didn't see now; he was using the welder for a while here on his handmade automatics, the stupid fool, it'll catch up on him eventually. There's no future here anymore, Australia's the place to go." As he shuts the sliding door with a bang, John is angry and confused. It won't be long until he's gone, as most of my family from mother's side, past and present, eventually leave.

Mother is already far away in her thoughts and father couldn't care less if the farm is sold and my brother follows his cousins to Australia. To live here now would certainly take a deep commitment. There was recently a cowardly ambush on the Protestant postman, driving into Newry on his rounds. Bullets travel faster than sounds, riddling his van, which ended upside down in the ditch, wheels spinning and the driver dead and fish-eyed, his blood spilt for what? The IRA sped away with whoops of savage, primeval, tribal satisfaction, horn blaring. And he knows where they're coming from!

Against the news of disintegrating, ruined lives, it seems importanat to me to get started on the silver chalice and paten. Looking in the laundry cupboard for a towel, I find the many-coloured ribbons of his war medals, including a blue enamelled patonce cross and a particularly attractive long, wide, poplin rose-pink and pearl-grey. 'For God and the Empire' is embossed in gold lettering on red enamel, circling old King George and Queen Mary. It is downright strange to think about the war these days. And yet they are lot more reasonable and uplifting than they could well have been, 'For Fatherland, Volk and Fuhrer' could have been written around the picture of Adolf Hitler.

I'm attached to the cross, blue as a clear morning sky, it's a shame really, to fold the ribbons away. But I return them to where they were hidden under socks and underwear. Warring Ulster. Ireland is where it all started, I suppose, the empire.

* * *

In the morning I check under the car, afraid of what I will find. I'm not looking for bombs. The problem is that the car is rusted and barely holding together. With another prayer and crossed fingers, I set out through a fog-bound, haunting wilderness from Pettigoe to darkened Donegal town. The town is lightly blurred and sounds are muted; people pass warily, floating and ghostly. I will just have to stay the night, I'm too exhausted and it too dangerous to drive on. Never mind the cost of a comfortable bed, hot bath and cooked breakfast. It seems I will soon be the only one of the extended family left in Ireland.

Dozing, I dream fitfully of the incomprehensible silver screen's depiction of the liberation of Belsen concentration camp. A British soldier bulldozes piles of skeletal bodies towards an enormous pit. There are distant voices and the faintest tapping. No, yes, there's a woman entering the room without turning the light on, the maid, not wanting to disturb me maybe. She stands there bold as brass.

I'm not dreaming now, as she unbuttons her blouse and her hands disappear behind her, to unhook her bra. She lets her clothing fall carelessly on the floor, then loses a tight-fitting short skirt, which she wriggles down her body so that still in high heels, she can step daintily out of it. Now she is just in suspender belt and stockings. This candy red-head is a fine looking woman. I'm fully focused now, but speechless. She stands in front of me, delightfully exposed.

"You are Joe Murphy, aren't you?" she asks from her quiet, alluring, fey, Donegal, reddened lips.

"Well no, I'm not actually." I answer foolishly, taken totally unawares.

"Oh, Jesus, Mary and Joseph. I do apologise for disturbing you." She exclaims hastily, putting on her clothes and rushing out the door.

"You don't have to leave." I call after her, stupidly. In Donegal town, of all places, I would never have believed it.

* * *

He said there was no hurry, but I finish off the gold angel ring without bothering to get it blessed, for how will he ever know? McDyer is still asking about apprentices and even the workshop rent, God forbid, I have to go to the Ulster Bank in Killybegs and open an account to get a draft for the silver order for the chalice and paten from Birmingham. Life's difficult enough without the long drive there and back, but I will be able to send a cheque to Birmingham next time, if they'll even take an Irish one. The joys of living in the Irish-speaking Gaeltacht. Although, so far I haven't heard anyone in Glencolumbkille speak it yet.

Bernadette's been to see me a few times, although it is always necessary to invite her into the workshop, where she coyly asks me, "how are you managing?"

She wants to try on a pair of earrings, which I was rather vaguely earmarking for Christmas maybe. We are so close and I can inhale her still youthful effervescence without the slightest intention of initiating anything, however how strongly I feel the invitation. Turning the county upside with a priest's housekeeper. What desperation must she feel to settle for a black Protestant I can hardly imagine. Not that Bernadette's job would ever stop, but life for her in Glencolumbkille would be difficult.

Another man might enjoy some fun, just short of commitment. But that's not me. And there's the crazy Catholic contraception laws. No wonder there are such large families here, given the belief in such nonsense. God knows what would come of a pregnancy as she's older than would usually be safe. Now she is sitting on the bench, swinging her pretty legs out of her pleated skirt, which is rather high just now. And she is laughing in a silly, nervous sort of way.

Looking after McDyer must be a right old chore, he can be a bit of a grump times. She's not getting any younger, mid-thirties or even older, I can't really tell, what with make-up hair and the likes. She's nicely put together though, no awkward edges to smooth out, making a pleasing whole. But a priest's housekeeper. Would she much into that supernatural stuff? Medieval and all, it really is for a simple, peasant people.

I can sense her desperation, here in Glencolumbkille, for what decent men are there here anyway? And who would want to be married and living in a dirty, thatched cottage of the kind that Father always hates having to go into? Worrying about the price of sheep and pigs? Bernadette is an unlit firecracker, waiting too long for someone to light her, but in danger of becoming damp and morose eventually.

The day comes when Bernadette's suddenly off in a huff, as if to express anger that she has been wasting her time. She doesn't give me another word. It was an awkward situation, I was unable to respond to her interest and was only being innocent and gentle with her. I read about a Spanish nun about Bernadette's age, who went mad, pushed over the altar, tore down Jesus crucified, toppled the Virgin Mary and screamed, "fuck, cunt, shite on you God!"

CHAPTER 45

When the silver finally does arrive, I hope the noise won't disturb the living and dead, as I gaze over the graveyard. Raising it with the definite purpose of getting it finished and hallmarked, the next week or two will take care of themselves. These playful hours are a celebration of creation and of the ability to construct, making my grey matter focus on the work at hand without interruption. Each hammer stroke sends a metallic ring through the village, but there are no complaints so far. I lay off the hammer during their Mass times and all day Sundays.

'Believing that the body and blood of Jesus Christ is present on these holy mysteries through the ineffable operation if God's grace and the virtue of the Holy Spirit. These things necessarily require faith, they do not admit to reason.' The phrases fall out from the dusty attic of my mind, how strange.

By chance, I am working in primitive isolated surroundings, but they are surely appropriate for such bygone endeavours. This silver will soon be locked away, taken out only for communion every other Sunday. That's probably the way it has to be now for the fast diminishing Anglican flock. In future years, it will be considered a curious piece of antique church plate hallmarked in Dublin. I can imagine someone wondering how they came to end up at Bishop's Caundle. Perhaps our future detective would take the trouble to check with the assay office to discover it was made by a silversmith with an English sounding name. So what was he doing in Ireland? Was he even Irish?

* * *

Joe calls up to talk about Pringle, saying old James gave the developer short shrift when he came to see the jewellry workshop. James said afterwards that he knew Pringle's sort and immediately smelt a very large rat. I don't know what to make of that. Unless James was aware that Pringle was in the Curragh with O'Connell, though I hardly think so. When I mention this to Joe, he becomes all agog at the thought, telling me that there is no smoke without fire.

He thinks aloud upon the implications of Pringle being friendly with O'Connell. Does it mean they are storing dynamite in McDyer's folk village? Two thousand pounds a year is an awful lot to be paying a high-falutin development officer (whatever that means) and what Pringle is supposed to be doing is hardly needed anyway, for sure, wasn't the whole country north and south established by his likes? Joe points out they only put away the guns a generation ago and gunmen are back in favour again today. For him, it all adds up to an IRA conspiracy that will destroy McDyer if the bishop finds out.

I find that Pringle is always helpful and he's interested in the silver making. He's no fool and is well read. I wonder why he'd be bothered with the Shinner stuff, it was perhaps a condition inherited at birth. To a romantic youth, perhaps it makes sense. And it did eventually get the British out after 1916. A religion for some, this orange and green. I couldn't feel either way now. I sense a quiet desperation in him, not least because he is without definite word about the job yet. Does McDyer even know himself where the money is coming from to pay for a development officer?

Whatever Joe says about the doctor being away on a bender with the village at risk of contagion and death, everything was normal enough the day went to see him about a bad cold and a constantly running nose. The doctor was a perfectly soft spoken gentleman, very capable. It was hard to believe his wife could throw a basin of dirty dishwater over him, shouting, "get away out of this house you mad bloody eejit!"

That story was told if Joe was there when it happened. For sure, what else is there to talk about at the moment? Never mind the wasting Atlantic waves and starry sky, or wandering over lonely bog lands and the melancholy cry of the curlew. I just have to get on with this life whatever way it takes me.

* * *

There's a gaunt, madly waving figure in the headlights; a man wearing a long torn coat, who forces me to bring the car to a halt. His distorted face is squashed right up against the window screen, like an escapee from a lunatic asylum and he obviously has been drinking.

"Will yez be going to the wake?"

"No, I didn't know anyone was dead." Despite myself, I reply civilly to this ghastly, unwanted intrusion.

"Ah, sure, come on, I'll take yez there; we'll get more of the drink, if ye know what I mean." He smiles crazily and is too quick for me to drive on without him. He gets into the back and my God, does he not stink of putrid, rancid, rotten humanity? He must be living alone in some lousy, mountain cottage. I take my unwelcome passenger as a warning that I should be careful and not become like him.

"Where are we heading?" I ask him, looking in the rear view mirror.

He directs me to a two-storey slated house, part of a tidy farmyard, where every window is lit. There are several cars parked to one side and a dozen people smoking outside the open doorway. I wouldn't know anyone. The outer darkness makes the glow from the inner commotion dreamy and transient. A scene bathed in gold.

My unwanted passenger, encourages me, "go on and help yourself." Then he's off into the crowd.

The paintings of Goya come to mind again, as I approaching the polite and puzzled gathering. A wake is a new experience for me. It a more a gossipy get together than a sad farewel. I recognise Norman the butcher, who slaughters his meat in the open fields where he has a sort of double gallows to hang the animals up to be disembowelled. Joe claims to often have heard their pitiful cries, though I never have.

There's plenty of food and drink. Going through to another room, I find an old woman lying dead in an unusual, narrow four-poster bed, all draped in clean whites. Her hands are folded and life has clearly evaporated from the candle wax face, the way of all flesh. From the other room, my companion knowingly raises his unsteady glass of Guinness to me, as if knowing my thoughts: you might as well enjoy yourself while you can. He'll be walking home on his own tonight.

Making to leave, I'm suddenly aware of another old woman, clothed in black and long dead, watching me from a large frame. It is a portrait of Queen Victoria, who is the last person I would expect to be venerated here. She is wearing the broad dark blue sash and eight-pointed, red St George cross star of the Garter and her image completely dominates the crowded chattering room for now. How extraordinary. And she even seems to be smiling.

I manage to slip away unseen, the car still filled with the heavy odours of the starved, wild, Irish mountain man. I imagine that the older I get living here, the more I'll become just like him, careless and unaware of his decay. Parking at the gate, I walk slowly to the cottage and look over the thorny hedge down upon McDyer's valley which seems to be sliding into the sea. Mary is over there. Across all that water. For her, Ireland was never meant to be, it will only be half remembered. Whereas I recall the sublime moments I have experienced here. Drifting like a lonely, feathered cloud across the rosy tinted moon are the words of England's Edmund Spenser, who lived for too long in Ireland for his own good sanity.

Huge sea of sorrow, and tempestuous griefe,
Wherein my feeble barke is tossed long,
Far from the hoped hauen of reliefe,
Why do thy cruell billowes beat so strong,
And they moyst mountaines each on others throng,
Threatening to swallow up my fearful life?
O do they cruell wrath and spightfull wrong
At length allay, and stint they stormy strife,
Which in these troubled bowels raignes, & rageth rife.

* * *

In the morning post, accompanying father's letter, as divorce papers for me to sign. I am deeply shocked.

* * *

Thankfully, just in time, the silver for the chalice and paten has arrived too. There is a bank strike, which makes business rather awkward. These are peculiar times, where cash is getting dirtier and dirtier as it circulates. But who needs real money? Certainly not the happy-go-lucky, retired English couple holidaying at the folk village, who occassionally call in to the workshop for a chat. I suspect the man in the couple is actually a woman. They are interested to see what I'm making and might perhaps buy something. Then, one day, out of the blue, they offer to buy the lot. In exchange for what? Well, all they can do is offer me a cheque to lodge when the strike is over.

What a sale. Money is no object to them. Easy come, easy go. But then, this would leave me with nothing to show if ever I get to Dublin to find outlets there. Pringle is enthusiastic about the prospect and mentioned he'd organise it. Going to Dublin with him is a confusing thought. Still, the windfall would be very welcome. I'd have a clean sheet to begin again, though why would they want to wear so much jewellry at their age?

I have to think about this, there is no hurry. Have two old dykes come to the rescue? Or when the strike is over, will I find myself with a worthless check and the jewellery all gone? Certainly, they seem a wealthy pair, ordering the best of foods from Donegal town. The day I was there with the prices I noticed steaks, Danish ham, various cheeses, chocolates, tins of fruit, bottles of expensive wine and cartons of Benson and Hedges scattered around the cosy cottage. I also noticed their diction, which was out of place: Londonish and lower class.

These are happy days; their offer goes around and around my thoughts. Even McDyer's dog has found a canine cornucopia with the many meaty leftovers put out for him by the side of their cottage door. Both are up at McDyer's, trusted, and well liked. They make bread and cakes with him. The weeks pass and I believe the cheque shouldn't be a problem. But I am undecided, cold cognition gradually taking over my daydreams.

* * *

The Reverend from the Church of Ireland was bound to call. Word amongst the few gets about. How did they deduce my affiliation? It is a mystery to behold and it was the same in Kilkenny. As the cottage window dims, I know intuitively that it is him, that he is feeling sad and apologetic and almost feeling he is a bother for what he is here to discuss. Did Jesus really walk on water, raise the dead and cure the sick? Hopefully, he is not here to talk about the *Ne temere* decree? I can tell that he is uncomfortable in my humble abode and he certainly isn't going to criticise the powerful Roman Catholic Church in Ireland, even inside these walls, it might get out. I feel a gentle sorrow towards him, for what does the Church of Ireland really stand for? That divine grace was a more effective way of gaining salvation than the purchase of indulgences? More like tea and polite conversation these days, avoiding the supernatural stuff, with his gentle hint that he would be so glad to see me at every other Sunday service.

* * *

As always there are the restless sounds of the wind and the sea in the workshop and I stop for a moment to listen at their mocking of my endeavour. Talk of the strike is now nearly over and it was wise not to have trusted the English couple. They were up and away without paying a penny, taking all McDyer's accumulated Mass money for the sick and dead from an upstairs drawer. Robbing a priest in Ireland was never heard of before.

It is a big surprise when Mother and Father arrive to see how their son is coping and stay in the just-vacated crooks's cottage. They bring a box of groceries and a large case of Armagh apples, imagining there might be hunger in Eire. The news is broken to me that the farm will be sold, my brother and his family are definitely emigrating to Australia, while they are moving to a bungalow in Newcastle at the foot of the Mournes. They had been threatened by the local UVF not to sell to a RC. Men had come, clan like, and masked, in the early hours when my parents were asleep and dobbed the yard with red paint: a Biblical warning. In the morning they awoke to that intimidating invasion. A visitation, as if from ancestral ghosts in the night. The UVF are fearful of their neighbouring race's Catholicism and its ancient tyranny. We are all held in the warm embrace of Ireland's past.

It is almost a burden showing them around this scarred emptiness enclosed by bleak mountains and sea. We are growing apart, for they are discovering a foreign land and my mother is inwardly dismayed that I am living in Donegal like this. I drove them to the top of Slieve League and the seagulls became encircling terrors. I wondered why he was so afraid, for they weren't Messerschmitts. But for a moment, maybe, they were for him.

The cramped, musty, old, turf-fired kitchen was a painful shock for them. They can hardly believe this is happening to their son. Mother was clearly uneasy, although she didn't say a word as she glanced at the lurid crucifixion of Christ on the wall. Imagine, that I would want to settle here, in that devil de Valera's neutral Eire! As always, she is wearing the RAF wing brooch on the lapel of her tweed jacket.

"Any word of Mary and the child? she asks, brightening hopefully.

"No, no, nothing, just the divorce papers. Signed and posted."

"So that's the end of that then," she replies mournfully.

"Yes, I suppose so." Words fall into silence, for Mary would be horrified by this cottage; I'm living as she once did near Freshford.

After they have gone, they remain standing like statues in my mind. They have grown old, the way we all do eventually. They leave in a dull red Jaguar, which has lovely leather seats and while putting it into gear Father's final words to me are, "why don't you do something in jewellery on the history of Ireland." This is a parting gift of some value. What can I make of his chance remark?

* * *

Out of dreaming night, old Ireland's history is magically awakened. In the consciousness of morning light, there's already a rough design in my head. A clever piece of cod-Irish jewellery with its story to tell. But where to start, where to end? Where to wear it? On the arm, ears, fingers or neck? And with such sadness to depict, it will perhaps be too much of a burden to wear; we shall see.

Twelve is a good number that divides equally. So I begin with Patrick's outstretched arms holding a crozier giving his converts a blessing; not that the boys and girls of Kilkenny Design would approve (they are getting a lot of publicity lately). Next will be a round tower, with a Viking unable to get into it and a laughing monk high above him. The idea came from a green booklet Coras Trachtala published that I kept. Will anyone know why the tall towers were actually built? Were they signposts to guide sup-plicants with bells calling them to prayer; were the monks climbing up closer to God? Or were they storing sacred treasure?

Next will be the wife-stealing Dermot MacMurrough, inviting the Norman Strongbow over to marry his daughter, to help restore the lands taken by the irate husband, so that after Dermot's death Leinster would belong to Strongbow. Then, fourth, is a chain-mailed Norman holding a lance and long shield. It is simple enough and I can then have their thick-walled castles appear as ominous features on most horizons. But they never wholly subdued the troublesome natives (much the same as in the north).

From a square-toothed castle it is only a walk around Protestant Belfast to see painted on their walls King Billy with a sword on his white horse at the Battle of the Boyne. And didn't he leave the country in the hands of the good old Protestant cause? Free from Popery, brass money and wooden shoes until the ninety-eight rebellion and the Act of Union in 1800.

The next image is obvious, the red saltire of St Patrick joined to the white and blue of Scotland and England's red cross of St George. Shove it to the Shinners, they won't like the reality of that, for we really are a quarrelsome lot. Is it any wonder so many left these islands to start an English-speaking empire.

I think that the skeleton sitting on the Londonderry coat of arms and juggling potatoes will do nicely for the great famines of the 1840s, with a ship symbolic of the emigrants leaving. I can have the GPO on fire with the green flag flying above it. Then, I will have the map of Ireland with the six counties separated, representing partition.

Looking out, I can see McDyer driving hellbent through the village again. He is going to kill himself or someone at those speeds and there's Tommy getting ready to dig another grave with his long shovel and pre-paring an old door to cover the hole when it has been dug. Looking to the future, will Ireland be united or not? Or will it join this European pro-ject. The simplest and last image can only be a question mark. *Quo Vadis* Ireland, whither goest thou?

I will start right away and make something easy to understand, a far cry from the silversmiths of old, like Paul Starr and Paul de Laramie. What am I doing here in Glencolumbkille, creating such nonsense? I paint one side of a gauge eleven silver sheet — one times eight-and-a-quarter inch — with white poster paint. Then I pencil in twelve images placed in line: the most complicated are the GPO, King Billy and Strongbow. Next, I drill small holes into each to let in the piercing blade to cut out each image and gently needle file the edges smooth. The twelve slowly appear complete. I make another strip of silver gauge ten — one-and-a-quarter times eight-and-a-half — borax both and hard solder the cut-out plate onto the second slightly larger one, making sure the solder has run everywhere. I leave it in the acid mixture until the hardened borax is dissolved. Now, I cut away the surplus edges and bend it into a circle and solder the edges together and then again in the acid until the hardened borax is dissolved, filing away any of the joins surplus solder. I finish the work carefully and finally wash it in hot soapy water.

It is not bad at all, in fact I am quite pleased. Rings and so forth will need to be made much smaller. That will be a long way ahead, if ever, given that I am without money for marketing and packaging. The grave is ready. Those crafty old seagulls are always on the lookout, there is a chorus perched on McDyer's Mass House roof. A complete indifference permeats every corner of Glencolumbkille.

The chalice and paten need hallmarking, so I go to get another empty box from Doherty's, which is a bright red and yellow fronted shop, but is gloomy and low ceilinged inside. And the paraffin smell is overwhelming. A horn toots behind me and turning I see that Pringle has a new car, well, a second or third hand car. He winds down the nearside window and leans over, determined to stay, whether he has the job or not. Has McDyer given up on the idea?

Would leaving a few murdered constables behind be of no consequence if the final goal was achieved?

"You were to let me know about arranging a trip to Dublin. I've a friend in Bord Fáilte who'd make a few appointments for us. It would look much better coming through them, rather than us just turning up casually off the street, unannounced," Pringle explains carefully.

"Well, yes, Peter, you're right, there's hardly any outlets around here apart from McDyer's craft shop and mine, if you can call it that." I knew it had to come to this eventually.

"I'll phone Blanaid right away, she'll make the appointments with the likes of Weirs and Mortons; she'll know best." Pringle is no fool and has a good business sense.

"Go ahead then Peter, it's jolly decent of you to arrange this."

"Ah, sure, I have to be in Dublin anyway and it's supposed to be what I am doing here as you know."

"You have the job, haven't you?"

"Well with McDyer. But I'm beginning to wonder, he did say 'yes' but there's no money coming forth yet, so I'm somewhat in limbo, living in hope that it'll come right eventually." There is a hint of anguish in his face.

"Thanks again Peter and you'll let me know?"

"Sure, if you can't help your fellow man then what help is there for humanity?" He raises his hand in a kind of salute and drives away with a purposeful glance. I am confused and a trifle apprehensive at the thought of travelling to Dublin with him. What have I agreed to?

So, Pringle knows a Blanaid at Bord Fáilte? They are underneath Córas Tráchtálta on the corner of Lower Bagot Street and Wilton Terrace by the Grand Canal, where I persuaded Hogan and Walsh to give me that once-in-a-lifetime commission to make a golden jug. It sounded like a good idea then, there was so much talk which drifted into the surreal as Princess Margaret arrived. She was a right little cracker, with Walsh beside her, proud as a peacock that afternoon. You could tell she was bored stiff with his obsequious Irish blarney as he showed her around the revival of ancient crafts in the dilapidated stables of the once powerful Ormondes.

Old Langrishe is still alive by all accounts, getting on a bit now, behind high stone walls and tall whispering trees, out of bounds for the Knocktopher peasantry, whatever wrongs they had been burdened with. I could even see the ancestral ghosts of those who might slosh petrol and ignite those fine walls, carpets and furniture. And it would be just too bad if the old dog was asleep in his bed upstairs. Pringle is beginning to loom large, imaginatively. There's a strange and dangerous fascination growing about him. He has the despair and struggle of centuries of Irish history written all over him.

CHAPTER 46

I've a good spread of jewellery to show in Dublin, priced and ready. Luckily, I never trusted the English pair and McDyer has the Garda on their trail. I heard they were last seen around Cork. Pringle has carelessly driven his pale green Escort up to the door, over the laneway. McDyer did the same. I make Pringle a cup of tea before our drive.

"So, who are we going to see, Peter and where can we stay?" He is rather shabbily dressed and I wonder if he will be coming into each shop like that?

"The North Star Hotel on Amiens Street, opposite Connolly Station; hopefully we'll get a room there and we've two appointments to start with: Weirs of Wicklow Street and McDowells opposite the GPO. Do you know them?" Peter asks, stirring three heaped sugars vigorously into his tea.

"I bought my wife a little diamond ring in Weirs, she was so proud when she first wore it, holding it up to the light, delighted with the way even the smallest of diamonds can reflect the colours of the rainbow."

"So, you were married?"

"In Kilkenny, where I worked at the Design Centre, everybody knows about it now. We moved to America where she went off with a photographer. He wore a snakeskin jacket, can you imagine that."

"Ah women, they're like a stone in the shoe one can never get out," he says wistfully. With his good looks, exciting many a woman with talk of politics and insurrection.

I am not going to ask about his exploits to free Ireland, he can tell me in his own good time. Those tyres look too worn to be going anywhere on them. I just can't help feeling uneasy with these Shinner types: on the surface they could not be nicer, but they are cold-hearted killers according to what you read and hear. How does anyone get involved? No-one needs to be shot in the name of Ireland these days.

There is a light drizzle and low, unbroken dark cloud. The little villages and towns we race through are blurred and depressing but I mustn't be too critical, I have chosen my path. The car thumps loudly into a pothole and narrowly misses another.

"Jesus, Peter you are driving much too fast for these roads and weather."

"Did I give you a fright? asks Peter, unashamedly amused. "She's a great goer all right," he adds, precariously lighting yet another Embassy Gold, brushing away the spilt ash on his crotch. Will he be coming into Weirs like that? It could be said that 'shabby' is the word for us both. I have to wash in a basin of barely hot water and the mildew gets into my clothes. A damp cloth just about gets the mildew out, but the whiff lingers.

The speedometer edges up to between seventy and eighty again. "You'll be the death of us all Peter if you don't slow down."

"Sure, maybe it wouldn't be such a bad way to end one's life, to never to grow old and decrepit, but out like a light," says he, with that mad Irish gambler's face. Give it a go, what's there to lose? Plant a bomb; load a gun. More for the devilment. Then stone dead in an upturned car. There is a sickly bang and the rear side tips down. It was bound to happen on those tyres, but today of all days! It is raining hard as he opens the boot, does he even have a jack and spare?

The wheel screws are too tight, so Peter jumps on the spanner and eventually loosens them. When he gets back in the car his hands are bruised and filthy, his hair and clothes soaked and he reeks of Embassy Gold.

"If that's not a warning about your tyres and driving, Peter, then I don't know what is," I caution him. Nevertheless, he drives as if it was a kind of dare, a game of Russian roulette. McDyer is the same.

"Not to worry, we'll get there." So, I say no more, I can always get the bus back to Donegal.

Night falls as we enter the outskirts of Dublin, forever the foreign, old, dishevelled, rebel city. We are suddenly at the North Star Hotel and a receptionist Peter obviously knows manages a room with two single beds. So we are sharing. There is plenty of hot water — a miracle of inventiveness — and a chance to wash away the day and Glencolumbkille with a mean square of cheap soap. Soaking in the bath, I feel a glimmer of hope. Sleep will be uneasy, if at all, tossing, disturbed near him, with the peculiar odour of Irish hotels: bodies, beer, regurgitated food and a long dead mouse somewhere. Lovely North Star light years away from your namesake in Dublin.

For dinner, Peter orders a mixed grill. I am content with just a pot of tea and toast that I can hardly keep down. His busy lips are concentrated and he delights in getting down kidneys, liver, sausage, egg, bacon and those revolting black and white puddings, all going from plate to mouth with surgical skill.

"Will we go to a film Peter?" I suggest, anything for an hour or two's escape.

He is surprised at the suggestion and glazes blankly for a moment. "Well, yes, if that is what you would like." So, *Anne of a Thousand Days* it is.

On leaving the splendours of the Tudor Court, something seems different. Admiral Lord Nelson has gone.

"Why on earth did they have to blow up Lord Nelson's pillar? O'Connell Street will never be the same; shame on them."

Peter shows his true colours, he explains that it was up there far too long and the lads did a neat job. No one was hurt. Nelson was a constant reminder of British imperialism and their bad government in Ireland. To have been still standing on the fiftieth anniversary of the rising would have been shameful. It was more like a mean and petty act, given that the merchants and shippers of Dublin subscribed to building the column, grateful to Nelson for keeping the seas open for them. The architect was an Irishman anyway, Francis Johnson. But I'm not going to get into an argument.

"Don't you think she's a grand old whore of a city?" Peter says, gazing towards the Burgh Quay and O'Connell Bridge, flicking his cigarette butt expertly over the rail, sparking into the dark waters of the Liffey below like a spent bullet. I must get a grip, this is about selling jewellery and making a living and I should not let spectres of the past intrude, as they always do.

"Are you cold?" he asks, concerned.

"A bit, all right Peter, we'd better get back," I reply. We are poles apart and yet together on our return to the North Star Hotel.

"Will you have a jar before we turn in?"

"Ah, no Peter, it's been a long day. I'll go on up. But don't let me stop you. You can follow me up later."

"Are you sure?"

"God, yes, Peter, I'm exhausted."

"Blanaid has us into Weirs from eleven and McDowell at three in the afternoon. We'll drive up and park in Merrion Square with luck, it's not too far a walk then to Grafton Street. After Weirs I'll leave you to go onto McDowell's and we'll met again back here. I'll be up in a while and try not to disturb you," he says, catching the eye of the lady receptionist who is looking knowingly at him.

Well, that's just how it is, he's a decent Shinner ready to help, with or without McDyer's job. And he tries not to disturb me, but in every way

he does. The door opens to the hallway light, Peter comes in and closes
the door quietly not wanting to waken me. Now I am accustomed to the
dark I watch him slowly undress, his hauntingly vulnerable naked body
floating ghostly, as marble white as Michelangelo's David, perfectly proportioned. Or is David doomed Adam, painted on the Sistine Chapel, a
better association? Perhaps Pringle should be painted as one of Durer's
Irish soldiers and peasants; or a lady on horseback, symbolising Ireland
with Pringle as her squire. Even somehow, Peter as the crucified Christ. I
will never understand what it is about this seemingly tragic man.

The curtain of sleep rises and falls upon us both, until it finally stays
down.

* * *

Broken fragments of memory sharply interrupt the morning sunshine,
I'm thinking of when I was with Mary by the Shelbourne that afternoon
when the future was promising.

On Wicklow Street, near where it meets Grafton Street, I approach
Weirs' high, carrot-coloured brick and frosted glass-lettered doors. A
sense of apprehension grips me. Where, if anywhere, is this leading? We
are entering a contracting world with time running backward and are
totally unaware of this. There are blue and white patterned floral plaster ceilings, beautifully made old fashioned mahogany and glass cases
crowded with reproduction Celtic and Georgian silverware and I wonder,
sadly, if this will be the shape of my life in Ireland, with no difference
between past, present and future.

A few loyal staff, male and female, stand immobile, part of the furniture.

"They're an old Prody-run family firm," whispers Peter.

Peter asks for Mr Parker and receives a startled look from the assistant
behind the glass-topped watch counter, who reluctantly goes to find him.
Mr Parker is long and lean; he greets us with a conspiratorial smile and
with loping strides leads us to a small room at one end of the second floor,
where the window overlooks the busy Grafton Street. My tension eases
somewhat.

"You boys are from Donegal then? Almost a place apart on its own
isn't it? Squeezed between North and South. It's your man McDyer's area
you're from, isn't it?"

"Yes, he's the parish priest of Glencolumbkille, where we both live,"
says Peter, confidently taking the lead.

"He's done a good lot of work there I believe, but he is supposed to be a
communist, or so I've heard?"

"Hardly a true communist if he is a practicing Catholic priest," answers
Peter boldly.

"Bit of a contradiction there all right. Wasn't it Lenin who said 'opium of the people'?" Parker sits opposite us, at this small, velvet-covered table. He seems an easy-going, decent sort, in his mid-forties, not missing a trick with those inquisitive, lemony-pale eyes. I have the feeling he would be easy to offend, that his sensitive nose would smell a rat at once.

"Which one of you is the jeweller then?"

I raise my right hand and experience his careful gaze.

"And you?" to Peter.

"I'm McDyer's — well I'm the Glencolumbkille development officer who arranged this, we're friends. The idea is to develop Glencolumbkille with various self-sustaining enterprises," he explains earnestly.

"So, let's see what you have got then," Parker says leaning over and taps the box I am holding, a wakeup call from the suffusing influences of McDyer's Glencolumbkille. We are interrupted by the door bursting open and two well-dressed gentlemen look down at us mischievously, as if delighted to have taken us by surprise.

"This is Paddy Moss and Douglas Bennett." Parker is clearly irritated.

Bennett is dressed like an undertaker: immaculate in grey stripped trousers; black jacket and a pearl tie pin. Moss wears a finely tailored single-breasted suit. Bennett could be an Egyptian, he is darkly handsome, sallow skinned and brown eyed. I guess both are of the good old Protestant cause. Since there is nothing doing on a dull day they are here for a bit of fun, but, after all they are hard-hearted business men and what they buy they must sell. As they pick and peruse my items a burst of sunlight floods the room.

"What's this supposed to represent? Parker asks about the history bangle, handing it to Moss who is impatient to see it.

"The story of Ireland, each image represents a period of our history from the coming of St Patrick."

"And what's this one, that looks like a spider?" Moss asks. I wish I had a suit like the one he is wearing.

"It's a skeleton juggling potatoes, representing the great famine."

"And this?" pointing to the question mark.

"*Quo Vadis* Ireland, whither goest thou, the unknown future."

"Bit of the old Charlton Heston what?" and he laughs in a peculiar, mad sort of way.

"This?"

"Strongbow."

"Ah, yes, I get it now. The others are obvious. Very clever indeed, what do you think?" he asks, but in returning the bangle too roughly to Parker it falls on the floor and rolls away to the far side under a heater. Parker gets down on all fours and Moss boyishly pretends to kick his arse. A slightly flushed Parker gets up and leaves the bracelet on the table.

"Yes, definitely, we should try some of this jewellery, it's certainly Irish and original."

Bennett picks up the bracelet and cautions, "our brave patriots won't like the Union Jack or the Question Mark either."

Parker comes back at him forcefully, "well feck them, all the more reason, a bit of controversy can do no harm."

They are an admirable threesome now, as their words float and fall honey golden as the autumn leaves that swirled and swept, seducing me on the Kilkenny Parade that Autumn of 1963. After a while, Moss and Bennett leave as Parker carefully checks each piece and writes out an order on head paper that states, 'Weir and Sons Silversmiths Manufacturers since 1869'.

"Make sure we get this by the end of October, well in time for Christmas," and he folds and hands me the paper. "You're not a Donegal man now are you? A bit of a mixture I'd say, not like this Pringle fellow who is surely a true Dub."

Peter jokingly informs him about my background. "He's a fearful black Protestant of the worst kind."

I wish he hadn't.

"Is that so? One of the dwindling few, like myself," he winks at me. "So which part are you from then?"

"County Down, Downpatrick."

"Near Belfast, where my brother's a clergyman at the Seaman's Missions, a dangerous place these days." He shook his head sadly, "I'm Castlecomer myself, my mother lives in Kells."

"Kells, Kilkenny?"

"Yes."

"Did you come across Langrishe of Knocktopher?"

Parker stops fractionally, evidently wondering why I ask. "Not personally of course, real gentry, titled, British army, real west Brits as your man here would say. So why do you ask?"

"I knew a girl there who worked at the Design Centre who was the daughter of the Terrence one, not that he ever recognised her."

"That wouldn't surprise me, we see the son Hercules very occasionally. He's married to Grania, Lord Powerscourt's daughter. I remember vaguely that he had a reputation, but wouldn't any man in his situation. So, you worked at the Design Centre? One of them came here, but we never bought anything, he was acting as if he was doing us a favour."

"Was he a German?"

"Well, yes he was. How did you know?"

"Just a feeling, that's all."

Parker looks puzzled but stands up and sees us out to Wicklow Street.

CHAPTER 47

"Jesus, we did well there," Peter enthuses as we walk towards Bewleys. "Play your cards right and you'll be well in there, that was a great order, will you be able to manage?"

"I certainly hope so, I'll need to order more silver as soon as we return." My mind rushes to the hurdles ahead. "I could phone Johnson Mattley from my home near Ballynahinch, we could go back that way and maybe stay the night, saving all the hassle of the Glencolumbkille post office trying to get through to Birmingham with an order and them having to send a proforma invoice. They could give the price there and then, so I can post a cheque right away."

"It's certainly a problem for you doing business there and I wouldn't mind going north in the least, I've never been to County Down."

"I'll get you a full tank of petrol on the way and I'll have to try to get thirty days credit from them, but it takes a while to build up a relationship and with you driving from Southern Ireland the people there might be wary, what with all this trouble going on." There is always a possible problem.

"Well, it's their fault and time they cleared out; there'll be no real peace until they've all gone."

"Can I get you a bite to eat or a coffee?" I offer, it is the least I can do for a decent man who helped me to get such a good order, no matter his views on Britain.

"No thanks, I'll be late if I don't get a move on, see you later at the North Star and well done." He crosses Grafton Street and disappears into South Anne Street.

* * *

There's a bare-legged beggar woman with long red hair holding a dirty child by the entrance to Bewleys, eyes belligerent and melancholy at the same time. A reminder I must not to let Weirs down. It's a chance of a lifetime, which I must take or else risk similar poverty. I share a table in the busy café with a companion who has his head buried in the *Irish Press*.

Leaning back, I wonder who all these people are? Celt, Gael, Norsemen, mixture of Norsemen and Gael, Norman, Anglo-Norman, Welsh Norman (called Old English), Elizabethans, Jacobites, Williamites, Cromwellians, Lowland Scot, Huguenot French and Anglo-Irish. All distinct from Native Irish, as if there are any natives left after the others have been here for so long.

I suddenly remember the chilling words of *The Wearing of the Green* and my mood darkens. Every face is now a mask, each wary and watchful of each other, their lives full of fantasy and talk, laughter and hate, outward gaiety, but inner suspicion. Some look as if they recognise someone familiar, then look away quickly.

I have to hurry away. To kill an hour or two in the daylight I walk around Stephen's Green, down Dawson Street and stop to gaze up at the tricolour as it writhes and twists to full-blown extent, falling and curling around the high flagpole above the Mansion House, never still, a symphony of green white and orange. It is constantly hypnotising against those fleeting blues, grey, pale peach and luminous white clouds. Other passers-by are glancing at the flag too, but without stopping or noticing it.

On O'Connell Bridge there's a cold wind blowing in from the sea, the river's waters are choppy at high tide. I fear this side of the Liffey, a fear derived from the myths and wartime chaos of my childhood. On reaching McDowells, 'The Happy Ring House', I just know this is not going to work out. Over generations this has been a place for couples wanting engagement and wedding ring on a budget. Couples that are in love, but for how long? I'm hawking my wares like the beggar woman, but without a blessing to give in return. It is a shop like Weirs, with old-style display cases walled to the ceiling containing similar silver merchandise and still with a depressing Victorian look.

"I've an appointment with Mr McDowell for three o'clock." I introduce myself and interrupt two young shop assistants who were deep in conversation at the end of the now-familiar glass-topped jewellery counter.

They turn with what seems offended astonishment but continue whispering for a short while, until one of them reluctantly disappears down the stairs, saying, "I'll go tell Mr McDowell you're waiting."

The other eyes me furtively as I look around the old shop. Is this going to be my future again?

"You may go down, Mr McDowell will see you there now," says the first, coming to the top of the stairs and they continue their whispering.

At first sight Mr McDowell reminds me of a heron at rest on one leg. His eyes are half-closed; he is a silvery sixtyish. McDowell shows me to a seat at a large green leather-topped table, seating himself opposite. We are surrounded by all-wood panelling and more fitted showcases. The whole shop must contain a fortune in stock. Just beside his sharp features there's a framed picture of a horse and jockey. I can make out the attribution: *Caughoo, winner of the Grand National 1947, owned by J. T. McDowell.*

He must be worth a few bob to own race horses. I lay out the jewellery as before, but there's nothing in this for him; he is just going through the motions. It is so different from Weirs. Without comment, he casts a brief, sceptical eye over the jewellery, arms folded. In any case, how would I cope with another large order? With the pressure of delivering it all on time? I feel I am under heavy rain, surrounded by the swelling sounds of cruel sea, that I'm drowning helplessly. McDowell gives a deep sigh.

"I wouldn't know what to make of this really, it's so very different, for us. I don't think it would sell, as you can see from what we have in the shop." There is a long pause. "But look here, you can give me six of these," he has picked up a small bracelet without even asking the price. It is the most plain and conventional of the lot and his decision is probably made more in sympathy than in expectation of sales.

One of the girls comes down the stairs and calls, there's a customer who wants to see him. He rises abruptly and leaves with no further ado. I gather up the jewellery thinking such is life and thanking God for Pringle and Weirs. On the way out, J.T. McDowell barely acknowledges me, he is in concentrated selling mode with a young couple enamoured over a tray of diamond engagement rings.

Passing the statue of Daniel O'Connell again it has the ever-present seagull on its yellowy, white-gooey head.

* * *

Peter drives as if possessed through Drogheda, Dundalk and Newry, as if someone is following on his tail and it'll be an even longer journey. It was the daftest idea bringing him home, never mind the convenience of phoning from there, I would have managed somehow. Coming down the hill in Newry we are stopped by a line of raucous — obviously Fenian —women. From a distance their stuffed guy looks like children in buggies.

The car has to wait as a British soldier of the Grenadier Guards, my grandfather's old regiment, slowly and warily walks past us with his gun held across his body. There is time for me to observe, as never before, the three-and-a-half walled, ruined castle, which was once Mountjoy's garrison. It has a tree growing in the middle. The stones are ivy covered and nothing much has changed here since then, other than nature taking over. Another soldier opposite acknowledges his partner this side of the road who carries on towards the bridge and railway line that connects Dublin with Belfast.

"Welcome to the North, Peter, we'll just have to wait, whatever this is about."

"Makes my blood boil; British Crown Forces on the streets of my country," Peter speaks vehemently as he watches the two soldiers.

"Should those two soldiers be shot, if you had the choice, Peter?"

"There wouldn't have to be a choice if they weren't here."

"But they are."

"If I thought it would get them all out eventually, yes, maybe."

"But Peter they are probably still teenagers, they'd know nothing about Ireland from England."

"That's war and it's always been the way here. Sure they wrecked Balbriggan, which we drove through, burnt every house to the ground, your teenagers from England." Flaming Irish Republicanism clearly shows in his eyes.

"A reprisal for something?"

"No excuse; they shouldn't be here."

After another half hour or so, the line of cars slowly moves on. The soldiers are now fraternising with the women and children at the bottom of the hill.

* * *

This could be the first ever time a man like Pringle was brought to loyalist Ballynahinch. It is dark when we arrive, Mother has heard someone arrive and is at the door, a lonely figure, stark against the kitchen light, fearful but defiant at this hour. No, no, we're not the UVF, and they must know by now the farm has been sold to Protestants. Mother fusses over me, no matter who this Peter Pringle is, makes us a hurried repast of scrambled eggs, toast and tea and says that my brother and his family will soon be in Australia.

My father comes in and asks somewhat boldly, "so what are you two boyos doing up here in our Orange Free State?"

Peter rises to introduce himself, shaking father's outstretched hand, with mother clearly upset that he's got a new audience to lecture on the Ulster situation and much more. Knowing Father, she diverts Pringle to the sitting room. I stay to work out the silver order for the morning. Mother drifts in and out, silent and ghostly, hardly aware, as if she has already moved to Newcastle, offering just a word now and then. I'm in this old house for the last time. I try to concentrate, feeling a sudden sadness for the low slate roof, ancient beams and memories. The house almost speaks in Jacobean tones.

With the order complete and ready by the telephone for the morning, I stay in the small television room, exhausted. What a day. I have left Peter with Father, whose voice echoes down the hallway, sonorous and other worldly, disconnected, and moving from one topic to another, unstoppable, a river in full flow. I hope to God Peter won't be justifying any of those dreadful murders in the name of Irish freedom, for Father would not approve.

I should never have brought him up here, for his idea of freedom is another person's prison, where you can't get divorced or buy Durex and where Rome rule is the order of the day. He should have thought about that before he joined the IRA and ended up in the Curragh.

Living here is almost too much sometimes, as my Father makes clear: "we get threatening phone calls and the RUC can do little more than contain the violence. The Provos can't win either, as long as the UK is prepared to go on losing soldiers and paying the bills for property damage and security operations. No wonder we're broke, and the days of sending in the gunboats and expeditionary forces are over, we're not in any shape to do that and the country wouldn't stand for that anyway, being tired of imperialism and colonisation. Britain is in the second league now, both economically and militarily, and it is not the slightest use pretending otherwise. All empires disintegrate eventually, ours was a relatively peaceful disintegration, lasting a couple of hundred years. Russia will go the same eventually, after all, only a handful of men are keeping two-hundred million Russians in line."

Peter hasn't said a word, Father pauses as a loud sigh of wind rattles the loose slates. All is futility but I hear him continuing stubbornly, "Great Britain is an old lady; the heady days of empire are long gone and basically our only hope of retaining even second class status is if we join the Common Market. But basically we aren't really Europeans, too many people still think we have an empire and distrust the French and Germans. In 1942, at the Russian Festival of Easter, Stalin ordered a big shake up in the Red army and navy, uniforms were smartened up, epaulettes were introduced along with badges of rank, swords for officers and warrant officers, and a mass of new decorations and medals. Anyone who had been awarded medals in the pre-1917 revolution were allowed to wear them. Guards units were instigated as were units which had especially distinguished themselves. They wore the orange and black ribbon on their cap bands, a high honour and highly prized."

Mother comes to the door, opening it, and says," I think I'll have to go and free your friend from him."

"Ah no, leave them alone, he'll probably enjoy listening to him, an old Group Captain and Irish Republican."

"Lordy me is that what your friend is? In the IRA? He's not getting you involved is he?" she asks worriedly and most surprised.

"God no, he's not in it any more I think, he's McDyer's Development Officer."

"What with the UVF here the other night. I really don't know where all this is heading, we're caught between the two. Your brother was right in leaving, although my heart's breaking. I'll make your bed and Peter can sleep in the wee room downstairs," she says, disappearing with a hot water bottle under her arm for Peter.

I fall back, despairing, on the chair, Father's words next door keep coming: "…having served in the North West Frontier, I can tell you, your wily Afghan is a very tough cookie, you can never find him when you want to have a shot at him. I wouldn't trust an Iranian or an Iraqi out of sight, the latter are really a treacherous lot. We had six Iraqi cadets training with me way back in nineteen twenty-seven, all of them were assassinated eventually in the many coups in Iraq… mistakes galore have been made in the past and none more than the British, the country should never have been divided but to reunite it now is just not possible, logic and compromise are not in their dictionaries and it wouldn't surprise me if the British got out of Ireland in the end …"

Another gust of wind brushes loudly overhead, fitfully interrupting the speech, which would sound in UVF ears like there's an Irish rebel here on good Protestant acres. The worst thing Father ever did was moving here for his eldest son. His voice continues: "…the Jews in the East End of London sorted Mosley's crowd out when he organised a demonstration in their area, not unlike Hitler's brown shirts and Mussolini's fascists and even the Blue Shirts in Ireland during the troubled thirties, except laughed out of existence… the Irish rebellion in nineteen sixteen and the Great War started the irrepressible slide and World War Two completed that slide with India independent in nineteen forty-seven… The Russian army in Petrograd was the spearhead of the revolution… God was on the side of those with the biggest mouth, like the ghastly Paisley, pedlar of a debased form of Protestantism learned at the Bob Jones University of South Carolina, a forcing house for bigots in the US bible belt… A divided Ireland is a nonsense in this day of interdependence and there will never be peace in Ireland until the British abandon their first and last colony; the British presence has meant bloodshed and rebellion, there is only one way to end it, clear out and leave it to the Irish to sort themselves out." Father is on his favourite hobby horse again. I have heard this so many times before.

Mother appears momentarily, distressed and beyond caring, "I've set the breakfast table out for you in the morning, so I'll say good night now, I won't interrupt them, he'll go on talking until the cows came home."

Father's drum beat continues, Peter's voice is subdued and I cannot distinguish his words.

"As I looked out of my National Hotel room on the Red Square in the dark days of forty-one to two, the Huns were then a bus ride from the Kremlin… and it is an absurd situation going back to Henry VIII and the reformation, where people by and large vote by their religion… one cardinal fact seems to have been forgotten, which is that Jesus of Nazareth was never a Christian but a Jew, executed under Roman law for being a revolutionary, the penalty being crucifixion, if he had been executed for blasphemy as the gospels maintain he would have been stoned to death, the Jewish penalty."

This has to stop. It will be a nightmare driving back to Glencolumbkille with Peter in the morning.

"Isn't it time we went to bed?" I interrupt, "it's nearly three o'clock."

Peter is slumped in the chair, barely awake.

As I show Peter where the bathroom is and his bed, he says, "Jesus your father's a gas man, really gas, I've never heard the like before."

In bed, I cannot sleep, the wind again sounds as if the dead have risen from the Magherahamlet C of E graveyard in dismay, aware of the unwelcomed visitor.

* * *

There is worse to follow, for Peter buys a bottle of whiskey for the road, what can I say as we drive through dreary Lurgan, Ballygawley and Omagh, until just beyond Pettigo we both have to stop to urinate. I glance towards the vulnerable man in this hostile environment, forever tragic and doomed, holding his pathetic, pale, limp member and letting loose the dam of sparkling corruption. I can't help but like this man who cared about my work and maybe got me on the road to fruitful endeavour. But somehow I know he could never be a lifelong friend.

When we are beyond Donegal he drives more slowly, his thoughts far away, reflecting on an Ireland that can never be. At last we come down into the village of Glencolumbkille.

"Shame about McDowells, but Weirs certainly made up for them. They've a great reputation, old Prody money, and they've been in Dublin for years," Peter explains knowingly.

"Thanks to you, Peter, the pressures is on to get it started. At least the silver is ordered and paid for and on its way. Father wrote them a cheque and said I needn't pay him back. That's double the luck of the Irish."

"Really gas that father of yours, well worth the long detour and night away just to hear him talk. Will I leave you up to your laneway?"

"No, this will do me fine here, a walk in the fresh air to stretch my legs and many thanks again for all your help Peter."

"No problem, anytime," he replies unconcerned, driving off towards the sea and his family. An extraordinary man. The sky is calm, with long high mauve and butter evening clouds; according to the archaeologists, there have been five thousand years of human habitation in this valley.

I open the door apprehensively and McGinley's dog jumps up in greeting.

CHAPTER 48

Days pass into late nights and become mornings, with too many unpleasant thoughts and dreams.

My fingertips are wearing thin, some even bleeding with so much filing and polishing of this hagiographic, Hiberniaesque jewellery. I never thought I'd be earning a living in Donegal. The sunlight suddenly pierces my thoughts as the rain clouds clear over Glencolumbkille. A piercing saw blade breaks going through my thumb and I have to pull it out with the pliers. I hope it doesn't become infected with creeping gangrene as Doctor Vere's not here.

I haven't seen Peter for some weeks and was wondering about him until the all-knowing Joe explains that McDyer was ordered by his Bishop to let him go, because of his time in the Curragh and continued IRA shenanigans, whatever truth there is in that. It's strange that he got on so well with an English Group Captain, but sure he never got a word in anyway.

There's a lot of ivy growing out of the thatch in the cottage he's living in, but another day, I catch Joe's eye and he says, "yer man Pringle's on the fishing boats out of Killybegs now."

Well, well, who'd have believed it? It sounds like an awful job and dangerous too, hauling in the jumping, gasping fish, an extraordinary sight under the unfathomable enormity of sky and sea. Then there's the noise of throbbing diesel and the shrieking seagulls that follow the boat. Sometimes they can be seen beyond Malin More. I hope he can swim.

* * *

One morning Peter arrives at the workshop with an enormous cod wrapped in the *Donegal Democratic*, I have a premonition of something obscure and symbolic. Is it a present or does he want to get paid?

"God, Peter, I am sorry your job fell through," I say, anxiously eyeing the cod.

"So you obviously heard about it and the whole village too it seems. That's the power of the Catholic Church in Ireland for you," he replies bitterly.

"Joe told me."

"I'm sure he did and that old James character will be delighted, but no matter, we'll survive." Peter speaks up bravely.

"I'm sure you will."

"Here, I've brought you a fine big cod, fresh from the deep only hours ago," he lays it on the bench very obviously.

I wouldn't be bothered to gut and cook it to eat it and an awkward little silence follows: is he waiting to be paid? The price of cod would be a pound or two, more like 10 shillings. I am bewildered, unsure how to do the right thing. What is he expecting? I don't want cod delivered every week. But the least I can do is to make him an offer.

"There's nothing like a bit of fresh cod Peter, how much do I owe you?"

"God, man, I'm not looking for money. I've one in the car for our supper tonight and I thought I might as well bring another for you.

"That's most thoughtful of you, Peter. How do you like working on the fishing boats?"

"Do you know I really like it. I was a bit sick at first and the money's not bad. At least I'm getting paid properly, unlike with McDyer."

"As bad as that was it?"

"Oh yes, between you and me he's a bit of a chancer. How are you getting on with the Weirs order then?"

"Just fine Peter, coming along nicely, and all thanks to you."

"I'll be moving with the family to Killybegs fairly soon, so good luck and give my regards to your father if I don't see you for some time."

"I'm sure we'll meet again Peter."

"Well I hope so."

I shake his outstretched hand and he's away, without subterfuge. I never thought cod grew that large, it gives me an uneasy feeling lying there, silvery grey, big mouthed, cold and dead, glassy eyed. From talking to some locals here, I can see that McDyer's not that popular. How did he get involved with Pringle in the first place? He would not have had much of a CV, I would imagine?

* * *

Past midnight there is an unusually clear sky and an amazing full moon has a pale, soft, golden light touching everything, making everything mysterious and beautiful as I walk through the village holding the cod by the tail. The incoming waves sound endlessly on the sandy beach. I am aware of subtle and mysterious movements above and beneath, of my utter helplessness and the futility of endeavour. Whether humanity exists or perishes is of no consequence whatever to the great cosmos. Along by the shoreline I pause to reflect on how Peter's gift is going to waste and on the few productive months of our acquaintance. Then I whirl the cod around like a propeller a few times, letting it go up in the air and fall into the cruel sea as if it were Peter.

There's a light on in McDyer's house on the higher slope and the dark figure at this late hour is McDyer himself, coat-tails rippling in the wind, all alone, staring strangely over the valley and up to the moon. I wonder did he see the cod, a symbol of the saviour Jesus Christ, God's son? He is reflecting on his faith and calling perhaps, confirmed or not by the bright heavenly objects above and everything here on earth. Is he musing that the Northern explosions are too small to achieve any good, compared to the blitz when he was a young curate in London during the war?

* * *

Glencolumbkille is a magnet for the disaffected who seek a different lifestyle, far from English urban living. One young couple of Irish descent from London want to start a pottery, another, with a small inheritance, are searching for a cottage with a few acres to grow vegetables and keep goats and hens. I can neither advise them one way or another. At first contact they seem foreign and naïve in their enthusiasm to start afresh.

A lovely new olive-green Mercedes Benz is parking opposite and a man gets out. I go down and meet Brendan O'Regan, who introduces himself as being from the Shannon Free Enterprise Zone; he has a friendly, easygoing confident manner. McDyer had mentioned to him that he should call in and see some of the new Glencolumbkille handmade jewellery. He immediately wants the history bangle that I have made for Weirs. Well, for cash in hand he can have it and I'll just have to make another, working day and night again. I count out those lovely Irish green singles and worn brown fives to thirty pounds, it is a really good price and much more than I can charge Weirs.

His car has seats of caramel leather; it smells of new, strong Germanic construction. It is a protective tank, an oasis of safety and warmth, with tyres and springs that glide over Glencolumbkille's disintegrating roads. The views through the tough waterproof Perspex will be of bog lands and overflowing streams, he will wonder in passing how does anyone survive in a land fit only for sheep. Away he goes, from behind the firm steering wheel of his top model Mercedes Benz.

* * *

The Weirs order is finished by the end of October and sent off in three separate registered parcels over a week. I will have to build up a stock of those history bangles and whatever other jewellery the design can be put on.

Days pass, stormy and wet. I am wondering when Weirs will pay; normally it takes thirty days from the end of the month in which the goods were delivered. So it could even be after Christmas. Now I'm living here, how can I ever escape? An Irish helot alone in a miserable cottage, with McGinley's dog for company. And at Christmas too. Still, I feel that something is bound to turn up.

On the walk home I enter the pub, two old men are seated somewhat apart, sipping their beer, making it last and not sharing a word between them. I join them with my whiskey.

"Will it ever stop raining?" I ask them both.

"That's the Glen for you now," says one.

"'Tis so," says the other.

The silence is deafening. When I leave, it is dark outside and there is a heavy mist, I am barely able to see a few yards ahead and the sense of panic is overwhelming. Will I eventually become like them?

* * *

Lo and behold, the cheque from Weirs arrives in the first week of December. Good old Prody time-keeping, on time and not a week later. *Sola gratia, sola fide, sola Scriptura.* It means a well-earned, joyful day away to the Ulster Bank in Killybegs, triumphant. I feel connected to the real world, savouring each purposeful minute, making out the lodgement docket with the lovely cheque, which I slide proudly over to the girl and am suddenly taken aback. I had almost forgotten the charms of the fair sex; I'm aroused by her smile and the proximity of her sweet-scented presence. A savings account that will earn interest for my money is opened: it is the beginning of my becoming a man of capital.

I stretch my time in the haven that is Killybegs to the full day, for there is no hurry. My happiness is completed with a leisurely cooked meal amongst a talkative hungry crowd. At the pier I watch the fishing boats below and inhale the briny, gutted odours of the air about. The strangest looking creature I ever did see lies dead on the deck of one.

Reluctantly I return to my cottage, where my doubts and insecurities start surfacing. Will there ever be another order from Weirs like that? Where else can I sell? For sale or return arrangements are not to be contemplated. I sense things have moved in the cottage, the landlord must have been snooping, does he have that right? Has anything really changed since the last century? I'm on shaky foundations with McDyer as there are no apprentices. I will never entertain them and the use of the workshop is therefore dicey.

There is a dead sheep on this side of the road nearing Glencolumbkille that wasn't there this morning.

* * *

I am kindly invited to share Christmas dinner with the widow McGinley and her two sons, but I feel a stranger and a sense of their innate otherness, bred of centuries of differences between their culture and mine. Her boys are curious about my coming to Glencolumbkille, probing me intensely and showing a wry amusement when I answer them. The jovial old Pope John XXII is dressed in Santa red, foxy white and gold, smiling across the table. It would have been rude to have refused, for I didn't feel like driving all the way to County Down and back in a car that's a dodgy heap. I have to get used to this way living into the New Year and beyond.

When January passes without paid work, a uncaring paralysis overcomes me. I am disconnected with everyone except McGinley's dog. It follows me down to the workshop, comes inside, then lies contentedly on the floor. This is how it could be, but I am hardly qualified to draw the dole. I must guard against negativity, becoming the quare one, sinking into abstractions and absurdities by living here.

* * *

Joe comes on his last week bursting with the news that a Mr Walsh from the Design Centre came yesterday, going to loan a Kilkenny trained goldsmith to work with Mr James, who is furious at the idea: what is McDyer up to now? And Joe has heard of McDyer's disappointment that there are no apprentices so far. I can well imagine that he sees me as working for myself rent free and not for the good of his community, but how much longer will it last?

* * *

Then, suddenly, there's a chink of light, a now or never opportunity of leaving Glencolumbkille. In February there comes from Weirs an order that is much the same as before. In a brief conversation with Parker to clarify ring sizes, he mentions an empty room on Dawson Street. Weirs would let me use it if I am interested in coming to Dublin.

"A man like yourself shouldn't be working amongst the culchies beyond the pale," says he.

"It's got its drawbacks all right, communications and distance being the main ones."

"How's your man, Pringle wasn't it, who we met last year with you?"

"He's left, something to do with an IRA background and the bishop getting after McDyer."

"That wouldn't surprise me in the least, there was something about him I'll never forget."

"I know what you mean."

"Well, come on down then and have a look at this room. I mentioned it to Moss and the old man Weir and they'd be delighted, it needs a bit of tidying up but that needn't be a problem," Parker continues.

Another upheaval lies before me and I wonder how will this pan out with Weirs? But I will never get a chance like this so the doubts can take care of themselves.

"I'll come right away, and get the bus from Donegal town."

"Good man yourself," replies he, a decent man.

CHAPTER 49

Arriving in Dublin at the beginning of the next week, I am given the key of the room at the rear of Hassett and Fitzsimmons, estate agents, on fifty-two Dawson Street. Ascending worn steps with iron railings, a thick Georgian door opens under a fanlight to a much-painted-over, high, stucco ceilinged hallway, with stairs going up. I'm directed down to another door, opening into a narrow passage leading to what must be the room. A curious, old metal switch starts the single length of hesitant, flickering, waking fluorescent light to reveal a blood-freezing, empty, grime-coated room of cracked walls and peeling plaster. A puddle of water lies on the floor from the leaking roof. It's a forgotten, empty place which has not had human contact for a long time. Amazingly, it used to be a silversmith's workshop with cut-out benches for four; there is an enormous stained ceramic sink, which has a large brass single tap, and turning it on there is a pent-up explosion of murky water. There's a small skylight and three filthy windows looking out to a small enclosed yard, where the sun probably never shines.

So here we go again, I am confused and disappointed and where can I live? Living this side of the border has meant dreadful cold and uncertainty, from Kilkenny to Glencolumbkille, and now this. There must surely be an end in sight somewhere. I can always say no, but that is not an option for I feel this has to be it. Weren't the old Kilkenny stables in very much the same condition? And this is in the very heart of Dublin. Extraordinary.

I have to stay the night at the North Star Hotel, which brings backs the vivid memory of when Peter Pringle came into the room late. How quickly everything passes.

I could just about finish the order here; I have Weirs' immediate approval to get on with it, they are most helpful. I can work out the details and relationship later. Perhaps with their backing I can get a mortgage and a house. So without further delay, while the tide is in, I hire a white transit van and return to Glencolumbkille.

This will have to be done quickly. I'm excited and nervous. There is not a lot to collect from the cottage, most of my belongings will come from the workshop, where the villagers will notice, everyone will soon know. I do not want a word said to McDyer, who may be looking for many weeks rent, annoyed at my ingratitude, without a single apprentice having been trained. I should at least have the courtesy to thank him before I leave. Roman priest though he is, he was so good to me, I feel guilty for the subterfuge of this sudden departure. But I can't. All I can do is flee. An hour or two is all I need to pack and be gone from Glencolumbkille; with a sad farewell for McGinley's dog. He follows me down from the cottage and for some distance after.

* * *

Speeding through the night, like a thief on the run, I leave the car left in Donegal town until I can collect it at some later date. Streetlights are fires of discord to my fevered imagination; threatening headlights drive up too close behind me. When they overtake, insane faces taunt me accusatorily. O'Connell's men are on the prowl, the leopards and hyenas of border territory, I am becoming fearful of this leap into the unknown. But, as Pringle reassured me, they have an old Prody, moneyed, above-board reputation. Arriving under the still dark morning sky at Dawson Street, I unload surrounded by confusing shadows. This is a most dismal start but there can be no return, for Dublin it must be.

* * *

A folding camp bed in the hallway is all that's needed, as I am not going to waste money in Bed and Breakfasts. There's a lavatory downstairs from Hassett and Fitzsimmons that I can use. I can boil water on the gas ring for coffee and tea, and get by on plenty of tinned soup and Bewley's coarse brown bread: a veritable feast. Weirs have arranged for the room to be repaired and painted, but after a few weeks they've still not started. Are they like the mystery of the Holy Trinity? Do I have to believe in an act of faith? Are they committed to what they're getting themselves into? A vagueness begins to permeate the situation, with obfuscation drifting from Dawson Street to Wicklow Street on a roundabout wheel of fortune. They are well meaning for sure, but I should have checked who was in charge and obtained a clearer commitment before leaving Glencolumbkille. I was much too much in a hurry, the grass isn't always greener on the other side. Is it a tramp or a qualified silversmith here awake at three o'clock in the morning? For there are no clear answers and sometimes feel I float helplessly to the wiles of this wretched country, where I should never have been born.

Having collected the car, I return nervously to Dublin. My bridges are well and truly burnt. Hopefully, it can remain parked safely for a few days by some out of the way railings and overhanging trees on Wilton Place. It is familiar to me from my old Coras Trachtalta days. And I look up to where Hogan and Walsh worked on the familiar corner building, turning left onto Lower Baggot Street.

* * *

Some days later I approach the car with a sense of foreboding, for badly scratched on the bonnet are the letters IRA. Two tyres have been let down and there window wipers are bent. The natives have been at work. Are northern cars fair game now? But how would they know which side of the divide the owner is on? Their sensitive antennas must be able to detect who owns it. The old Morris did just about get me around Donegal and to Dublin, with the help of a St Christopher medallion I found in the cottage and which I foolishly attached to the rear-view mirror. That should have been enough to deter them, if they had bothered to look.

Maybe they did, but were far too acutely tuned to be fooled. And there's a Protestant church on the Stillorgan road with its stained-glass window broken and daubed in disgusting, large green letters is the slogan: 'HITLER WAS A GOOD FELLOW.'

* * *

The streets and names of Dublin become familiar from the easy walk from my workshop to the Assay Office on Lower Castle Yard. Early afternoons mean entering by the Ship Street Gate and waiting between shadowed, narrow, high brick walls, in a small cubby hole, for a hatch to open and someone appear. I stand with a few others, silently waiting, and on some days we have to press together to shelter from the rain. The hallmarks need to be checked, they are never deep enough, and I always have to hand them back to be punched deeper. It is something they should know how to by now.

Here I am, in Dublin's ever-mischievous airs again. The curtain of rain lifts suddenly to sunshine, firing the front of the State Apartments momentarily made of dazzling diamonds and gold. I can wander around outside the deserted former British Army Ordnance Office, where through grimy windows can be made out the overgrown faded bundles of tax returns for 1953. They are long forgotten references to hard-earned money taken and to worries about paying.

The garden before the heavy, grey stone, mock medieval coach house (where the Viceroy's coaches were kept) is overgrown. In the Chapel Royal, I gaze up to the balconies above, to the many beautiful carved, armorial bearings of past Viceroys with their names beneath the portraits, covering over seven hundred years of rule. Kildare, Talbot... and there's Ormonde's shield, familiar from the high door of Kilkenny Castle on the Parade. I shook the old Marquesse's hand that day in the stables.

Taking in this dilapidated historical brew, I stand by the massive drum Record Tower. The Treasury building has near perfect Georgian, biscuit-coloured brick symmetry. Little clusters of cherubic cloud hurry over the Bedford Tower, near to where Fortitude, on the right, holds a long spear, with a dopey dog-sized lion behind his legs. Justice, parallel to the left, holds the sword and scales. I walk through the Palace Street Gate, where the first policeman was ruthlessly shot in 1916. The the same beliefs that caused the Rising are still unchanged for some.

"He's threatening to blow up the Assay Office," calls Captain Ronald Le Bas, the Assay Master, getting out of his car, angry and flushed, waving a sheet of paper in the damp air.

"Who is?" I ask, as I pass with a parcel of silver to be assayed.

"That mad man from Tipperary."

"Who's that?"

"Padrig O'Mathuna. Maintains the Crown on the Harp is a symbol of British misrule in Ireland and has no place on the Republican hallmarks: can you believe such petty nonsense?"

Well, there's certainly plenty around like him these days. The Crowned Harp is part of our history surely, it's been on Irish silver long enough and actually is rather attractive."

"He says it is the badge of the RUC, oppressors of our brother nationalists in the North, an illegal occupying force, he even files out the Crown on all the silver he gets hallmarked, stupid man." Le Bas sounds increasingly flustered and upset.

"Weird, to be that concerned."

"Likens it to the Germans still using the swastika."

I worry the Assay Master will get a heart attack. "Hardly the same, by a long chalk."

"I've already reported him to the Gardaí, showed them his letters, and look another one's arrived today."

"Maybe the Tans roughed up his father or much worse."

"Whatever happened long ago is best forgotten. Of course he's a rabid

Provo supporter. I wouldn't put it past him to do something stupid, at least he's open about it, but, really, how bitter can one get?" continues this most distraught Assay Master, who wouldn't be here but for the St Bartholomew's Day Massacre and subsequent persecution of Protestants. It will be nearing the fourhundredth anniversary of those events soon. The Assay Master is a small and strong man and the fact he holds on to his military rank is a signal not to cross him.

"So O'Mathuna is a silversmith from Tipperary? I remember it well."

"If that's for assay I'll take it then," Le Bas holds out a hand and I pass the parcel over to him; he is calming down a little.

I feel that this incident has been blown upon us out of the history of this place. This is where it mostly started. Sectarianism is still smouldering beneath the musty atmosphere of Dublin Castle, or Chaislean Bhaile Atha Cliath as some would say. I well remember Mary with her second helping of apple pie and cream, God love her, wherever she is now. The past is always ready to haunt us, even for this Padraig O'M… Patrick Mahon more like. I hadn't noticed before that the badge of the RUC indicated sterling silver.

* * *

When the workshop is finally put right (at Weirs' expense) there's a generous two thousand pounds of their capital and eight hundred of my own, that includes the value of furniture and equipment from Glencolumbkille. So they'll be the majority shareholders, giving me a monthly salary of a hundred-and-sixty pounds, but hopefully it won't stay at that for long. It has to be a limited company, named Dublin Silver, with Weirs ultimately in control.

Without warning, at Weirs' insistence, two men arrive from Alwright and Marshall, the silversmiths. The reasons for this are obscure. I will have to take on Desmond Taaffe and Joe Doyle, but it is difficult to find enough work to keep them busy. In fact ,it will be bloody awkward with me sleeping in the hallway and wondering what to give them to make. I'm unaware of their talents at present. They make tea from a large aluminium teapot they have brought over with their tools, explaining that they both worked here until Weirs bought out a Mat Staunton who was competition for repairs and silver and they didn't like being undercut. They were sent over to Alwrights who make a lot of silver for Weirs. I'm becoming confused by the mercurial airs that blow mockingly over Kilkenny, Donegal and now Dublin.

* * *

I fell for Parker's siren calling to this and still have nowhere decent to live. Doyle is a polisher and no silversmith, whereas Taaffe certainly is. I can only sell wholesale and not to customers coming off the street, so there is just a small brass plate on the outside door for the postman to see. Whatever I am getting into once again, I will just have to get through it, however fraught the situation is for the moment. There are many riddles and interlacing pathways through a land shrouded in mist and fog.

There are occasional visits from the three boyos from Weirs I met that time with Pringle. Their conversation is full of phrases with dubious meaning but dreamily comforting. They watch the new enterprise with their innermost thoughts covered with colourful curtains. And with a certain amount of laughter. Parker's that hoot of a Protestant man, surreptitiously giving me the low-down on Weirs, where Moss has family connections and Bennett is their antique silver salesman. He has just published a book on Irish Georgian silver, which costs twelve pounds, and flicking through the pages at Hodges Figgis I find that it is an accurate and well-researched illustrated history, but doesn't enter into the tumult of a silversmith's wary and insecure head.

* * *

I am getting to know the two silver polishers and three engravers over at Weirs and the one who never forgave Moss for bending his raised finger like a hook, calling his name and motioning him to follow. Many sleights and grudges are left simmering. While signing for a parcel, the postman carelessly imparts to me that he had been a soldier with Montgomery's Eighth Army in North Africa, where the head of a soldier beside him was blown off, the neck still pumping blood. Something that no longer seems of any consequence these days, delivering mail on the neutral streets of Dublin. On mentioning this to Taaffe and Doyle they glance at each other knowingly, without comment.

* * *

I am startled by Father McDyer hurrying out of Bewleys Oriental Café. What is he doing down here? His eyes, in the moment we made a connection, looked betrayed and disappointed (after all we did for you, you left without a word and never…) and he looked so small, shrunken almost, in his priest's shabby ill-fitting clothes. I hurry along Grafton Street followed by remorse and guilt. Taaffe's well able to make a silver tea set, he can be left to get on with it, but there's nothing for Doyle to polish. I wish he wasn't here.

* * *

A gentle day, that holds me in a soft Irish hand, finds me on Molesworth Street, walking towards the National Museum, where a conspiratorial group of whispering women are gathered outside on the steps of Buswell's hotel. Once Leinster House, now the Irish Parliament, the Dail once belonged to that long line of quarrelsome, proud FitzGeralds from Norman times, who largely ran the country then. The one named Silken Thomas, having heard that his father was to be beheaded, threw off his allegiance to the British Crown, surrendering on the promise of a full pardon. This was violated by Henry VIII, and Thomas was hung, drawn and quartered at Tyburn, together with his five uncles. Imagine such butchery in one day. Then, wondering at the sacrificial bog man with red resin shaped hair, whose leathery half remains are crushed flat, in haunting, cruel antiquity. Close up, sideways and mirrored underneath the Ardagh Chalice says it all. Life in Ireland must have been bizarre and I'm incredulous from one exhibit to the next. And yes there's old James' shrine of St Lachtin's arm… amazing. I'm not going into the Rebellion rooms. I don't belong there; I feel like I don't belong anywhere.

I move on down Kildare Street, sorrowful and melancholic, shaken, suddenly imagining the winged black box marked 'Langrishe Estate' flying out of the Kildare Street Club to remind me of Mary. Mary's father could well be in there. In my daydreams, the unlocked lid opens, spilling secrets yet again of those ancestral High Sheriffs, Deputy Lieutenants, JPs, Master of Hounds, Heiresses, Archdeacons, Privy Councillors, Commissioners of Revenue and Excise (coining it), as well as Clerks of the Peace, a Gentleman Usher of the Black Rod. And not a mention of Mary and her poor mother. On a day like today, I can't help wondering enviously what living in Florida would be like. What is she doing, while I go back to bread and soup heated on the gas ring?

* * *

Parking meters are being put in Merrion Square, so I move the car. With night time enveloping the streets, by street lamp I see a well-shaped pair of lighted long legs, high skirted. She is walking down one side of the Pepper Canister Church on Upper Mount Street, a storm-lashed island of the Reformed Faith in a sinful sea. Turning around the church and returning past her, my heartbeat quickens, as she's now moved forward to acknowledge me. And why not? It's natural as moon rising and spring daffodils. Around I go once more and my mind is made up. She steps out from the pavement, arm outstretched, motioning me to stop. I am transfixed with anticipation. I roll down the window to see a pale, alert face, short dark hair, red lips and eyes sharp to the dangers of her profession.

Who cares? I drift along the changing seashores of life, feeling unconcerned tonight.

"It's three pounds for a ride and one for a blow," she informs me defiantly.

"Well you better get in then," I reply, as she runs around the front of the car, lithe and sinuous, quick as a bird under the dim lamp light.

"You're from the North aren't you?" She has a strong smell of cigarettes and an attractive, pert nose.

"Yes." Those plates again.

"Terrible going on there these days."

"So where do we go?"

"Over the bridge, right and straight over Lower Baggot Street and first left."

A dark lane, what am I getting into? Seeing those legs out of nowhere… but now I don't want to end up with a disease. But what the heck.

"Stop love, this will do, now what will it be?"

"The ride."

"That's three pounds first then and you'll have to wear one of these yokes," as she hands over a Durex, and me the three pounds to her. Thank God for that, better safe than sorry.

"How do you manage to get these?"

"Ah sure it's easy enough, there are two Irelands, as you'd well know. We don't all mind what the bloody priests say, feck em's what I say." She speaks with a rasping, deep-throated laugh, pulling up her skirt and opening her blouse. "Here, have a feel of these to get you in the mood."

It has been so long, touching her small warm moist breasts, the effects are immediate. "Go on, then ride me and you'll soon come and be done with me," she shouts in coarsely Dublinesque.

Sodden and emboldened, I crush her underneath, over on the passenger seat, until she gently pushes me away.

"Are you finished?"

I kiss her ever so lightly on the cheek.

"Ah God love you Sir, no need of that," she is somewhat startled, putting herself together and lighting a cigarette.

"Where to now?"

"Where you found me by the church," she replies. It is a baptism of sorts, for the rest of my life here for sure.

* * *

Between her and the bog man, sleep comes fitfully as I lie on the folding bed. I wake to Taaffe and Doyle gazing down upon me mischievously. I am in distress and vulnerable like this and imagine scenes of my helpless body on the undertaker's slab but still alive, then taken to near the banks of the Nore, where obsequies are performed by McDyer, before I'm buried in an unkempt broken graveyard in a winter mist, which shrouds the leaning and broken, roofless Kilkenny church.

"Have you nowhere to live?" asks Doyle.

"He's a refugee from the North," says Taaffe.

More like a beggar in a Dublin doorway I think, no difference. I get up to make the coffee. If only I could just be able to wash in warm water, lie on clean sheets and eat properly. They know well I'm from the North and it's easy to tell my persuasion, but I am not going to discuss the situation one way or the other, that is a road leading nowhere with us working so closely together. There's little conversation. They are unassuming and cautious, so different from the two Londoners I brought to Kilkenny. That was unreal.

CHAPTER 50

Slowly, the orders start arriving as word gets around, from Weldon, Mortons, Wine, Danker and of course Weirs, each one as different as day is to night. There's also work to be had with antique silver repairs, mostly cutlery. It is such a shame to be filing off beautifully engraved Georgian crests. There is, say, the stringed harp, a demilion rampant, one of a mount vert, a falcon rising or, as the heraldic language would put it, another of a set of twelve spoons of a cock resting its foot upon a rose. They are all quite extraordinary, all brutally erased with the rasping sound of a file. The anonymous Irish engraver with his clever creations was paid a pittance then and now has been totally forgotten.

The days pass secretly, each still weighing the consequences of working at Dublin Silver. I sense there are no certainties. Doyle finishes polishing the silver tea set Taaffe has made, leaving it on the bench. It is a surrealistic sculpture of harsh plain lines. I question, as I so often do, whether anyone makes silver these days by such hand raising methods, anyone not subsidized like Kilkenny Design is. I remember the laughter of the old Marquess of Ormonde when he was with Haughton, considering this kind of manufacture taking place in his stables.

On holding up the tea-pot to inspect it, I see my shrunken face on the highly polished plain surface. In the momentary silence, it is left back on the bench. I have discovered now there is an unfathomable relationship between them and Weirs. There's a peppercorn rent for the room I haven't been asked to pay yet, a few pounds each month according to Taaffe, and who's the landlord? A strange vagueness permeates everything, with nothing much agreed upon, a perpetual penumbra, as it was at Glencolumbkille. It is a tightrope of uncertainty, challenging my ingenuity as though I have entered a maze. The jazz of those Celtic interlacing designs is again leading everywhere, baffling and absurd, I must try to survive.

"So, what do you think Des, will Weirs take it?"

"It all depends on the price and it may be too modern, they have a huge mark-up remember. Have you worked it out yet?" he replies somewhat doubtfully. With a longish nose, pale face and pale blue eyes, he is a mixture of Norman and Gael, a lot came over to Dublin from Bristol in the Middle Ages. Doyle is native to his papish bone, looking freakish in his dirty apron and sinister cloth dust mask, with lustre blackened face and hands. He looks ready for murderous rebellion — burn the big house down – not long before he would have been a White Boy. He has croppie ancestry from Tipperary. The other half of Mary's side.

"Yes, I reckon we'll need at least a hundred and fifty pounds to cover your time and the weight of silver."

"So, to buy it from Weirs you would have to spend at least three hundred and seventy pounds."

"Wouldn't you wonder who'd be paying the likes of that these days?" comments Doyle, his livelihood depending on it, as for us all.

"There's plenty of hidden wealth around this country, look at the farmers, they pay no income tax and keep all their money hidden in the North, with tax free interest tax." Adds Taaffe knowingly. Now that's most interesting.

"But they'll hardly spend it on silver tea sets, and there's a new value added tax coming son." Doyle is hardly being helpful.

Taaffe shrugs. "Weirs have to carry a lot of stock, though, before any is sold. They've even silver bought before the war and even some as far back when the Brits were still here."

"But they'd put the old prices up every few years with inflation," explains Doyle.

"Like money on deposit," comes Taaffe, faintly smiling, flipping his head. Then he turns to me with a penetrating eye, as if to ask, *do you really know what you're doing?* "This can't be like Kilkenny Design you know? They are way out of touch with their fancy talk, grants and unfair competition — no middlemen and all that free publicity — and all their choice commissions. You should know that." His tone is almost accusatory, but he is grinning, to show no offence is meant.

* * *

The ancient Canning polishing lathe brought over from Alwright and Marshall is so well made and balanced, that the two spindles keep on revolving with a continual fading sound, minutes after Doyle has switched it off. The running down of energy, gravity and time.

"What about Alwright and Marshall, Des? How do they manage? Were Weirs in control?"

"They were not," Taaffe replies emphatically, "Alwrights always did their own thing, a mixture of repairs, church and domestic plate, medals and trophies, silver and gold plating."

I've another question for them. "And Royal Irish Silver, they seem to be all reproduction Georgian in really heavy gauge. They are employing thirty to forty workers fulltime, how do they manage? Where do they sell to?"

It's Taaffe that answers. "Weirs won't touch them because they do a sort of retail, like special events selling in hotels. A lot goes to America, but there's trouble brewing from what I've been told, what with the price of silver and things going missing, that sort of thing."

"Theft you mean?"

"You said it not me."

"They were Gunnings originally."

"Yes, they had to change after Vatican II when church work began to dry up. The Bank of America and the IDA put money in. Toddy O'Sullivan of the Gresham was involved, along with the three Gunning brothers, Peter, Larry and Kerry. Reed and Barton, an American crowd, are now involved I believe." Taaffe is certainly well informed.

"Angelo Giuseppe Roncelli is the one to blame then," I say to myself as I turn away.

"Who?" Taaffe asks, curious.

"Pope John the twenty-third."

"Was that his name?"

"Yes, an Italian."

"You're well up on the Popes then?"

"Only the bad ones," Maybe I shouldn't have said that.

"Which one's were they?"

"One of the worst was Alexander Borgia the sixth who purchased the position, had children by his mistress and other women when he was still a cardinal, and he authorized the burning of Savonarola in Florence. There was Innocent the eight who started the witch burning craze; Sixtus the fourth provided for nephews and favourites and made relatives cardinals, one of whom died of his vices at the early age of twenty-eight, to name but a few. There are many more, not forgetting the late Pius the twelfth who never once condemned Hitler for his murder of six million Jews."

"Phew, my goodness me... being a Protestant, does that give you satisfaction?" Taaffe asks wide eyed to the ceiling, leaning backwards, while

Doyle listens gobsmacked.

"I wouldn't call myself one now."

"A leopard can't change its spots," he says looking at me most directly.

"St Paul did."

"That was divine intervention."

"How did you know I was a Protestant?"

"One can usually tell after a short time." He stretches himself, hands behind his head. We had best return to the silver trade.

"Bernard Fitzpatrick's Irish Silver, how do you rate them?"

"You're changing the subject now, however they're very traditional and the silver's much lighter, paper thin in fact. It's very clever how they manage it, but it is nearly impossible to repair, Weirs stock some of it. They've a great spinner over from England, a Mr Cartwright."

"And that's what we need here, a good spinner and no more of this hand-raising cod as we don't have a spinning lathe; it can be done outside as we find the work. I can get us someone. He's a chaser as well. Paddy Johnston in Weirs is their best engraver, he does nixers at home."

"I'll leave it to you then Des."

The telephone interrupts us, alarmingly it is from the Blood Transfusion Service in Leeson Street. Doyle is wanted for his unusual blood group type, it means he'll be gone for at least two hours, he is delighted.

"That'll be a nice glass of Guinness as well," he says, washing himself at the sink and obviously happy to be leaving.

"You can always go for the biscuits and tea Joe," an amused Taaffe calls after him; there is no reply but the sound of the door shutting.

*   *   *

With my head bent to the tiny, sand-like grains of silver accumulated on the pull-out shelf above my knees, I draw a picture of the crucifixion with the point of a needle file, then blow it gently away. A day in the life of two silversmiths and a polisher. Metal working was one of the most distinguished arts of Celtic Ireland, an art form that began long before the Celts and a tradition that exists to this day.

*   *   *

Weirs do buy Taaffe's tea set from this dark room hidden behind Dawson Street. It can be seen floating magically on grey velvet and nicely spotlighted, sparkling in one of their Wicklow Street window displays. It is there for no more than a week or so before it is sold. An enquiry came from the Department of the Taoiseach looking for antique Irish silver and seeing the Dublin hallmarked, modern hand-crafted malarkey, had purchased right away, money no object, for a presentation to maybe the Prince and Princess of Monaco. I soon find chasers, polishers, platers, spinners and engravers coming along the narrow laneways, up the creaking stairways to our grimy, acidic, sour-tasting Georgian rooms of this fractious, secretive and suspicious trade.

CHAPTER 51

I am finding a place to live through Hassett and Fitzsimons, where there are pretty sales girls and many homes for sale. With a letter from Weirs (thank goodness) there is a chance of a mortgage from the Educational Building Society. I have an eye on a cottage on the bend of the Brennanstown Road. Up from the Cabinteely Garda Station. This is a solidly built construction, made for the R.I.C. There are bullet marks opposite, on Hardy's newsagent. A local remembers the ambush that took place there and knows fine well who the rascals were; they are still living here and grown old as she.

"The Black and Tans, you'd have seen them?" I ask her.

"Oh God, I did, they were gorgeous," she replies, bold as to brass, and unafraid of who her preferences were.

The cottage has a corrugated iron roof on top of thatch, which is painted red. It is single storey, white-washed, with an attached tank at the gable end. How did they ever get planning permission for the septic tank to be so near beside it? The view over the narrow road is to a high ivy-covered wall, behind which the land falls steeply to the Druid's Glen of thick foliage and trees, the Carrickmines stream and a Neolithic portal tomb, which is where, I am told, a poor family once lived during the famine. The price is all I can borrow, it needs a bit of renovation but there's privacy surrounded by more high, ivy walls. There could eventually be a workshop in the front sunroom and any amount of noise could be made hammering.

* * *

I enter Donal T. McAuliffe and Company Solicitors, Commissioners for Oaths, fifty-seven Merrion Square and into the fan-lit corridor of a bygone age. There is a whoosh from the thick, majestic-sounding sprung door closing behind me. It has attached to it a wire cage of important looking mail in long brown envelopes.

"Donal won't be long," the receptionist says, smiling sweetly as she gets up. If only I could be in the moment.

I'm shown to a large stucco ceilinged room, where a swirling heavenly configuration of white flowers, fruit, busts, birds, violins, clarinets and trumpets on blue are above me. Vainly, I attempt to enumerate each one. There's a magnificent, most likely Irish oak, long table, matching chairs, sideboard and red patterned wallpaper which feels like velvet. The pre-Union aristocracy were good for interiors, decorations, cabinet makers and furnishers. The minutes waiting become dreaming hours. Waiting, waiting, listening to distant footsteps and murmurings, just as it was with Poe and Kiely when I bought the land in Kilkenny. Within my exquisite loneliness and feeling resigned, I drift in the embrace of sublime Irish time. The door suddenly opens to bring me back to consciousness again.

"Donal will see you now," she says, as I follow after her I detect the faintest trail of bodily and applied scent.

Donal's wary eyes zero in on mine, looking up from above severe steel, round-rimmed glasses which balance at the end of a sensitive nose. Fair skinned and boyish in appearance, he sits shirt-sleeved behind an over-flowing desk of legal papers. There are shelves of thick legality on his left, the large window on the other side has a panoramic view of leafy Merrion Square, bathed in bright sunshine, lightening the rosy coloured bricks of the beautifully proportioned Georgian mansions.

"You've no second thoughts about this?" says Donal, direct and gruff, looking up from a letter, leaning over to shake hands.

"The cottage needs a bit of renovation, but it's as fine as can be in the circumstances."

"I mean this letter from the Council about road widening, the vendor wanted to add another storey but couldn't get planning permission from them."

"So, what do you think yourself, should I be worried?"

"Well it's a possibility all right, long term though."

"Long term?"

"Ten or fifteen years and you would be compensated and of course it may never happen," he says with a quick smile.

"It's why I can afford it probably, and the area's beautiful, almost countryside."

"As long as you're sure."

"And as you say, I would be compensated... yes, I'll go ahead."

Unfolding the long, creamy Indenture, pink, treble-border lined, with red stickered spots to show me where to sign, he calls for Kathleen, his receptionist to witness it. She is bending so close, her long, almond hair lightly brushing the Indenture, I inhale her scent even more deeply; scents are as ephemeral as a passing shadow.

"I'll give you a call when I've checked all the deeds, shouldn't be more than a week or two," says Donal, impatient to be finished, another client is waiting.

An Irish cottage indeed, I never thought I would see the day. My earlier thoughts are evaporating and I'm angry now in a dark miasma towards everything Irish.

* * *

A week later I am back at McAuliffe's.

"Make sure you put these safely away," says Donal sternly, handing over a lengthy, heavy package. Such weighty deeds for so humble a cottage.

This time I am not left to wait amidst the splendours of Georgian interiors and delightful dreaming, Donal seems to have hardly any time to spare. The receptionist is familiar with my face but that's all, continuing her typing and barely acknowledging my leaving. The car is parked outside, so seated under a dull sky, which is beginning to rain, I open the package and peruse the numerous, folded documents, words written in an almost secret code. Would the touch of her hair on the Indenture be still there, microscopic and infinitesimal? There are harp-pressed green seals with flowing, intricate Celtic-like surrounds over the pages of some. The main Indenture must have at least five or six thousand words. I glance over it:

'...made the Thirtieth Day of July in the year of our Lord one thousand eight hundred and thirty eight between... in the County of Dublin and by virtue of a certain lease to him these granted by Charles Lord Archbishop of Kildare Dean of the Cathedral Church of the Holy Undivided Trinity Dublin... subject to the yearly rent of forty shillings by the acre together with sixpence in the pound receiver's fees, and other covenants therein... legally vested in John Barrington of the City of Dublin... made and passed in the third and fourth years of the Reign of his late Majesty, An act to amend the laws relating to the temporalities of the Church in Ireland... one thousand eight hundred and seven... and Sobieski Kildahl for the considerations therein mentioned, and according to their respective rights and... Executors and Residuary Legates in the proper Ecclesiastical Court... reserved rent... all taxes Tythes assessments and declarations whatsoever parliamentary parochial or otherwise... late Plantation measure being equivalent to... English Statute measure or thereabouts...'

Hand Search, Negative Search, Statutory Declaration, Assignment, Bankruptcy Office and even the Probate of Last Will and Codicil of a Frank Malone Esquire, deceased, second day of April 1905. So much legality for so little.

The gable and water tank are overflowing. An old woman is leaning over the end wall and shakes her head at it. "I'd never have bought it you know, it's subject to flooding, the water comes up from the ground at the back when it rains a lot."

Through small windows I can see restless tall tree branches growing menacingly towards the cottage, as if wanting to grasp it and the moaning winds are the lingering presence of the dead from Neolithic and Famine times. Occasional car lights illuminate the old ivy stone walls at night, turning them to shimmering golden, crossing over to the open-gated sloping field where there's a large, ugly modern house to the right, foreign and intruding over the valley. The portal tomb has been clearly visible for the last five thousand years, an arresting, mysterious pale coffin-shape on three fat legs. Bathed in moonlight, it sometimes seems that anything is possible.

There's a disturbing and slightly mocking mute telephone in the cottage that can't be connected as no line is available yet. It could be ages it seems. Florrie Baker was the old woman, a widow who lives the other side of the high wall behind me. She comes down most afternoons for a smoke, to watch the traffic and chat to any passing neighbours. Late evenings I can hear her calling, "Gambit, Gambit ..." her (sometimes) cat, smoky, grey and fat, watching.

My days are but dreams that tumble this life about from the past, present and into the future, briefly connected episodes that ultimately lead nowhere, as strange as the pointed stone follies by the roadside, faery-like and surreal. There is solitude by Tolleymore Forest Park, a dense blanket of fir trees with falling, clear water from the Mournes and secretive, small, fast-moving creatures. Earl Annesley once owned much of this land, where now their abandoned big house lies empty in spacious laked parkland by Castlewellan, echoing those faded sepia-tinted yesterdays.

CHAPTER 51

My parents are wearing a heavy shroud of sadness. I've travelled to find their new bungalow in Slievenabrack Avenue, Newcastle. Both are as well as can be expected, except for the ever-advancing veil of years and a confused vacant air. We have a simple tea of boiled egg and toast accompanied by father's all-too-familiar comments on the Ulster situation. How's the living in Dublin? I am asked. Mother speaks about Mary and Lucy; they haven't heard anything and are not likely to now.

There's a loud explosion in the night, bringing mother into the bedroom without turning the lights on. We are aware of some danger outside. She makes a nun-like figure, staring out from the window, curtain slightly drawn back. What is going on out there? The face of a good-looking young nurse can still be seen in Mother's features and I can imagine the many young Indian army officers who would have wanted to dance with her.

"Did you hear that?" she asks nervously.

"Yes, of course, it woke me up."

"What have they done now? Another dreadful outrage no doubt. You know they murdered a young constable on the main street in broad daylight last week."

"I heard it on the news."

"He was only twenty-two. they have no heart. Vicous and cowardly, for what?"

"It's probably the IRA trying to destroy the Slieve Donard," comes father's voice wearily and faint from the adjoining bedroom. He's not bothering to get up.

"God forbid, it's such a fine hotel," Mother replies.

"They've put bollards around to stop cars getting too close, but maybe they've managed to carry the bomb inside. It's never really that bad, apart from any deaths, you should see what we did to Hamburg and Dresden!

"Come on back to bed, it might not be the hotel anyway, it could even be themselves. We'll know soon enough in the morning," continues Father. Mother departs and I am left ,lost in the silence of a smouldering resentment of ever having been born to them, which I suddeny felt for no reason.

I hardly listen to the news at the morning breakfast table. Both of my parents are leaning towards the wireless, which is on far too loud, waiting for last night's explosion to be raised amongst other news. They want to know whether it was indeed the Slieve Donard or not? I, on the other hand, am watching a blackbird swooping down cleverly on the newly mown lawn to pull out a worm. It is truly amazing that the bird could spot the worm from on high, or even hear it's movement under the ground. The blackbird flys off at the sound of the telephone ringing.

Father gets up to answer a long-distance call from Australia, to where a whole generation of my cousins are emigrating and her Majesty's head is still on the coins in the pocket. Even uncles and aunts follow their children, selling whole farms. In a couple of years there'll be none left. The phone call has a rejuvenating elixir for their day, as with it comes a litany of all good news my brother has to tell. Taking over the call, I feel a little envious at what he discloses but I know it is impossible to leave Ireland again.

* * *

Along the shoreline of Dundrum Bay I walk over timeless material. How many grains of sand are there in the whole world; what mighty force acting over millions of years pushed up the Mournes? The Sunday newspapers are collected for my parents to read: a dog catcher was murdered, lured up a narrow laneway where they were waiting for him; a young female census distributor was shot and even a Pakistani cook — minding his own business — was killed for no obvious reason. That's just how things are at this long moment.

"Did you make that History of Ireland thing yet?" Father asks, putting down his paper and gazing inquisitively at me, suddenly remembering his visit to Donegal and evidently still feeling a warm glow that his eldest son is doing so well in Australia.

"Yes, Weirs liked it, they bought some and they're selling."

"Make me three then and I'll send them to Australia."

"Three?"

"Yes. How much will you charge me? It should be a keen price for that many and I am your father," he says this as if wanting me to confirm it.

"Eighteen pounds each is the best I could do; there's a lot of tedious work with each."

"I'll give you fifty for the three then, how about that?" he replies, and knowing he'll be giving them away to his daughter-in-law and the two cousins in Perth, I will have to forego the four.

"I'll get the money for you now," and he gets up stiffly, momentarily falling back again, a warning of his borrowed light growing dim. After he returns with the money, he asks, "when will they be ready?"

"The end of the month maybe, I'll post them individually and under-priced as presents, to avoid any tax they might charge you."

"They've destroyed the customs post this side of the border."

"Yes, the place was a wreck when I passed."

"Terrible goings on. Your brother was right to leave; we would if we could, but it's too late at our age."

"No, you could still go and join them. You'd enjoy a place where none of this old history is endemic, is in the air we breathe, inherited at birth." I'm thinking of old uncle Leslie, who at seventy-seven is about to leave.

"You didn't inherit any of it did you?" he asks pointedly.

"Well, I'm certainly no lover of Catholicism."

"It takes all sorts. Mary was lucky to get her divorce in America, for she'd never have managed to get one down south."

"It might not have been needed if we'd stayed, but she just had to get away from Kilkenny and memories of her childhood."

"Understandable of course."

"I'd have been the same if I'd been her, though in a strange way I've never left Kilkenny, considering the effects it has had on me."

"More so than County Down?"

"Well no, I wouldn't go that far, but the more I'm up here the more I'm a stranger now. You can sense it as soon as you cross the border, these days especially."

"I can well understand the feelings… this country…" his voice fades away mid-sentence and his eyes close. When he has gone to bed, I look out of the front window at the flat, calm, silvery shining Irish sea. The night sky is clear and there is a full moon, turning everything mysterious. Slieve Donard has become a Prussian blue. Mother is wearing her long white dressing gown and holds a red hot water bottle under her arm. She tidies the room, an ephemeral, ghostly presence, as if in league with the moon.

"Good night then, I'm away to bed too," says she, with a gentle whisper as though from an abandoned country cottage.

* * *

Returning to Dublin, I feel an acute homesickness for Down and a dull feeling of helplessness at the border crossing. On through the mean, badly lit streets of Dundalk and Drogheda, desolate and bleak. And it is raining, raining over the Boyne waters. The cottage will be waiting. I know full well I have sealed a binding contract with this Irish wretchedness and misery, care of Donal T. McAuliffe and Company. Half asleep on my camp bed I hear things moving: the brush of the trees overhead; gusts of rain (intermittent now); soot coming down the chimney; mice behind the wainscot. It will take a while to sort all this out.

But then morning is mad with sunshine, the valley's greens are alive.

It takes a good half hour to drive to work, depending on the traffic. I have to get a grip on this silversmithing nonsense, how on earth did I ever end up in this career? I have been given the name of a metal spinner by Taaffe, with directions that indicate he is not far from where I live. I eventually locate the place in a row of single storey, abandoned dwellings, where I can hear the moan of a lathe.

After I bang loudly for attention, the doors open hesitantly, no this is not the Gardaí or Revenue. There is a man in filthy blue overalls, wearing goggles, and he reminds me of the face on the tenth century gaming board made of yew found in a Westmeath bog. No doubt he can read a look of deep anguish on my face at his situation. Amidst a confusion of disassembled lathes, there are shelves bending under the weight of numerous metal, nylon and hardwood chucks. On the floor are finished spinnings of brass, aluminium, copper and a few of silver. He has a calendar of a half-naked women from the year before last. Another man, with stooped back, is polishing what must be communion rails and a large sanctuary lamp. As they have no extractor, the polishing dirt is getting everywhere and mixing with the smell of oily wood and metal shavings. As he turns around (wearing a blackened mask with no respiratory protection), his suspicious eyes confront mine. A blinding moment of spiritual transcendance comes to me: this is a noble and splendid space of magic endeavour, the abject squalor is of no consequence, this creativity of unrecognized brilliance turns reality upside down again.

"You must be the man from the North. Des Taaffe said you would be calling; so what have you got there?" asks the Spinner rather petulantly, eyeing the parcel of silver circles and my cylinder of designs.

"Yes, I have what you quoted Taaffe for here, can you give us a rough idea when they'll be ready?"

"You know I'll have to make all new chucks for these and it'll cost you on top of the spinnings, but they'll be yours or Dublin Silver's, whichever you decide. They're a shrewd lot, those Weirs who you're working for, real

West Brits to the bone, if you know what I mean?"

"Is that so?"

"A bit like yourself, maybe?" he laughs but seems to want an answer.

"So, when will we have these?" I lay the parcel and cylinder by his lathe.

"A week or so, I'm fairly busy right now."

"Are you on the phone here?"

"No." Is there one in hiding, tucked away out of sight, purposefully hard to locate?

"Will we say this day week then, for collection?"

"Now, don't you be putting me under pressure, I'll let you know when they're ready on my own good time," he replies, taunting me almost, as if it is a game, *ready when they're ready*, that could mean anything.

The polisher stands silent, watching as an ancient tribesman, with a communion rail for a spear. He is listening avidly.

"Any silver scrap turnings you'll collect and return with the spinnings." No harm in asking him.

"Will you listen to him Billy, a real Northerner, having even to ask. Get away on with you now, I'll be in touch," this reply is both amused and irritated. Billy nods his head in agreement.

On the bright side, there'll be goblets, whiskey measures, salvers and anything else can I can think of, magically spun out at Sallynoggin. *Ready when they're ready* is a beautiful distortion of time and meaning and it is only a matter of getting used to such behaviour, then it needn't be a problem. After all, one worry just leads to another. When a problem's solved there's always another and another. Spinning is a lot more sensible than the old hand-raising methods, whatever those Kilkenny Scandinavians in their tall towers might think. At the end of the day, I have to make a living first and foremost.

I feel a trifle distressed on leaving Sallynoggin, a poor area of ugly warehouses, with a large monstrous, yellow brick Catholic church and lowly dwellings. Coming down Kildare Street, I feel a sudden, instant shock, as a car parked ahead of me, by the railings of Trinity, lifts into the air with a stretched, rag doll-like person flying helplessly higher, seemingly in slow motion, but in reality the very opposite. In the infinitesimal time it takes the loud explosion to travel and be heard, both fall back on the pavement amidst smoke and red, yellow and blue flame. I break to a fearful halt, as there could be more. A deadly silence ensues... then shouts, people running, siren sounds. I was about to turn into Molesworth Street and I hurry along, knowing there is nothing I can do, Death appeared suddenly out of nowhere. Up the steps of fifty-one a, the familiar sounds of the workshop are welcoming. I explain about the bomb, but they didn't hear a thing. Both stop what they're doing and look over to each other.

"It could only have been the Loyalists," says Taaffe.

"Or even the British army," offers Doyle.

'Perhaps,' Taaffe sounds hopeful. "An IRA own goal when they were about to drive north?" He doesn't want to believe the northern violence has come here.

"That's highly unlikely," Doyle replies.

"The loyalist crowd then," Taaffe is convinced.

"It could even be the RUC, I wouldn't put it past these boyos," says Doyle.

"They'd be across the border, back in Belfast by now."

I join in, "we'll probably never know, unless whoever it was claims responsibility."

"But it is not hard to guess, one way or another," says Taaffe as he turns to me.

"My guess would be that UVF crowd," says Doyle "and the Brits will have to get out of Ireland in the end. Like they did down here."

"But is it worth one single death to make them do so?"

A long silence follows my question.

"Only time will tell," shrugs Doyle to himself.

"To do something like that though," says Taaffe shaking his head slowly.

I nod. "It was shocking all right."

"Bastards..."

And so it continues. As we soon discover from Hassetts, there is more of the same seen on Nassau Street, so for the rest of the working day we switch between work and talking interminably about bloody deeds.

* * *

When they have gone and I lock up, I am confronted by a bearded phantom-like figure, lurking in the darkened, shadowy, low-lit hallway. I am reminded fearfully of a much older Ireland, that spirit of obstinate rebellion, of suffering brought upon themselves and the vicious comedy of the penny-a-peck, simian-faced, Paddy malcontent holding an ancient gun in the old *Punch* cartoon. Fears arise out of the bottomless pit of my subconscious. The man looks haunted, with eyes of desperation, searching for some sort of Holy Grail that he is unable to find. A will-o-the wisp, a green, white and gold illusion of freedom, disappearing in the never-ending search that gives his life meaning.

"Jesus Christ, it's Peter Pringle, I didn't recognise you with the beard. How did you know where to find me?"

"I was over at Weirs to see how your silver was selling and the Parker one told me you'd left Glencolumbkille and were working here. And you didn't even say goodbye to me!"

"It all happened so quickly Peter and you were away working on the fishing boats from Killybegs."

"I don't think McDyer was too pleased either from what I heard."

"I can well imagine, but there you go, one can't be forever grateful. When an opportunity suddenly arises, you have to put yourself first."

"I suppose so and as for McDyer, it is best I say nothing, you know my story."

"Weren't those explosions today terrible?"

"It looks like an all-out war now, mark my words," says Peter sadly. What is it about this man again that draws me towards him? But I dare not enter those nightmares.

"So where are you living now, Peter?"

"We've a house in Killybegs and I'm still on the fishing boats nearly all the time. Mind you it's hard work and often dangerous, but I love it, if you can understand."

"At one with the seagulls and sea? A kind of understanding with nature, the true reality?"

"Yes, you could say that," replies Peter, eyes fractionally distracted and wistfully far away. Yet somehow I wish he'd never called; he looks dishevelled as if he had crawled through a hedge. "How are you getting on with Weirs and this new enterprise?"

"Just fine Peter, Weirs have been great and I've a house near Cabinteely now, all thanks to you or I'd still be in Glencolumbkille. Can I get you a drink or a bite to eat maybe?"

"Ah no, I'll be on my way now, I'm glad it's worked out so well for you. If ever you're up to Donegal give us a shout, or at least give Clarrie a call if I'm not around; she'd be easy to find as Killybegs is a small town," he gives me a friendly touch on the shoulder and he's gone.

CHAPTER 52

I could have been in that explosion. My delayed reactions are exhausting. I found both Taaffe and Doyle irritating, then Pringle had to appear. Driving home, the evening sky is an amazing pale turquoise, holding big, slow-moving, fluffy, peach-coloured clouds, which are fantastically shaped. Coming from Foxrock village, the half-moon is beginning to appear over the Brennanstown Road.

What a waste of time it is, driving in and out of Dublin every day. And free parking is getting more difficult to find. Home, I mull over the awful events of the day. As the evening becomes night, sleep gently arrives.

I'm awakened by someone at the door; who could it be at this hour? What is David O'Connell doing here, a most unwelcome disturbance. He has a meaner, hardened, fanatical appearance, no holds barred for the cause. I'm hypnotized, feeling shocked, surreal and helpless in his presence.

"I need you to do something for me," he says more as an order than a request.

"Yes, certainly David, if I can," is my obedient reply.

"Can we go inside?"

"Of course, David."

"Now shut the door and lock it."

"Whatever you say, David," I'm powerless to his commands.

"I want you to hide these for me," and out of his jacket pocket, which is covered by a long, dirty, frayed raincoat, he takes an automatic hand gun made from sinister black hardened steel and with it a red and yellow packet of bullets, marked made in Czechoslovakia.

"Jesus, David, are you serious?"

"Never you mind, just do as I say." He is not to be argued with.

"Are the Gardaí after you? Have you murdered someone?"

"Whatever it takes," is the resolute reply.

"I think you're mad David, it's not worth taking a single life for the sake of Ireland."

"That's not for you to decide: we're both diametrically opposed to each other. Are you going to help me or not?" This is threatening now.

"Just this once then, but never ask me the likes again, David."

"Where will you hide them?"

"I don't know, let me think... we'll leave them on the floor between the wall and the rear of the old Milner safe."

"Let me see you do it then," is the brusque order and there is no
way out.

"Are you Chief of Staff of the Provisionals, David, inventor of the ar bomb?"

No reply. The gun and bullets are wrapped in the creamy brown-bordered, Selvyt polishing clothes. Then the deadly contraband is hidden away. "They'll be secure enough there, Peter."

"This won't be for long and you're here most days."

"You've got me involved now Peter, which is the last thing I want."

"Not to worry, you're a decent man for a Prod." Pringle holds out his skeleton hand for me to grasp; his face is a hideous laughing skull now. I'm shaken awake, bolt upright from this nightmare. Thank God, it is only a dream, a dream of Daithi O'Connell.

* * *

The Spinner hasn't been heard from all week, I will just have to go and find out what is happening as the works are urgently needed. So at half past ten next morning, I am in Sallynoggin's abandoned street. No one is there, but there is hysterical barking of a fierce dog inside. Do I wait a while or leave? It could be all day. A boy on a bicycle arrives without greeting me.

"Will they be here soon?" I ask.

"Should be, you can never be sure though," is the reply.

"Will I wait on?"

"You can if you want." His answer could mean anything and he climbs like a monkey onto the roof, the dog whining excitedly at the familiar voice. Opening a skylight, he squeezes through, then, in no hurry he opens the door.

"Have you no key?"

"No."

The dog is an ugly black-and-tan Rottweiler on a heavy chain and it sniffs feverishly at my feet. If it's that easy to enter, it doesn't bear thinking about with all that silver I gave him.

"Has he spun the silver I gave him yet?"

"He was working on it all right."

"Does he keep them here when he leaves?"

But the boy doesn't answer, feeding the hungry dog heels of stale white bread from a Dunnes Stores plastic bag. The wretched boy is hardly a mine of information. I will wait a while outside, where I can look at the Sugar Loaf mountain, floating magical and carefree far beyond.

"He's got the Archbishop's wagon now you know," the boy calls over.

"Is that right?" What does he mean?

"A real beauty, rides on air, she's pure heaven."

"What are you saying?"

"McQuaid's wagon, he's just bought her."

"Is that so?" I'm none the wiser, but the mystery is suddenly solved, as a long low top of the range black Citroen 5270 glides startlingly into view, the spinner at the wheel. The Archbishop's car indeed; he died just up the road in Loughlinstown hospital and it was said that his last words were, "nurse do you think I'll go to heaven?"

"The man from the black North again; didn't I tell you I'd call when they're ready," he glares at me as he gets out of McQuaid's wagon, which is parked across the laneway.

"I was in Dun Laoghaire and just wondered how you were managing with our spinnings."

"You needn't be coding me to believe that now." He ignores me, going on into the workshop, catching the excited dog's head with both hands, giving a rough head-to-head twisted greeting to this simple-minded creature of habit.

Surely, it isn't too much to try and elicit a delivery time? I know, thankfully, that this will pass; the moment's frustration will soon be forgotten. No one's indispensable. There are plenty of good spinners in Birmingham, but it is a nuisance though. I will just have to be patient, and really, a week or so isn't that long, not with the new chucks having to be made. Why annoy him like this? As I gaze high above, there's a beautiful radiance, shafts of light from behind clouds, the sky a golden monstrance, the host as the sun behind the veiled glass, centred over Sallynoggin. I shall not worry about the silver being stolen, I will just have to take a chance on him. My natural anxiety is a burden at times, and didn't the boy say he was working on them? So I tread warily and leave him alone. Taaffe said he's a natural born genius at what he does, and there's other work I can be doing.

* * *

Waiting outside for the Assay Office to open, I feel there's a clinging sense of despair from the omnipresent breath of dreadful history in the damp atmosphere of Lower Castle Yard. That peculiar atmosphere of Irish neglect and decay. It is not helped by my having to urinate under the entrance archway, behind a wall to one side entering from Ship Street, where it smells especially foul on warm days. The whole Castle complex has a general air of treachery. I'm reminded of those shifty figures of corruption, the many informers, the aborted uprisings and agents of English oppression of Ireland. This history always makes the place feel suffocating. Here comes Christy, always the first to arrive, early for work.

"Morning Christy, are you well?"

"Not a bit of bother and yourself?"

"I'm all right Christy, just thinking this old place could do with a good facelift, it hasn't changed a bit since the Brits left."

Christy eyes me blankly without comment, shrugging his shoulders as if it doesn't matter. "Miserable old day isn't it, however," he says rubbing his hands, doing a little dance to warm up, just as it's beginning to rain. He lights a Silk Cut. Christy has lost most of his dark hair, is short and stoutish and turns everything into a joke, as if all of life is a charade of doubtful meaning.

"Here, you can take these, Christy," as I give him the box of silver to be hallmarked, "make sure they're spread the same size, you needn't be scraping them for samples as there's plenty of scrap there for that."

Christy is well aware I always repeat instructions and replies with his mischievous knowing look.

"I'll collect them this afternoon."

"Game ball, they should be ready."

"Are you busy these days?"

"So so, we're kept going; you know how it is."

"How's the Captain treating you?"

"Ah, sure you know how he is, his bark is worse than his bite, a gas man, he's all right though."

"Speak of the devil here he comes, I'm away Christy."

The bold Captain drives around to the front of the Assay Office, he has a brand new Japanese car of a type I've never seen before.

I could almost envy Christy, oblivious to the dark and ghostly memories within these walls. Recurring nightmares of O'Connell came again last night. I almost believe that the gun that never was is still there behind the safe.

I get soaked on Fade Street, having pressed the buzzer for the caster to let me in by the automatic door lock. On ascending the worn, creaking stairs I find the Caster is there, with two other men who are ever ready for a sparring, sitting on tall stools together at a long, fitted worktop, making numerous blue waxes for casting everything Celtic that one can imagine. Six silver christening mug handles were promised from an old pattern Weirs gave me. The Caster is somewhat slow getting up to the smaller room and asking, "have you brought any scrap?"

He produces a circular tin of the scrap silver. He then weighs the monster-headed, winged handles on his electric scales on top of the safe and awful little yokes they are too, making up the weight out of the tin.

"I'll write you a cheque, then." I have a grey-blue, AIB company cheque book, Grafton Street branch, with Moss's signature already on them.

"Sixty pence each, you said."

"Correct," he replies, sounding strangely far away.

After examining each one carefully first, I look up. "You'll have to cast me another, there's a hole in this one, see?" I present the culprit back to him to inspect.

"Sure, you can easily fill it with wire and solder," is the unconcerned suggestion.

"But I shouldn't have to if you did right."

"You're an awful fuss, for all the time it'll take you." He does not want the bother of casting just one. "You'd hardly notice it anyway."

"I'll take these five and call next week for the other and pay you then."

"You're a terrible man. Pay me for the six now and I'll have it this day week."

"Give me an invoice then."

"Have you no cash? It's a small amount."

"No, I haven't."

Reluctantly going over to his desk, he writes out a barely legible invoice. What's the point of arguing? The two other boyos have stopped working, listening avidly, delighted at the inconvenience I'm causing, as I make out the cheque to him.

"This day week then. I have your word?"

"Do you have to ask?" The other five seem rather porous, but sure, they'll just have to do. On leaving I inspect their array of waxes.

"What are these ones?" I ask about a curiously primitive Christ crucified, at first sight it seems more out of Africa than Ireland.

"Penal crosses, we poor Irish were terribly persecuted by the British you know. We had to be taught behind hedges and our priests tortured and hanged," says Caster, the larger of the two, looking up at me accusatorially. I'm not going to get started, so I hurry away out of this
twilight zone. I will have to make do.

* * *

The now familiar faces of Weirs' employees are going to work as the shutters are rolled up, another day, much the same as always. The staff who stay for a lifetime become somewhat Weirized. Parker mentioned that their basement can become flooded from the Liffey if high tides coincide with heavy rain. It was built on marshy ground and odours linger even after ruined carpets are taken away. All along the river's banks are Viking remains, like a shoe, a walk way or a comb.

"The spinner called; the silver's ready," says Taaffe, concentrating on his careful soldering. The room is warmed from the large blue-and-yellow roaring torch flame in his left hand. He is holding a stick of solder the other and speaks without turning. "He said to make sure to bring plenty of money," Taaffe bends to check the solder flow on the base of a large cup he is repairing on the revolving soldering stand.

"That'll be the price of the chucks as well no doubt," I say quietly to myself.

"What the man said." Taaffe overheard me, turning out the blow torch, inspecting his soldering, slowly turning the stand, then waiting for it to cool and pickle. The room is becoming shrouded in Liffey mist, or the Nore's, for there's no difference now, as I sit down, hands around my head contemplating, a profound depression taking hold. I think of Mary coming up Patrick Street, a vision of intoxicating loveliness, as I waited in the Mini for her outside the Club House. The whispered sighs of those days are suddenly like a sharp knife through the heart, when even the pain is exquisite.

At the midmorning tea break inconsequential conversation lifts the mist of bereavement somewhat. I know the relationship with Weirs can't last. The History of Ireland jewellery is selling well, I will have to get the design registered, protected from the magpies of the Dublin trade.

*　*　*

The hallmarks always have to be checked before leaving the Assay; they need to be punched deep, with no fear of damaging the silver, easy to read and proudly Irish. From Dawson Street to Ship Street, a journey of a lifetime, from one world through that entrance again to the much older.

"Are yez all right?" I'm shouted at drunkenly. This is followed by a rasping chuckle of lunatic laughter from the beggarly figure in a filthy, tattered, dark brown overcoat far too big for him. The Lower Castle Yard's fool, this broken-winged bird, crippled dog, hobbling and gesticulating, a frightening reminder of defeated Ireland, forever jumping out of the past. Why is he here, does he have an official job even? The madness of hopelessness is etched on his reckless but defiant face, somehow I know that his forebears were once the High Kings of Ireland.

It's the gorgeous Marie Mulcahy at the hatch this time, with a smile to quicken any man's heart beat. The Harp Crowned and Date letter guarantees this codology, with an extra commemorative mark every so often now, from the Rising of 1916 (sword of light) to joining the European Community (which just had to be the Glenisheen collar found in a cleft in the rock of County Clare). A few minutes chat with her bathes me in warm scented thermal caresses, her wafting womanhood. Her very name, the lilt of her voice and the light of her eyes makes me believe it is good to be alive. If only ...

"I'll get Christy for you now," says Marie, sweetly, as I awaken from an erotic dream.

"The man himself," says Christy, displaying both hands wide. "Your silver I think is ready."

Returning, sliding under the counter, opening the hatch door this side and quickly checking everything to Christy's obvious amusement, for life's just a silly game here. I find a napkin that is barely marked.

"You'll have to do this again Christy," I put it under the window hatch along with the money charged on the assay docket. Christy examines it closely, shakes his head without comment and disappears, then comes the sound of him striking the Hibernia, Harp Crowned and Date letter again. A few familiar people arrive, curious, and Christy passes over the errant napkin and change. Many desperate moments are spent collecting the silver I'm now carrying.

* * *

Why would the spinner want to own the late Archbishop's car? Hearse like, it is parked ominously outside their workshop. The driver obviously seeks attention. Is McQuaid himself risen from the dead to drive it? The dark-eyed, heartless, unforgiving Spanish Inquisitor. A Catholic fanatic in his rich gear and Borgia ring on a long accusatory finger; the gullible expected to kneel and kiss. A psychologist would be intrigued, reading much into the Spinner's purchase. Will we now have a tortuous song and dance routine? Or a beneficial interaction for us both? There must be easier ways to make a living, than waiting for his curtains to draw apart.

"You got my message then, good man yourself." A fair weather change indeed in his demeanour. Though his appearance is still that of figure on the yew gaming board from County Westmeath.

"Yes, how did they turn out?" I ask apprehensively.

"The silver was shite and easily cracked; I've never seen the likes before."

"You're joking; that was special cadmium-free silver, specially made for spinning." So here we go again.

"Come with me." Heading over to the car, he opens the boot to a large cardboard box, presenting it proudly. "They're all there," and they look just fine, amazing in fact, with a tidy little bag of crunchy silver turnings.

"I think you took me for a chancer," he is suddenly serious now.

"What makes you believe that?"

"Ah, you lot with Weirs in Grafton Street, and we mere Irish ,soiling our hands, not proper gentlemen if you know what I mean. Let me show you something." I follow behind. "These chucks are yours, so you'll know," as he waves at them shelved neatly together. "The lot come to ninety quid with the silver at sixty-nine."

"Can't complain at that. Have you an invoice so I can pay you?" I take out the cheque book.

"No doubt you're all above board with Weirs, but make sure you don't cross it," is the reply, writing in his small duplicate page and tearing the invoice out. Yet again, I am hardly able to decipher it.

"I left school at a very early age ,if you know what I mean," he says, winking, handing me the paper. I feel like I'm riding a dark horse over dangerous ground full of ditches. I will have to get used to it and not fall, but at least I have the measure of things now. It's only natural to survive. All the while, Billy's polishing a large Celtic-edged silver salver, swaying it from left to right against a Reflex, or is it a G mop, with his rouge bar touching down lightly now and then. Changing to a Swansdown, he uses an oval crocos bar and rouge powder mixed in paraffin, taking care not to burn it. Finishing the salver with cotton wool soaked in white spirit, Billy wipes it clean. A master class of silver polishing; they certainly know what they're doing.

"Away with you now," says the Spinner; Billy turns to acknowledge me.

CHAPTER 53

I make a stop on South Anne Street to gaze through the window of Danker's antique shop. There's a fine display of Irish and English silver from the last two-hundred-and-fifty years or so: cutlery, tea sets, salvers, those peculiar Irish dish rings, sauce boats, tumblers, cups and more. Compared to England, Ireland was a poor silver buying country because of its turbulent past, for who but the aristocracy could afford to purchase silver and keep it safely? From the fifteenth, sixteenth and seventeenth centuries, there is nothing much but a few chalices with that simple, early circular silver salver there, with a trumpet-shaped foot decorated with gadrooning.

A gentleman's helmet with worn engraved arms of saltire, between each arm ermine, with a lion in the fourth left, a crescent in the cente, a demi lion rampant above and flowing mantling all around. For that silver is truly old, I'd say it was about seventeen hundred when those outcast, hungry faces around Freshford and Knocktopher. Back then, fearful nightmares of reality were never far away. Bribed and corrupt peers with their illicit pensions and titles commissioned some silver. Then came those angry victims of the new landlords who assaulted, murdered and burned the many country houses, with any silver present taken away to this day.

In our times, Ledbetter's shop on Nassau Street was emptied, the silver stolen out through the roof. And Parker's nephew was murdered by the IRA in Belfast recently.

What can one say to him when he tells me the news? The poor boy had just bought a pair of runners the day before. When he did not return home after the many explosions, his distraught father at the morgue knew immediately it was his son by the runners protruding from under the covering. Parker is bitter telling me this; infuriated at remarks by some that it was an unfortunate incident in a just war being fought until all Ireland is free. I am asked to meet his brother, a Reverend C of I of the Seamans Mission Belfast, to see about a silver memorial chalice, crucifix or whatever he thinks would be appropriate for his dead son. A favour owed; I must go.

It is a long tiring journey, with heavy rain, thunder and fork lightning between Maybridge and Castlewellan. Cars are a death trap. I arrive in the Square, Ballynahinch, outside the Ulster Bank. This is where father lodged many a pig cheque, a vault of borrowed hopes and secrets, saved security where there is none.

The Roman-numeraled clock marks the fearful eye of passing time. It is beside the Union flag, a bold statement of who they are. Unionism embraces this wary old Protestant town. Why we have arranged to meet here at this late hour, with my having to drive this far, seems a cheek. What's wrong with telephoning? Well, no, I can imagine what state of mind he would be in, days and sleepless nights, helpless with grief as a physical pain; the hour and place is of no consequence.

I am an apprehensive ,sympathetic spectator, inhabiting the thinnest layer on the surface of this molten sphere. The cross section through the earth is seven thousand six hundrend and twenty-six miles but the habitable hard crust is only thirty one miles and that is less than seven miles high. A precarious existence, with Ireland once part of a land mass that is breaking up, so that the country is now an island in the sea.

The Ballynahinch lighting makes me feel uncertain, I am unable to see clearly, lean shops and dark alleyways lead where?

When I returned from America alone, I got off the bus here. One can never really know another person, but with hindsight it is plain to see that America was an escape to sanity for Mary. The other day, a girl in Hodges Figgis was strutting around on high heels. The difference it makes to their legs. Lifting their arse, teasing, their walk sexually advertising. She bent to the lower shelf and knew I couldn't help watching. But there's no one who will ever replace Langrishe's daughter.

Ballynahinch is the world of the surreal, where subversive conspiracies encroach, where burnt remains of stakes from London's Smithfield during the reign of Queen Mary were unearthed.

Out of nowhere comes the Reverend Parker. "You must be the man from Dublin. Will you come over and we can have a chat about this in my car," he calls over.

Just as well, considering the condition of my heap, which is thankfully camouflaged by the gloom. As I get in, I just know this meeting is a complete waste of time. His car is pleasantly newish smelling and warm; I imagine his grief. What we are experiencing here seems like an extension somehow of those dreadful religious and political French wars of the sixteenth century, in which Protestants were slaughtered at Wassy or St Bartholomew's day in Paris,. He has the austere appearance of a Geneva pastor in the time of Calvin and is clearly submerged in his great loss. A torrent of words come my way. He needs someone, anyone, to listen and listen to his purgative litany of bitterness. Understandably, he forgets the whole point of meeting… he'll soon be gone.

"What sort of memorial do you have in mind for your son?" I eventually manage.

Silence. He has totally forgotten why he's come, gazing ahead, then turning to me intently. "You're a Southener aren't you?" he asks in a somewhat accusing sense.

"What makes you say that?"

"You are, aren't you?" he's convinced.

"I was born in Downpatrick."

But he doesn't seem to hear. He can believe what he likes, it doesn't matter. I want to hurry away from this claustrophobic encounter of no consequence, the windows are fogging up fast, I'm unable to see out; I'm suffocating.

"Have you any ideas yourself about this?" I try again.

"The memorial to my dead son, ah yes indeed, the memorial."

At last. "Yes, the memorial."

"Well now, let me think, the memorial… what about yourself, what would you suggest?"

Having arranged all this, he has nothing in mind. Well, death isn't an everyday occurrence. According to his faith, this man would believe his son to be in Heaven. "Depends on the amount of money you want to spend."

"The money, always the money, isn't that so?" this is a sad whispering reply, more to himself, but it had to be asked.

"What about a chalice and paten in silver to be left in whatever church you'd decide? That would perhaps be the most appropriate memorial," I suggest, at least get him thinking and hopefully an order will materialise. There is a long pause…

"That sounds interesting, yes," his voice comes from afar, "look here, let me give it some more thought and I'll let you know, there's no great hurry to do anything yet. You'd best to be going, it was good of you to find the time. You're a real Southern gentleman to travel this far."

Turning the ignition on, he lights up the dashboard. It's all off his chest now, for a while, until the next time; there's nothing more he wants to say.

The Square is cold as I watch him disappear forever, the state he's in, his very own Calvary, a Southern gentleman said he, but that couldn't be more wrong. Is that how others see me? Perhaps.

The country turns upside down, people fall off, they are rearranged all the time without noticing. I drive slowly towards the old homestead. In this light it seems that nothing much has changed, but there are strangers asleep in what was once my home, a low and whitewashed house now a useless bulwark against native hostility. It has emptied a generation to Australia. Familiar fields and secret places rise to that ancient ring fort, which is fully covered in foliage in summer, now standing sentinel, unconcerned, against the dull sombre night sky and a faintly illuminated glow from Belfast. I stop to get out and urinate by the iron gate of the water works. Across memory's horizon comes forth the strangely comforting, golden words, *PRIMO ELIZABETHAE*.

Driving on towards Newcastle across the familiar landscape of my fragmenting soul, what else can there be coming towards me out of the dark? I had better not awaken the past. From Newry to the border checkpoint, where a British soldier with a head light waves me to stop. He's like a circus clown, or a black and white minstrel, only armed and wary. It would be exciting for him, almost, if they weren't targets for patriot killers. The badge on this young soldier, as I wind the window down, show s the sword and wings of the SAS Regiment.

"Driving licence, Sir. Where are you coming from and where are you going this late hour?" His accent is from the north of England.

"Newcastle, where my parents live, heading for Dublin where I work, my father's a retired Group Captain." And I produce the small, blue Northern Ireland driving licence with its Ulster cross and six-pointed star beneath the Imperial Crown.

"What's his address?" he asks as he scrutinizes the licence with a thin torch. Poor lad to be doing this; my heart goes out to him.

"Twenty one, Slievenabreck Avenue."

"Away you go then, safe journey." Handing back the licence, he smiles satisfied, sounding foreign now. There are two other soldiers barely visible behind him on either side, holding their standard self-loading rifles at the ready, pointing, real or imagined spectators to history.

Why didn't I say Ballynahinch? In unforeseen situations one says anything. They might have thought I was IRA. Three nervous fingers and a sudden move to eternity, visiting the Group Captain indeed.

Drawing towards mother's dirty old rebel city, as though helpless from the power of an irresistible force, I recognize the Sugar Loaf very faintly far beyond, the early morning light breaking palest rose pink over Dublin. Feeling faint, with a sickness of tiredness, I'm going to vomit, but not over the seats, for there's a large, dull entrance that's the Archbishop's palace or house on the Drumcondra Road? Sure, he won't mind, or maybe he will, turning in, I park to one side under tall, gloomy trees. It must be something I ate, or a touch of the flu about to take hold.

Spinning around and around like millions of tiny stars, my vision seems mixed with blood, it is writhing and confused. I lean out of the open door trying to get sick... nothing doing. Life's convulsions weigh me down. I feel I have too much to carry. Is my heart stopping here of all places? The seat of the representative of the great Roman Catholic God.

Touching my throat a few times with two fingers brings a kind of relief, not in my head though. Jesus Christ, there's a young priest gazing down upon me. Wouldn't you just know.

"Are you all right?" asks he.

"Just a bit sick, had to come off the main road."

"In front of the Archbishop's house?"

"It can't be helped."

"You've been drinking haven't you?"

"No, I certainly have not," is my reply. Probably, this is a very young seminarian, all in new priestly black, overcoat and matching felt brimmed hat, soft leather gloves and trousers bicycle clipped above polished laced shoes. Well protected from worldly contamination, set apart from the rest of us. He is astride the latest Raleigh bicycle, it has silvery dynamos attached to lights front and rear, he has one foot on the peddle the other the ground, holding the bicycle upright. A young Catholic aristocrat, so well outlined and sure of his calling.

"The drink is a terrible course, just look at yourself. And you shouldn't be here, you should leave."

"I told you, I haven't been drinking."

"You're in denial; when were you last at confession?" The pale pinched face asks, accusatory eyes narrowing behind thick, black-rimmed glasses.

"I'm a Protestant heretic anyway, we don't believe in that nonsense," I answer him, and he is visibly taken aback.

"Well, God help you then," he replies glaring but also with condescention and without further comment he peddles off. From behind he looks like a crippled crow. Another day, another incident soon forgotten.

Passing the GPO brings a chain reaction of thoughts. It is hard to believe I was alive when the Germans were gassing the Jews. De Valera's attitude and invitation to Hitler without anybody knowing about it. There was an awful fear of Germans over the fields of County Down. They still appeared the other night, when I was dreaming beneath thatch and corrugated iron in the old cottage on the Brennanstown Road. It was all arranged so that Hitler would be buried in an unmarked grave in Tipperary or was it Kilkenny? The church door was bolted for the politicians sworn to secrecy and senior clergy, attired like monks of old. The service was nothing too flashy, ony the screaming red and black crooked-cross flag draped over his coffin. A priest was called just in time for his confession and last rites, extreme unction isn't it called? For Adolf was a Catholic and didn't want to go to the Hell he created, perhaps a little purgatory would be enough cleansing for his church. After the midnight hour he was anonymously taken to a disused graveyard of leaning gravestones and broken slabs. Sure it could have been Knocktopher or Kells even, for nobody will ever know now where it was. The coffin was lowered beside the dark cypress trees, with a bombers' moon above. May he never get out. By the hedge, curious cattle cautiously approach, before they suddenly turn and gallop off, sensing something awful, as only animals can. Everyone is standing to attention with arms outstretched, a last "Sieg Heil" for the Fuhrer... and no memorial for those Germans buried at Glencree.

CHAPTER 54

The torturous mechanics of this Dublin trade can be secretive and slow to understand. Late nights somewhere; somebody doing something for me; waiting in a spotless little sitting room gazing at a picture of Swiss Alps, with green valleys and picturesque chalets below, the good wife going to find him at the rear, finishing a fitted box almost ready for collection. It's a visit to the engraver or the spinner again. Something that is never straightforward when I'm collecting the silver. Usually, I have to go through another song and dance routine while I listen to his thoughts on the latest Northern outrage and who is to blame. It is not always the Brits. Is he testing my sensibilities? I'm careful always to agree, or not to comment, although he knows full well I mostly think the opposite of what he is saying. My only purpose is to collect, pay and leave.

The demise of Gunnings — which had become Royal Irish — occurs amidst rumours of mismanagement, misappropriation of grants, machinery that went from grey to blue and missing silver (whole tea sets in fact). Their de Valera anniversary plates were beyond belief. The silver model spitfires for the RAF, mounted on Kilkenny marble plinths, didn't go down too well either, having been made and hallmarked in Ireland. According to one story, they were sold by the dozen for a quickfire sale to get rid of them. Their seahorse candlesticks mysteriously appear now and then, long after Royal Irish have gone. Whatever comes along, it is about making a living and whatever it is can't be helped. The real heroes are those who survive here.

As always, there are the harsh realities of having to employ people, pay taxes, cope with the ever-changing price of silver and disgruntled employees. Every workday comes polishers, casters, chasers, engravers, spinners, jewellers and silversmiths along that ancient stairway, which is hard to locate, fit for demolition and a definite fire hazard.

* * *

The few importers of Irish-made bric-a-brac most can afford are the sombre Ronfed brothers, funerary attired, who converse with me cautiously in their second-floor room overlooking Wicklow Street. One stands behind the counter, the other silent, to one side, listening and watching. A very dark place for them to occupy, day after day, perhaps leaving them with a few orders for bolt rings or chains.

Then there is the lovely wee girl serving in Darby brothers, who walks deliciously back to get a few green, gold-lined bracelet boxes; she is absolutely stunning. The older woman from Shamrock Chambers, collecting a leprechaun from me, says gaily, "Sure change is as good as a rest; it comes to men and women you know."

I think about her remark while going slowly over to Philip J. Dix on Aston Quay. He has everything needed for manufacturing, where his walls are painted cod grey and the Liffey outside is a grim reminder of movement nearby. Phil can be seen inside at his desk from the window and on hearing the bell he looks up with a mischievous smile, rising and hurrying over to open the side door, wondering what will the contentious topic be today. During the purchase of a few needle files or a polishing mop, I listen to his gentle chiding of Dublin's Protestants, a secret society of well-heeled Freemasons. An historical debate is more important to Phil than waiting customers and money in the till.

"Ah, the man of the reformed faith indeed, come to my humble establishment and what can we do for you today?" Phil asks mockingly. He is a soft and gentle Corkman, good natured, with a touch of the devil though and those dark eyes are strongly opinionated.

"I'm in an awful hurry Phil, parked just outside on Anglesea Street."

"None of that now, you walked over from Dawson Street, so I'm truly honoured by your esteemed presence."

"I need three packets of Number Three Ideal piercing saw blades."

"There's a special tax on those for Protestants for the tithes your lot levied on us poor Catholics you know," says Phil leading to the store room. "Do you hear me now?" he searches through a shelf of numerous files and saw blades. On his table is an open box of little silver St Christopher medals in cellophane packets, that I have never seen closeup before, but on taking one out I hear a command: "put that back at once," Phil has a mock-horror tone, "we don't want to be giving the wearer bad luck from the touch of a black Protestant, do we now?"

"Jesus, Phil, will you ever stop; sure it'll give the wearer a touch of good old Protestant common sense, no priests or popes between us and our God, divine grace being a more effective means of salvation than purchase of indulgences, do you know what I mean?"

"But see how you made us suffer under the Penal Laws, that was Protestantism for you, until we eventually threw you out."

"To let the Catholic Church take over, where the use of contraception is still a criminal offence."

"It's a filthy habit anyway, except for procreation. Protestants wouldn't understand that lust is the disordered desire of sexual pleasure, morally repugnant when sought for itself and not for its procreative purpose, do you understand what I mean?" He glares at me forcefully, without malice, but still wanting to strangle me with both hands.

"Sure, Phil, it was much worse for the Protestants of France when Louis the Fourteenth expelled them all out with Revocation of the Edict of Nantes."

"That was then."

"But you can still feel the whole ethos of it here however distant it now is."

"Why are you living here then, from the North of Ireland, too?"

"You may well ask Phil, for that I cannot truly answer, except that I was born here and in some strange way I belong and wouldn't want to live anywhere else."

Phil doesn't reply, his eyes momentarily pityingly me. Then the phone rings, he goes to answer. He makes out the invoice, payment made with small change, saw blades handed over, with amusement in those dark eyes showing he has another trick to pull.

"My grandfather was in the Royal Navy at Jutland and an uncle went down with the *Hood*," he whispers, as if it is a secret to keep under my hat. Then he shows me out to the mournful, seagull-crying quays, where the poor are waiting for buses to Blanchardstown, Palmerstown Cemetery and Heuston Station. Distraught mothers are inwardly hysterical at their predicament again, holding and scolding little shrieking wayward children. Then there are those too old to care, queuing at the soup kitchen by the Royal Barracks amidst hysterical laughter from the grave. The refuse of the dispossessed is much the same now, how Ireland's history can suddenly awaken me unawares.

Mentioning Louis the Fourteenth reminds me of Kilkenny again and those books by his military architect Vauban, what was that all about then? The night I took them, after seeing Mary home, I had the key to the Marquess's estate office and could have taken anything. A thief, careful and shaded in that night's mysterious magic: the once powerful Ormondes, their castle, stables and possessions are as out of dreams now, the mirage of memory forever deep inside me.

* * *

It is good to see Johnson Matthey's new branch opened at one-o-one Grafton Street, they stock plenty of gold and silver and so I've no need to keep so much on the premises now. Head down, hopefully invisible to Weirs, I go past the second floor where Douglas Bennett is writing antique valuations for jewellery and silver on Weirs-headed paper with his new assistant youthfully awed, keen to learn about makers' marks and hallmarking. A black loop in one eye makes Bennett a pirate of antiquity on the high seas of human vulnerability. I reach the fourth floor on the back stairs, where Michael Muldoon and Paddy Johnstone are the engravers and explain in mild undertones what I want from them surreptitiously on the side. Johnstone looks up from engraving a large silver two-handled cup from the Royal Dublin Society, which is an annual affair for him. Muldoon briefly turns from standing at the window, something has his attention. There's a photograph torn from a page stuck on the wall near the door showing a ragged beggar man, arm outstretched, cap in hand, running for a few pence after the open horse drawn carriage of King George the Fifth who is top hatted, his companion likewise, both laughing highly amused at the poor man. Probably this was at Ascot.

"Jesus Christ, look at this," exclaims Muldoon, pointing across to Switzers. A young girl in a buttercup dress is climbing out from the high window almost opposite. She hesitates, then jumps purposefully, fearlessly freeing herself, falling brutally onto Wicklow Street, a good drop below. Splayed beneath us, with a last shuddering motion, blood oozes as stunned, horrified, onlookers gather around hesitant and shocked.

"Broken hearted there, silly girl," says Muldoon without sympathy, ghoulishly photographing the scene with his German camera. Johnstone remains silent, crossing himself and returning to his bench ashen faced, then he calls, suddenly annoyed, "Jesus, Mick, will you ever stop that, for God's sake put it away." I concur too. "He'll be showing them to everyone soon," whispers Johnstone as the siren sounds eventually come.

Life goes on. I hand him the small silver bowl with the name and date to engrave on it. Johnstone is a small man with dark, going-grey hair on a crinkly face, he's about fifty and the salt of the earth. Muldoon is younger, with a fey mocking appearance and a disregard for the rules. Brooding and inwardly tormented, he is a brilliant engraver.

I'm unable forget the buttercup girl and to go back to silversmithing in the afternoon seems an absurdity.

* * *

Dublin's jewellery outlets are a chequer board of slow, emerging twilight figures, which can gradually be discerned through the gloom. Suspicious and cautious when I first enter the room of their mind, their mirrors reflect the very opposite of what is before me. They have to be alert to tricks and illusions, of being fooled or ambushed. They must survive on ground that feels tremulous beneath them. Is there any difference from the past?

Making knotted pins and brooches, those golden yokes, big and small, looking out to the same crow and fox, salmon leaps and herding cattle, or depictions of bloody confrontations and human sacrifice (which are much the same today with the IRA). I praise the creeping night's sweet oblivion, which evaporates away my fevered melancholy.

Certain late evenings see me drive through Stillorgan and Donnybrook, a lonely trespasser turning from Leeson Street to Grand Parade and on up to the Crumlin Road. The swans are drowsy white, heads curled into their bodies; others glide awake on the dirty old canal. Whores go to work boldly around Fitzwilliam Square, an unchanging profession, just as the women who gathered around the Colosseum in ancient times under burning torch light, waiting for the sated crowds to leave, looking gloriously obscene with painted bodies and wearing masks inviting fornication. I glance at a shapely, tempting rear and view a long-legged girl who disappears.

Then I collect the engraving and cases I need from Crotty Avenue and Balfe Road East, Walkinstown. Where formerly the father went over the top with the many, returning with the few. He was a case maker by trade, handing on the skill to the son, a handy little part-time earner that he does more as a hobby, away from his job at Post and Telegraphs. The demands of the silver trade are not what they once were. The hall light is turned on to reveal an easy-going, shambling sort of man carelessly dressed. I'm shown to the sitting room, a refuge of normality, apart from the picture of the snow-covered, towering Matterhorn against a clear blue sky. He leaves to collect the condiment set cases he's made; has he ever been to Switzerland? On the mantelpiece the ticking clock says it is a quarter past ten. I hear a woman's voice from the kitchen. Their terrier dog checks in, sniffing, wants a stroke, then scampers away. The old soldier himself is there in kilted uniform in a faded, famed photograph, the resemblance clear.

My craftsman returns with three green cases smelling of elephant glue. They have tiny brass hinges and are clasped, opening to the pepper, salt and mustard set, each fitting snugly down into black silk, with matching elastic bands holding the ball-hammered mustard spoons. There are cod castles, round towers, the Sugar Loaf Mountain, Glencolumbkille's angels and cross gravestones cut around each. I feel a sense of pride at having made them. I'll do whatever it takes for the customer, who'll believe anything. But how long will it take for the salt to spill and corrode the silver to a cancer of black spots? Or sweaty hands cause a relentless disintegration?

"So how much do we owe you?" I ask.

"Aaa... now let me think," he replies with a low whistle, as if working out time and materials is an awful inconvenience when it's only a hobby, what with his secure job. He's suggesting it doesn't really matter from sweetness of his sublime indifference, in contrast to my working reality. Good man yourself. "A pound, two... fifty, two-pounds-fifty each then, how does that suit you?"

"Whatever you say yourself, that's just fine, you've done a lovely job as always." It is not nearly enough though, but I can hardly offer more, it is his affair. I feel like I'm robbing the blind here. Althought it is late, it is only a short drive to Paddy Johnstone the engraver.

The Company of Goldsmiths coat-of-arms is being engraved on a three-legged silver round salver on Paddy's kitchen table, he's just finishing. *Te Radiante Virebimus* is scrolled beneath two tiny, harped upright, standing unicorns. Paddy is so sure of hand, their manes and tails appear almost to me moving. The salver holds a quartered shield with harp on first and fourth, covered cup and two buckles on second and third. A gentleman's helmet mantling flows gracefully on either side. With a flick of Paddy's sharp engraver, a harp-chested, long-haired girl's outstretched hands hold the weighing scales and touchstone, the sun rising behind her. Paddy has an unrecognized talent that's meanly rewarded. Such artistry now earns no more than a cobbler or plumber. Martin Schongauer and Albert Durer come to mind, perhaps Paddy is not in the same league, but he's roundabouts there anyway.

Paddy's eyes are bleary from intense concentration and he should be abed, after a long day's work at Weirs. These strange Walkinstown late hour encounters set me adrift through time, as though I were meeting the builders of Newgrange or the makers of the ancient objects displayed in the National Museum.

"That's fantastic Paddy, you've done a brilliant job."

"A difficult enough coat-of-arms, but I think I have it right now," Paddy leaves down his loop and engraver, leaning back, arms stretched wide, yawning.

"You certainly have." I take a closer look. Engraving is a tedious enough job, without colour or body, working on small words that have to be magnified. Loop on again, Paddy puts the full stop on the last Latin word, whatever it means, the strong light reflecting harshly from the polished salver. Here is continual heat and movement.

"So when did you first get into this business Paddy?

"Nineteen forty-two, and I can remember the day as if it were only yesterday," he answers, gazing fixedly to more than thirty years ago. "I was coming down South Georges Street when there was an almighty roar, growing louder, then right above me was a German plane followed by a Spitfire, both very low. Whatever happened to them I don't know, everything about the war was censored then."

"Over Dublin? When the Republic was neutral? They were a bit out of their way, surely?"

"I could see the black cross and the red blue rounded quite clearly."

"On your first day at work Paddy, you'd certainly remember."

"It brought the whole war home to you."

"It most certainly would."

"How and ever." Fast forwarded back to the present, Paddy gets up, "just a light polish over this and you're right," he presents the finished salver to me.

"Fantastic, Paddy, how much?"

"Thirty-five."

"Will you take a company cheque? I won't cross it and I'll make out to cash."

"Not a bit of bother; no problem at all." Easily said, but what else could he have replied? A good London engraver would charge at least three hundred and more for the same work. But sure, this is Ireland. I write out the cheque.

As he shows me out, on the hallway wall there is a picture of three young soldiers kneeling around a machine gun. "Who are they Paddy?"

"That's Joe Walsh, me father and Paddy Nolan, together on the Western Front," Paddy proudly explains, pointing to each.

"Which regiment?"

"The Dublin Fusiliers."

As I drive home I ask myself are these places a hidden state of Nirvana? Lowly Walkinstown, Sallynoggin, Swords, Ballinaclash and others too. But I am shocked out of my thoughts by the tottering, headlighted whore on the window screen, a screaming mad fury, a ball of contorted rage comign from the footpath, as if out of the grave from ancient Ireland, reminding me of past and present wretchedness on the narrow Mespil Road. I am shaken.

"Watch out, ye feckin bollocks yez; try to run me down would ye? Yez all the dirty same Irishmen."

"Are you all right?" I stop and ask, calling to her.

"Ah get away with ya, has anyone ever been alright in this feckin country?"

* * *

Woodlice on nocturnal pursuits move slowly and become stationary on both sides of the cottage front door when I open it. There is much the same sight, albeit to a lesser degree, on the porch inside. I pick them off with soldering tweezers, these pin-eyed, many legged, crunchy little monsters that can grow dog-sized in my nighttime nightmares.

Living in Cabinteely is surreal at times. I feel adrift between the Horse and Hound, the Garda Station and the garage of the three taciturn multitask mechanical men with their clock in the pediment above stuck at twenty seven minutes past eleven. Christ, on the mosaics of the gable of St Brigid's parish church, is red, blue, white and golden. The abomination that is Mass is celebrated here.

The Carnegie library has books on history, including one about Himmler and the Holocaust. The nightmares of the twentieth century are real, not dreams. On the Brennanstown Road by old walls, high railings and overhanging branches, at the bad bend where Garda Kerry Dan knows a thing or two. He is standing watchfully, guarding the British brigadier McMullan, the military attaché. There may be bloody assassinations tonight and often on Sunday mornings I notice the untroubled tweeded mustachio, walking up the hill past the cottage to Tullow Church with his wife. He should be more careful, he's an easy enough target.

The atrocities swing back and forward like a pendulum clock. Somehow, I knew a man was pretending to fix his bicycle outside on the pavement, suspiciously, a few yards away from the Brigadier. I registered his face later. They kidnapped the dentist around the corner at Manor House for ransom, if I remember correctly. Imagine, they cut off his finger with a hammer and chisel. It was left I a matchbox inside a Carlow church, at the feet of the Virgin Mary. Get a move on with the money, or it is an ear and eye next time. There is no messing with The Irish National Liberation Army.

CHAPTER 55

There are many uses the trade has for imported Johnson Matthey Celtic silver wire. It comes in three widths: four, six and nine millimetre looped snakes of fine grain, bordered between circular, decorated studs. It is to be soldered on salvers, christening mugs, single and double napkins, rings, whiskey measures... There is an endless list of possible silver items. I have thoughts about leaving Dublin Silver and Weirs.

In the land of Israel, the Holy Temple is the centre of Jerusalem. I always pausing to check Dankers' crowded window and when I do, nearly two millennia of Jewish persecution comes to mind. At Dankers are the lovely Joy and Gayle, with their Biblical good looks and their uncle who would never never bc driven in a Mercedes Benz or make of similar German origin, and quite rightly so, considering. the Gestapo had a list of four thousand Jewish people here. I wonder would de Valera and McQuaid have acquiesced to Hitler's demands to hand them over if Germany had been finally victorious? Hungry did, also France, Romania, Ukraine and the Baltic States.

* * *

Irish Hallmarks are probably the Best Guarantee in the world. I'm dealing with these little lies and deceits again, tall stories to fool others and myself. Some days I strive for a useless immortality with special creations to be left behind when I have departed. God love the le Bas, a decent family, with a most helpful son and daughter now, securely positioned in the warm, amorphous airs of family connections to past generations. Position has been handed down along with their inside knowledge and family name. Their concerned attention comes my way occasionally at the hatch and, if it is her, it comes seductively. Not that she knows it. Without her realising, I daydream of entering the castle's erotic Garden of Eden together with her. Walking through vapours that are rising from the hard asphalt on the lower castle yard after heavy rain, now under hot sunshine, I feel drugged with metamorphic confusion.

* * *

The state becomes overbearing on the resources of its hard-working citizens. I find it best to keep silent about my finances, knowing most people are the same way, especially those with their hands on the levers of power and on money that can so easily be diverted their way. Making theft legitimate in the eyes of the law, they contract to help themselves, human nature being what it is. At secret locations, around the corner from McDaids, say at an arranged time when no one will notice and nothing is said, packages change hands surreptitiously. Confidentiality in all institutions is assured, this is not corrupt, it is sound business practice.

It is as though they are still haunted by an alien land system, with its lack of security of tenure and evictions. They have inherited fear, as if the British authorities are still here. Somewhere between a lie and the truth, I set the price for an honest day's work and support the state — unwillingly — by adding such a high rate of VAT. I am now falling, unaware, into the funnel of Irish sensibilities, making lodgements at the Ulster Bank and Irish Nationwide Building Society.

It will not be a problem working in the cottage, there is enough room front and rear. The finger of providence is pointing into the future and I am aware of the slow-burning fuse of the inevitability of my leaving Dublin Silver. Weirs are no fools either, they expect this departure and even help me move my equipment to the cottage in their van. Now I am alone again, anxiously confident with my History of Ireland design and many others. For how long, though, can I manage without a telephone?

I'm up the laneway to good old Florrie Baker, using hers most days, pressing the bell and waiting, waiting forever. I can't just phone and leave, she likes a lengthy chat after avidly listening to my business and I am glad too, to bring her contrary, old, laurel-green Morris Oxford to life with the starting handle. It's the same as my own. I don't really mind these encounters, as all hours are working time for me.

At night, a dreamy nonchalance takes hold of me, as I listen to my neighbour after making a phone call. She becomes a witch with Gambit, her off-and-on cat, unbelievably, urinating while perched on the edge of the cool scuttle. Once he did so on top of the television and it went crazy, before steaming back to normal again. I begin to know her stories, which are repeated again and again. Like the spring morning they took Alan Bell off the tram, she'll never forget that. As a teenager, she watched horrified as the man – a senior police official, taken out of retiremet to end Michael Collins' fundraising – was shot dead. His name and the tram's bell became synonymous she always maintained, remembering it like yesterday and through nightmares long after.

Her late husband's market garden behind the high wall has gone to rack and ruin, I can take whatever I find, says she. I discover tomatoes, raspberries, black currants an a few autumn apples (which she calls Beauty O Baths). These apples have a gorgeous orange-yellow colour and an unforgettable, slightly bitter taste. The greenhouse is falling down, yet she still manages somehow to do the flowers for the Gresham Hotel.

* * *

Pringle. His name shouts out, shocking me, on the wireless and on every Irish newspaper I can see. He has been arrested for supposedly shooting two Gardaí while fleeing from having robbed the Bank of Ireland at Ballaghadereen, County Roscommon. He'll be sentenced to death if found guilty, although it will hardly be carried out though. But for the rest of his life he'll be in gaol. What a waste of an intelligent man. It is hard to believe the story, knowing him and thinking about the last time I saw him. I find it impossible to believe he would ever shoot a Garda.

What is life here about anyway? For Ireland can't possibly exist only as Florrie's recurring nightmare. And now this. My distorted grip on reality leads to feverish dreams. Something happened, yet didn't. I'm at Dublin Silver again, where O'Connell's gun is still behind the safe. I will have to get rid of it, immediatcly, but where? Where? At the bottom of the Liffey, which is an apt resting place. Bhaile Atha Cliath means the dark pool. The gun will be metamorphed into badly rusted iron ore when it is eventually discovered, probably hardly discernible, lying there with ancient battle axe, sword and sliced skull six hundred years later, with no difference between now and then. Our descendants will be curious at the remains displayed in the National Museum, alongside a beautiful, beaten bronze shield from near Lough Gur, County Limerick and much more. Such artefacts will partially reveal thoughts and secrets from long ago, just as the wind does that sighs eerily through Langrishe's tall trees at Knocktopher.

I go furtively down the steps into Dawson Street and away, around by Trinity and past the extinct Parliament, night lighted, soot-brushed ghostly white, with Ionic tall pillars of sweeping nobility. The big Hanoverian coat of arms is still there. I make no eye contact with the garda approaching and I keep going on to O'Connell Bridge, stopping half way across. How did it ever come to this? Leaning over the parapet, left to right is busy enough, so I let the gun fall away beneath the balustrades into the moving cold waters. Nobody notices. *Summa Theologiae* with Mary on the bridge at Inistioge again.

I keep walking past Eden Quay and into O'Connell Street as a moth drawn to a burning flame, conscious that ambush and treachery emanates from seemingly gargoylian encounters in a foreign land. Hypnotized and horrified at the loud Dublinesque I hear, I'm fearful they'll sense that I am an outsider, in the way pack animals can kill an interloper, I saw the pigs do it. Head down then, I keep moving until at the Garden of Remembrance in Parnell Square. The heavy sliding gates are shut, locked with the little bishops and bronze-copied processional cross. I can see the sunken, shallow blue, green and white wavy mosaic-bottomed cross-shaped pool. Oisin Kelly's enormous children of Lir creation is at the far end, the once copper green-coloured bronze turned black and dead, with the limp, wet tricolour to the rear above. All under the ominous heavy impenetrable mirrored city lit sky.

I heard somewhere about Barry's Hotel, to the right and somewhere around Denmark Street, and, yes, there must be a dance on, there are women in pairs and single men following them to where there's faint sound of music. From remembrance of the dead to the rebirth of the nation from casual couplings to be found here in the snares of Irish womanhood.

So I go nervously into the narrow, crimson-lit corridor towards a very large woman seated behind a table, reminiscent of a gypsy fortune teller, heavily made up, dressed in black, eyed as Cleopatra, purple lipsticked and with matching long nails. Two pounds, ten shillings is needed for her outstretched, many-ringed hand, she gives a warning glance. To warn me to be careful who I dance with downstairs.

Descending to what seems at first to be a loud, bacchanalian scene, I push through the crowded smoke-filled room. It is a struggle to reach the bar, I just managing to catch the overworked barman's attention for a glass of Smithwicks to nurse, while watching the dancing. What an assortment, I really should leave although there are one or two good looking ones no doubt.

"Would you believe such a crowd; have you ever been here before?" I ask the pink, sweating man standing unsteadily beside me, his stomach out above his belt, shirt unbuttoned halfway, hairy chested.

"A few times all right, but you know these Dublin girls can be very choosy who they dance with, be warned." He obviously knows.

"Is that right?"

"The country girls are much nicer and, sure, what am I doing here anyway?"

"Where are you from?" I ask and decide I might as well stay a bit longer at least.

"Drogheda. Not a bad little town, mind you, and yourself?"

"Downpatrick." Does it even exist from down here?

"Whoo, the North, you don't have the accent though, I'd say you're more English, but who cares? Never been up there much, 'specially these days." He drains the last of his pint glass of whatever.

"Would you drink a lot of that in a night out?"

He smiles, reckless, eyes rolling. "This is my eighth, I think, from around seven that is."

"That's a lot," I believe he's got a problem there.

"Do you think so? What about yourself then?"

"No more than a glass or two of this; a whiskey now and then," I'm conscious my glass is still full.

"It gets you relaxed and out of this world."

"I suppose so," he does have a point.

"Have you seen anything you fancy?"

"One or two maybe and yourself?"

"Ah, sure, you know they can be so bloody rude, ye see her, blondie one over there? Told me to get lost." I can't be sure of the woman he's pointing to. "I don't dance with farmers like yerself says she, the cheek of her, and thought it a great laugh with her friend."

"No need for that," I sympathize.

"The little bitch; they're all whores in Dublin anyway, I tell you now." Shaking his sorry head, his shirt is stuck to his back with sweat and male desperation. He moves to the bar once more.

How did I ever get here, was it by chance after disposing of a misguided patriot's gun? But wasn't that a dream? Mysterious forces are ever-present, made to feel stronger by coincidences and my forgetfulness. Soon I'll see if they're choosy or not, the worst they can say is "no". The flash one in tight red has a laughing face, close-cropped dark hair and a figure that taunts me brutally to ask her for a dance. Unfathomable emotions are stirred in me at the thought of discovering the reality of how she might tremble beneath my touch. She's on her own now. There is no time to lose or she'll be with another partner again.

Surprisingly, she comes with me onto the dance floor. It is a wonder to hold her young femininity, she is light and sweet scented, a bird in the hand to break or want to keep.

Having told me she is from Finglas, she almost is accusing. "You're not Irish are you?"

"Whatever you want to think is all right by me," I reply, unconcerned.

"Why are you here?"

"I was just passing, the music drew me in with curiosity."

"Go on with you, there's more to you than meets the eye."

"How so?"

"Never mind, there's just something about you I find hard to figure out. It's your voice and the fact you're not the usual rough I'd find here. Will you get me a drink?"

"What will you have?"

"A Carlsberg Special," she says without hesitation.

"A glass?"

"No. Pint of course," is the cheeky reply.

Blimey, she's lizard quick and cute as a fox, drawing me into a momentary happiness with life. She doesn't seem to mind her religion's disapproval of what we are embarked upon, since her body and her touches are sending me encouraging subliminal messages.

After midnight we are underneath the porch of what was once Lord Charlemont's fine house on Parnell Square. Outrageously, without shame or embarrassment, for there's no one around and she doesn't seem to care if there is, we enjoy ourselves. Standing somewhat shadowed, lifting her skirt waist high, I find her nicely lubricated now, wanting me, legs apart, encircling me greedily to oblige me to go as deep as the gun into the Liffey waters. Drowning in her exquisite dark pool... but taking hold of myself, in a panic, I pull out just in time. There is a flash of anger from her disappointed, fevered face. Dashing away, straightening her dress, she immediately runs off, stops and turning shouts, "you're a fucking gobshite; no Irishman would do that."

How very strange of her to say so and this a worry for her too, with consequences long into the future. There is always a chance, it just takes one determined microscopic seed out of millions. Hardly though. But if so, it seems I'll never know.

Her scent is still upon me as I cross O'Connell Bridge. How deep is the Liffey water? Gazing down, I wonder if it is ever dredged, for surely the changing tides of moon and motion will hide and pull apart the gun. Will I never return and try to see her again? For she was gay and spirited, carelessly indifferent and hungry for what's natural and free, the most intimate of all human contact. And I didn't even ask her name.

CHAPTER 56

Silver is always made at a price that's never enough to make something inspiring and worthwhile, so to heck with artistic creations. I have to cut corners to survive, without much thought to design. Irish codology has to be at the fore, while the History of Ireland jewellery will always keep me busy. The parsimony of the Irish situation, however, is a creeping paralysis bringing blight to my activity. Working undercover, I have to slowly find the means to live, by conspiracy and subterfuge, creating my own kind of Republican Brotherhood, sworn to overthrow the harness of constraint in order to lead a decent life. Diverse talents and personalities join my society, amidst swirling seas of doubt and worry of discovery by the legality of tithe collectors and foreign landlords. Power was handed on to the new native masters and exists much as it always was for the peasants.

I read that Mary's father had died recently. How the once powerful eventually disappear, deep beneath the wet earth, which must be settling nicely over his fresh grave at Knocktopher. Where the wood-pigeons will have taken fright at his funeral, but the crows wouldn't have noticed or cared. Whatever Mr David Kiely didn't want me to know about will remain a secret. The big house is sold and the contents auctioned. I'm told the former became some kind of time share.

* * *

We wait, squeezed between the Assay and former Army Ordnance, glancing at each other silently, each one unto him or herself. It is impossible to avoid the occasional cute hoor of the trade. Anything can be stolen and copied and made cheaper elsewhere. As with a meteorite, magpies can suddenly hurtle out of orbit without conscience or originality, ever watchful for easy pickings, they pass off my work as their own. Called theft by another name, they know that court proceedings are an expensive undertaking, which those of limited means are afraid to go near. Over the years, there's a lot more to contend with from the loss of sterling to Ireland's part devaluation: the price of silver soars through the roof without warning. VAT is an outrageous thirty-five percent, which really puts the frighteners on the whole trade. Will it even survive?

* * *

Collecting a rhodium-plated silver ring from Joe Malone on South William Street, I scent a strong smell of frying pan grease up the dirty carpeted stairs. There are sixty steps, which I count from the narrow Georgian entrance. There is a warren of various enterprises on each of the four floors, the ever-present nightmare of self-employed artisans dissolves in the light-hearted banter, quickly returning when I'm alone and unable to sleep at night. Joe's door is always unlocked on the top floor, allowing me to go from one world to another in less than a nanosecond. Joe looks up on hearing me, switching off his small, spinning polishing motor. I can see the day's endeavour has brushed his countenance an ashen grey in the small room, which is badly lit by a fluorescent strip.

"You have a ring for me Joe, how much do I owe you?"

Smiling weakly on recognizing me, without replying, he finds the tissue-wrapped ring and comes over with it. Joe is dressed all blue, his head capped, he's wearing a dust mask and there's no extractor.

"Three pounds will do," Joe says, still far away. He's not one for needless conversation. Finding three Irish-harped silvery coins, I put them into Joe's rouge-tinted, outstretched hand.

"There you go Joe; how's business?"

"Things are very quiet. I'm not open Fridays for the moment."

"That bad?"

"Afraid so," he answers, flicking his head to the ceiling.

On the landing at the foot of the top flight of stairs I open the tissue to check the ring, perfect as always. The mysterious rhodium coating is brighter than silver when polished. Orbiting electrons keeping the silver from oxidising and the solder join covered until eventually it wears off. These are these tricks of the trade.

Weirs are steadfast, pay well and on time, with occasional treasonous thoughts being expressed to me now and again, when one or other of them deliver an order to me. So-and-so has left and so-and-so could be next. Family run firms always have family blood to the fore.

Every month without fail comes an enormous green cheque for one hundred pounds from F. Brennan of Patrick Street, Cork. This is for me to make and send whatever I think they would like.

Mortons on Nassau Street are church of the reformed faith. Brothers David and Johnathan are stiff-suited men, wearing Venetian masks that they are literally unable to ever take off, while their father is inscrutable, all seeing, motionless, seated low behind the counter, Buddha-like. It is as if I have entered another side of reality, an anxious otherness overtakes me on entering their shop. The picture of their establishment is a union flag flying, which was taken during Queen Victoria's last visit to Dublin. It is framed at the bottom of the stairs. Fine old sombre wood and tall glass cases are from the same period. In them is stacked plenty of reproduction Georgian silver; idyllic country scenes of dairy maids churning butter beneath summer trees, with horn players, dancing dogs and distant castles; helmet-shaped cream jugs with legs of lion heads and seashells; S and C scroll handles with bird beak terminals; a most unusual set of sugar tongs, star engraved, with pendant flowers and bright cut borders and no end of antiques. I feel an exquisite uselessness for today, for who would ever want to use this? Usually they might have a few repairs for me or German silver sheets to cup up in their basement, or to take home and fit on ligneous plinths. They sometimes order silver hollowware, with two-and-a-half percent discount paid on the VAT as well, but I can't complain of their good business sense, it takes all sorts.

* * *

In the narrow space of Brereton's shop on South Anne Street there's a dual of religious opinions some days, with light hearted innuendos and mockery without malice. I pretend to agree and hold on to my secret thoughts, for I can't push Diarmuid's Catholic upbringing too far. He fishes for information that he knows fine well, laying many a false trail, asking how an Irish Pigin is made, wanting to make another exactly the same, and could it be cast? A perfect gentleman, soft spoken and courteous. There was a Brereton who was supposedly one of Anne Boleyn's lovers, who met a ghastly end. Brereton's stock much the same as Mortons and there's even the same unusual engraved star. Another piece has the stag's head, one a crowned demi-lion holding the sun between his paws. Which leads my thoughts to the custom and demise of the old Anglo-Irish Ascendancy. He orders letter openers, book marks and money clips mostly.

On leaving one morning he earnestly advises me — writing it down on torn paper — to learn St Luke two, verses ten and eleven. Assistant Dan from Tipperary, still a pup, is visibly amused.

* * *

The Celtic cross topping the front of St Anne's church in Dawson Street, that I'm now facing, is detached and floats strangely on the soft, hallucinating Irish airs. I feel as if I'm walking alive at my own funeral procession.

* * *

The essential phone calls are becoming a trial. I'm interminably up and down the laneway to Florrie's once-fine house. Her roof is coated in green moss. The house is slowly becoming uninhabitable, behind the ever-mysterious old ivy-coated high wall, like a scene from Grimm's Fairy Tales. There is a smell of cat on approaching the front door. Eventually Florrie appears, dishevelled and toothlessly disfiguring sometimes, glad of the intrusion and the chance to discuss the weather, tax demands and hopefully she does not recall Bell's ghost today.

Picking up the filthy, black rotary dial telephone, I find that Captain le Bas is not available for another half hour or so. To go or stay? I might as well stay for I have the time to wait and she's delighted as I take the seat before her. My extremities become frozen; I'm unable to extricate myself and pretend to listen. There's raw liver on the floor of a cage with a lattice door.

"I used to catch the train across the fields of Barrington Tower at Carrickmines station into Harcourt Street when I worked in town before the war. They should never have closed it down, it was that Tod Andrews to blame and I never liked the man anyway..." She talks and talks, until morning becomes night. I'm falling into a dream of her, where her voice echoes, strangely far away.

She's delivering up to Brennanstown House, where there is no mistaking the man behind the bushes. Whatever is he doing? He is surprised by her, while she hurries past and mentions it to the rest of them. They just laugh and say she is seeing things: a look-alike. For he is dead. But she could tell they are upset and want to nip this in the bud, so the news does not to get out. Imagine if everyone knew that Adolf Hitler was living safely in neutral Eire. There he was, with his little moustache, and hypnotizing, mad, eyes. Furious at being recognized. It gives her the shivers to know he is just next door. For she wouldn't be surprised at what Dev's crowd were capable of and there were others as well...

I'm tossing and turning, the old cottage is adrift in unchartered waters and those twentieth century nightmares. There are dreams I am unable to extricate myself from, the ever present ones of my earliest years, which are a heavy burden, casting dark shadows over the fields and boglands. I remember the horrors discovered on the liberation of conentraction camps. Horrors I am unable to understand.

"Well, I certainly believe you Florrie, for I saw him a few times myself in Kilkenny and Tipperary some years ago." I confirm her sighting of Hitler.

"So, there you are now, I knew I was right," she replies, clapping her hands, stamping her feet, delighted.

"He'd be dead by now though."

"In his nineties at least. You wouldn't remember Oliver J. Flanagan during the war, or was it just before? He said the Jews had it coming to them for crucifying Christ."

"I thought it was the Romans; for wasn't the penalty for blasphemy for the Jews stoning to death?"

"We'll never know," says Florrie.

"The whole Nazi thing about living space, master race and world Jewish conspiracy, Judeophobia, German mass hysteria, it was all madness really, wasn't it?"

"We had fierce censorship during the war and didn't really know what was going on, apart from old Haw Haw and I found him hilarious. Some were even pro-German, young Haughey and his like, I remember it well."

"Did you know, Florrie, there's a carving of him on a tree there just behind the wall by the gate at Brennanstown House? Wearing his peaked cap, with Hitler written below; it certainly adds up to what you saw."

"I'll take a dander down to have a look, as I've never seen it before."

"I spotted him right away the first time I came up the hill, you can't miss it on the right."

Waking with an awful start, I get up, go to the phone and call le Bas.

* * *

When the price of silver reaches an almost unaffordable high for the making of hollowware, it's time to think of an alternative. Some are quick to notice, a large sanctuary lamp is stolen from Enniscorthy Cathedral, then cut into small pieces to be melted and sold as bars. It was found in the boot of a patriot's car; the once finely-made lamp destroyed. For another piece of recovered silver, the Shankhill Gardaí ask me to come and value it. I can just make out ILB, the Victorian forebears of Captain le Bas.

Much to the annoyance of some retailers, especially Market Ireland, the state-subsidised Kilkenny Design have opened a shop in Nassau Street, where they'll take a few pieces of jewellery of mine each month. I wonder about a range in brass, while the price of silver remains high. I

offer to take Kilkenny's designs. They can leave the manufacturing to me.
Delighted with the idea, but without a word about payment (or royalties,
if they were ever collected), the shop takes most of the brassware I make.
It is worth a try. They design a set of bowls, containers, trays and candle
holders, which need to be lacquered or continually polished, even if silver
plated. The polishing will be a tiresome, filthy affair, difficult enough for
the Spinner, who concurs at the idea, now that silver is no longer possible.

* * *

I have a new pale blue Volkswagen Beetle, bought in Armagh, because
by the vagaries of the Irish situation it is much cheaper there. For how
will they know I'm resident in Dublin? If asked, I can show a Northern
Ireland drivers licence to match the bright yellow number plate, And it's
handy for free meter parking, that I supposedly live up there. My only
reservation is the German make, but at least it is made to last.

I haven't been to Kilkenny since I left, it will be interesting to return
there. On the familiar road back through Naas and Athy, I feel a growing apprehension. At wide, leafy Castlecomer the past now is breaking
through the barrier of my thoughts. Electrical disturbances in my mind
tumble in airs of memory: I see green flashes as well as more calming
smoky blues. Mary's there, alongside a physical pain that floods through
my head with every mile of this elegiac journey. Driving on the parade,
I see the lime green and cream J.J. Kavanagh bus to Urlingford via
Freshford. It is waiting with Mary about to board. I almost cause an accident. A loud beeping car coming opposite jolts me forward to the present.
Stopping a while, shaken and confused in the front of the castle, I decide
to park further up the road that goes to Hubert Butler at Bennetsbridge.

Kilkenny Design couldn't have been nicer, but all through the conversation I feel a careless, surreal, soporific state of mind. We talk over coffee
and beautiful, detailed designs are produced on blue paper. With plain
rounds and straight sides, they have developed a sort of peasant-like,
rustic style, which is totally useless apart from the bowls and fat candle
holders. The rest would be used more as decoration about the house.

All the faces are new and mostly English. Des Byrne, a Dubliner, is
now in charge of the metal workshop. He is friendly and likeable, a leprechaun living at the bottom of a well or hollow of a tree, glad to meet
me. He has the low, subversive word of what's really going on. I'm given
a detailed overview of Walsh's forcible retirement and the financial problem that is brewing. Peter Donovan stayed, but left to manufacture and
teach at Grennan Mill Craft School. Others are mentioned, people I only
vaguely heard of, but who are long gone. The workshop hasn't changed
since it was first laid out. It still has the familiar stakes and tools bought in

London, the same, green, angle-poise lamps, spinning lathe and polishing motor. They obviously were the very best of everything needed, a silversmith's dream. I feel somewhat envious.

Now the summer day is long enough, why not drive to Knocktopher and maybe see inside the old bluebeard's lair?

Old Ireland forever beckons through the open gate. I walk up the gloomy, unkempt, potted driveway with the high enclosing walls. The hoarse "caw cawing" call of those rooks is a haunting welcome back to the past. What am I even doing here? Obsession makes me unable to turn around. A few cars are parked on the wide open space in front of the large, grey, early Victorian, lancet-windowed three-storied house. Swallows dive and rise, twittering "tswit tswit tswit" as sounding faerie bells to the falling sun. There are cattle grazing everywhere on lush grass fields. There is a tall splinter of a tower and the remains of an ancient church in a graveyard to one side beyond.

All is peaceful and calm now, as if the poison has been drained, the boil that has been festering over centuries has been lanced. The evidence is here. The other side of the building has a splendid expanse of overgrown lawn and yew trees, with parts of much older stonework visible alongside the more recent. It was a stately home for a loyal Irish MP, bribed to vote for the abolition of the old Irish Parliament and for the proposed Union. He was rewarded handsomely, receiving in excess of thirteen thousand pounds, a fortune then.

Opening the heavy thick perpendicular shaped unlocked door, I enter nervously, well imagining Mary's mother as a young, innocent girl from the village doing the same, though probably she came in to the rear. There's a grotesque, bearded, life-sized knight in aluminium armour grinning a welcome. It is some sort of a hotel alright, it has a receptionist's desk with a buzzer to call. I press a few times, no one answers. There are only ethereal voices, faint and far away.

From the high ceiling hallway rises a wide mahogany staircase, carpeted ruby dark, heading up to what secrets? Through a door marked "lounge" the same coloured carpet flows, where from a gilded frame on the opposite wall a red-uniformed, silver-epauletted officer stares distastefully at the intruder, wanting me to be gone. Whoever you were, you must have been a leftover from the auction, the black sheep of the family, best forgotten. It is a fine big room with tall, dark, curtained windows, a billiard table set to play with, a massive button-upholstered sofa and matching settee. The very same on which Mary's father sat in dinner jacket and bow tie by the black Kilkenny marble fireplace, warming himself on a foggy cold night. I wonder would he have given his rape of the maid a thought?

The whole place looks as if pre-arranged for my visit, the timing of which seems fortuitous. The place is empty, but for those voices, wherever they're from. From the stairs to the second floor, the windows look out to the loveliest of once-stolen views, the girl, on her own, would have flet fearful about the many maze-like rooms. I can well imagine him undressing, with the devil in his eyes, a snake ready to strike its prey. A matter of only of a short, brutal time. Perhaps to occur repeatedly thereafter.

Wretched and confused, the consequences in Catholic Ireland would be her father's wrath and the arrival of the priest. A microcosm of Ireland's suffering sorrow. From Norman footsteps to the more recent past, what are eight hundred years, or even five thousand, but sparks of the endless eternity? The servants in the other wing would not have been disturbed. His wife would have been away. And Mary's mother would have been easy. There for the taking. There are suitcases and items belonging to guests visible in some of the rooms. What a reversal of fate. If he could only see it. Presumably the heir, Hercules, had to pay capital gains or whatever, forcing a sale. On the third floor a tiny room is empty but for a single iron bed without mattress and I have a strange, sudden certainly that Mary was conceived here.

Hurrying past an area of small gravestones on the lawn, I wonder were they for horses or dogs? The names are now covered by lichen and are unreadable. Did the family prefer its own pets to the natives?

There are Mass goers, most likely leaving the church across the main road from where I am parked, a man is about to get into his car but on seeing me comes over.

I greet him with a question. "Excuse me, if you don't mind, would you know anything about the big house and the Langrishes who used to live there? Were they liked and good landlords over the years?"

"Well, yes. Yes they were all right but from what I remember, very distant. I've been farming here all my life, just up the road, and hardly ever saw them. They have been living there for hundreds of years you know. Why do you ask me?"

Although it is natural enough, I feel caught off guard by this question from this upright Kilkenny man (early sixties, kindly faced) and I'm unsure what to say at first. "My wife was the daughter of the last Langrishe that lived there, the Terence one, the mother a maid, a Margaret Malone, if you know what I mean?"

"Well now, that wouldn't surprise me the least. His wife Joan left him for such behaviour, it was said, amongst a lot of other things." He sounds wistfull and knowing. "Your wife wouldn't have been the only one either, I have to say, and from the stories I've heard handed down his forebears were much the same. That whole class holding power then took their pleasure on our women as a common right, whenever it suited them." He says this without bitterness, more as historical hindsight, then holds out his warm hand for me to shake. "The name's David Rice by the way."

I return the same.

"My family's been in Kilkenny for generations, came from Callan originally, Edmund Rice, the founder of the Christian Brothers, is related. So tell me how did all this come about for you?" he asks, curious now.

"Chance, really, as in all things, I was supposed to have met a man in the Club House, Kilkenny, I'm sure you know it. He never turned up, but she was there working behind the bar, barely seventeen. I'll never forget the evening. At the time I was working at the Design Centre."

"Is that so?" He eyes me keenly, encouraging me to continue.

"She was beautiful."

"I can well imagine, he was a handsome man, I wouldn't have known the mother, the name's familiar in these parts all right."

"An old woman near Freshford looked after her. Boarded out I think they call it, the district nurse told my wife, Mary, that she had good blood, that she was a Langrishe. Her mother later confirmed it when I met her not far from here."

"The same midwife that would have delivered me too. She's dead now, but her two sons live in the village. It's extraordinary you telling me this. How the generations come in circles. So where is your wife now?"

"We went to America where she met someone else, kept the daughter I never got to know and I wanted to come back to Ireland. End of story."

"I'm sorry to hear that," he replies genuinely sympathetic.

"Do you know she's never really left me? She's always there. The whole Kilkenny experience is a recurring dream, whether I'm awake or asleep. I went up to the place. An unlocked invited me in, set me imagining what went on." And I won't tell him I saw Adolf Hitler one evening walking down the Parade.

"I can well understand how you feel; the house is a timeshare now, I'm not sure who owns it. It's all very mysterious."

"Maybe I'm becoming obsessed about this, but I'd love to have confronted Langrishe before he died. When you remember the awful conditions Mary was brought up in Roscrea and Freshford."

"It would have done you no good, he'd have closed the door in your face, if indeed it was himself who actually answered it. He was in British Intelligence during the war, a very private and suspicious sort. A Lloyds Name I think, but definitely no farmer. Most of the land was sold off. He had what they called an iron horse, with a special permit to get petrol, I remember, just after the war. A two-handled yoke, you walked behind it rotating the soil. But sure, they were English to the core, to them we were a different species, like the Indians or blacks of America." He continues with a history of Kilkenny. Langrishes, Hume Dicks, St Georges, McCalmonts, Butlers, Tighes, Smithwicks and Desarts.

Finally, I get the opportunity to ask where he is buried.

"Over there by the sign to Knocktopher church in the walled cemetery." Pointing towards it, "he's buried by the old tower, beside his father Hercules. I remember the funeral, we weren't supposed to go inside their church but we did."

An acute awareness of vanished worlds strikes me. I'm no longer married. Maybe I never was. Maybe I was a victim of the ethereal and faerie tricks of Irish weather and distorted time. My memories of her will taste bitter-sweet forever. Floating extra-terrestrially, incarcerated in Kilkenny's warm evening airs, I walk carefully through grave stones, to what was once Matthew Fitzgerald's late twelfth century Norman tower, so the notice reads. Underfoot somewhere are his remains, from whence came the miniscule seed, brutality transmitted, mixing and mutating and eventually still alive in Mary.

Gazing into the archway of the tower, which is locked by high gates on both sides, I can see dusty, spider-webbed, broken fragments of indecipherable scattered memorials. A raised, near-life-size medieval husband and wife lie together, carved from dark stone. The scene is wonderfully framed from this side, becoming an extraordinary evocation of the big house into which nature is slowly invading. They lie against a background of ineffable luminous greens, eerily tragic, yet hauntingly beautiful. Once more I have found an encapsulation of old Ireland. Waist high, there are the two plain-cross gravestones for Sir Hercules and Sir Terence Langishe. I feel a strong urge to urinate on his, but no, let the old dog lie. He was the last of their selfish breed; the Catholic natives have risen and are in charge now.

* * *

The Bridge House Bar is unpleasantly cowded, nothing has changed, the barmaid is a beautiful, dark-haired young girl busy serving on her own, totally unaware of being watched and or that she reminds me of another, as she hands the large whiskey over. Later, somewhat comatose, I drive in the direction of Freshford and beyond. As if she'll be waiting at the cottage. The windows and door are boarded shut. There is the small gable room window where she slept with Kevin Barry, which I gaze up towards, as long ago.

When I bethink me on that speech whyleare,
Of Mutability, and well it way:
Me seems, that though she all unworthy were
Of the Heav'ns Rule; yet very sooth to say,
In all things else she beares the greatest sway.

Which makes me loath this state of life so tickle,
And loue of things so vaine to cast away;
Whose flowring pride, so fading and so fickle,
Short Time shall soon cut down with his consuming sickle.

Then gin I thinke on that which Nature sayd,
Of that same time when no more Change shall be,
But steadfast rest of all things firmely stayd
Upon the pillours of Eternity,
That is contraryr to Mutabilitie:
For, all that moueth, doth in Change delight:
But thence-forth all shall rest eternally
With Him that is the God of Sabbaoth hight:
O that great Sabbaoth God, graunt me that Sabbaoths sight

I walk down to the crossroads where I left her that first night. Over to Clontubrid church, which is unlocked for some reason. I take a seat. Near the altar, the sanctuary lamp glows faint red. I'm dimly aware of Jesus and Mary opposite in each corner. The mystical ties of their religion drifting into superstition. There are no moving miracles here. That is where the priest came out, signalling me to go into the vestry, a gratuitous Catholic insult. Miracles at the rear of the church, under the first hint of new morning sky, Kilkenny stretches undulating and impenetrable towards Maryboro and the Queen's county. I fall asleep somewhere between Athy and Naas, carrying too heavy a burden, exhausted, waking by Ardskull.

CHAPTER 57

The Spinner does an excellent job on the brass designs, but I have to listen to his long tirades about the Brits and the Falklands War — he pointedly calls them the Malvinas — and how Maggie Thatcher is in for a big surprise, with an exocet missile up her behind as the islands rightly belong to Argentina. I agree with every word and therefore annoy him, ignoring the bait.

Apprehensively arriving to collect and pay cash, I wonder what the topic will be today, since the Argentinians are fleeing. Joint sovereignty is on the cards, until the United Nations vote for the Brits to go, says he. The burning friction of polishing brass, in the smoke filled-shed, induces dirt into every pore and makes me an African look-a-like, a runaway slave thinks Florrie.

For almost a year I deliver these brass items to the Kilkenny shop on Nassau Street, wondering do they really know what they're doing stocking the likes of this? They are sold as the Kilkenny cowshed look (it says in an accompanying brochure). Whatever it takes to survive.

Gradually, the price of silver returns to a more affordable price, enabling me to make of hollowware again. Thankfully I'm able to leave the brass behind. The Kilkenny orders dwindle to an occasional silver-plated, cut out lidded bowl, such as was presented to the twined town of Annecy in France one year. I sense Kilkenny Design is in trouble and running down.

The high price of gold and silver didn't much affected jewellery, so the choice is between casting or stamping for the History of Ireland design. Orders are growing and I can no longer produce enough by hand. Casting can be porous and produce fire stains, while dies are expensive, the rings, stamped flat, have to be rounded and soldered and filed inside and out before polishing. The joint line can become visible in time, the purchaser calling it a crack. But stampings are sharp and cut deep.

I'm advised by Ronnie le Bas, the Captain's young son, to go see Fergal Morrissey, just off Lower Mercer Street.

Too late, I realize I am entering a torturing mirage of false promises. I'm ambushed and hung upside down, helpless and ripe for the plucking, anguished and confused. The time and money wasted creates a powerful anger in me.

Egan demands payment up front, before the dies are started and gives me the feeling they'll be his, that he's doing me a favour. He even charges for removing the plastic covering on each piece stamped. Because the dies are always wrapped up well in a parcel of supposedly finished work, I'm unable to check them until later. Even so, he insists on immediate payment.

They are double stamped and off centre by at least twenty percent, nor have they been annealed in the protective atmosphere of his furnace chamber, which was promised at no extra cost. I have to do this myself with the gas flame. A fire stain appears and soon a die breaks that should have lasted indefinitely. He demands payment to replace it. Then he's suddenly producing the Story of St Patrick in a similar style to mine. This is some change from his usual gate bracelets and Claddagh rings.

Enough is enough, I will take the dies and give them Johnson Matthey in Birmingham. The English have never minded much about Irish history. For them, the Irish are a quaintly superstitious and troublesome race on the western approaches of very recent and bitter memory. So I plan to go to Morrissey's with the element of surprise. Obsequious (and hopefully disarming), I will explain that I want to take rubbings from the dyes for an explanatory booklet, he can hardly object. On Friday afternoon he'll be relaxed and unsuspecting; that's when I go to see him with paper, pencils and a strong bag for the heavy dies. His office is at the top of high concrete steps from a small yard below, entered by a heavy metal bar gate.

Reduced to such subterfuge, having to act the thief to take the property I have paid for is absurd. But he'd only be looking for more money and God knows what else. I feel as dispossessed as the Meath man, axe concealed, surprising de Lacey at Durrow with a blow on his greedy Norman head. Here goes, I put my finger nervously on the button. The door is opened by his smiling girly secretary, who leaves me to go back to find Fergal behind his desk, on a revolving chair. He is not expecting me.

"I just want to take a few rubbings from the dies, Fergal. I can do it here on the floor if you don't mind, it won't take long."

He doesn't reply, but leans back with his hands behind his head, stretching, swarthy and with dark, quizzical eyes. His brain is at work calculating; he is not to be caught out.

"It's for a new booklet, I'd like the old Irish stone rubbings on the cover, it should look good, black and grey you know", I offer this explanation to his silence. Does he believe me?

"Can you come again next week? Its closing time; I have to lock up, the dies are all over the place,." Does he smell a rat?

"I need to work it out for the printer, there's a deadline and there'll be more stampings for you as well."

He leans forward, staring intently, "I don't know what you're on about however." Still, he picks up the phone and calls a Tom to bring the dies up.

Both of us are frozen in the cold of Ireland's new ice age, time moving too slowly, both suspecting something is afoot. What will it be? Tom arrives with a large wooden tray, I motion to leave it on the floor and praise the Lord the clipping tools are there with the dies. This isn't going to be easy, but I am determined to succeed. As a bewildered Brendan departs, Fergal stands right beside me, he's a small man. Laying each dye out carefully, checking they're all there, I'm ready to put it all the bag and make a quick exit to the door. But he might call Brendan back and more of his staff.

"I could take these home Fergal, it would give me more time, and not be holding you up," I suggest, but he's no fool; he's watching me intensely.

"You might not return them."

"They are mine."

"Not until fully paid for."

"I thought they were."

"Only half."

His phone rings, requiring him to go behind his desk to answer it. I seize the fortuitous moment and pile the dies into the strong bag as he continues talking. I'm angry at this charade; no more of this nonsense. I make boldly to the door.

"You're committing theft," he calls out angrily, throwing down the phone, running over.

"Fuck you Fergal, they're mine." I push forcefully onwards as he tries to grab the bag. Down the steps and I'm off. I turn to see that he's gazing down at angrily.

He shouts, "you'll be hearing from my solicitor!"

I am somewhat shaken. Such a carry on, amongst the wiles of this trade's perpetual and rancourous double dealing, theft and confrontation.

* * *

There are beggars along Johnsons Court, one is playing 'Danny Boy' on his violin, a mournful tune that I can well understand. It plucks a heartstring deep inside me as I enter Sleater's shop. A cheesy fog of dark crimson, a fortune teller's, a place of libidinous unions, I have to enter the song and dance routine of getting paid.

"He's upstairs with a customer," says gnomish Tony the watchmaker, "I'll take that if you like, he could be a while."

"No, no Tony, I'll have to wait, it's way overdue and I've already sent him two," I reply wearily.

"You'll have to talk to him yourself then," Tony says as he disappears.

From left to right foot, holding the statement... until voices and footsteps herald Geoffrey appearing down the stairs with a customer, seeing him out only for another to arrive and another, damn them. "If you're back in about an hour I'll have this ready for you," says smooth-talking Geoffrey taking the statement. He is a might irritated, although nicely pale suited, washed and scented with aftershave.

It could have only taken him a minute to write a lousy cheque for one hundred and sixty-eight pounds from him, I think, sitting exasperated in St Teresa's church opposite. Instead, there's a large, filthy hand on my shoulder. I turn to a man maddened by the drink, out of it, who asks, "a few bob sir, any loose change will do."

"Get you away from me!" Leaping up, I shout at him in surprise, disturbing those kneeling at prayer. I stride angrily away to crowded Bewleys for coffee, returning in an hour.

"He's gone for his lunch," explains Tony, now looking like he has fallen out of *Scenes from Peasant Life* by Pieter Bruegel the Elder.

"Did he leave that cheque for me?"

"Maybe he did, but I very much doubt it," says Tony going to the little side office. The bell rings on a curtained door as it breezily opens to a very large, effervescent, pink woman who's obviously a friend of Geoffrey's, by Tony's friendly greeting to her. The cheque is obviously not written. I converse with herself until Geoffrey arrives, glancing at me, as if to say: are you still here? Not asking for any favours, I hover awkwardly.

"This man was before me Geoffrey," the woman says kindly, thank God. Geoffrey reluctantly retreats. As he begins to write out the cheque, I am so relieved that I feel benevolent and suggest, "why not get Louis le Brocquy to design something in gold or silver? It might be an idea worth trying, you know, with limited editions, as he has such a great name."

Geoffrey pauses, pen in hand, cocking his sleek, cunning head, thinking, forefinger pointing at me, "you could be right."

"I'll make whatever he comes up with, you can do the advertising and packaging, he can only say no. You won't have to stock anything, the money can be paid with the order."

Silence, watching... he is onto a winner. He probably already thinks it is own idea even. "Leave this to me then, wherever he is we'll find him," Geoffrey signs the cheque with a flourish, handing it over to me at last.

This is what it takes to get my dues; the mires one has to cross.

* * *

Intellectually serious stuff, his isolated beings are blue and white paint mixed with sand. Here are the disintegrated faces of Beckett, Joyce and Yeats, portrayed with subtle flicks of yellow and reds. Le Brocquy lived in the South of France, as did Picasso, where there are fine wines. He speaks fluent French of course. He has a Chevalier de la Legion d'Honneur; scarlet riband and white enamelled five-ray crossed, double-pointed, each point tipped with a silver ball, with green enamelled wreath of oak and laurel. Observe the female head, symbolic of the Republique, surrounded by the blue riband bearing the words, *Republique Francaise 1870*. The reverse has two crossed tricolour flags with the wording, *Honneur et Patrie*.

It is hard to beat that, but there's much more to Ireland's most famous artist, would we even get a look in? A self-taught painter, he has regularly exhibited internationally and won major prizes. No, I wouldn't stand a chance, he is too rarefied to descend. His paintings hang alongside Hogarth, Constable, Blake, Picasso, Matisse, Mondrian, Braque, Kandinsky. My feeling is that the quantity of sales could be enormous: *Limited edition by Sleaters of Dublin. Designed by the Irish artist, Louis le Brocquy, and made by hand in the Republic of Ireland by... myself.*

On entering Grafton Street, I pass men maddened by the drink. Dear God, what a state to let yourself get in Ireland.

* * *

As though a strange arrival from the firmament of deep space, an occasional Irish silversmith can suddenly appear as a newly discovered star. The distant light becomes brighter, flashing mysteriously closer. This one survives in the old school house, Ballinaclash, Co. Wicklow, where one can occasionally hear the wolves of insecurity faintly howling above the valley, never far away.

Owl wise at night, the windows are lit and the sound of thymic hammering stops; a machine is turned on; it stops to be replaced by the rhythmic hammering again and through the window I can see a room of racks holding numerous shaped-metal stakes, hammer and files. There's a strangely constructed lathe, a rolling mill, press, ancient lead-capped vices and a tree stump with a flat iron attached.

Alone, secretive and cunning, the man moves with the concentrated stealth of a fox; from his bent, bald head comes an extended Optic Visor. A great locust of prehistoric times, a beetle at work, a moth at this late hour and light, extraordinary creations are strewn about. On white-washed rough-cut stone walls are copper green faces, darkly repellent, with designs that are intricately uncanny and puzzlingly ambiguous. He has the most creative imagination and wonderful technique. His artefacts are mounted on storm-torn slates found under nettles and thorns. On the bench, he has a magnificent, near-completed, silver pitcher, base chased on a stippled background, set with a jade handle. And — God Almighty — a shrine-like cover for a large book, a Bible most likely, magically woven in silver, set with semi-precious stones. For how many hours has he dared to fantasise No one else could or would do this without a customer in mind. He's completely unaware that I have entered.

"Are you right there Brian?" I ask and he is visibly startled.

"Jesus Christ, you gave me an awful fright! What are you doing here this late hour?"

"I had supper on the Vale View; just had to get out of the house for a while and be served a hot meal for a change. And come see you as well."

"A long way to come for something to eat," says Brian, a touch grumpily at being disturbed. Taking off his visor, he wears large round glasses over pale blue eyes.

"What are you making?"

"A christening spoon for a neighbour," he replies tired and wearisome, throwing it down before me. I pick up the quirky, little, grinning-faced bowl creation.

"Who's the book cover for? It's amazing."

"No one, I just felt like making it."

"There's hours of work in that Brian and the price of silver as well."

"God, don't I know, Eavon was complaining."

"Fair play to you, someone's bound to want it."

"Let's hope so."

With only half a bottle of red wine left, poured into coffee cups, I open the lavishly illustrated pages of a recent catalogue which he has obtained from London's Goldsmith's Hall. I'm envious at the work English silver-smiths are getting. Our conversation is inconsequential. I look around. Silversmithing here of all places is truly a heroic endeavour. I feel loneli-ness of the solitary artist's insecurity, his wondering each day whether any work will come.

* * *

I'm in the suburbs of Dublin's Northside, where the dismal, monotonous estates of St Columbus Heights, Rises and Avenue are located. Always driving late through the miasma of city streets, to avoid traffic, I am still uneasy in this territory. Approaching the broken remains of Swords Castle, I sense history's foul breath: Edward, the murderous Bruce, Boru lying gutted overnight under a sterile moon with Caravaggio-lit hooded figures murmuring above. The porch door I want is laminated shiny white: a long, narrow side window reflects my face. I look temporary and incidental.

Shane's familiar face appears behind the glass, subversive and apprehensive, dissolving on recognizing me. Bathed by Ireland's many historical grievances (he read avidly) he knew about many obscure men, such as martyred Bishop Conor O'Devaney or Father Patrick O'Loughran. He was drowned in Catholicism at an early age, and he has a unique understanding of jewellery formed early from George Bain's Celtic Art and is able to chase anything, such as panels of masterful composition on Joyce's very round Martello tower, resting on a garden of every flower mentioned in the famous book *Ulysses*. Is Shane Ireland's Florentine, Lorenzo Ghilberti? Nothing much is beyond his astonishing capabilities and the work he can do from his garden shed.

When I'm in the shed, I contemplate a complexity of interlacing limbs, bodies of humans, reptiles spiralling out of control, together with pictures of the Devil. Once angels momentarily illuminated the shed, said Shane, praeturnaturally proving the existence of God. After many lengthy phone calls, reverberating with orange and green, I know the story of his life like the back of my red hand. Shane attended with his father the forbidden football match, Ireland playing Yugoslavia.

Largely self-taught, he is an artist with a highly individual vision. I recently made a chalice for him to chase Pope John the twenty-third's coat of arms on. The triple crown, crossed keys, winged lion of St Mark holding the book of his gospel, and a fleur-de-lys on both side of a tower, (all wanted by a priest) are masterful. I'm here to collect the casting pattern he's making for the Lord Mayor's Awards. The three towers tipped red to be cast in nine carat gold, then cold enamelled blue. A nice little order every year or so and no bother over the price. Delivered to the Mansion House on Dawson Street and usually exchanged for a free cigar that Gerry the doorman nicks from the Lord Mayor's office for me.

"You have my job ready, Shane?"

"Indeed, I have sir, step in," he says light heartedly, opening the door.

The miraculous Dublin housewife's warm interior, spotless and with scents of flowers wafting faintly, whereas my cottage is beginning to have the hygienic appearance of a pigsty. Aidan is a smallish man, a true Celt one could say, dark curly hair and laughingly confrontational, not to be taken seriously but as I get to know him, I appreciate his raisin-coloured eyes never miss a trick and that he always remembers a slight long afterwards. I am shown into the sitting room and seated.

"I'll be back to you, this'll just take a minute."

I gaze at Van Gogh's night sky and sunflowers, I've experienced that he tends to be absent-minded, is the job even ready? Does it still need a final touch? For you can't hurry a good artist. Fame, honour and virtue are not easily attained on this island. Shane was born too late in the wrong place; he could have known Donatello if he lived then. What is he doing?

"Would you like a cup of tea or coffee?" his wife Mary asks, head around from the hallway. She is delicate and gay, the queen of his heart, an attractive mother earth with a backbone of steel. A woman of domestic virtue and common sense, who has to satisfy the dancing aurora of Shane's spiralling imagination.

"I'd love a strong coffee Mary, with just a little milk, no sugar."

"And where is that man of mine?" she says to herself as she disappears, calling, "will you hurry up Shane, you're keeping this good man waiting."

He appears eventually, holding a saucer-like paten with the finished design of the consecrated host, himself the dissolute priest. "Body of Christ, you fearful Protestant heretic, take, eat in remembrance this Body of Christ." He kneels before me, lowers the saucer towards me, giving a Mass for the amazing little jewel he's lifting, with casting spruce all ready to go. The words *Obedienta-Civium-Urbis-Felicitas* are perfectly readable, yet so small. I hold it for a while, silently admiring the craftsmanship. So much better than the old one I had previously made.

"That's perfect Shane, dare I ask you for an invoice?"

"Did I give you a price?"

"Ninety-six, including the VAT."

"Are you sure?" he looks puzzled.

"Yes, that's what you said, I've the cheque already made out," and I take it from my inside pocket and hand it to him. Shane scrutinizes the figure, somewhat upset.

"There was a lot of work in that, small that it is."

"I can well imagine, do you need more?"

"Ah no, I'm a man of my word. I'll get you an invoice for this then."

It was his own fault and so I do not make another offer. Mary puts a mug of coffee and a plate of assorted biscuits onto the small table, bending beside it. She is a golden triptych with ivory, delicate hands, a Monroe blonde. But I must get a grip.

"Has he left you again?"

"Just to get an invoice, he won't be long."

Soon I hear voices from the pair of them somewhere, seemingly far away... where are they?

"There you are now," says Shane returning with the invoice.

On glancing at it, I see that it is cunningly scripted. Shane sits himself opposite; it can't be helped it's done. He looks up, "how do you find the Assay these days?"

"They're ok, but you do have to check everything before leaving, and they're almost afraid to punch their marks deep."

"Well, wait till I tell you this. I had some donkeys in the other day, small charm-size, you know the sort, with creels of turf. Guess what they did to get an assay sample?"

"Nothing would surprise me."

"You won't believe this: they cut two of their tails off for samples!"

"God, I hope you kicked up a stink, Shane."

"That Gerry, you know the one, he said they had to get a sample and it would be no trouble for a man of my talents to make and attach two new ones. The cheek of him."

"My goodness Shane," I reply, concealing my amusement with difficulty, donkeys returned without tails. "I always give them a few bits of scrap for samples, usually does the trick for me. But they'll always need to make a few scrapings."

"And they were porous as well."

"Awkward all right."

Now he's becoming very strange, his words cease making sense, as in a dream. Donkeys without tails; fire stains; the mounting misdemeanours of the Assays office ... Mary calls him away to bed from the top of the stairs, I should be gone too and Swords isn't Freshford. Sadly, I return down the leafy Brennanstown Road. The moon goes in and out of clouds behind trees, the dramatic mysteries of night, the moment reminds me of Sebastiano del Piombo's pieta, with Jesus dead at her feet. And I turn into the cottage

CHAPTER 58

There's faint tapping on the window, a voice that's low and gentle, calling
me back to daylight's reality. Florrie has a message that someone is on the
phone; she is confused as to who. The caller must be patiently wondering
what sort of business am I running? I dress quickly and run ahead, with
her following slowly after, whatever she's saying. Drowsily sunning himself on the steps, Gambit doesn't bat an eye or move, the doors are wide
open and the unhooked phone is waiting: who could this be? Taking hold
of it, I wonder could this be a life changing moment?

"Yes, hello?"

"Can you meet us at the Shelbourne tomorrow at eleven?"

It is the smooth-talking Geoffrey from Sleaters, le Brocquy has agreed
to produce designs for me and wants to discuss how this should proceed.

"Have you seen them; what are they like?" I ask, surprised the idea has
taken hold.

"Yes, he posted them over from France. They're very abstract based on
heroic Irish sagas, I'm delighted he's agreed," explains Geoffrey, running
away with this now.

I'm delighted le Brocquy has agreed. It was in 1963 that I first met him,
in the Kilkenny stable yard with Walsh and Sir Basil, baronet, Goulding.

"I'll see you tomorrow there at eleven Geoffrey, well done," I put down
the phone and feel an upsurge of concern about what I am now getting
myself into.

Le Brocquy must be short of a few bob to get involved with Sleaters;
has he ever been inside there? Incomprehensible. It is any wonder that
Geoffrey arranged to meet at the Shelbourne. I must get this right from

the start, the price of gold and silver is ever changing, so I will want payment up front, written in black on white.

* * *

Geoffrey strides purposefully towards me, beaming. Grey stripe suited and matching tie on white, dressed to impress, the man about town, carrying a long cardboard tube, it has the blue stamps of the Republique's helmeted Lady Liberty.

"Let's have a look then," as I motion to take them.

"Not now, he'll be here soon," Geoffrey pulls them away, like a child with a new toy. No doubt le Brocquy will be late, as the elite usually are, building suspense and excitement before appearing. Five, ten, twenty minutes later, there he is with his wife; Geoffrey now becomes a fawning obsequious courtier. A table and three chairs are available in the lounge, with difficulty we find a fourth.

"Coffee for everyone?" asks Geoffrey.

"No, no, we can't stay long and we're just had our breakfast," replies le Brocquy.

His blonde wife Anne is dressed colourfully, she is young and noticeable, wearing black-laced, high heeled boots. While he is in soft muted grey and blues, with his familiar low-countries appearance.

"I met you in Kilkenny with Bill Walsh, it must be well over fifteen years ago; he was showing you and Sir Basil Goulding around the stables." I say, looking at him; he doesn't reply, acknowledging me only with a weak smile.

Geoffrey turns to me blankly; Anne shuffles her feet, head down. Is there a fleeting sense of embarrassment at my attempting familiarity? Geoffrey pops the plastic lid at one end of the tube and pulls out the designs. There are bold circular red abstractions, I've seen them somewhere before. The paint has been swirled around, allowed to fall by chance into these shapes of barely-controlled chaos. Rotating galaxies, a foetus, molecular cloud, writhing snakes, dog sick, leftover dinner on a plate. Ochain, Dubán and Lámthapad, each one named as a shield from the warriors of the eighth century epic, *Táin Bó Cúailnge*. I was never into those cattle raids and bloody Cuchulainn blarney, the Hound of Ulster resisting the armies of Medb and Ailill, queen and king of Connacht.

It is clever enough, I suppose; he's certainly hit on something all right, as they draw me into eerie mists of half memory.

"So how shall you use these?" Geoffrey asks from afar. All eyes are upon me, looking puzzled. I take up each design while they wait expectantly. I enjoy the moment, deliberating.

"They seem to lend themselves to plain silver bowls, flattish about an inch deep and eight wide. They'll have to be etched and then gilded or oxidized to contrast the design against the silver. We could even do them in twenty-carat gold, which has the uniquely Irish fleur-de-lys hallmark and would be quite something." They listen intently as I explain to them.

"If someone has a pen I'll do a rough sketch." Geoffrey immediately produces a flash ballpoint out of nowhere, clicking the point down.

"Can I draw on these," I ask le Brocquy.

"Oh, yes, please do," he replies ever so encouragingly.

I draw a cross-section roughly the size of the bowls I have in mind, then in three dimensions to give them an idea. "There you go, simple enough, the design standing boldly out from the inside of the bowl," I say hoping they will agree. Le Brocquy studies the sketches without comment.

Anne leans into him affectionately and he turns to her, "what do you think darling?" he asks.

"Yes, it looks fine, but we'd need a made-up sample first," she says, too easily eyeing it over.

"Should be most interesting, definitely yes. Certainly, a sample of each, for in Ireland the attitude so often is, sure it'll do. This has to be right for me to be involved." How easily he speaks of wanting all three. "You're getting Kilkenny to design the boxes and brooches you said," continues le Brocquy, turning to Geoffrey.

"Yes, with your approval of course, and we'll have these samples for you as soon as possible," Geoffrey answers, pointedly glancing at me to get a move on: you heard what he said.

* * *

Geoffrey heads across to the top of Grafton Street, with me following well behind the pair into Kildare and the Taylor Galleries. The arrangement requires no sweat on their part. Whereas I will have to wait for their approval indeed. What am I getting into? I need to find someone to etch and the bowls will have to be spun, so the Spinner will know everything. These designs now, were they illustrations for a book I once saw?

Standing by the railings of the Green the first autumn leaves are already underfoot, when I recognize Paul Hogan, on crutches, drawing nearer. As he has not noticed me, I let him pass on. Those early years when I knew him are long gone, but also it can seem like only yesterday that he was with Mary and I the Freshford wedding. Whatever happened to him? I stop to watch his slow progress, with morose thoughts at his disability and on the disintegrating effects of time. I drive home to turn le Brocquys abstractions into concrete silver form.

* * *

There's an ethereal presence on Killiney Hill. To the far horizon of the Irish sea, under ancient woods covering deep hollows and giant lichen-covered stones, impatient dogs scamper down the steep steps, freed from their owners' leads, but always checking to look back for them. The land abruptly rises through pine trees and gorse covered slopes to an ugly galvanized radio mast, a bricked-up tower and the sheer drop at the top of the old quarry's blasted face. From here came the stone that built Dun Laoghaire harbour.

Dublin stretches out beyond the Poolbeg power station's twin chimneys. Much further north, I can imagine that I can see the Promised Land of God's chosen, the thirteenth tribe of Israel, besieged Ulster's good Protestant people. Going nowhere in particular, by chance this evening, I make my way towards Dalkey Island Hotel.

Cars are filling the adjacent car park, as dim figures hurry towards the brightly lit entrance. Hush-voiced, with seemingly illicit intentions, there is an air of subdued excitement here; I might as well go in. The bar upstairs is busy enough and there is a man there I know from the post office in South Anne Street. I acknowledge his mischievous greeting; his eyes are alight, as if something is afoot. Bearer of whispered, manly tales, Conor Doyle has the appearance of an Irish Traveller, the man with the piebald pony and trap, wiry and quick, who doesn't miss a trick.

"Are you looking for women?" he asks, beside me now.

"What makes you think that?" For wouldn't be such a bad idea.

"Sure, this is one of the best places to come, though Alcoholic Anonymous is hard to beat, where the women are vulnerable and grateful for the interest you show and easy to please."

"Well I certainly didn't know that Con; I've never been here before."

"Go on with you now." He cocks his knowing head and closes one eye disbelieving.

"This is all new to me Con, so where are these women anyway?"

"Downstairs in the basement, it's always the singles night dance on Thursdays. A great hunting place, plenty of choice from single, separated and the married. Some of these older ones will give you a great ride, if you play your cards right," he says knowingly.

"Aren't you married Con?"

"Ah, sure never mind that. She threw me out of the bed one night and said never again; it was her Catholic upbringing and couldn't be helped. So I says to her, don't expect me to remain celibate for the rest of my life. And we have a sort of arrangement now and she doesn't seem to mind what I do."

"And you're still living together?"

"Oh yes, we've two children, so there'd be too much bother and expense separating and she's glad to be without the sex, as some women are you know," he explains incredulous, as if it is a dark and hidden secret, most unnatural. "So, what'll you have? Then I'll take you below."

"Here let me get this Con." I catch the barman's attention for a glass of Smithwicks and a pint of cider for him.

"You shouldn't be without a woman to ride most nights, it's what life is all about." He speaks adamantly.

"Is that right?"

"I know I'm right, the rest is just shite!" He is strangely likeable, generous and light hearted, whether you'd believe him or not. Spreading the good news of what is (seemingly) available out there, maybe sensing something's missing in me.

"There's a bird down there I know would suit you just fine. I've bottled her a good few times myself, likes a jar and loves a good ride, lovely tits and get her started right, she's juicy as a ripe peach between the legs and boyohboy when she comes, she erupts like a howling dog, I tell you now."

"You're something else Con."

"I used to fuck her when she was drunk, leaving her home in the car outside her flat. But listen a word of advice, don't be spending money on them, no fancy restaurants to impress. Maybe a few drinks at the most. That usually gets you the job for a while, then you can move on when they start getting serious and wanting more. Come on and I'll introduce you to herself." Curious and quickened, I follow this pirate of female flesh, this serial philanderer, to the crowded, hot basement below.

"Will you just look at these boyos standing around. There's nothing more vulnerable than a man looking for his hole! Now do you see the little dark one over there talking to her friend, who's incidentally a great ride. I could never get it away with her, very nearly did once but not quite, and didn't she make me wet me bloody pants." Con nods towards the two seated women, who are smiling over weakly at him. "In a way you have to hand it to them though, letting us men put our dirty ould dicks up them. Do you know what I mean?" Con muses to himself, then, "see the tall one, in the greenish jacket, with yer man in a white shirt."

"Sort of blue with the grey skirt?"

"That's her all right, you be wary of her, the husband committed suicide, threw himself in front of the Dart. Leave her well alone, she's a fucking spacer."

"What makes you say that?"

"After I rode the arse of her on the first and only night, she pushed me off and screamed the place down. Threw a vase at me, a big heavy yoke it was too, broke into pieces. Don't get me wrong though, she was all for it at first, must have been a sudden feeling of guilt or something afterwards. The ghost of her dead husband maybe. You can never tell with women I tell you, they're the strangest of creatures."

"What do you mean Con?" It is hard enough to hear him, with the loud music and many voices. There comes a strange and sudden transformation in him. Like a fused light bulb switching to darkness, he becomes one with his distant forebears under the heavy burden of Celtic superstition. I can imagine him covered by animal skins and a participant in fearful bog sacrifices.

"I'm from Galway you know and as a child I must have been about eleven or twelve at the time. There was this ould one, ah, sure she was probably no more than thirty-five or forty, for you know the way children are when it comes to the ages of grown-ups. She lived in a thatched cottage on her own, across some fields from where we lived. So one evening when it was nearly dark, with a friend we peeped into her lit back window and Jesus we nearly died..." says Con, pausing.

"So what did you see?"

"She was down in her hands and knees naked, being fucked by her dog!"

"You're not serious?"

"On my mother's grave, I swear to you. We used to come most nights, in the hope she would be at it again."

"It must have been a big dog."

"And black as the devil, we thought it was, and she a witch. It became an obsession with us for all of a year. We never told anyone, for who'd have believed us there anyway. She had a right queer look and you could smell her in passing; she wore bright red lipstick, which was unusual in the country for those days. I'll always remember that too. In a way I think she even knew, leaving her curtains open, not caring. Can you imagine, in Holy Catholic Ireland!"

"Jesus." Why does he have to tell me all this?

"Yes, you wouldn't know what goes on behind closed doors in this country, we're all savages at heart, in spite of all the pious nonsense we get from the pulpit. Did you know Dublin was once the slave capital of Europe many years ago?"

"No I didn't, that's news to me."

"Well it was, I read it from a history book recently, there's a lot we don't know about our past and the church for that matter, it's well worth looking into it." All the while he talks, Con scrutinizes intensely the dancing couples and those seated around the floor.

"There's the one I have in mind for you, just ended a relationship and she's married as well. But don't let that put you off. See the short-haired blonde with the fat one? Together by the far corner."

"I think so, yes."

"Well, away with you now, I'll try the young chick on her own, the one just come in." His narrowing eyes focus like a snake on its prey.

I identify the woman I think he means for me. She is sitting sideways, nose sharp and nicely curved, a touch pointed too, saying she is not to be messed with. The shape of the nose is as important as their legs. Without saying a word, I hold out both arms, inviting her.

She's certainly surprised and gets up with a fluttering smile, to the annoyance of her fat friend who was in full flow, telling her something, but who is now glaring at me. I guide my parnter into the maelstrom, she is a mature woman and shoulder height to me, I look down on her big brown eyes. Her hair smells of cigarettes and something that makes me think of the wild woman, wreathed round the temples and loins with laurel leaves. I sense her approval from her movements; she is getting closer.

She's the one Con said would… well, we shall see. Con has the young chick he targeted beside him now and he gives me a lascivious grin, winking and putting his thumbs up behind her back, saying, go, go for it man, go. Her first words will connect to a yes or no immediately, they are make or break. I'm not going to ask her does she come here often. Yet despite the intensity of the moment, my thoughts stray. I have to get pure alcohol and boric acid from Dix in Aston Quay to mix and paint over six sugar bowls before soldering their bases on, or they'll be covered in fire stain for Weldon.

I remember now that once, when I was bringing a parcel to his counter, Con explained to me the way that women are. In the morning, without their makeup is a fright and that's the time to get out fast. But is there really any difference? All flesh and bone has to die in the end. I will have to get the etchings right for le Brocquy's bowls, even if no-one would know the difference but himself. And there's a statement to pay from Johnson Matthey.

She is the colour of vanilla ice cream, dessert sweet and tobacco sour in the trickery of enclosed lighting, where her message is becoming clear.

"Did you know Dublin was once the slave capital of Europe?"

"Well fair play to you, I'd never have known," she says haughtily, deep throated, lightning quick, the west of Ireland somewhere.

"Con Doyle told me that, you know him I believe, as he pointed you out to me just now."

"Well, did he indeed?" Raising her nose (yes, a very nice one) she draws back as if from a bad smell, not wanting to comment any further.

From the long evening walk on the eroding shoreline of the sweep of Kilkenny Bay, to Con's talk, and now to the concluding phantasmagoria of a pagan dance. It is time to leave. And yet the prospect of returning to the empty cottage alone is enormously crushing. I've work to be done, being here is only a distraction here. The anticipation is always much tastier than an act that can sometimes only take a minute or so to consumate. Escorting her back to her friend, who's like a suspicious hen hatching a poisonous egg, I undecided about what to do.

"Will we see you again?" she asks.

"I need to go to the loo first." I smile weakly to her, unable to resist inclining the head positively.

"Well how did you get on?" Con is suddenly beside me undoing his fly hurriedly.

"I think she wants me to ask her out."

"You're on a winner there then, so don't be hesitating, I tell ye."

Unashamedly taking out his member, I can't help thinking it an absurd attachment and so small for all the pleasure it supposedly gives. He lets out a great gush of unusually phosphorous-coloured pee, flooding the butt-blocked bowl. "Whoo there she goes... now you can do the same to yer one and the relief will be so much greater," says he shaking it dry, knees bending, putting it away.

"What about yourself Con, how did you get on with the one you fancied?"

"Game ball, I'll bottle her in a day or two, not tonight though, I'm jacked. You're the lucky one, so don't even hesitate."

"What's her name?"

"It's Maria, she's a school teacher, moved to Booterstown recently, not far from where you are," he explains as he washes his hands, flicking the excess penguin-like on the floor, at the pull-out towel that's wet with no more give. "Jesus, I hate these feckin yokes, they're all the same." He gives it a thump, then faces the mirror and carefully combs his hair and turns and says, "you'd better hurry or she'll be gone.

CHAPTER 59

I waken to a new world. The cottage is invaded with an unfamiliar, sweet and sour smell. She is now breathing, still sleeping. Some of my items have moved mysteriously; there is a shock of scattered clothes, skimpy bits of cardinal red shout loudly amongst my shirt, underwear and crumpled trousers. How did this happen? And who is this carelessly generous person, with her charms. She never hesitated and was like a pawing cat, with contented yelps and murmuring pleasures from head to toe, as I slowly explored her reckless nakedness. Hers was a gift. It was as if a final cry of Irish womanhood was lighting a fire of defiance against the dark forest of Irish history. She's beyond caring. I believe that her glowing complexion proves this is good for a woman's health and wellbeing.

"Are you leaving me?" She appears at the door wearing my coat, without make-up on. I wonder what Con would think, to my eyes she looks well.

"Yes, but only for an hour or so."

"Will you get me twenty Silk Cut?" and now she's suddenly an unwelcome intrusion. A dishevelled demanding stranger, bare footed, returning to my bed without another word. Twenty Silk Cut indeed, getting her priorities right first thing this morning. Elastic and fast-moving memories beckon through time as shadows in sunshine and soft rain. I can see the face of Mary, Mary Malone, who once-upon-a-time softly enveloped me. So, get out of my bed Maria whoever you are and go home. Or is this the future for me? Who can tell what is to come? I gaze down upon her in the first light, troubled.

At the Assay, Gerry is a touch grumpy; rolling his eyes towards heaven having heard my instructions so many times before. And he's no fool. Leaving through the freakishness of the Ship Street entrance, I observe how two parallel worlds drift aimlessly far apart, as always. The cod intricacies of hallmarking. Then I return to the school teacher waiting in the cottage for her twenty Silk Cut. I don't have to get them, but will, considering her generosity last night.

When I return she's still in bed, so I leave her well alone and in any case there's work to get done. Anxious, I'm aware that another person is invading the innermost secrets of my livelihood. Putting on the filthy, torn blue warehouse overall, a dust respirator mask, head covered in a knitted wool hat, it must surely be as a sinister spectre as I now start to polish.

I was Saint John Chrysostom, living in solitude until visited by her. Sinning. And she did say it would be all right as her monthlies had long dried up at an early age. But I'm not happy to be seen like this, vulnerable and awkward, a lowly self-employed artisan tradesman. She has been watching. For how long? I was unaware due to the noise of the polishing motor?

"Did you get my cigarettes, I'm dying for a smoke?"

"You'll be dying all right with that filthy habit, haven't you heard what it does to your lungs."

"Oh, do shut up, it's none of your business; did you get them?" It's the cry of addiction.

"Yes, they're in my jacket pocket."

It is difficult to concentrate, with her sitting on the low wall just outside the shed watching, still in my coat, and smoking.

"You look really weird, what are you doing?"

"I wish I knew sometimes; these are silver rings I've made and am now finishing."

"So you're a jeweller."

"Silversmith really."

"Well I never, how interesting. I teach, myself."

"Should you not be at classes then?"

"No, I'm taking the day off."

"How do you manage that?"

"I'm entitled to so many sick days, so I might as well take them all."

"But you're not sick."

"I know, but it's Friday, so a long weekend for me."

"Will you lose pay?"

"Oh no."

"Lucky you," I reply, knowing I must collect the assay later and work tomorrow and Sunday to deliver on Monday as promised. It is difficult to find time for so laid-back a woman as this, sitting there calmly smoking, with her fine pair of crossed high-heel-shaped legs well exposed, making it difficult for me to concentrate. There is obviously something on offer again. Such uninhibited availability. She flicks away her cigarette and shares with me a knowing glance, giggling coquettishly, whatever I want I can have. Positioning her with each hand on the left and right spindle of the motor, as I remember doing with another, I bend her forward, lifting the coat up, entering from behind the well-rounded flower of Ireland. I'm almost annoyed at the distraction but unable to resist. Her loud sounds, on the other hand, say that she is thrilled to be fucked by a masked stranger in his garden shed. How dangerouns and kinky. She'll do just fine.

Without a clean cloth to wipe it away, I must leave the whiff of sperm. The lustre and carmine-coloured rouge of her sex is the same as her lips.

"You know where the bathroom is if you want to go first."

"Oh, Jesus Christ you must be a Protestant." She pulls away, confronting me disdainfully.

"Why do you think that?"

"It's what we've been brought up with. Prods are always cautious, clean and tidy, counting the pennies and quick to wash away the mess of too careless Catholic procreation without contraceptives. You are, I can tell."

"Yes, but a non-believer."

"Non-believer indeed. A Protestant is always a Protestant, it's in your genes, in your blood anyway, non-believer or not. Always a Protestant. Asking me last night was it safe to stay in. I immediately knew."

"You didn't want to get pregnant, did you?"

"No, I didn't, but there are times when you should throw caution to the wind."

"And live with the consequences long after."

"Maybe, but life is short and anyway I'll leave you alone and do as you suggest."

"Make yourself a cup of coffee and have a piece of toast, I've to go into town this afternoon," I say to her as she disappears.

The inside of the overall will have to do. This must get finished. Work is the only sanity and I recall the the saying of a wise old Chinese proverb: when sudden disarray comes about unexpectedly, remember to carry on as usual, do the work that you know best.

Eventually, I hear the front door close and her car starting. There was no farewell. That was as intimate an experience as one can get, an unexpected cornucopia from this generous Galway woman. She has left, but remains in small ways as I notice certain pleasant changes. She made the bed; tidied the bathroom; kitchen; washed the dishes; cooker and picked a lovely white rose from the side of the cottage, placing it in a glass of water on top of the mail.

There is an unwelcome, familiar, harped brown envelope from the Revenue Commissioners and on opening it I read: *Collector-General Division,* on a wavy pink sheet with green and black type. *I acknowledge receipt of the payments below with thanks. In all correspondence please quote Registration No 9271833S Notice No: 00718339 – 0004T* ... and so on scanning the sheet. The sheer banality of the document, after last night and this morning, causes me to throw it back on the table and dash the crumpled envelope against the wall, where the four striped medallist Group Captain of the Royal Air Force stares sternly down upon me from beneath the gold braided peak of his cap. forever the stranger in this troubled land.

* * *

On the radio is another atrocity, a reminder of where I am living just now. Irish Republicanism, today at least, has the dark instinct for horror found lurking in old antiquity and pagan ritual. A demand for victims and a prostration before the dreadful abstractions of nationhood and the dead. Their activies are from the fanciful romance of Ireland's mysterious twilight landscape, such as the delicate tiny pink and purple flowery veils that cascade over the old high walls behind me. Through rising mists and golden imaginings, Mary's still there and waiting. The vision quickly disappears when I open an assay parcel containing far too many cod Irish pieces to sort. I am descending into mediocrity and madness even.

Maria drifts in and out of the cottage whenever the mood is upon her. The pattern seems to be that she stays overnight on Holy days, and all these many sick days. For midterm breaks, she stays a whole week and of course she has three long months of summer holidays as well as weeks at Easter and Christmas. So like unto golden hooks, *she with flattering smiles weak hearts doth guide.* At times, it seems I have made a pact with the Devil. Eve, in skimpy cardinal red underwear, looks for vice in the arms of a satyr. And there is a high price for this, as I soon discover. Maybe I should have listened to Con's advice. I'm told that a dress by Diane von Furstenberg from Brown Thomas would be nice. Also, comes the question, where are you taking me to dinner tonight?

"For a gentleman would never expect a lady to put her hand in her pocket," says she, a little too often. For the moment, it is worth paying, but these requests create in me an ineffable feeling of fragile impermanence. Abducted by naked witchcraft, disguised as a national school teacher, she's bound to move on from me. She's not going to wait around for entertainment and company from June to September.

* * *

For a while I recover from schizophrenia, as le Brocquy's bowls eventually turn out right and I gain the order of designing a new chain-of-office for the Deputy Lord Mayor.

Where does one begin with a commision like that? In the thirteenth century, naturally, using the Dublin City seal as the reverse side for a change. *SIGILLUM COMMUNE CIVIUM DUBLINIE* is deeply engraved around a full-sailed ship with a pennant on the mast and an anchor at the bow. Embattled platforms rise fore and aft, each carrying a figure blowing a horn. Below the sail a man wears a crown, standing by a chainmailed helmeted soldier, as another's about to drink a goblet of wine. There's a sailor behind and all are afloat on a choppy sea full of fish. Such quirky and wonderful minute details, taken from the mind of the hell-haunted middle ages. I cast it in nine carat gold, taken from a rubber mould poured on the original. This should do nicely, as the main part hangs below the collar, which is made from linked scenes telling the story of Dublin, with the Liffey flowing down from top to bottom, it will take a few days to draw all this out on paper for them to consider.

"Are you going to be working all day?" Maria asks, looking over from the front door, about to open it.

"I have to, yes."

"Well then I'm off, byeee."

So be it, as this has to be done. Studying the picture of the old seal (created at least seven hundre years ago), I'm drawn towards the man who made it. Really, it is much the same then as it is today: metals; sky; sunshine and rain, whatever about happiness. The everyday brutality of burnings and beheadings have now been replaced with those of a revolver or rifle and a fast getaway. Melancholy, like a shadowing cloud covering the Carrickmines valley on a summer's afternoon, I attempt on paper to portray Dublin's past on twenty-five linked panels: a toxic mixture starting with the first Viking longships and ending with the Easter rebellion. I sort out in sequence Strongbow's shield and his Normans, scaling the city's walls. Henry the Fouth's forget-me-not inscribed silver gilt-handled sword, that he presented to Dublin in 1409. The spire of St Patrick's cathedral and, say, the argent saltire of Garret More, the great Earl of Kildare. Sprinkle it with Tudor roses and the arrival of Oliver Cromwell or should it be King William? The Great Mace of Dublin takes me to Molly Malone's wheelbarrow and the thought of Mary brings sadness again. Oisin Kelly's statue of Larkin in O'Connell Street; the Lord Mayor's coat of arms and those ever-present seagulls. The Reformation's split chalice of wine or Christ's blood; Joyce's Martello Tower; the plain people of Dublin to the Ha'penny Bridge; not forgetting a large rat for those of this trade, who would steal my copyright and patent without my knowing. Gazing over the GPO on fire towards the Dublin mountains, nature is indifferent and at peace, the sun is smiling above. Sure, I could even put Langrishe, eating his shepherd's pie in the Kildare Street Club. It all comes slow and easy, drawn as if I was part of it all.

There's a budget of six thousand pounds that Arthur Guinness generously donated to design and make it and it is a most interesting commission to get. It came from supplying a pair of silver napkins to a feisty lady. She was part of an inner circle of master wardens and brethren from the Corporation and the Assay Office and was hoping to be soon nominated as one of the brethren, with her dusty, recently acquired, knowledge of hallmarks and antique silver plate. She stands a good chance as becoming the first woman ever in the long history of the Irish assay since the reign of Charles the First.

Too much work is, curiously, as bad as none sometimes, for customers can't be kept waiting, or they'll go to another person soon enough. Orders can suddenly stop. And then too come the stomach-wrenching feelings on discovering my designs displayed in a shop window, on sale even more cheaply than I could make them for. Never mind rewarding the ingenuity of my originality. *Stop me if you can*, is the message that emanates from them. *It's going to cost you a fortune in convoluted legality*.

Who is going to make this chain of office? I would need a whole month and more without interruptions to finish it myself. So I'm away to Ballinaclash with the design to put it in the capable hands of Brian Clarke who agrees to start. There he's at one with the amazing display of the starlings, whose ever-changing formations sweep the evening sky, surviving the attacks of predatory hawks, which are unable to penetrate the flock.

The tiny village of Ballinaclash is not of this world. It is an outrageous dreamland where imagination thrives so well. Formed by luxurious airs, it is a momentary land of sweetness and light. Here, I enter a make-believe place of what should be. There are gentle words and the sound of silver whispering ever so faintly (so I can never quite grasp what it is saying) amongst the sloping fields and thick, blackthorn hedges. The land rises to fir plantations and the purple coloured high ground of County Wicklow. His wife, Eavon, is a mysterious woodland queen, all flowing white astride a unicorn, quickly disappearing with the magic that is found in the old school house of Ballinaclash and surroundings.

* * *

On a cold and late November evening, I am going along the dimly lit corridors of the Four Courts with barrister de Blacam and McAuliffe's pretty assistant, Kate Tooher. I have a fearful sense of being buried beneath the massively intimidating, classical, domed structure. The bewigged, strutting vultures of the legal profession embody legal absurdity in motion. Here I can feel the breath of history, the real theatre of Irish life, past and present. An air of subterfuge, lies and treachery lurks menacingly in every room. I think of the famous Curran, who defended the United Irishmen. Or Emmet's final speech from the dock and his ghastly sentence of being hanged, drawn and quartered for treason against the Crown, handed down to him by the notorious hanging judge Lord Norbury. But it is even more shocking today, as Peter Pringle has been found guilty and sentenced to hang for a bank robbery in Ballaghaderreen where a garda was shot. It is in every newspaper, on television and radio.

I haven't seen or heard from Peter in nearly ten years. I always liked the man, in spite of his beliefs; are they really going to hang him? The circle turns, nothing much changes. I find it hard to understand.

I shouldn't be here, but my History of Ireland design was stolen. This is my creation but they tried to take it by flinging base lies and legality at me, trying to frighten me away. There is a profusion of accusatory letters between McAuliffe and his solicitor on Upper Fitzwilliam Street. I have to go through such time-consuming legal expense to stop them. The cute whores exemplified, brazen without conscience, they're going to hold out to the bitter end.

Antiquated phrases I never heard before are put before me. It is raining Affidavits and Equity Civil Bills, Book of Pleadings and a correspondence of over forty letters showing the nature and grounds of their Defence. A Mandatory Injunction is issued, directing the Defendant to forthwith deliver to the Plaintiff all dies and other devices in its possession and used by it to manufacture copies of the Plaintiff's designs on the defandant's Newgrange spirals, Ogham-lettered names, the numerous, carved, standing stone, miniature gold and silver copied crosses.Man bites dog is engraved on whiskey measures from the Book of Kells; the Warrior Shield Brooch is based on the original shield found in Lough Gur, County Limerick; the Moylough Brooch found from the seventh century AD and there are various other artificats and twisted torcs. And my History of Ireland jewellery, the cheek.

For nearly two years like a malignant disease, the legal case continues, with constant deliberating, until finally, at the door of Chuirt Chuarda, they agree to stop and pay up: undertaking not to reproduce my designs in Ireland or elsewhere, without the license of the Plaintiff.

My satisfaction is somewhat diminished on getting McAuliffe's bill, but I have made a reasonable profit nevertheless. And it was well worth protecting the unique, cod-Irish design, which brings a steady income, even if at times I feel like drowning in the stuff. Lying awake in the bedroom beside Maria I stare out the half-curtained window at the racing moonlit brushed clouds. She could be dead on a mortuary table, so motionless and mentally frozen is she. Turning away, fearful. First love, my love, amorphous and both unable to comprehend it. From intimacy and laughter to ... what is it Con said about women?

I remember the lonely bog land road again between Pettigoe and Donegal. I was with Pringle then, who now is jailed, waiting apprehensively to die. Maybe not though. Is it their subconscious wish? I'm mindful of Pearse's words: *without the shedding of blood there is no redemption.* No matter who the dead are.

My real Ireland lies by Ballynoe Stone Circle, or even with the remains of Knocktopher Abbey and that first evening at Kells and Kilree's Round Tower and High Cross. I am forever on the road from Kilkenny to Freshford; my thoughts multiply incomprehensively. For it's not Mary beside me.

"So what are we doing today?" Maria asks hopefully.

I know I have to work on le Brocquy's bowls, with an order for two sets of three, amazing, in twenty carat gold. Their etched shapes take hold of me in a curious fashion, the abstraction evoked from his powerful imagination is of the heartfelt sadness, beauty and mystery of Ireland. It is necessary to finish these, even if Maria's not going to wait around. Whatever she does is her own affair.

I drive down to Ballilnaclash every week checking with Brian until he has the Deputy Lord Mayor's chain completed. Then to the Mansion House with it, nicely cased, fitted in blue and white satin. I'm shown into the stately, honey-coloured, plum-blue furnished drawing room by Gerry, who wants a quick look at the chain. Reluctantly, I open the box to show him.

"Jesus that's a great lookin' yoke, how much are you gettin' for that?" He is unable to resist touchin it and it is with difficulty that I prevent him from taking it out.

"Six thousand Gerry, and to be honest, it hardly covers the cost of materials and labour."

"Get away with you now, I'm sure it's more than enough, the Mayor will be delighted," he stares down at the chain, shaking his head. "I'll let him know you're here, he's with someone at the moment, but he shouldn't be long, have a seat and make yourself at home."

The Mayor this year is an undertaker I believe. Alone, I savour such splendid quietude. On the near wall is a large portrait of the Earl of Westmoreland, Lord Lieutenant of Ireland 1790, with sword, wearing a brown, brightly buttoned slanting coat, silk stockings and black buckle shoes. The blue sash of the Garter (or is it The Most Illustrious Order of St Patrick) rests over his left shoulder? It's hard to tell in this light whether it's dark blue or sky blue. His back and shoulders are covered by a long, crimson, gold-threaded cloak and mantle of ermine, which has an extraordinary gold and enamelled collar, linked with knots of cords, discs that are vaguely harps and crowns. The centre has a large crowned harp from which hangs a circular, gold-rimmed, saucer-size medallion of a shamrock with the argent saltire of St Patrick superimposed upon it, hanging to his navel. The powdered wig comes just below his ears, eyes look to the left, a touch pensive on his aristocratic, handsome pale face. He holds a rolled parchment in his left hand.

On the adjoining wall, either side of the late Georgian mirror, over the fancy tiled, Doric-column-sided, black marble fireplace and matching clock are two enormous portraits in magnificent rococo-carved gilt wood frames. One has George Viscount Townshend, Lord Lieutenant and General Governor of Ireland 1771, leaning on shaded dark furniture, standing on his stockinged left leg with the other nonchalantly crossed over it. He wears tight blue breeches, high heeled brown leather buckled shoes, a turquoise waistcoat embroidered with gold thread, an elaborate red-layered coat edged with gold, alternating red and white borders left open, clasped at his throat, beneath ermine or similar material over the shoulders and behind to the left side, draped abundantly down and out onto the floor. There's an open-facing letter in his right hand that can hardly be read and what could be his own short grey hair, neatly tufted at the back of his round, fair pinkish head. His was an affable presence I would say.

The other Lord Lieutenant is the Earl of Northumberland. At first sight he seems all dazzling silvery-white and rose-reds. He wears tights and frilly shorts, a mantle of blue velvet lined with taffeta and the encircled red cross of The Most Noble Order of the Garter, which is barely visible at his shoulder. Visible too are the hilt of sword and a golden cord of twisted strands from his neck to a large tassel between his thighs. He has a collar of gold, composed of alternative buckled garters, each encircling a red enamel rose, with knots of cords enamelled white. Suspended from the collar is an enamelled figure of St George fighting the dragon. On his left leg below the knee, a garter of dark blue velvet and gold bears the motto, *Honi soit qui mal y pense* in golden letters. I know it well. He's wearing somethig like gilded sandals. Obviously he was a man of command and substance, this emanates from his stern, chalk-white face and the way his right hand is perched on his hip, the other resting on the lining of his mantle. Bending closer, I see it was painted by Sir Joshua Reynolds even, in 1765.

Feeling disorientated and dizzy, I am unable to resist the fine detail on all three. Taking a seat on the thick buttoned, peach pillowed sofa, I gaze up to the ring of bulb lights hanging from feathery wheels above them on the ceiling. They seem to be spinning, spinning somehow in the company of these long dead, born-to-rule Englishmen. What am I doing here? I sense the same thoughts from them too. These surroundings are a rich dessert to be slowly savoured if only time would hold. Sunshine is streaming through the high, open-shuttered windows, brightening the room and warmly embracing me. I see myself reflected in the mirror, an extraordinary and mysterious transformation of Irishness. I'm captivated and on the edge of answering the real mystery. Ireland is wayward yet sublime, I am a child again in the comforting arms of Hibernia, soporific and content with the whole Irish experience, no longer ill at ease. This is where I want to be, here.

Hearing footsteps and boisterous laughter approaching outside, I'm suddenly confused, wanting to hurriedly awaken out of this heady phantasmagoria. Facing me is Dublin's Lord Mayor, Councillor Stafford, wearing a dark, double-breasted suit, pristine white shirt, blue and white striped tie. He is followed by Charlie Haughey's son, Sean, who is easily recognisable, identically suited but with a tie of navy and pink spots on blue. The city's coat-of-arms of blue and red enamel is suspended from a gold Celtic-inspired chain around his shoulders. Then as now, this new republic continues the tradition of wearing fancy gold chains and rightly so.

The friendly moustached, grey-haired Lord Mayor is in his late forties I'd say, his hair is receding. Haughey is shorter and younger, pinch faced, with thinning brown hair parted to one side. Are they looking at me in a funny sort of way? Like they suspect me of drinking? Introducing themselves, I find it strange to shake hands in the flesh, so unreal is the moment at first.

"So you're the man with our new chain, we've been looking forward to this, isn't that so Sean?" greets the effusive Lord Mayor, turning to his companion, who is quietly confident as an elected parliamentarian, son of someone important. He has the touch of the black-arts politician with the right connections. I sense that the pair of them are as mischievous as school boys and are in for a bit of malarkey here.

Fingers crossed then, I take up the case, made compliments of Yeomen Case Co, sixty Albion Street, Birmingham, good-hearted (if a little rushed), well-made British craftsmanship. I rest it on the fat arm joining the back of the sofa and open it. Silver on blue, ancient and modern, the story of Dublin, hopefully to their liking.

"Whoo, look at that Sean, did you ever see such a yoke?" Both are clearly intrigued, but are ominously silent for a moment though.

"So what do the symbols mean? I can recognize the city seal all right," the Mayor asks. Didn't he see the drawings that explained each link?

"The story of Dublin from earliest times, Vikings and Strongbow, around to the present, there you have the Easter rebellion with the GPO on fire and that's Larkin and..."

"I see, I see," he interrupts, bending closer. "How very clever, what do you think Sean?"

"You better try it on to see how it fits; it's enormous," Sean replies, taking the chain out of the case. Up above the Mayor's head it goes and is lowered on to his shoulders. Then he walks over to the mirror to look at himself, swaying strangely, with his arms outstretched. "Would you know me now Sean?" he asks mischievously.

"You look like Brian Boru in that gear, here let me have a go." Sean is eager to try the chain, awkwardly helping the Mayor take it off and putting it on. But he's in the wrong side of the crossing chain, so the seal slides down to his crotch, looking ridiculous now.

"You have it on wrong, lift it over your head and lower it again with the crossing chain behind your neck and shoulders. Here I'll show you how," I do it for him, but it hardly looks much better.

"Jesus, Sean if your father could see you now, he'd be so proud." The Mayor is taking the piss, laughing as Sean goes to the mirror. It's not right on him, and never will be, he's too small. What do their lordships think? I catch Northumberland's disdainful eye, watching these Popish natives behaving like children in a dressing-up game. They'll soon have it all twisted, with the links broken and in need of repair if their antics continue. For goodness sake put it back in the case I'm thinking. But yes, the chain is far too wide.

"There's a fair old weight in that now to be wearing it for long," complains Sean, struggling out of it and handing it to the Mayor, testing it up and down in his right hand.

"It has a good weight all right, but sure, it's modern for a change and an amazing piece of creative silversmithing, don't you think?"

"Well it's certainly different, I'll say that," Sean replies ambiguously; the little shit.

Now I want to get out of this in a hurry. I feel faint from the portraits and these clowns. I'm in a boiling miasma of rumbling pasts and the present, engulfed and stultified, experiencing an overwhelming sickness of heart that my moods can change so abruptly. I'm like the weather here, from sunshine to the dark night Hitler arrived: the U-boat commanders even coming ashore for their supper along Donegal's neutral coastline. Eventually the chain is put back in the case, I feel the Mayor is pleased enough, never mind little Haughey. I must not forget to present the envelope; I'm most eager to get paid.

"There's your invoice Lord Mayor, at the price agreed and I would much appreciate being paid as soon as you can."

"Not a bit of bother." He takes it from me. "I'll get this to accounts to settle right away." The Mayor shows me out past the large, draped tricolour in the hallway, under the portico that Gerry once explained was built for Queen Victoria, so she wouldn't get wet or cold as an old woman, the last time she called here. Down the steps and out the cobblestone entrance below, at last.

I'm in Dawson Street, by Danker's, where I'm never allowed enter. It is the holiest of holiest, with thousands of years of history reaching back to Moses and King David. One could even say the Big Bang or the beginning with Adam and Eve, whichever one chooses. I have to meet old Mr D around the corner from McDaids, as he doesn't want Taaffe, still at Dublin Silver, to know.

Diarmuid Brereton is standing forlorn and contemplative behind his glass-fronted shop door. He raises a limp hand on recognizing me, so I do the same to him. Three pigeons are fighting over a few crumbs on the pavement entering Grafton Street. It is survival of the fittest, each in our own way, we have no handle on time, anything.

Maria will be over tonight, expecting a bottle of good red wine. I mustn't forget that on the way home... a fair exchange for the mutual use of her tinderbox. Afterwards, she'll be ever so softly sobbing.

CHAPTER 60

"Will you put that silver away and come and listen to me, I've got something to tell you."

This sounds ominous; I don't know what to expect when Maria arrives, seating herself opposite me.

"Is there something wrong?"

"I'm pregnant!"

This is unexpected, given what she had assured me about her condition.

"Congratulations, isn't this wonderful news." Surprising indeed, I will have to get used to it, one way or another now.

"Congratulations says you, no way. I'm not having another child at my age, no way. I just couldn't face it."

"Didn't the doctor tell you you'd never?"

"Never mind that, the fact is I'm pregnant and you should know, before I go ahead with this."

"Like what, go to England?"

"No, no, it's called D and C, and I'll say no more for I've already arranged with my gynaecologist. A sensible man I've known for ages."

"What are you saying?"

"It will be taken care of, and you don't say a word about this to anyone, understand."

"You're already decided then, are you really sure?"

"Yes, I am, it's all so easy for you bloody men, gobshites the lot of you I think to myself sometimes. Did you get any wine?"

"I'll get you a glass right away." Blimey, what can I say, it's her decision anyway. Her mind is made up. I didn't think it possible here. But I suppose there is always a way if you know the right person; some sort of an operation is it? I've heard of it. The poor little mite will hardly be formed yet, just beginning from an infinitesimally small collection of cells. A I pour out the wine, I watch the barrelling machine turning around and around, powered by a rubber belt from a two-hundred-and-forty RPM electric motor. A great little yoke polishing thirty history rings by the constant friction a of small round steel slot with a few saturns in soapy water and a hexagonal barrel revolving continually. It saves the tedious bother of polishing each separately, leaving a bright even finish in an hour and a half roughly. I wash them out under cold, running tap water.

"Where's my glass of wine?" she calls loudly.

"I'll get you some roast duck and California corn chips from the Chinese takeaway in Cornelscourt," I offer, as I hand her the glass.

"And you might as well get another bottle of this in Dunnes before they close." Gobshites the lot of us, I'm not so bad now.

* * *

Florrie will miss our chats from when I used her phone, as one finally arrives courtesy of Telecom Eireann, in their new grey, blue and white logo-covered van, I knew at once it had been created for them by Kilkenny Design. I experience moment of joyful gratitude at the first ringing call; a great inconvienience has been lifted. The phone sounded strangely loud at first and I was apprehensive. Who can it be? It came with a crisp, new directory and my name is in the yellow pages.

* * *

Dilatin Caretlage means cleaning the womb. Like a wind blown out of the past, I remember what Anna Rose said under the archway onto the stable yard from the Parade. Kilkenny Design is closing down. It never became self-sufficient and gave all sorts of reasons for ever more grant aid before accumulating losses of over a million. Paul Hogan writes in *The Irish Times*, '...that the time has come to call it a day and for Kilkenny, always an innovator ...its work accomplished, to lay down its tools and go onto well-merited retirement.' It was most peculiar, that time under the archway into the stable yard from the Parade. I experience it like it was only yesterday, Mary barely seventeen, forever waiting for the J.J. Kavanagh bus to Urlingford via Freshford. Dear God, sometimes things never change.

* * *

Maria is still in the arms of another. The man about town, who seduced her from a straight and narrow Catholic upbringing and cautioned never to sit on her father's knee. He was something like a chief engineer, in county Waterford or Wexford, where her mother used to put slack on the fire last thing at night. Going to bed was an abiding childhood memory for her. Getting married was exciting at first: until the day when dragging a bag of coal between them up the steep steps and he, coming down, shaved and double-breasted, hurrying away.

* * *

I take her to Rome where, on the mysterious Via Appia Antica, there are those peculiar-shaped dark green trees, striking against the burning midday summer sky

She did assure me about her condition, free as a bird: must have been when it happened on the Carrickmines bridge. In starlight over gilded water flowing fast underneath. And now as Bernini's St Teresa of Avila widely abandoned on a fallen Corinthian capital taken by a mad black Protestant as an added fillip for her pleasure. Those saints that so appalled Luther, one the colour of marzipan in a glass case beneath an alter. Mussolini's lot were a lousy shower in the war. Imagine him hoping to ride in Alexandria on a white horse. Victorious indeed, unable to make up their mind's whose side they were on, watching a very old cardinal dressed in that extraordinary red that I will always find nightmarish, leading a procession up the nave of the basilica of Santa Maggiore. He suddenly turns an eagle eye towards me. They can smell a heretic any-where!

* * *

Flying into Dublin, which looks grey dirty and poor below me, I think to how it was once a fortified Viking Settlement by the sea. I'm still in a fearful, dark mood, back to the reality of cold and rain. Maria will be away again, brooding, isolated and sad. Struggling with the immensities of existence.

A journey with her up to Belfast, in heavy traffic on the Lisburn road, grazed the rear of a man's car and an awful argument ensued. Not want-ing to hang around arguing about whose fault it was, drove off, until the RUC Landrover came behind, siren and flashing blur warning to stop.

Constables Stewart and Patterson, heavily armed, escourting us to the station. Maria was terrified as never before. I had to hand over sixty pounds sterling before they'd let us go. Their voices were so different and harsh, she recalls. And 'why did you hae to take me up to fucking Belfast?!'

I do like her, but sometimes not.

CHAPTER 61

The days slip slyly by, stealing whatever's left of my life, this being as good as it ever gets from now on. I walk towards the long-abandoned Tully church on the pretty, high-hedged tree-lined narrow road. I feel disaffected, a complete chancer, who never having made anything of artistic worth. Everything always rushed at a price, there was never enough time for my own work. As if it really matters.

I gaze at the overgrown gravestones, fallen and angled over by the sharp axe of time. In the roofless little church chancel, with its thick recessed windows, the fine round arch is in perfect order, wider than the outline of the nave which is completely down. The sign says it was dedicated to St Brigid. Probably, she was a mad old cow of a woman praying non-stop day and night to the wonder of all those around her.

There are two ancient gravestone slabs, one of concentric circles, another with a Latin cross with knobs under the arms and cup marks on each arm and centre. They are so worn as to be barely visible, each leaning on the channel walls. Thick ivy is eating one side of the wall and gable end, on the bumpy, much dug-over graveyard there are numerous stone stumps. Markers of what must once have been there and the others that can be deciphered are from the seventeeth to nineteenth century.

Trees of many sorts are scattered amongst the graves, shading this memorable scene. An island of contemplation amidst the growing city that will eventually surround it. In a field on the opposite side of the road is a tall standing cross so badly disfigured I am unable to know what it ever was, apart from the vaguest figure of a bishop holding a crozier.

Returning towards the plain granite wheel cross, left at its original height by enclosing the ground beneath it in a wall of masonry when the road was lowered, there is a battered dirty-cream, two wheeled caravan, incongruously parked with a bright yellow cylinder of gas attached. I notice in passing a man and two small boys inside. The wretched and dispossessed are forever appearing, as were those in the previous century, who lived in the tiny chapel near Kells, County Meath, in the 1840s. And now the very same again by St Brigid's in the 1980s. Those two ragged boys climb atop the ivy, sapling-sprouting stone roof, monkey-like, with their father seated, resigned on the ground below. My worst thoughts of Ireland are here; nothing has changed or ever will.

I have the sudden, gut-wrenching melancholy that I felt when Mary's mother showed me her first communion picture. They wouldn't look after Langrishe's daughter and had her boarded out. My memories are more real than today's reality.

* * *

These things happen and can't be helped, I should really go and see Maria for the rest of the evening, instead of soldering silver bracelets most carefully so that the solder doesn't run and lock the links tight. A call comes from the Taoiseach's office via the Assay recommending me to make a freedom box for Charlie Haughey to present to Nelson Mandela when he arrives in Dublin next week. This doesn't give me much time to have it hallmarked and engraved in English and Irish as well, so I go to get the lettering from John Teehan at the National Museum.

Another rushed favour is needed from Paddy and for me late evenings out to Walkinstown delivering and collecting. There is no time to make a hinge, it will have to be a cylindrical lift off lid, like most of the old Irish ones were anyway. Looking at their photographs from the loan of a book, there's a beautiful gold one by Thomas Bolton in 1707, lid engraved with the arms of Freeman and underneath those of the city of Dublin, both with infoliate, floral and scroll motifs on the surface around. The first mention is of one presented to the Duke of Ormonde returning to Dublin when the monarchy was restored and he was made Lord Lieutenant again. This from the records of the Dublin Corporation for July 1662.

I remember his namesake, pressing my flesh, who I first met in the Kilkenny stable yard. A soft day it was, with big, white, slow-drifting clouds and a hot summer sunshine that made me drowsy, bewitched and unaware I was entering an isometric existence.

* * *

I live as a monk in solitary prayer and fasting: up early and late to bed. The box is made and is ready for hallmarking and collecting the same day. The spread marks are struck exactly as I wanted. It is set, finished and polished for Paddy to engrave. I emphasise that the Celtic letters and spelling must be done exactly to Teehan's meticulous instructions. I wait parked by the National Gallery on a wet Sunday morning in Merrion Square. Then I'm on my way to Ireland's notorious Taoiseach, Charles Haughey, who wants to meet me with his freedom box at Abbeyville, Kinsealy, Malahide.

John Teehan is a pleasant, soft-spoken Kerry man, seemingly fey and easy going. Keeper of the Art and Industrial Division, a nicely indexed comfortable position, on half pay when retired, whatever a keeper there actually does. Polish the silver? No? Maybe move it around, so it looks better in one case rather than another. All correctly spaced, explained and spot lit, with an occasional piece to write, like: Irish silver in the seventeenth to the nineteenth century was fashioned by skilled craftsmen in articles of remarkable beauty. Or an article: the Development of Irish Silver, Dublin Hallmarks, local marks and styles of Irish silver. There'd be cultural exchanges, with an exhibition at the Smithsonian (all expenses fully paid, no doubt) as well as the compiling of text from numerous catalogues. Well, fair play to him

At our first meeting he mentioned he might order copies of some of the items from the museum's collection for their new shop, which they hope to open soon. We drive through the unfamiliar, dreary suburbs of north Dublin. It is now raining heavily.

"He's a bit of a boyo this Haughey from what I hear, John, what do you think?"

"Ah, now, there's no smoke without fire."

"It's mostly about the money. Where does it come from? That he can live in such style?"

"Bit of a mystery all right, he has a mistress too I believe," says John, a touch admiringly, with the flicker of a smile too.

"Didn't he marry Lemas's daughter?"

"He did indeed, a smart move."

"And guns for the IRA in Belfast. That was never really sorted during the arms trial. Then there's his island and bloody big yacht; something's not right there John, it's a mystery how he ever manages on a Taoiseach's salary."

"They say he's a shrewd business man, made money from property: buying and selling land."

"You'd wonder though... and what's the name of his island, isn't it off the county you're from John, somewhere?"

"Inisvickillane it's called."

"Inishvickillane that's right. Now what why would he be wanting a bleak island in the middle of nowhere?"

"To call himself High King of all he beholds."

"Of Inishvickillane."

"Inishvickillane" John repeats to himself.

Inishvickillane... and didn't Haughey burn the union flag outside Trinity on VE day, whatever the story was, and curry favour with those Argentinian thugs over the Falklands war, emphasizing the name Malvinas just as the Spinner did.

John is driving, he stops at a gated entrance on the Malahide Road where a garda, ascertaining our business, waves us through to a sweeping driveway leading to a large Georgian establishment, bayed at both sides, I count twenty-five windows, not including the smaller basements.

"God he's doing all right for himself here John."

"The new landed gentry if you ask me."

There's a helicopter over on the lawn, its long, black rotor blades quivering, spider-like in the wind, ready to pounce. A well-dressed woman in tweeds answers the door, showing us into a mirrored hallway, leading to a milky-green drawing room of Georgian taste and furniture. Here is a sideboard of silver and fairly recent oil paintings, with a large one of himself beside a tricolour. The very image of a patriotic Irishman, proving to himself and the world that he isn't a fraud. He's with President Mitterrand of France in a wide silver-framed, coloured photo, as if to give him an added aura of worth.

The dubious Frenchman, with his supposed career as a Resistance fighter, is a lifelong friend of Reneé Bousquet, secretary general of the French police, who willingly obliged the Germans by rounding up French Jews with their little children in dawn raids, to be sent to Auschwitz to be gassed. Surely, that was the most infamous deed in the history of the French nation and Reneé never got his just deserts. He was almost forgotten long after the war was over, without remorse,and with so much blood on his hands. These ghastly deeds momentarily intrude on my thoughts.

John and I are both somewhat amazed and subdued in these lovely new surroundings, however they came about. It has stopped raining and a beautiful bay horse is led past the windows by a lithesome young woman in jodhpurs, helmet and fine leather riding boots. I hear the wealthy clip clop sounds of an aristocracy.

"Who pays for this John?" I ask, as I reach inside for the box, my work wrapped in acid-free tissue paper.

"God only knows." John grimaces at the floral stuccoed ceiling and all around, shrugging his shoulders and displaying his empty hands wide.

"Not the house John, the box."

"Oh, try sending your bill to Foreign Affairs ,or maybe the Department of the Taoiseach would be more like it."

Haughey enters silently, wearing slippers and a thick, white Aran sweater. He is small in stature, with long, thinning hair.

"Ah, the two gentlemen with my Freedom Box and how does it look?"

He holds out his hand for both of us to shake, getting straight to the point.

I hand the box to him. He takes the lid off and on again, off and on a few more times, for it fits perfectly. The engraving is checked, I wonder would he be a fluent Irish speaker, as Mary certainly was. This thought awakens a deep sadness. I imagine being buried in the ditch of the laneway leading to her cottage, under the blackthorn's cruel piercing memory, with nature's disintegration taking me mercifully away.

"Mandela should be well pleased with this, an exceptional example of modern Irish silversmithing. I like how you've spaced the hallmarks, and the lettering is perfect, an historic reminder, nothing too ostentatious for his stay and with connections between us all in our longing for freedom," he catches me eye to eye, distinctively clear voiced, speaking slowly. It's strange how human contact can dissolve people's misapprehensions about one another.

"I didn't have time to get a presentation box made, unfortunately," I have to say something at least.

"Sure, we don't need to box a box, isn't that right John?"

"Yes of course Taoiseach, just the way it is," he replies smiling, relaxed now, his responsibility to deliver is complete.

Haughey holds the silver up admiringly, as if it is a bright star, catching the sunlight coming out of the dull, clouded sky, which clears to touches of Irish blue behind the far window. It is miraculously enthralling, clear, golden. Hallucinating, I am unable to understand a word of their conversation... Irish football in Italy. Half awake, I know I'm not dreaming when the Irish Taoiseach Charles Haughey says to me on leaving, "how would we have managed this without you?"

CHAPTER 62

Father's coffin is draped with the union flag at the Roselawn Crematorium, Belfast. The flag looks somewhat foreign now, so close, a great burst of exploding red, which is then carefully folded and handed to his eldest son, home from Australia. The naked coffin moves with eerie slowness, disappearing behind heavy golden curtains to fiery oblivion. The few mourners wait in mutual awe, all too aware of the same fate awaiting them eventually. And why wouldn't he want that flag anyway? Fighting for Great Britain those dreadful war years to final victory, vanquishing unspeakable German wickedness and genocidal inhumanity, he was lucky to have survived.

Whatever he thought of the same flag representing an awkward tribe over here was another story. My brother's acquired accent is annoyingly disconcerting. He feels the damp and cold and is bewildered that nothing has changed, saying, "how can you still want to live in Ireland?"

Mother despite her age, will soon be leaving to join him. It is definitely decided upon, which I find surprising. There are a few bits of memorabilia I can have, but there's no point, as I've no one to pass them on to. A few photos of him are enough. Glancing back, a large puff of smoke is ascending from the crematorium chimney, the same coloured blue as the uniform he once wore. He is rising to oblivion, far from the bitter airs of Belfast.

*   *   *

On a quiet morning, working, my once-fraught memories of him are unwelcome and strange, interrupting my life in Ireland. The postman calls to leave a package addressed in mother's familiar but now shaky hand. On opening her farewell letter, I find the one photo of him I always liked. Father is with the six airmen at Archangel in 1941, frozen in time and seemingly transcendent.

*   *   *

After inspecting the Lord Mayor's Great Chain last week, I have been asked to give a price for creating a replica. Made in 1698, with its large central medal of King William the Third, it has worn badly. That period was a very bad time for the Popish natives; it was the beginning of the Penal Laws. The links of roses, knots, harps and S-shaped snake heads joining the rings have been repaired so many times there's a danger of it falling apart when on the Lord Mayor. Made in London, with high carat gold but not hallmarked, the constant rubbing of gold on gold inevitably wears. Thickening it with solder year after year has weakened the links. So to preserve it for only the most important occasions the corporation want an exact replica made for everyday use. It shouldn't be too difficult, as three castings are repeated on the chain linking. Another two for the portcullis and one medal, in nine carat to keep the cost reasonable. It does add up to being expensive enough though, I'll need eleven thousand five hundred punts, including the VAT.

The next day I receive the letter for the go ahead for the replica chain on headed paper from *Leabharlanna Poibli Atha Cliath*, Dublin Corporation Libraries, Information and Cultural Heritage Services. It is signed by Mary Clark, City Archivist. I wonder where Maria is today.

I am at the old Irish Parliament the Bank of Ireland, for no particular reason. Glancing into what was the Commons, there are long counters of numerous tellers and their customers to be seen. Then to the Lords, with his two enormous tapestries: The Glorious Battle of the Boyne and the Glorious Defence of Londonderry. The high-rounded, coiffured gold bussed ceiling room of past glories is empty and curiously silent, despite the noisy world just outside. It smells of old, varnished wood, dusty, thick woven fabrics and darkly warm airs suffused in history's intricate warp. A few pale busts of Ireland's past worthies (including the Duke of Wellington) surround the room. Display cases show the first Free State bank notes and coins, items associated with the Parliament and the early bank then. A printed copy of the Great Parliament of Ireland 1782 has a numbered key with the name of each member beside it. And I look to see, startlingly, the ancestral one himself, Sir Hercules Langrishe BT, Borough of Knocktopher.

So how many generations on would Mary be from him? The first baronet of this malevolent family looks well fed, seated comfortably, expensively dressed with his many contemporary Protestant parliamentarians. It cannot be avoided; I'm swirling down the vortex of Irish history again, which I find helplessly debilitating at every turn. There's no escape and is that Kiely's black box on the far table over there marked Langrishe Estate? Spilling secrets, convolutions of my imagination. I had better get out of this place in a hurry, but to go where?

Buswells, for a bite to eat, where the carvery lunch of roast beef, potatoes, carrots, cabbage with thick gravy poured over is warm and filling. Reading the *Irish Times*, another memory rears up from the past. Peter Pringle is free: the evidence used to convict him was insufficient. Well, good job they hadn't already hanged him. His picture reminds me of that first meeting in Glencolumbkille. Something was always deeply enigmatic about him, though I always liked him and he helped me get started in Dublin. This despite his Socialist Shinner shenanigans and being in the Curragh. He was once a friend of O'Connell, Daithi Death more like, those killer's eyes I remember well. I will never forget how they mirrored the fanatic heart of a religion, the ends justifying the means. I look now to see if there are any dogs for sale in the pages of advertisements.

From Buswells, just across Kildare Street, is the National Museum. I might as well go in, to the darkened mysterious worded *An tSeodlann*, The Treasury. *Éire san Iarnaois agus sa Luathré Chriosti*, for Celtic and Early Christian Ireland once again. Church-like, yet feeling far more sacred and profound, I admire the remains of ancient Irish endeavour, these weirdly wonderful creations. Mostly, the artefacts are fragments, there are few complete finds. Mellifluously calmed from their once superstitious beliefs, I walk to see The Cross of Cong and The Shrine of St Lachtin's Arm (which old Mr James, the Englishman of Glencolumbkille, would know in every engraved twist and turn, having meticulously replicated it). The Tara Brooch and the many other broaches are just not of this world.

Hallucinating mischiefs are everywhere, disturbing me. Unnatural, ethereal waves, the whispering of the tides, the language even, *Chriostaí*. *Chriostaí*, however it is pronounced, has a certain ring to it. A ring that the same bell might make that I am standing before. There are rows of tall, four-sided display cases softly lit as is the whole room. Bending to get a closer look at The Ardagh Chalice I see extraordinary, fine-worked golden detail. It is unnerving. For who were these people? They must have been from the far side of the cosmos. Straightening up, feeling dizzy, so I go through to the other side of the glass and exactly opposite me is Mary Malone.

Dear God, what is she doing back in Ireland? She looks amazing. My hopes momentarily rise. I look excitedly straight into those eyes, the tricks of light dancing on the glass. She is a heart-breaking exact lookalike.

Dressed in flowing white, goes from to one case to another as a cloud. I observe her discreetly, hypnotized, she is gracefully unaware. Now she's now at The Hoard of Silver Ingots, Rocky Island, Dysart, County Westmeath. Ghostly and ephemeral, the sharp glance she throws me wounds me like a spear. She knows she is being watched now, and, like the rarest of birds, hurriedly disappears down the steps to the gold finds of The Early, Late and Later Bronze Age.

Let her go. I study the malicious magic of each detail displayed, until it is closing time. With the haunting experience of Ireland's early imagination echoing still, in mine, I wait for the 145 or 46A bus by the dirty-green statue of a past Protestant Archbishop of Dublin. Those eye-aching creations are a kind of prayer and penance, a foot on the ladder to heaven. Their working conditions must have been appalling, wattle huts, rat infested, using charcoal to melt metal by candle light.

* * *

Who is left these days? There's plenty of the cod, cast-copied Celtic silverware, with leaflets explaining the design. Thus: *The Maireadach Cross is a miniature work of art, one of the most beautiful of the High Crosses of Ireland.* Pronto printed in emerald green, and, God forgive me, there's my own History of Ireland.

The better ones I know are Clarke; Harron at Killyleigh; Taaffe; Donovan and always Breen of course, that cunning contortionist of gold and silver, having the very freakishness of the ancient Celtic race deeply engrained in his work. His secrets are well-kept, as only he knows how to make the likes of The Broighter Hoard. Those snakes, birds, trumpeting coils and faces come out of his shed, where the wood louse and spiders play. He has a mongrel dog attuned to every tap tap of his chasing hammer. He's no longer earth bound, heaven's light is his only guide at the rear of a very ordinary Swords semi.

"Will you just look at him this hour, away with the fairies," says Mary, tossing her pretty, miffed head, letting me out to his mysterious shed, as though I've just landed from a faraway place. Wives give up on craftsmen. Maria is much the same, with me for the long breaks, then gone for days.

* * *

So who's going to cast the replica Lord Mayor's Great Chain? For that's what it really is, with the original reluctantly borrowed from Mary Clark, her forefinger raised, warning me to be most careful. She informed the Cabinteely Garda station that I have it in my possession. I am to keep it for as short a time as possible. I wouldn't want to get on the wrong side of Miss Primed Torpedo. She is straight to the point, having agreed the price, she wants a definite delivery date. It will take approximately four to five weeks, assuming there are no unforeseen casting difficulties, I explain to her. She's icily unimpressed. Gerry warned me about her.

As Brian Clarke is not one for casting, who shall it be? I have to disregard the views of the fractious rivals, who speak well of nobody in similar occupations. I consider the personalities in this shop and that, many of whom want exclusivity and who deal mostly in half-truths or outright lies.

There's the man from South Africa married to Donovan's daughter, he worked for Johnson Matthey and is now with Cookson. I will see what he casts there. He has moved to Kilkenny and is worth a try.

Between Bennetsbridge and Thomastown, in the old artifice county yet again, my darting melancholy returns, becoming a sacred shrine within me. I am a reliquary without the gold and silver encasing, my memories are the heaviest cross to bear. I eventually find the Afrikaner in his new, modern bungalow, workshop attached with all new equipment. It is incongruously set amidst idyllic countryside that I find as bewitching as ever.

Given an audience for his overweening confidence, this Afrikaner likes to talk, not least about the price of casting gold. He explains the basic stages of the casting process: with the lost wax investment; the quality of the castings being dependent on the quality of the original master pattern; that he will have to make in nickel silver for each link, considering the worn state of the originals. Sprues of the right size, put in to the right position, are of paramount importance to successful casting, they will be attached to the thickest part of the pattern. The master pattern will be finished to a standard that makes it indistinguishable from the link when new on the chain, where contamination of the melt can result in brittle castings, porosity, rough surfaces and inclusions.

* * *

It's going to be a long day: from rubber moulds to waxes, the gold grain is melted at last in the hot investment flask on the centrifugal spinning casting machine. Amongst the links, King William eventually emerges, still warm on the hand, a copper orange colour most fitting for a Prince of Orange. Then with his wife Mary. The King and Queen of England, Scotland, France and Ireland, Defender of the Faith, a strange saviour of the good old Protestant cause in Ireland.

The casting is a job well done. I find myself thinking the Afrikaner wouldn't be here if I hadn't made the call to his father-in-law, working at Naylors in London all those years ago.

Sitting in a very small pub alone, somewhere between Kilkenny and

Carlow, low lit and almost dark as the night outside, I feel most strange
after inspecting King William again. When he's placed on a Smithwicks
beer mat, I feel even stranger. The room is small, the old barman mute
and shadowed, watching me from behind the counter. The glass of
brandy is pure liquid comfort beside his majesty. Old barman, brandy
and King William, a Holy Trinity. A benevolent calm is emanating from
them. Ireland is a woman of easy virtue, I raise the glass and silently give a
toast, 'to the glorious, pious and immortal memory of the great and good
King', who is lying on a Smithwicks beer mat, how extraordinary. At a
mile or so outside the village there's a dilapidated, ivy choked entrance I
remember passing early this morning; then I could see a driveway leading
up to tall trees, half hiding a large grey establishment. It is gone in the
night, another Knocktopher.

* * *

"You can tell Mary I'll have the replica finished by the end of the week,
Gerry." I hand the original back to him, a concern lifted under the por-
tico of the Mansion House, on a soft, damp, overcast day.
"Ah, now don't be talkin about it, and I'll be saying no more."
"Is there a problem?"
"I'm sure you know what I mean."
"About your one, without mentioning any names."
"Game ball, bulls eye," he replies with a wink.
"I see, I see, well at least you have the original back, and she'll be pleased
with that."
"Let's hope so, the Mayor will certainly be glad he can wear the original
tonight," is somewhat wearily said.
"There you go then Gerry, sunny side up, I'll be on my way." Without
another word, he closes the heavy door behind him, not his usual self
today, and no cigar. Is there a deep melancholy in every Irish heart?

* * *

The replica is completed, filing the sprues, I make joining rings for each
link. After a light polishing, the replica shines as the original would have
when it was new. A good weight, the Assay only charges pennies, treating
it as a necklace.

* * *

There are two dozen, very old, pistol-handled knives and forks from
Danker that he wants to be repaired in a hurry. The handles are split;

rusty blades and forks are loose and have fallen out; the shellac is broken and missing inside. I wouldn't know where to get it these days, I will have to use pitch and plaster instead. Gently heating each handle to melt out the remaining shellac, I file away the rust on the prongs, use a light, abrasive polish on the blades and forks, then lustre them to rouge. They certainly look much better as a result. Nearly all need a thin strip of silver inserted between the split, which is easy to solder from both sides. With the piercing saw, I cut away the excess fin, filing it carefully without touching the original surface, which is so worn and fragile it would be destroyed. I leave a barely visible line of new silver holding it all together.

I use the blow torch to melt the broken pitch with a spoonful of plaster in an empty peach tin squeezed to a pointed spout. Wearing thick gardening gloves, I pour the pitch inside the handle up to the hilt, lettign it cool but when it is still soft, gently insert the prong, slightly heated, into the handle until both are tightly connected. The pitch hardens after a few minutes, any that spilled is easily picked off, the handles lightly polished.

Between the knives and forks and the Lord Mayor's yoke, I do what I can to survive. It is like being on a shooting star, hurtling through space. I'm afraid to let go; where will I fall to. The smell of pitch is in my hair, clothes, everywhere. I did a filthy job, long into the night, as a favour. The first gentle blush of new morning light comes over the Carrickmines valley and the Neolithic tomb, the new day beginning just as it would have started some five or six thousand years ago. Taking a breath of fresh air outside, I can see Maria through the window, asleep, gone to the world, at one with the great mystery.

* * *

The rough seas of Irish litigation are never far away, seeping through the letter flap onto the floor are those familiar buff envelopes, which are most upsetting. The cute whores emerge surreptitiously like poisonous mushrooms in the forest of evasions and circumlocutions. Despite my Registrations of Designs and Trademarks, they fight me with letters marked 'without prejudice'.

Maria finds this all highly amusing, to judge from her uncaring remarks about them, not realising how angry this makes me. I'm considered fair game, the peasant poacher's right. Whatever they can get away with, they are entitled to. They take the History of Ireland again and again. In this latest offering, all they have changed is the last symbol, which is now a shamrock, how inadequate and pathetic can they get.

'Stop me if you can', their products cry, 'we murdered Lord Leitrim and no jury would dare convict us, as nobody owns Ireland. And you know how smuch solicitors charge.' A shamrock stamped over the question mark, apparently it was bought from an English bagman. I never heard of the likes; it is unbelievable. Eventually, after protracted correspondence and after threatening an injunction, I finally secure a written agreement to desist. But the final reckoning of Matheson Ormsby Prentice is exorbitant.

* * *

In a clean white towel, I unwrap the replica chain, pleased it has turned out so well. I'm doing so before the expectant gaze of Mary Clark and Tom O'Connor, over at the Mansion House. There is a long silence... the dying man's life flashes before my eyes. Once again I'm awakened in bed by someone shouting at cows, hoofing across the yard below to the byre. On the news is more about the bombing of Berlin. Germany is being hit on a massive scale now. The Russians liberate Kiev, reaching Korostern and Zhitomir, but the Germans counter-attack on their flanks driving them back.

"The roses and knots are the wrong way around!" exclaims Mary pointing sharply, like a cat would pounce on a mouse, with eyes boring up to mine. She is seated beside me at the magnificent, long, mahogany table in the dining room, where at the far end is the portrait of the Duke of Richmond, watching us.

"My mistake there Mary, sorry about that, it can be fixed in a few hours." I should have checked with the original before returning it to Gerry.

"And it looks far too new; they'll know it's not the old one, I won't accept it like this," she continues. It is most upsetting, having to scrap this, getting only a fraction of what I have already spent.

"But does that matter Mary? Why would you want to pull the wool over their eyes? Whoever they are. And of course the colour of the gold is different from the original, anyone can see it's much paler."

"Don't you dare patronise me, do you understand? You will have to make it look the same, our people would be aghast at their Lord Mayor appearing without the original on," she says angrily, so whatever she wants to be done, I have do to in order to get paid. O'Connor standing behind her, gestures with both hands, making ready to strangle her, grimacing menacingly. I can well imagine the friction between them.

"I'll file and polish the links down, it's not a problem Mary to have it like the original, and you'll be well satisfied."

"You do see to this then, and we'll meet you here again as soon as possible." Mary rises abruptly, somewhat flushed, leaving the room, as O'Connor raises his right arm abruptly and straight in the Nazi salute as he follows after her.

She's going to destroy this even before it is delivered, to inflict a couple of hundred years fake wear and tear on it is a shame. The only thing that can be said of this inconvenience is that I will gain a few extra grains of gold from vandalizing each link, except from the badly worn medallion which I left alone, other than using it as the casting pattern. On the third visit I'm nearly there, but not quite. Mary is satisfied most of the alterations have been carried out, but the petals of the outer and inner roses of the first six Tudor Roses to the front of the replica are to be further worn down and their texturing removed. Each portcullis on the replica, including the raised dots on both, are to be further worn down and blunted to resemble the portcullis on the back of the original chain.

I miss the antics of O'Connor behind her back, who's not there today for some reason. The Principal Officer City Manager Department has asked her to inform me that the invoice will not be paid until she's satisfied that the replica matches the original chain and so it continues.

Finally, on the fourth visit, I emerge liberated without the chain at last and she'll pass the invoice on for payment. For any queries regarding payment to contact Willie McEvoy at the City Manager's Department at six, seven, nine, six, one, one, one.

"Can I speak to Willie McEvoy please?"

CHAPTER 63

Maria insists on taking me to occasional marriages, first communions, confirmations and baptisms. Tiresomely seated as far back as possible, the old masterish, gloomy dark stations of the cross are incongruous in the mostly straight-lined modern churches of reinforced concrete and kaleidoscopic stained glass colours. The older ones have those awful, Christmas-cake like altars. A catwalk of mothers and daughters in short, tight-fitting skirts saunter up the aisle, carrying fancy handbags and the latest cameras, thoughtlessly crossing themselves with a cursory bended knee, displaying a well-rounded rear.

Dispersing left and right onto long hard pews, they are attentive to who's here and who is wearing what. I pity the poor priests, who are unable to avoid these devils in disguise, their church being always wary of women. After a long hour viewing the flower of Irish womanhood, the children troop past: little girls in varieties of white, heads veiled of course, with the boys to one side. Again, I think of the photo Mary's mother kept in a biscuit tin. Wasn't it her first communion too, that day beyond Knocktopher?

There are mostly teachers here. One must be the Vera that Maria is always on about. She has told me about Vera's affair with a Chicago undertaker, of the husband she grew to hate, ever since he insisted she had to take the bus to work, while he always had the car. Also, about the kidnapper Vera fancied when he held her hostage while the other two robbers made the manager of the AIB bank in Grafton Street open the safe early one morning. Then there was the summer when topless men weere digging a trench by the school; she just couldn't help herself imagining being with them. Maria convinced that a child is being abused over there.

Perusing the *Irish Catholic* during for the service, I read that the Inquisition was, in reality, a mild affair. Unbelievable.

* * *

At a wedding reception, the priests at the raised top table, knife and forking it greedily, the conversation from lovely Evelyn is unintelligible, her Longford speak is too fast and the boyos are tanking it up noisily. It can't be helped if I gaze around at the wide varieties of nature's call; change is as good as a rest. Thinking of Maria across the table, God love her, she has suddenly grown old and looks Queen Motherish; her lipstick is too red.

The other evening we were at Russells of Glasthule for a surprise birthday dinner. It certainly was a surprise when the bill came and I had to pay it. On holiday in Spain, Maria insisted on taking me to the awful bullring in Seville, under a still merciless evening sun. I was aggrieved at having to watch the macabre carnival of death at an exorbitant price. She was as excited as any Roman ever was at the Colosseum, couldn't keep still, at one with the Spaniards, encouraging the ritual killings.

* * *

Somewhere between Longford and Mullingar we stop, for Maria can still be bewitching. But it only takes a minute before I withdraw, dizzy and exhausted. She's annoyed twisting, her skirt back down. I sense she's already seeing someone else. Continuing in shades of dark anxiety, I notice mysterious loughs gleaming silvery beyond, under a clear night sky and moon.

* * *

It is extraordinary reading *The Evening Press* report headlined, 'Peter Pringle freed as case dropped by State.' So why was he sentenced to hang? And committed to forty years, if he's innocent now, having spent fifteen years incarcerated in Portlaoise Prison? I will never really know. The Irish struggle is a subconscious preternatural craving for martyrdom these days. I wish him well though; he enabled me to get started here.

I'll leave it all behind someday, the gold and silver at least. Not Ireland. Maria has gone now without even a farewell or last words, just as the wind would gently drift broken egg shells apart in the lonely landscape between Pettigo and Donegal town, without tears. The sighting of a man on her arm when our eyes meet momentarily was all that was needed. It was a liberation in fact.

I work as a hermit, almost without distraction, but sensing time as a locomotive gathering speed. When thoughts of female company intrude unbearably, I ask Conor Doyle's advice about where to go.

We agree to meet at a venue called the Spawell, finding it with difficulty towards Templeogue, late Thursday evenings again. There's a large car park, nearly full, it looks like some kind of sports centre. To the sound of music, I head towards the open lit doorway, another Dalkey Island hotel (which is now demolished, replaced by newly built apartments). Once more I am among the inestimable mysteries of Irish femininity, perhaps able to discover some kind of solace here for ten punts. There is a crowded, low lit dance floor, reeking of cigarette smoke, sour sweat and too sweet perfume. A good live band is playing.

In order to have something to do at least, I go to the bar, ordering a glass of Smithwicks so as not to appear a lost soul, surveying the dancers and those seated around the walls. Up comes Con Doyle. Acknowledging each other, we drift closer, absorbing the atmosphere, noting the women. He's a touch greyer and somewhat dishevelled, with a couple of day's growth. He sports a large, many-dialled, fancy, atomic watch; at least I think that's what they are called.

"So, what about ye?" asks Con grinning. "On the loose again? I'm much the same meself after the last one was getting a might too possessive." Is he kidding himself? A might too possessive, indeed. But I'm glad to see him, his outrageous comments are warming and strangely reassuring. "And yourself with Maria, what happened?" he continues.

"Sure Con, the way it is with teachers, so much time off, wanting to be entertained, the eating out, she never paid for anything."

"Well, that's your own fault. I told you set the parameters right from the start. Give them an inch and they'll be looking for a mile."

"Well, yes, of course, with hindsight you're right Con."

"But there again, wasn't she a great ride?" he replies with an even bigger grin, rolling his eyes to heaven. Without replying, I notice a slight and beautifully proportioned, curly-headed blonde, standing in a group of men and women chatting. She seems delicate and and to radiate a fragile innocence.

"She's nice there, Con, do you see the little blonde one?" I nod towards her.

"Well then, Jesus man, what are you waiting for? Go and ask her to dance. Come on then, I'll take you over." Whether Con has a belief in kind fate or whether it is just his determined bravado, he goes boldly up to her and introduces us.

"Would you like to dance with my good friend here?"

The group are somewhat surprised at Con's cheeky intrusion, but she looks up at me with all the startled beauty of her clear blue eyes. And yes she will, without saying a word though, moving closer, gesturing me onto the dance floor where we are even closer. My arms are around her now. I gaze into her creamy, blush, fey, almost childlike face, which seems without artifice. She has an extraordinary angelic presence, that I want to take hold of.

"A difficult place to find the Spawell, coming from Cabinteely; it's my first time here, and yourself?"

She doesn't reply, seeming faintly amused. It is as she is telling me that I don't really have to say anything. I can't let the moment pass as this will be over too soon, sensing this is the chance of a lifetime and I must say something before she's gone.

"Would you like to come out with me some evening for a meal, or whatever would suit you?"

"Oh no, I'm only here for the music and dancing and never go out if anyone asks me," she replies in her slow, far-away voice.

"You must be married then?"

"Well no, I'm not actually." She's as light as leaves falling, a will-o-the-wisp, ethereal and dreaming. I'm awakened to the ending of the dance.

"Here, if you do change your mind, I'll give you this card."

She takes it and puts it into the little pocket of her lacey white top. Maybe she is just being polite. She is wearing a pleated black skirt and kitten-heeled shoes. Every movement of hers is as alluring as I could ever hope to see. Walking away from me, I realise I don't even know her name. Maybe I can catch her on the way out, at closing time.

No. She walks right past me, talking to someone without noticing my presence.

* * *

On Friday night I fall into a disturbing sleep of dreams, of a big old house that proves to be Knocktopher Abbey. I'm viewing one of those clever triple portraits made from vertical strips of wood painted on each side. Facing me head on is the mysterious woman I danced with on Thursday night, who I am unable to forget, to the left is Mary and moving to the right, a child whose appearance is barely visible on the swirling mysterious mists of what must be the Nore, stretching out her hand to hold mine. Now I recognise Lucy, looking the same as Mary did in the faded, old, grey photograph she showed me of when she was a child.

* * *

There's another dozen spun sugar basins to planish, so they look hand-raised, with their separate bases to be attached. I find the centre point with dividers, then scribe a circle to mark where to solder the base on after coating it with borax. Then I coat the entire surface inside and out with boric acid mixed with alcohol to prevent fire stain, once again not wanting to polish out the hammer marks. The subterfuge of it being hand-made is possible because Irish hallmark only guarantee the metal, not the design and quality of workmanship. I do whatever it takes to make a living.

The memory of the woman from the dance is a disquieting presence. The old cottage whispers in fractional movements and sighs. Outside, there is a spot of rain, the sky is blue to grey with big, white, puffy clouds that colour pink towards evening. The new moon, when it rises, is a golden crescent thread. On checking the click of a trap in the kitchen cupboard, I find there's a dying mouse with his tiny, dark, accusatory eyes and the same red blood as ours.

Poor creature, valiant hearted, I drop him onto the footpath where the fox or owl might find him. I gaze up to the branches advancing across the road, as Ireland is enveloping, threatening and eventually embracing the cottage. The sugar basins are soldered, I leave them in the bucket of diluted sulphuric acid over night, to dissolve the solidified boric acid and borax.

* * *

I lightly polish a space for striking my mark, then on Monday go up to the castle for Hibernia, the crowned harp and the date letter to be spread beside them. I notice the black roof of a hearse coming slowly down the laneway behind the ivy clad wall to take Florrie Baker away forever. Charlie Breen from the cottage around the corner said she'd been dead for nearly a week and might have been there much longer if he hadn't gone up to her. Alone here, fashioning gold and silver into the future, is this a foreboding I will experience the same fate?

* * *

The phone rings on Monday evening, I wondering who it could possibly be? I'm certainly not expecting anyone at this hour. Setting the hallmarks, filing any excess solder off, I put away the assay docket and samples (they've done a great job, the trick now is not to damage them while polishing, it shouldn't take long tomorrow). The Assay office feel like an extended family, I have got to know them well enough. The bold

Captain retired, with his son Ronald taking over, no questions asked. Somehow it was automatic. I could let the phone ring out. Probably, it is a wrong number, of no consequence. It would hardly be the Spinner or Chaser. Perhaps it is an order for that lunar-like, wide, tapering torq collar that was talked about. I was thinking of soldering an inch-wide strip of eighteen carat gold together into a dog collar, hammering it on one side to stretch it out until it is almost flat, then cutting away the excess to resemble the crescent moon of last night. I think all this in the time it takes to reach the phone.

"Hello. You asked me to give you a call, I'm the one you danced with at the Spawell, my name's Kathleen, do you remember me?" Her voice is as soft music, enchanting all over.

"I certainly do; so when can I take you out?"

And from there we move on exponentially. At times I am almost levitating with her, my work dissolving into all the other gold and silver ever made, tossed to the ever-changing Irish sky, forgotten and mocked by the harsh cries of Dublin's seagulls.

Spinning out of control, I know Ireland is an illusion, but I'm unable to escape. The years pass and, imperceptibly, I'm getting older. Kathleen is light as the butterflies I noticed in a summer field when walking from the station to Thomastown.

Here, I sense those Normans again, in the thick walled remains and also in some faces. I sight Peter Donovan on the other side of the street, he doesn't notice me. He is a star of the trade and deservedly so. I let him pass, as the years since Kilkenny have flown; what is there to say or ask? He never went back. His daughter is as native as any in Kilkenny since the days of Strongbow.

* * *

Ireland is a mirage that rears and disappears. Grasping Kathleen's hand, where she's waiting outside Hodges Figgis, I read on the nearby chalked blackboard that Peter Pringle is going to give a talk on 'Surviving Ireland's Death Row'. My goodness that's a coincidence; it is starting soon on the second floor. There are chairs laid out and people waiting to hear him.

Coming in forty years later, he looks much the same, still with the full head of hair, bearded and now all snow white. He's certainly moved on; he's quite a celebrity in fact and reads parts of his book describing his life and incarceration. Peter is delighted to meet me again and introduces me to his new American wife, who suffered a similar fate, that somehow brought them together. He signs his book for me, *About Time*.

"I've always felt a bit guilty about Father McDyer and leaving

Glencolumbkille so suddenly, without thanking him, or a giving a farewell explanation, or taking on an apprentice."

"Well you needn't, he was a rogue and gave me the run around the time I was there and never paid me; so don't be feeling sorry. He wasn't even liked by most of his parishioners. I know that for a fact, as I'm sure you'd know yourself."

"So where are you living now Peter?"

"Casla in Galway by the sea. So if you're ever down that way give us a call, but ring me first as we're often away,;here I'll write the number in the book for you." Then he turns to others who are waiting impatiently.

"Did you know him well?" asks Kathleen, as we head out into the growing darkness of evening.

"Well yes and no, in the early seventies for a short while, up in Donegal. As much as you'd ever get to know anyone, especially Peter, with his youthful involvement in the armed struggle and republican socialism shenanigans, for all the good it did him, spending fifteen years in gaol," I look into her innocent, bewitching blue eyes, that so captivated me at the Spawell.

* * *

Peter has even written how to contact him on the internet, which I was never interested in getting, nor the use of a mobile phone either. Watching people on the bus glued to their tiny screens, whatever it is they see, it's clear that the old Ireland is fast fading away, as am I. My aged appearance is reflected in the mirror of the Killiney post office, when I queue on a Friday to buy stamps with at least a dozen pensioners. There's a free travel pass, TV licence, portion of electricity and, most amazing of all, a small pension electronically transferred into my bank account. It is quite extraordinary how it comes through the air, or is it via a line? The figure miraculously appears on a screen; it means there's cash to be collected, compliments of the Irish State.

Much of my gold and silver jewellery is now sold on the internet, too much in fact. I let my best designs go for a reasonable royalty on everything sold, by those of the oldest persuasion I can trust, never an Irishman though, including myself.

* * *

One morning, at the first light of day, I awaken to notice the top of a ladder, just above the high wall behind me. Someone was cutting the ivy probably, yet curiously it remains there for some time. The reason is eventually explained to me by a retired former Assistant Garda Commissioner, who is attempting to serve a summons on my neighbour and is enquiring as to where he could possibly be. The ladder is a lookout for my neighbour to see who was there to avoid.

Unable to help this craggy, grey, upright, determined man, on a hunch I ask him about Pringle.

"They were beginning to let those boyos out anyway,"he replied.

And so it goes.

* * *

Being in Geneva for a week feels as long as a lifetime working here. I gaze into the fast-flowing Rhone river on the Port des Bergues, the water beneath me reflecting the city's night lights as whirlpools of sparkling diamonds, swirling and constantly changing, canary and brilliant abstracts. Swans and ducks are sheltering by the little island of Rousseau, where I had a croissant and coffee this morning, watching the famous hundred-and-forty metre high white plume of the famous fountain beyond on the lake side. Geneva is a city of big, colourful flags.

I visit the Reformation museum at the cathedral of St Pierre, where the great Protestant reformer Calvin had his chair. At the Patek Philippe museum, I marvel at their mechanical watch creations through the ages: what are my talents compared to all this? Slowly, from the Rue du Rhone, with its luxury shops displaying so much jewellery, fashionable accessories and watches, I go up the steep steps to the old part of town again, ordering fondue in a charmingly quaint restaurant down a narrow side street, just off the Place de la Madeleine.

I'm alone, yet Kathleen's beside me eating apple tart with cream as she did on afternoons at Powerscourt. For they have all gone, surprised by time, just as the old queen was. I don't want to lie dying, helpless in an overcrowded Dublin hospital, but on my own day of choosing.

For could Ireland really exist from here?

Seriously. The strangest things can happen. What we think we know, but don't know about time. Switzerland celebrates each specific hour in so many different ways, such as on the face of a small dial carried on my wrist, not much bigger or thicker than a few old half-crowns. I could well have been a Swiss watchmaker all along, waking from a faraway place in the weirdness of a dream, a dream of Ireland.

I arrive at the Gare de Cornavin, where the train to Zurich is waiting.

I am shown into a blue metal-clad structure with a bed, table and chairs inside. The doctor inserts a medical line onto my arm, connected to a button.

"Press the button whenever you're ready," he says gently.

As I do so, I can see Mary Malone coming slowly up Patrick Street under soft lamplight that first night, nearer and nearer, ever more beauti-ful, waiting in the Mini outside the Club House hotel, I gesture to her to get in beside me ... Ireland was only ever a dream. It could never possibly have existed.